W9-CAT-538

1983

Science Year

The World Book Science Annual

A Review of Science and Technology During the 1982 School Year

World Book, Inc.
a Scott Fetzer company
Chicago London Sydney Toronto

Merchandise Mart Plaza, Chicago, Illinois 60654

ISBN 0-7166-0583-X
ISSN 0080-7621
Library of Congress Catalog Number: 65:21776
Printed in the United States of America

Preface

Science writer Arthur C. Clarke once formulated three scientific laws, one of which says: "Any sufficiently advanced technology is indistinguishable from magic." This "law" describes a fundamental challenge for science writers and editors. Just as we know that so-called magic can be explained, so do we know that science and technology can be explained—in language that literate people, if they have sufficient interest, can understand.

The difficulty lies in bringing all subjects in science to a common level of understanding. Different areas of research have different degrees of complexity. Stories about the environment, endangered animals, or advances in medical research can be described in ways that are relatively easy to follow and that we can relate to. This is not necessarily so with stories about high-energy physics or molecular biology. Here, researchers compose theories and use mathematics to describe the fundamental pieces of the universe—in language that is incomprehensible to the average reader.

This range of scientific endeavor and the editorial approaches to it is reflected in the current *Science Year*. In the Special Report, STALKING THE MEDFLY, for example, a description of the insect's simple life cycle and fruit-destroying habits is all that is necessary to set the scene for a social-scientific story about how *not* to handle a scientific problem. NEW LIGHT ON THE ANCIENT MAYA describes the life style of an ancient people. Since we all have a life style, it is not difficult to relate to this anthropological story.

On the other hand, to appreciate CATCHING NATURE'S VANISHING ACT, the reader must first learn what a proton is made of, and how its parts behave. Understanding DIVERSIFYING OUR DEFENSES—how a million different types of antibodies are made from a substantially smaller number of genes—requires concentration and a good memory for new words.

The same things can be said of the Science File. There are interesting, easily related stories told in ENVIRONMENT or NUTRITION or ZOOLOGY. For SOLAR ASTRONOMY, or OCEANOGRAPHY, the reader has to pay a little closer attention. And if he undertakes to learn about what is going on in CONDENSED MATTER PHYSICS, or GENETICS, he must be ready for some serious reading.

The editorial staff works harder to reduce the more difficult concepts to readable terms. We think that the interested reader is also willing to work a little harder on these subjects. The reward should be a better appreciation of the scope of science and technology; a better understanding of the magic. [Arthur G. Tressler]

Contents

Staff

Editorial Director
William H. Nault

Editorial
Editor
A. Richard Harmet

Executive Editor
Arthur G. Tressler

Managing Editor
Darlene R. Stille

Senior Editors
Marsha F. Goldsmith
Barbara Mayes
Beverly Merz
Jay Myers

Contributing Editors
Gary A. Alt
Sara Dreyfuss
Irwin Saltz

Research Editor
Irene B. Keller

Editorial Assistant
Lettie Zinnamon

Art
Executive Art Director
William Hammond

Art Director
Roberta Dimmer

Senior Artist
Nikki Conner

Artists
Rosa Cabrera
Alice F. Dole
Margot McMahon
Valerie Nelson

Photography Director
John S. Marshall

Photographs Editors
Karen M. Koblik
Sandra M. Ozanick

Research and Services
Director of Editorial Services
Susan C. Kilburg

Head, Editorial Research
Mary Norton

Librarians
Sharon Glinski
Mary Kayaian

Head, Cartographic Services
H. George Stoll

Index Editor
Claire Bolton

Product Production
Executive Director
Peter Mollman

Director of Manufacturing
Joseph LaCount

Director of Pre-Press
J. J. Stack

Production Control Manager
Barbara Podczerwinski

Assistant Product Manager
Madelyn Krzak

Film Separations Manager
Alfred J. Mozdzen

Film Separations Assistant Manager
Barbara J. McDonald

Research and Development Manager
Henry Koval

World Book, Inc.
Robert H. King, Chairman of the Board and Chief Executive Officer

Executive Vice-Presidents
Michael J. Goodkin — Direct Response/Distributors
James L. Jackson — Marketing
Grant C. Malchow — Finance
Peter Mollman — Manufacturing
William H. Nault — Editorial

Editorial Advisory Board

Joseph Bordogna is Dean of the School of Engineering and Applied Science at the University of Pennsylvania. He received the B.S. and Ph.D. degrees from the University of Pennsylvania in 1955 and 1964, respectively, and the S.M. degree from Massachusetts Institute of Technology in 1960. Dean Bordogna's contributions to his field include work on communications, space electronics, and television applications of holography. He helped develop a program of engineering study for high school students.

Alexander Dalgarno is associated with the Harvard-Smithsonian Center for Astrophysics and Phillips Professor of Astronomy at Harvard University. He received the B.Sc. degree in 1947 and the Ph.D. degree in 1951 from University College, London. After a 16-year association with Queens University in Belfast, he joined the Harvard faculty in 1967. Dr. Dalgarno is Editor of the *Astrophysical Journal Letters* and is on the editorial boards of several physics and astronomy journals.

Thomas Eisner is Jacob Gould Schurman Professor of Biology at Cornell University. He received the B.A. degree in 1951 and the Ph.D. degree in 1955 from Harvard University. He was a member of the Board of Directors of the National Audubon Society from 1970 to 1975. He received the American Association for the Advancement of Science Newcomb Cleveland Prize in 1968. Professor Eisner is co-author of several books, including *Animal Adaptation* and *Life on Earth,* and is on the editorial boards of several journals.

Dr. David W. Martin Jr. is Professor of Medicine, Chief of Medical Genetics Service, and Professor of Biochemistry at the University of California, San Francisco, Medical Center. He attended the Massachusetts Institute of Technology and Duke University, from which he received the M.D. degree in 1964. Dr. Martin's research has centered on diseases of the immune system and metabolism. He is a member of the Recombinant DNA Advisory Committee of the National Institutes of Health.

Walter E. Massey is Director of the Argonne National Laboratory and professor of physics at The University of Chicago. He received the B.S. degree in 1958 from Morehouse College and the Ph.D. degree in 1966 from Washington University. He joined Brown University in 1970, where he was professor of physics and Dean of The College from 1975 to 1979. At Brown, Dr. Massey was also director of a program to prepare high school science teachers to work in inner-city schools.

Mark S. Ptashne is Professor of Biochemistry and Molecular Biology at Harvard University. He received the B.A. degree from Reed College in 1961 and the Ph.D. degree from Harvard in 1968. He was named a Fellow of the American Academy of Arts and Sciences in 1977. He won the Eli Lilly Award for Biological Chemistry in 1975, shared Le Prix Charles-Leopold Mayer de l'Académie des Sciences, Institute de France, in 1977, and won the U.S. Steel Foundation Award in Microbiology in 1979.

Leon T. Silver is Professor of Geology in the Division of Geological and Planetary Sciences at the California Institute of Technology. He received the B.S. degree from the University of Colorado in 1945, the M.S. degree from the University of New Mexico in 1948, and the Ph.D. degree from the California Institute of Technology in 1955. His research has included radiogenic isotopic systems in rocks and mineral resources, geologic evolution of North America, and lunar exploration.

Contributors

Adams, Richard E. W., Ph.D.
Professor of Anthropology
University of Texas, San Antonio
New Light on the Ancient Maya

Adelman, George, M.S.
Editor & Librarian
Neuroscience Research Program
Massachusetts Institute of Technology
Neuroscience

Alderman, Michael H., M.D.
Professor of Medicine and
Public Health
Cornell University Medical College
Medicine, Internal
Public Health

Auerbach, Stanley I., Ph.D.
Director, Environmental
Sciences Division
Oak Ridge National Laboratory
Ecology

Bell, William J., Ph.D.
Professor of Entomology and
Biology
University of Kansas
Zoology

Belton, Michael J. S., Ph.D.
Astronomer
AURA Inc.
The Hairy Stars
Astronomy, Solar System

Busby, Colin I., Ph.D.
Vice-President
Basin Research Associates, Inc.
Close-Up, Archaeology

Caldwell, Frances, B.A.
Managing Editor
The Physician and
Sportsmedicine Magazine
Fundamental Facts About Fitness

Cromie, William J., M.A.
Executive Director
Council for the Advancement
of Science Writing
Norman and Leigh Anderson
Where There's A Smoke Detector,
There's Safety

Dewdney, A. K., Ph.D.
Associate Professor
Computer Science
University of Western Ontario
Close-Up, Physics

Dewey, Russell A., Ph.D.
Assistant Professor of Psychology
Georgia Southern College
Psychology

Dickinson, Terence
Free-Lance Science Writer
Close-Up, Earth Sciences

Fermanian, Thomas W., Ph.D.
Assistant Professor of Turfgrass
Science, University of Illinois
Making the Grass Greener on Your
Side of the Fence

Fisher, Arthur, A.B.
Group Editor
Science and Engineering
Popular Science Magazine
The Promise of Videodiscs

Gates, W. Lawrence, Sc.D.
Professor and Chairman
Department of Atmospheric Sciences
Oregon State University
Warmer, Wetter Weather Ahead?
Earth Sciences, Meteorology

Glickson, Jerry D., Ph.D.
Professor of Biochemistry
University of Alabama, Birmingham
Close-Up, Medicine, Internal

Goldhaber, Paul, D.D.S
Dean and Professor of Periodontology
Harvard School of Dental Medicine
Medicine, Dentistry

Gump, Frank E., M.D.
Professor of Surgery
Columbia University
Medicine, Surgery

Hartl, Daniel L., Ph.D.
Professor of Genetics
Washington University School
of Medicine
Genetics

Hester, Thomas R., Ph.D.
Professor of Anthropology and Director
Center for Archaeological Research
University of Texas, San Antonio
Archaeology, New World

Hood, Leroy E., Ph.D.
Professor and Chairman
Department of Biology
California Institute of Technology
Diversifying Our Defenses

Jennings, Feenan D., B.S.
Director, Sea Grant Program
Texas A&M University
Earth Sciences, Oceanography

Jones, William G., A.M.L.S.
Assistant University Librarian
University of Illinois, Chicago Circle
Books of Science

Kay, Robert W., Ph.D.
Associate Professor
Cornell University
Earth Sciences, Geology

King, Lauriston R., Ph.D.
Deputy Director
Sea Grant Program
Texas A&M University
Earth Sciences, Oceanography

Konishi, Masakazu, Ph.D.
Bing Professor of Behavioral Biology
California Institute of Technology
The Ear of the Owl

Labows, John N., Jr., Ph.D.
Associate Member
Monell Chemical Senses Center
Our Most Mysterious Sense

Lamberg, Lynne, M.A.
Free-Lance Medical Journalist
Close-Up, Drugs

Lemmon, Richard M., Ph.D.
Associate Director
Laboratory of Chemical Biodynamics
University of California, Berkeley
Close-Up, Science Awards

Lewis, Richard S., B.A.
Free-Lance Writer
Space Exploration

Lubs, Herbert A., M.D.
Director, Genetics Division
University of Miami
Close-Up, Genetics

Lujan, Enrique, M.D.
Instructor in Pediatrics (Genetics)
University of Miami
Close-Up, Genetics

Maran, Stephen P., Ph.D.
Senior Staff Scientist
NASA-Goddard Space Flight Center
Astronomy, Galactic

March, Robert H., Ph.D.
Professor of Physics
University of Wisconsin
Catching Nature's Vanishing Act
Physics, Atoms and Nuclei, Particles and Forces

Maugh, Thomas H., II, Ph.D.
Senior Science Writer
Science Magazine
Time Bombs in the Blood

Meade, Dale M., Ph.D.
Head, Experimental Division
Plasma Physics Laboratory
Princeton University
Energy for the Eons

Merbs, Charles F., Ph.D.
Professor
Department of Anthropology
Arizona State University
Anthropology

Moffat, Anne Simon, B.S.
Free-Lance Science Writer
Plants that Eat Animals

Murray, Stephen S., Ph.D.
Astrophysicist
Smithsonian Center for Astrophysics
Astronomy, Extragalactic

Olson, Maynard V., Ph.D.
Assistant Professor
Department of Genetics
Washington University School of Medicine
Molecular Biology

Orbach, Raymond, Ph.D.
Professor of Physics
University of California
Physics, Condensed Matter

Patrusky, Ben, B.E.E.
Free-Lance Science Writer
Stalking the Medfly

Pennisi, Elizabeth J., M.S.
Free-Lance Science Writer
Zoology

Piel, E. Joseph, Ed.D.
Chairman, Department of Technology and Society
College of Engineering
State University of New York at Stony Brook
Should You Buy a Home Video Game?

Posa, John G., B.S.E.E.
Contributing Editor
McGraw-Hill Publications Co.
Electronics

Reed, Michael, B.S.
Free-Lance Writer
Classrooms in the Clearing

Reidenberg, Marcus M., M.D.
Professor of Pharmacology and Medicine
Cornell University Medical College
Drugs

Salisbury, Frank B., Ph.D.
Professor of Plant Physiology and Botany
Plant Science Department
Utah State University
Botany

Smith, Harding E., Ph.D.
Associate Professor of Physics
Center for Astrophysics and Space Sciences
University of California, San Diego
The Brightest Beacons

Snyderman, Ralph, M.D.
Chief, Division of Rheumatic and Genetic Diseases
Duke University Medical Center
Immunology

Shurkin, Joel N., B.A.
Science Writer and Instructor
Stanford University
Close-Up, Chemistry

Thompson, Ida, Ph.D.
Associate Research Professor
Center for Coastal and Environmental Studies
Rutgers University
Earth Sciences, Paleontology

Trefil, James S., Ph.D.
Professor of Physics
University of Virginia
Curbing Those Electricity Gluttons

Verbit, Lawrence P., Ph.D.
Professor of Chemistry
State University of New York at Binghamton
Chemistry

Visich, Marian, Jr., Ph.D.
Associate Dean of Engineering
State University of New York
Energy

Wenke, Robert, J., Ph.D.
Associate Professor
Department of Anthropology
University of Washington
Archaeology, Old World

Westman, Walt, Ph.D.
Professor of Ecosystem Analysis and Conservation
Department of Geography
University of California, Los Angeles
Environment

Wittwer, Sylvan H., Ph.D.
Director, Agricultural Experiment Station
Assistant Dean, College of Agriculture and Natural Resources
Michigan State University
Agriculture

Zakem, Brian, M.A.
Director, International Phototherapy Institute
Editor, *Phototherapy* Magazine
Bringing Images to Mind

Contributors not listed on these pages are members of the *Science Year* editorial staff.

Special Reports

The Special Reports give in-depth treatment to the major advances in science and technology. The subjects were chosen for their current importance and lasting interest.

New Light on the Ancient Maya

By Richard E. W. Adams

Scientists are adding modern tools to the classic ones in their attempt to uncover the story of the rise and fall of a once-flourishing civilization in Central America

Patterns are often a key to solving mysteries. Detectives use them to solve crimes. Archaeologists use them to find clues to the past. Such patterns showed up by chance in the laboratory one day in 1979. I was leaving the room for lunch when I noticed that a strip of radar pictures I had been studying still lay on the surface of a light table. For no particular reason, I slapped a piece of plain white paper over the pictures.

Suddenly, I could see a network of gray lines that formed grids. Were they watermarks in the paper, or something showing through from underneath? The patterns were located on the radar map in a part of northern Guatemala that I knew was occupied by a large swamp. That was the clue I needed. I suspected that I was looking at canals—waterways that might have been dug by the ancient Maya, a people who lived in what is now Guatemala, Belize, Honduras, and Yucatán in Mexico from about 800 B.C. to A.D. 1500.

Archaeologists have been fascinated by the Maya ever since their ruined cities were discovered in the mid-1800s. In lands that are now sparsely populated swamps or dense forests, the Maya built a great civilization. They developed the only true writing system in the New World, created a sophisticated system of astronomy and mathematics, and devised two complicated calendars. They set up an elaborate religion and built magnificent temples and palaces. They encouraged the production of fine and applied art, and established an extensive trading network throughout Central America.

This remarkable civilization reached its peak from A.D. 250 to 900—which archaeologists call the Classic Period—then suddenly collapsed. No one knows why. Efforts to learn about the Maya run up against a historical stone wall. When the Spanish conquered Maya lands in the 1500s, they destroyed almost all the written evidence of that civilization.

Archaeologists followed traditional research methods there. They dug and examined the remains of buildings and graves, uncovered pottery and paintings, and attempted to translate the hieroglyphics carved on stelae, or stone pillars, found in plazas and temples. And by the 1920s, they arrived at certain theories about the Maya.

The mysterious Maya ruins posed three major questions: What were the cities for? How many people lived there? How did they feed themselves? For a long time, the answers dug up in the 1920s seemed adequate. Scientists believed the cities were ceremonial centers where only a few thousand elite—members of the Maya aristocracy or nobility—lived full time, occupying themselves with priestly and intellectual activities. They thought Tikal in Guatemala, the largest Maya city-state, might have had 15,000 residents. It seemed likely that most of the population lived in the countryside. They came to the centers only for religious and political affairs and spent the rest of the time producing food by slash-and-burn farming. In this method, the trees are cut and burned to make their nutrients available to the soil. This fertilization lasts only a short time.

However, in the more than 50 years since these theories were developed, evidence has been accumulating to cast doubt on them. Archaeologists have uncovered other cities, devised better ways of estimating the population, and deciphered more of the carved and painted hieroglyphic writing, or glyphs. Consequently, our view of the Maya has changed radically.

Most of the new work has come to light in about the last 10 years. Scientists learned, for example, that Maya farmers lived in pole-walled, thatch-roofed houses built on earth mounds. By counting the remaining mounds, archaeologists can estimate how many people lived in the area surrounding a city. They also came to believe that the cities were true urban centers, not just ceremonial sites. William A. Haviland of the University of Vermont in Burlington estimated in 1969 that at least 50,000 people lived in Tikal. A slash-and-burn

The author:
Richard E. W. Adams is a professor of anthropology at the Center for Archaeological Research at the University of Texas in San Antonio.

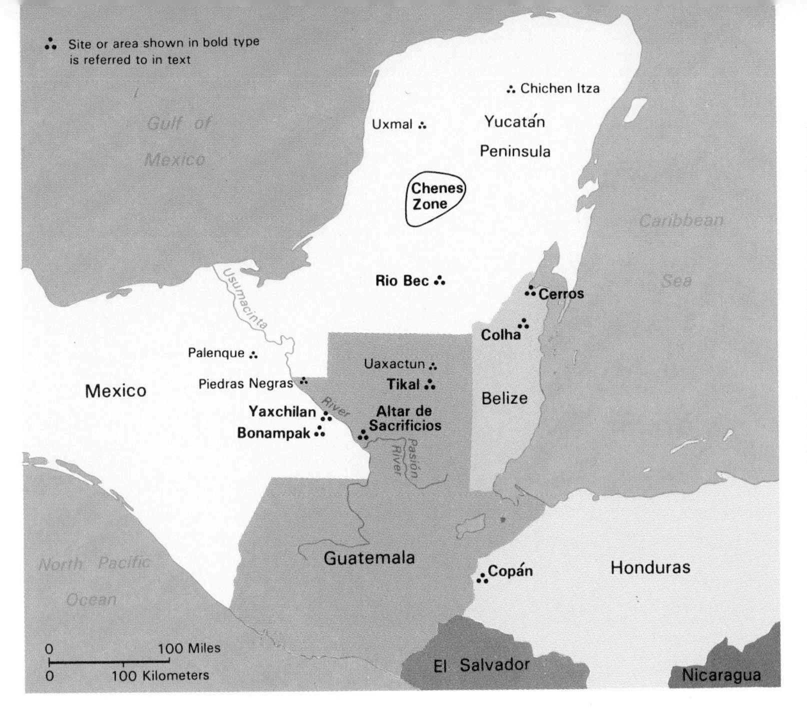

Ruins of Tikal, *above,* a Maya metropolis in the midst of a rain forest, have sparked interest in the fate of a civilization it housed more than 1,000 years ago. It is the largest of dozens of Maya sites scattered through about 250,000 square kilometers (97,000 square miles) of Central America, *above left.*

system of agriculture could not produce enough food for so many people, so how they were fed was still a puzzle.

Jack D. Eaton of the University of Texas in San Antonio suggested one answer. In 1968, he discovered thousands of square kilometers of terraced hillsides and fields surrounded by stone walls. This was evidence that the Maya understood and practiced an advanced form of agricultural engineering. Further work done in 1973 by B. L. Turner, Jr., now at Clark University in Worcester, Mass., supported this theory.

The following year, a group of scientists interested in the origins of Maya culture met at the School of American Research in Santa Fe, N. Mex., to consider what we knew and coordinate our future activities. We realized that we still needed a great many pieces of information. Among the most important was a complete count of the cities and discovery of their supporting farmlands. This would help us check our population estimates and learn how far the Maya dominion extended.

Accordingly, anthropologist T. Patrick Culbert of the University of Arizona in Tucson and I decided to make a new aerial survey of the ancient Maya homeland. In October 1977, Culbert and I flew over the territory in a plane equipped with special radar instrumentation designed to look through clouds and vapor on other planets. We hoped it might also penetrate the dense canopy of foliage that covers rain forests on earth and reveal what was underneath.

When I saw the canals in the photo lab in 1979, it seemed that our mission had been successful in at least one way. Finding that an extensive system of interlocking canals connected many of the known waterways clarified a discovery made in 1968. At that time, geogra-

A terra-cotta ballplayer with an animal headdress, *top,* is one of many figurines from Yucatán that are clues to Maya practices and beliefs. The ceremonially dressed man on a stele dated Nov. 30, 849, *above,* was found in Guatemala.

pher Alfred Siemens of the University of British Columbia in Canada and archaeologist Dennis C. Puleston of the University of Minnesota in Minneapolis had found canals in a river valley in western Campeche, Mexico. They confirmed that the raised fields between the canals could have been used for farming. But scientists had no idea of the extent of the canals—maybe those were unique. Our radar surveys indicated that there were from 1,250 to 2,500 square kilometers (480 to 960 square miles) of raised fields and canals.

Culbert and I began to make a ground check of the radar grid patterns in February 1980. Using boats and airplanes, we found several of the Maya waterways and their associated raised fields in Belize and Guatemala, including one in a swamp east of Tikal. Other scientists working in the area helped us. For example, Turner, along with Peter D. Harrison of the University of New Mexico in Albuquerque, was excavating in a place in Belize that British colonists had given the wonderful name of Pulltrouser Swamp. Their discoveries suggested how the canal and raised-field system worked.

Maya farmers dug both large and small canals. The larger ones were dug in parallel lines about 18 meters (60 feet) apart, while the smaller canals were about half that far apart. The farmers removed and saved the material dredged from the bottom of the swamps. They put a pad of *caliche,* or crushed limestone, into place between each pair of canals. Then they replaced the fertile material on top of the pad to create a growing surface. It was 60 to 90 centimeters (2 to 3 feet) above the water line. Plants growing on the raised field could benefit from moist soil without being water-logged.

Thus, rather than being simple slash-and-burn farmers, the Maya seem to have been intensive cultivators. The raised-field cultivation system was a fundamental part of the Maya economy. Combined with hillside terracing and orchard cropping, it could have supported the estimated 14 million to 20 million persons who lived in the Maya lowlands from A.D. 600 to 900. In addition, the canals were water highways. We used to think each Maya city stood isolated in the forest—the way the ruins stand today. But we know now that cities were built at the edges of swamps to make trade and communication between them as easy as possible.

The new picture of food production and population location is augmented by advances in other areas of Maya studies. One rich source of new information is the hieroglyphic writing Maya sculptors painstakingly carved into the thousands of stelae. Earlier, archaeologists believed the purpose of the stelae was to show calendar corrections and images of the gods that ruled a particular period of time. In 1960, architect-turned-archaeologist Tatiana Proskouriakoff of Harvard University's Peabody Museum of Archaeology and Ethnology undertook the extremely difficult task of deciphering the glyphs. She proposed that they recorded historical events in addition to myths, astronomy, ritual, and religion. Proskouriakoff's prelimi-

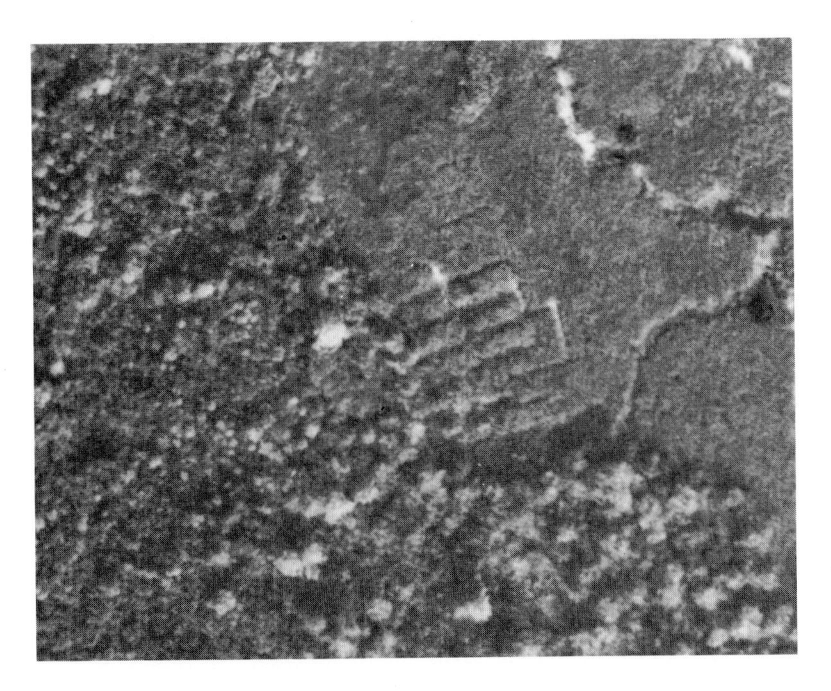

Gridlike patterns on radar photos, *above,* of Maya territory in what is now Guatemala hint at what a visit to land reclaimed by the forest in Belize confirmed. They are remains of a vast system of canals and raised fields, *below,* that the ancient Maya used for farming.

nary work has proved that this history was about ruling dynasties and the city-states they controlled. Rulers are named, their titles given, and the importance of their families emphasized. This tells us that the Maya had a complex, multilayered society. For example, in 1962 and 1963, Proskouriakoff deciphered the texts of stelae at Yaxchilán in Guatemala. She read the history of a ruler named Bird-Jaguar II from the elements in his personal name glyph—a symbol that appeared close to the ruler's body. Bird-Jaguar II came to power in A.D. 752, succeeding Shield-Jaguar, his father. He is described as having conquered a number of communities and their rulers during his reign. At Tikal, a sequence of rulers from about A.D. 350 to 870 was established through studies of tomb furniture and sculpture begun in 1975 by Christopher Jones of the University of Pennsylvania in Philadelphia and Clemency Coggins of Harvard University in Boston. Fortunately, the records interlock. That is, the Tikal glyphs mention other cities and other rulers at less important centers, so that we can check their accuracy.

Combining these histories of dynasties with the depictions of warfare and the known fortresses, such as the one Eaton and I excavated in Guatemala's Rio Bec region in 1970, gives us the impression that the Maya were often at war. Furthermore, glyphs recording warfare increased in frequency from about A.D. 600 on, hinting at internal troubles that may have led to the collapse.

The Maya elite were concerned throughout the Classic Period with burial ritual, and they built sumptuous tombs to honor the distinguished dead. The evidence in some tombs reverses the idea that the Maya were isolated. They appear to have influenced and been influenced by surrounding cultures, such as the then-great Mexican city of Teotihuacán. It also seems that the elite of various Maya cities were in close contact and many rulers were related.

Canals cut through the forest served the Maya in at least three ways – as a constant water source for crops growing on the piled-up earth fields, as a local fishing area, and as travel routes for intracity trading and social relations.

Hieroglyphic records, supported by the contents of the tombs of the rulers at Tikal, tell of an intrusion into the Maya area in about A.D. 378 of a ruler who was allied with Teotihuacán. This man established a line of succession that seems to have been broken, then re-established later by another man archaeologists know as Ruler A. One possible interpretation of Ruler A's name glyph is Kal Cacabil, meaning "Producer of Chocolate." This name seems appropriate, because the Maya placed a high value on cacao beans, from which chocolate is made. They used them as a medium of exchange. Ruler A also was one of the first to have an extraordinarily large burial monument. After he died in about A.D. 730, a colossal temple 40 meters (130 feet) high was built over his tomb. Into the tomb itself went an immense quantity of valuable items, including 7.5 kilograms (16.5 pounds) of jade and much polychrome pottery. There were also several animal bones beautifully carved with canoeing scenes, along with a pair of bone tweezers engraved with his name.

As might be expected in a civilization that set great store by its ancestors, funeral ceremonies for the elite class tended to be elaborate. We can reconstruct some of them from excavations. There is one striking scene recorded on a polychrome vase from Altar de Sacrificios, a small city on the Pasión River. I was part of a group under the direction of Harvard University archaeologist Gordon R. Willey that dug into a very large temple there in 1962. Inside the structure, we found an earlier building where two burials had been made—one in an elaborate tomb and one in a simple grave.

The tomb contained the bones of a middle-aged woman along with 15 pieces of pottery and jade and costume jewelry. This indicated she was a member of the elite. The grave contained the bones of a young woman in her 20s. Her filed, jade-inlaid teeth indicated that she was also of high status. Four pieces of pottery were found near this woman. One of them was a superbly painted polychrome vase depicting four dancing and posturing human figures. Hieroglyphs explain the scene and identify the people. The date is A.D. 754. One of the dancers is Yaxchilán's ruler, Bird-Jaguar II. Another figure, identified as coming from Tikal, may be Ruler A's younger brother. Still another person comes from the highlands of Guatemala. The fourth figure is a dead or dying woman whose throat has been cut.

I have interpreted the ceremony as the funeral of the older woman buried in the tomb. The person with the cut throat was apparently the young woman in the simple grave—a sacrificial victim required to accompany the older woman into the afterlife. The other persons from various places must have attended the funeral and brought with them the other pottery we found.

Maya fortresses, built of mud, had spectator sections. Protected by a moat, noncombatants watch from the ramparts as elite warriors meet invaders from a rival city-state to defend their own ruler's supremacy.

Figures and glyphs on a funeral pot, *above,* from A.D. 754 depict elite rites and relationships. A painting made to show the whole scene, *top,* reveals that the funeral required a sacrificial victim (left) and the presence – and presents – of neighboring nobles come to honor the dead.

I believe there were at least 12 Maya regional states, some of them occasionally united under one capital, but many of them independent and competing. Within the regional states were the city-states and smaller cities, surrounded by farmland. We think the elite classes lived in the cities most of the time, because we have found so many palaces, each containing several apartments. Excavators have also found lower-class residences, warehouses, workshops, reservoirs, and roads in a typical Maya city.

There must have been considerable variety in the way society was arranged within the political boundaries of the states. It was probably based in most places on a feudal system, where the lower classes gave allegiance to the upper classes in return for the use of farmland and protection against invaders. Historian Woodruff D. Smith of the University of Texas in San Antonio and I suggested in 1981 that the Rio Bec and nearby Chenes districts north of Tikal may have been organized somewhat loosely along feudal lines.

Eaton had found rural housing remains consisting of small house platforms and farmsteads on hilltops surrounded by the terraced hillsides. In this scheme, the commoners or peasantry lived on the land and farmed it for the elite owners off in the city. Scattered around the landscape are small courtyards surrounded by somewhat larger house platforms and, in many cases, a small stone building. These might be the residences of the "squirearchy" — an intermediate class of people not quite nobility but a cut above the commoners — who managed the estates and farms. Less frequent, but interspersed among the common houses out in the countryside, are single and multiple palaces or "manor houses" for visiting nobility.

It is pretty easy to imagine what peasant life in the Maya countryside was like, because farmers the world over share certain traits. They generally have large, close-knit families because "many hands make light work." Also, their lives are tied to the seasons and to cycles of weather and of crop and animal reproduction. For the Maya living in the swamp zones, some agricultural activity was possible throughout the year. But the annual cycle in the hillier and drier parts of the Maya lowlands consists of a wet growing season from June through November and a dry season from December through May. During this latter, relatively idle, period, the commoner population must have been mobilized for building projects.

Both country and city palaces show the effects of constant change and enlargement. This implies the existence of part-time craftsmen — farmers who also had a skill such as stonecutting. While the farming cycle may have occupied most of their year, these people must also have spent a good deal of the dry season working on buildings and renovations. Temples were built when someone important died, of course. Reservoirs, roads, and other public works were probably built as need dictated. Need often dictated a great deal — for example, the combined capacity of the reservoirs at Tikal was about 10.5 million liters (40 million gallons). Another example is the raised Maya roads, which are usually broad enough for at least a dozen people to walk abreast. They ran quite straight across the countryside, providing rights of way through a landscape crowded with farms. At the city of Copán in Honduras, they also led to the country estates of the nobility. Mapping and excavation work done by Harvard University's Willey and Richard W. Leventhal in 1977 turned up a sort of early expressway — a roadway that led out of Copán with small paved exit ramps leading to elite-class housing located at various points along the road.

The many building tasks in the Maya empire naturally required many tools. The digging done at Colha in Belize from 1979 to 1981 by Thomas R. Hester of the University of Texas, San Antonio, and Harry Shafer of Texas A&M University in College Station showed that hundreds of thousands of high-quality stone tools were produced. Most of these seem to have been exported. In fact, Harrison and Turner found some remnants of Colha tools in the raised fields and canals of Pulltrouser Swamp in 1980 and 1981. We had not realized that so many tools were produced as items of trade.

Other commodities traded between the various city-states included honey, raw cotton, and probably such manufactured goods as henequen cloth. Their weight and the difficulty of packing them on the backs of human porters make it likely that these things were shipped by canoe. Despite their advances in so many areas of civilization, the Maya never used wheeled vehicles, and had no pack animals. There was a lot of canoe traffic around the Yucatán Peninsula in the 1500s. David A. Freidel of Southern Methodist University in Dallas and his colleagues, who dug at Cerros in northern Belize in the late 1970s, uncovered an early port there. While it is not certain what was shipped out of Cerros besides the Colha tools, it was a

successful enough community from about 250 B.C. to A.D. 250 to erect moderate-sized temple structures. However, after about A.D. 250, the ports in the Maya lowlands were no longer independent. William J. Folan of the Center of Historic and Social Studies in Campeche, Mexico, suggested in 1980 that each major prehistoric city in Yucatán controlled a smaller coastal community that functioned as its port. The larger city would protect the smaller from enemy raids while itself being less susceptible to other risks such as hurricanes.

Trade proceeded on several levels. Access to the most exquisite and costly items was confined, as you might expect, to the uppermost levels of society. Impressive pottery and stone gifts undoubtedly played a great part in elite personal and political relationships. Maya fine arts and crafts, such as sculpture, stucco work, jade carving, and other highly skilled endeavors, were undoubtedly the product of full-time specialists. These people not only had to learn the complex skills of their art, but also master the Maya rules of symbolism and the hieroglyphic writing system. Because such artists produced wares for the elite class, it seems likely that they were attached to the households of the great lords more or less permanently.

Maya artists were concerned with depicting the gods and ancestors of ruling and distinguished nobles, whose ancestors were often considered to be gods. The artists also recorded the history of rulers and their states, and symbols of supernatural and secular power. They painted vases, produced folding-screen books on paper, carved wooden boxes and lintels or house beams, sculpted stelae, and managed to wrest beautiful forms from extremely hard pieces of jade. These items added to the prestige of the elite and went with them into the afterlife, or at least into their tombs.

Before they went, the Maya elite seem to have led a fairly pleasant life on earth. Undoubtedly, most of them were waited on; servants and retainers are pictured in the sculptures and such paint-

Pomp and circumstance characterize a coronation. As thousands of his subjects celebrate in the great central plaza, a new Maya ruler ascends the steep temple stairs to receive a priestly blessing and to make vows to his gods and ancestors.

A thatched hut built by Lacandon Indians living in Yucatán today, *above,* is probably very similar to those of Maya farmers. A young Lacandon, *below,* bears a remarkable resemblance to one of his Maya ancestors.

ings as the remarkable series of murals at Bonampak in Mexico dating from A.D. 752. Ceremonial and court protocol—the framework within which the business of politics was carried on—probably took up a great deal of time. Alliances were formed, plots thwarted, intrigues spun out, and all the familiar features of personal and palace life in other cultures had their time and place in the Maya empire. The elite were far from being just philosophical stargazers. Unfortunately, we know few details of those daily matters, and so miss much of the quality and tone of Maya civilization. But, now and then—as in the case of the funeral pot I helped find—some new information comes to light that illuminates our understanding and engages our sympathies.

For those of us committed to learning all we can about Maya culture, this makes it harder to bear the knowledge that this richly civilized society suffered a catastrophe that still evades our full comprehension. Generations of archaeologists have pondered the collapse of Maya civilization. Based on the evidence they have found so far, most of them believe the collapse was probably a mix of different factors at different places. No area seems to have been able to recover once difficulties became severe. A downward spiral in which one disaster fed on another is probably the best way to visualize the Maya collapse.

We know that starting in about A.D. 600, Maya population grew and the people expanded into new areas. Farmers drained large areas of swampland, terraced hillsides, and built walled fields. But producing enough food for this population proved difficult.

In 1973, physical anthropologist Frank P. Saul of the University of Ohio Medical School in Toledo studied many Maya bones. He found that evidence of scurvy and other diseases caused by poor nutrition increased toward A.D. 900, especially among the lower classes; they were probably eating more root crops, which provide little protein. In addition, Saul's studies showed that the Maya population suffered many diseases. Those that occurred regularly included malaria, yellow fever, trypanosome or Chagas' disease, and possibly syphilis. In addition, hunger and famine could lower resistance to disease, and so pave the way for epidemics. These, in turn, further depleted the manpower needed for farming.

Another reason for poor harvests may have been climatic change. Joel Gunn of the University of Texas, San Antonio, and I pointed out in 1981 that a warmer, drier weather period began about the time of the Maya collapse. A general decline in rainfall would have dried up even the swamps and increased crop failures.

Some scientists think the Maya elite may have made bad administrative decisions that led to revolt or war. Archaeologist A. J. Taylor of Texas A&M University found evidence in 1980 for a massacre of the elite class at Colha in about A.D. 850. She found that about 28 persons of various ages—indicating they were not all warriors—had been executed and their heads piled into a pit along with smashed pottery. The pit had been dug in front of a palace building—perhaps their home—which was then burned down. Nearby were the scattered remains of at least 20 more persons, who may have been killed in battle. We are not certain whether this represents a military intrusion from the northern cities or a revolt, although it seems more likely to be the former. We know that outsiders conquered the Maya at about that time in at least five other cities.

Thanks to the work of Proskouriakoff and her colleagues, the Maya writing system is being unraveled, but we are a long way from having a complete transcription and translation of all the texts. Between 1975 and 1982, Ian Graham of Harvard University published eight volumes of a projected 50 that will eventually be an accurate record of all known Maya texts. The task is an urgent one because, in addition to enabling scientists in the future to work on the glyphs, it will provide photographs of the strangely attractive stelae sculptures before they are gone.

Unfortunately, it is now a race between archaeologist and looter. It is illegal to steal and trade in ancient artifacts, but that does not deter thieves. Our work must be completed as soon as possible, because the black market for antiquities is contributing to the destruction of records of the past.

The Maya collapse still haunts those of us who work in the field of Central American archaeology. Because we cannot figure out how the civilization fell unless we know what held it up, we are exploring new research trails. For example, we are just beginning to learn the structure of Maya society. We need more understanding of the agricultural system, and we need to know further details of the urban networks and rural settlements.

There is much to be learned and much work to be done.

The Ear of the Owl

By Masakazu Konishi

As a night hunter, the barn owl owes its survival not just to keen eyesight but to a sense of hearing more accurate than that of any other animal

The barn owl sits motionless on a high rafter, listening intently to the sounds of the night. As it picks up a faint rustling in the dry leaves below, it swivels its head abruptly, pauses for a split second, and swoops from its perch. It positions its talons in mid-flight and makes its strike. Within seconds, it returns with its daily dinner—a small gray field mouse.

As an animal physiologist engaged in the study of hearing in the barn owl, I have watched this scene hundreds of times. My research over the past 16 years has shown that, to this owl, life depends upon a sense of directional hearing that is more accurate than that of any other animal studied. Yet, each time I witness the owl in action, I am fascinated anew by its ability to track its prey solely by the sounds they make.

I am not alone in my fascination with the owl. Its round face, wide-eyed expression, and plump body have made it a favorite subject for artists, sculptors, and toymakers throughout the world. The ancient Greeks interpreted its habit of perching motionless while other birds fluttered about as a sign of intelligence. They designated the bird the pet of Athena, the mythical goddess of wisdom. To some primitive Asian and African cultures, the owl's nocturnal hunting made it the embodiment of evil spirits. However, although the owl has been adored, revered, and even feared, people have until recently understood very little about it.

One common misunderstanding about owls is that they can see in the dark. Zoologist Lee R. Dice, of the University of Michigan in

Ann Arbor, disproved this in the 1940s. He scattered dead mice on the floor of a totally darkened room and put a series of owls in the room. None of them found a single mouse.

How is it, then, that most owls hunt their prey — field mice and other small rodents — at night? For one thing, night is seldom totally dark. And owls have very good vision, which helps them to locate objects in dim light. But there are conditions when acute vision cannot account for the hunting owl's accuracy. Scientists began to suspect that they were using another sense. Live mice in nature do one thing that dead mice on a laboratory floor do not; they make rustling noises. Could the owl be using its ears as well as its eyes to locate its prey?

I knew very little about the owl until 1966, when I came to Princeton University in New Jersey as an assistant professor of biology to study sound perception in songbirds. Our laboratory was something of a sanctuary for homeless birds and, one day that fall, a local bird watcher brought in three baby barn owls he had rescued from a church that was about to be demolished. This gift was to change the focus of my research. I decided to use these owls to study how the owl's brain located the sound that its ears heard.

I raised these owls and subsequent generations of owls with the aid of Michael Watson, a graduate biology student from Australia, who was interested in studying the development of hunting skills in the barn owl. By the end of 1967, our barn-owl population numbered 20, and I began to plan my research project.

The author:
Masakazu Konishi is professor of behavioral biology at California Institute of Technology in Pasadena.

First, I needed a tame subject. Although all our adult owls had been raised in captivity, none could be considered tame because they had been raised with other owls. Only owls raised alone develop a close relationship with the trainer.

I took a baby owl from the last clutch born that spring to hand-raise in my apartment. I named the owl "Roger" for zoologist Roger S. Payne, who pioneered the study of barn owl hearing. It was not until 1975 that I realized that Roger had been misnamed — that was when she began to lay eggs.

I hoped that Roger would teach me two things — how accurately the barn owl tracked the source of a sound, and which variables in that sound provided important clues that helped the owl locate the sound source.

Roger Payne, working at Cornell University in Ithaca, N.Y., in the early 1960s, laid the groundwork for our research. Payne set up a movie camera that would photograph in infrared light in a room he built on campus and covered the floor with dead leaves. He made the room absolutely dark and set mice loose. He placed an owl in the room and turned on the camera. When he viewed the film later, he saw that his owl had caught the rustling mice easily. When he repeated the experiment, substituting a speaker broadcasting tape-recorded mouse sounds for the live prey, the owl struck the speaker.

A drawing made by 16th-century Dutch artist Hieronymus Bosch emphasizes the owl's tendency to sit motionless, as if analyzing the activity about it. A legend with the drawing reads, "The field has eyes, the forest has ears, I want to see, be silent, and hear."

Payne then trailed a ball of paper from a string attached to a mouse's tail and replaced the dead leaves with sand to muffle any sounds the mouse might make. When the owl was set loose, it struck the ball of paper, the source of the sound—rather than the mouse. These results indicated that the owl does not detect its prey by smell or body heat—its only clue is the sound the mouse makes.

The barn owl's hearing is developed to an extraordinary degree. Although no bird can hear sounds at as high a pitch as humans, owls can hear higher-pitched sounds than any other bird. They can also hear extremely faint sounds that are not perceptible to humans.

The barn owl's great sensitivity to sound is largely due to the sound-collecting property of the facial ruff—the wall of stiff, densely

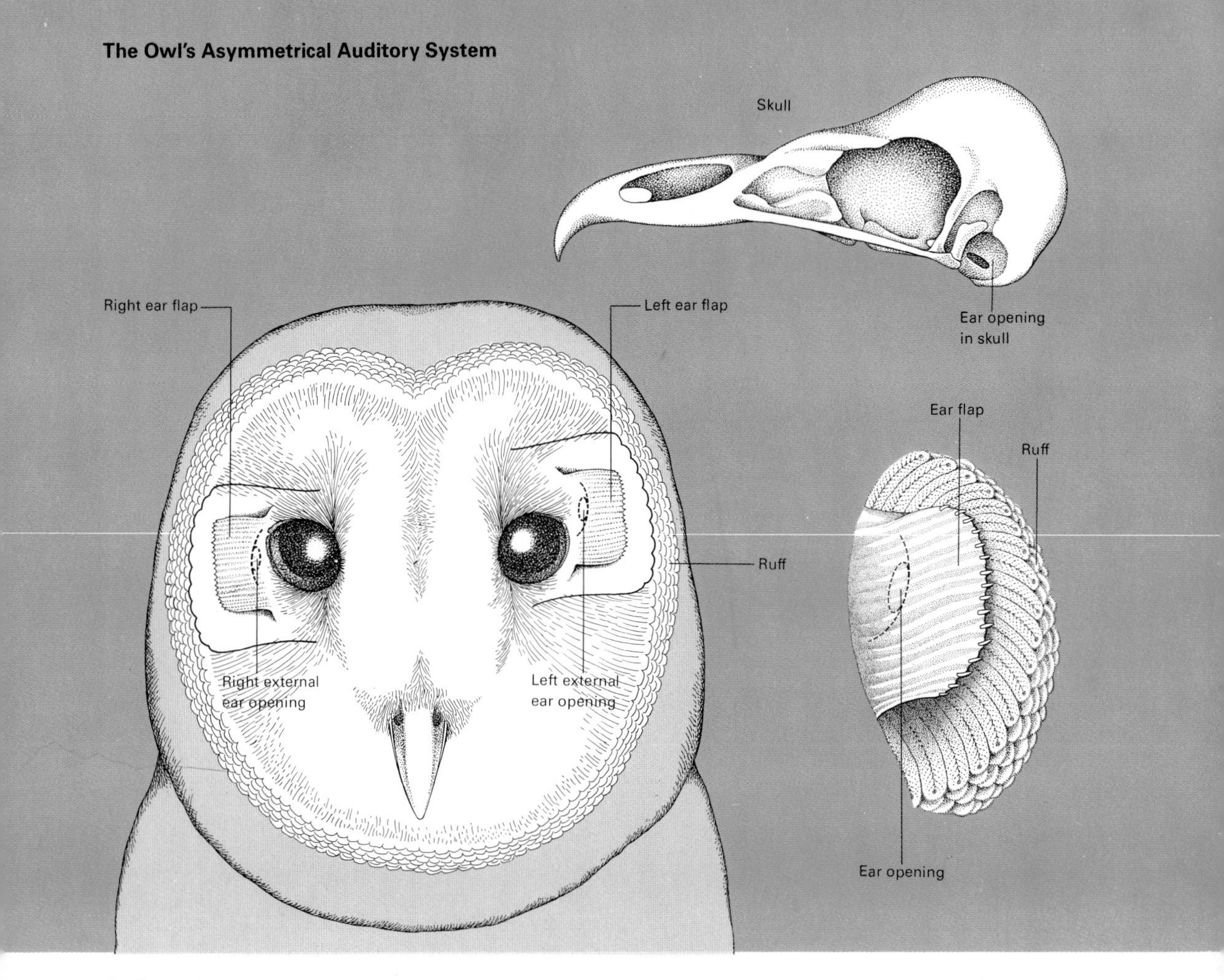

Auditory Asymmetry
The owl's skull, *top right,* is small in proportion to its face, *above,* which is extended by the ruff, a thick band of feathers that collects sound. The ear openings in the skull are symmetrical, but the right earflap and external ear opening, which are directed up to catch sounds from above, are slightly lower than the same structures, *above right,* on the left, which are directed down to catch sounds from below.

packed feathers that makes a heart-shaped outline around the face. Each side of the ruff extends from the owl's forehead, behind its ear opening and down to its "chin." The two walls of the ruff meet in a feather ridge at the midline of the face. Like a hand cupped behind an ear, the large surface of the ruff collects sound and channels it into the ear openings. Owl species that hunt at night, like the barn owl, have larger ruffs than those that hunt during the day because they need the extra amplification that the larger ruff provides.

Roger and I began with slight variations on Payne's work. I wanted to know how accurately the owl pinpointed sound and which variables in that sound were important to the owl. I trained Roger to strike a small earphone lying on a sheet of soft clay. At first I put a dead mouse next to the earphone and broadcast the sound of a mouse rustling. Roger flew down and grabbed the mouse. After several successful trials, I removed the mouse. Roger then struck the earphone, and sometimes even seized it in her claws and carried it back to the perch.

The pink flap that lies over the barn owl's ear opening has a structural resemblance to the human outer ear. Feathers on the outside of the earflap and in the ruff behind the ear act like cupped hands to funnel sound into the opening.

However, I was dissatisfied with my system of measuring Roger's strike accuracy. I had to measure the distance between the earphone and the claw markings and smooth out the clay after each trial. This was tedious and less than precise.

To solve all of these problems, in 1970 I designed a new system. I equipped the test room with six loudspeakers hidden under a false floor. The surface of the floor was crisscrossed with a network of microswitches. At the slightest touch, these microswitches turned on a corresponding light on a panel in the control room.

I broadcast mouse noises from one of the six speakers in random sequence, so that Roger could not remember their positions. When Roger struck the floor, a light indicated her position, and I could immediately calculate the distance between the speaker that had broadcast the sound and her strike.

I learned many things about the barn owl's hearing using this system. I frequently varied the type of sounds that I broadcast, testing Roger with sounds of various frequencies and bandwidths. The frequency of a sound is determined by the number of times the object making the sound vibrates each second. One vibration per second is called 1 hertz (hz). The higher a sound's frequency is, the higher its pitch will be. The bandwidth of a sound refers to the range between the highest and lowest frequencies that are encompassed within that sound.

I found that Roger, and other barn owls I have tested, struck most accurately at sounds with frequencies between 6,000 and 9,000 hz. These experiments also revealed that the barn owl can pinpoint the source of sounds such as hissing noises, that encompass about 16,000 hz, much more accurately than narrowband sounds like a whistle, which may be only 300 hz wide. Thus, the barn owl can easily pick up the field mouse's wideband rustles.

Once I had learned which particular sounds the owl located best, I was eager to discover exactly how it did so. I needed an even more precise system of presenting sounds and measuring the owl's ability to pinpoint them. In 1975, I moved to my new quarters in Beckman Laboratories of Behavioral Biology at the California Institute of Technology (Caltech) in Pasadena. When I arrived, a crew had already begun to construct a very large soundproof, echoless room for my research.

The snowy owl, *above,* does not rely solely on its hearing, and must hunt while there is still light, *top*. The barn owl, a night hunter, *opposite page,* swoops down upon a field mouse in complete darkness. The feathers of its facial ruff, *below,* focus sounds, enabling it to locate its prey with great accuracy.

Because I wanted the owl to locate the speaker without striking it, I took advantage of something I had noticed in my work with Roger and other barn owls. I had observed the owls pinpoint sound by turning their faces toward the source of barely audible noises. I would train an owl to remain on its perch while I broadcast the sound and develop a way to measure precisely the direction that its head turned in response. With this system, I could also eliminate the possibility of errors that might arise due to the owl's inability to fly directly to the target it had located. Thus, I could determine more accurately how the owl had located a sound.

My neurophysiology colleague Jack B. Pettigrew and I conceived of a device that could move a small speaker—5 centimeters (2 inches) in diameter—on a track around the owl's head. We asked technician C. Herbert Adams, a machinist who had participated in the construction of equipment for the United States aerospace program, to help us design it.

Newly hatched barn owls are raised by humans and away from each other so that they will be tame enough to train.

A room lined with foam polyhedrons provides a lightless, soundproof laboratory in which to test the owl's ability to locate sound. The owl is centered under a semicircular track that can be rotated 360°. A small speaker travels along the track, permitting sound to be broadcast from any point on an imaginary sphere surrounding the owl.

We developed a semicircular track, 2 meters (6½ feet) in diameter, for the speaker that formed a 180° arc around the owl's head. Both ends of the arc were fastened to tripods by adjustable screws that allowed us to rotate it almost 360° around the owl. This allowed the speaker as it moved on the track to cover every point on an imaginary sphere surrounding the owl. I used this device not only to continue my studies of the owl's ability to locate sounds, but also to begin new studies of the owl's auditory neurons.

Gary G. Bladsdel, a Caltech neurophysiologist, developed the measuring device I needed in 1977. We anesthetized the owl and cemented a small ceramic socket onto its skull. We then mounted a small coil, called a search coil, in the socket and placed the owl between two pairs of larger coils — one pair directly above and below the owl; the other to its right and left. An electric current flowing in

A small search coil mounted on an owl's head receives a current as it intercepts the magnetic fields generated by pairs of coils above and below and on either side of the owl. The strength of induced current indicates the precise position of the owl's head as it turns to locate the source of a broadcast sound.

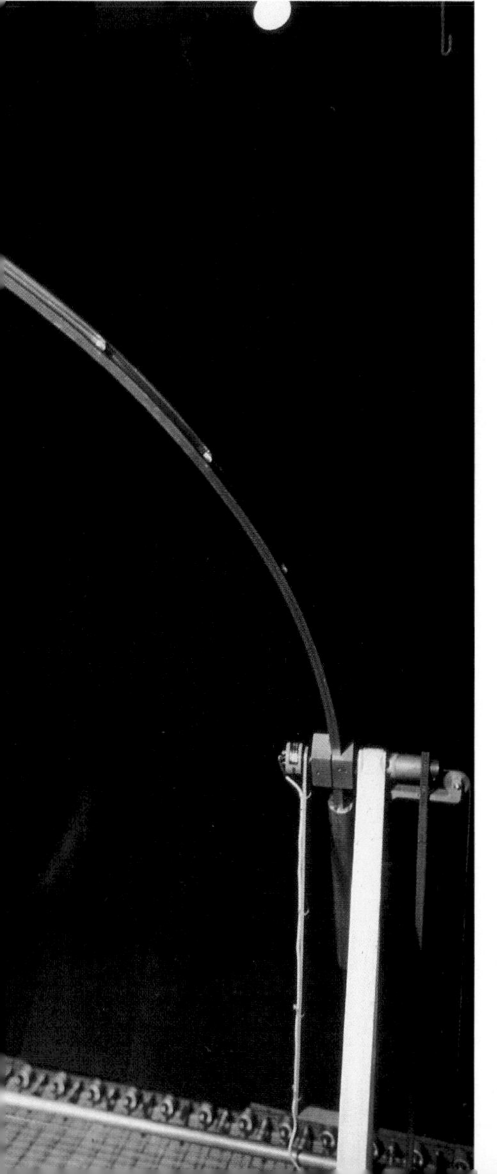

A researcher operates the computer that controls the speaker and monitors the owl's responses in the laboratory next door.

each of the large coils sets up two magnetic fields — a vertical field between the first set and a horizontal field between the second set.

When the search coil moves in either field, an electric current is induced in it. The amount of current in the search coil depends upon its position in relation to each pair. When the search coil is parallel to either pair, as when the owl faces directly downward or to the left or right, the maximum amount of current is generated in the search coil. When the search coil is perpendicular to either pair, as when the owl is facing directly forward, it receives a minimum amount of current. Thus, we were able to pinpoint the precise horizontal and vertical position of the owl's head by measuring the amount of electricity flowing through the search coil.

We then positioned the speaker on the track and broadcast the mouse sounds over it. The owl responded immediately, turning its head toward the direction of the sound within one-hundredth of a second. Our device showed us how accurately it pinpointed the sound. We repeated this test with the speaker in other positions.

Using this method, my postdoctoral student, Eric I. Knudsen, and I could measure how accurately the owl positioned its head to face the speaker. We found that when the speaker was directly in front of the owl's face, the margin of error was the lowest — 1.5° in both the vertical and horizontal planes. In a range within 30° from the midline of the face, the owl can locate sound more accurately than any other land animal studied, including humans.

We also noted that even if the sound was broadcast so briefly that it ended before the owl turned its head, the owl was still able to pinpoint the sound accurately. This indicated that the owl's ear and brain system can determine the position of the sound almost instantaneously — even before the owl begins to turn its head toward it. It therefore must pick up special auditory information — some cues unique to each location in space — to locate the sound.

Our next step was to determine exactly what these cues were. We knew that there were two types of auditory cues: monaural — those that provide the same information to either ear; and binaural — those that present different information to each ear. If the owl was processing only monaural cues, it could locate sound as accurately with one ear as with both. We tested to see if the cues were monaural by plugging completely each of the owl's ears in succession and testing to see how well it could locate sound. The owl could not locate sound at all with one ear, so we concluded that the cues were binaural. But what kind of binaural cues does the owl use?

Because the head is between the right ear and the left, a sound emanating from the right will seem softer to the left ear. Naturally, the closer the sound source is to the middle of the face, the smaller the difference in intensity.

We partially plugged the owl's ears to determine how it used this difference in loudness. We found that the owl directed its face well

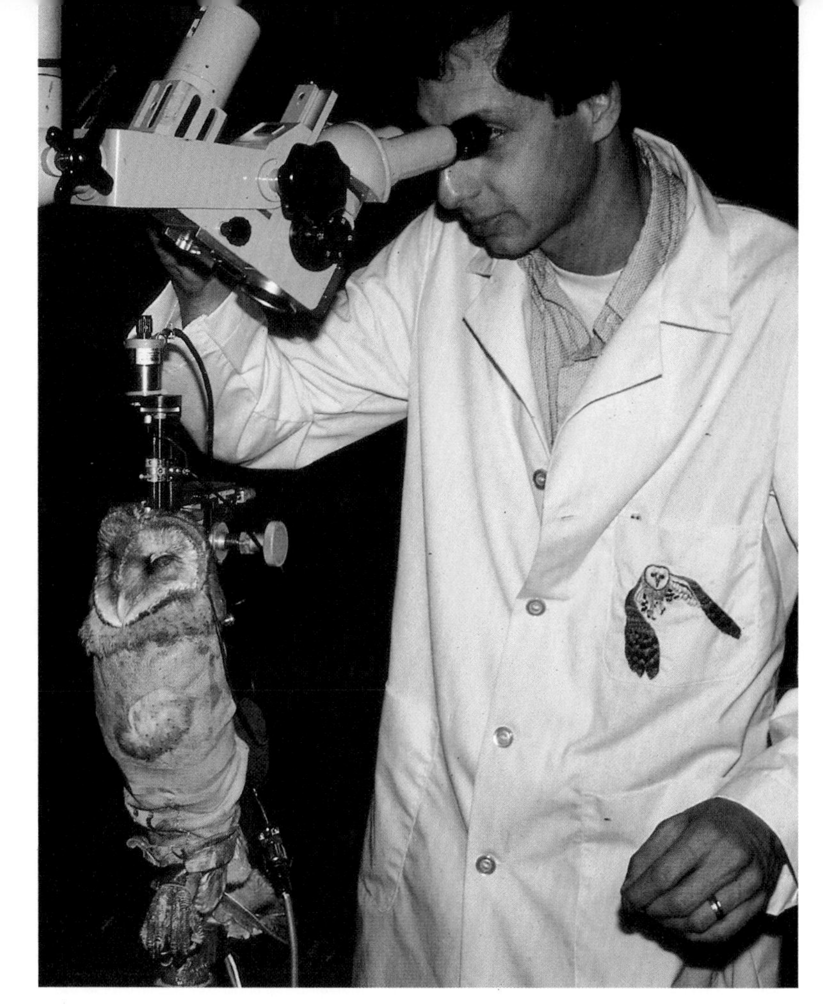

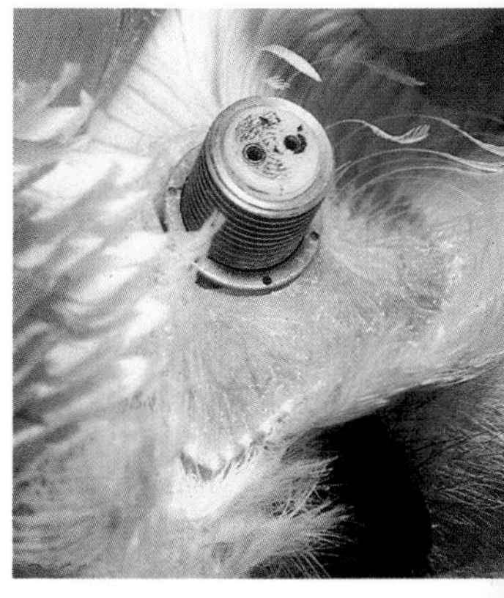

A small earphone is fitted into a ring sewn into the ear of an anesthetized owl, *above,* and an electrode is implanted in its brain, *left,* in preparation for tests to determine which neurons respond to certain sounds registered in the ear. The owl is constrained by a leather jacket to avoid its injuring itself.

above and slightly to the right of the speaker when its left ear was plugged, and well below and slightly to the left of the speaker when its right ear was plugged.

The owl's response to this test also indicated to us how the asymmetrical makeup of the owl's hearing system comes into play. The owl's right ear is located slightly lower than the left and is surrounded by a slightly upward-pointing ruff, which makes the right ear more sensitive to sounds emanating from above. The left ear has a downward-pointing ruff, making it better equipped to pick up sounds from below. Thus, when the left ear is plugged, the owl hears a more intense sound in its right ear, indicating the sound source is "high." When the right ear is plugged, it hears a more intense sound in the left ear, indicating that the sound source is "low."

While this cue accounts for the owl's ability to locate sound in the vertical direction, it does not explain how it locates sound in the horizontal direction. On the horizontal plane, another factor becomes important. The right ear hears sound coming from the right of the head slightly before the left ear does. My co-worker, neurobiologist Andrew Moiseff, and I in 1980 began to explore how the owl used this time difference in pinpointing sound.

A. J., one of the author's prize subjects, displays an extracurricular interest in the piano, perhaps suggesting a similarity between owls' and humans' perceptions of sound.

Since the owl's head is small, the time difference is minute—only a few microseconds. (A microsecond is one-millionth of a second.) We measured these differences and found that when the speaker is 20° to the right of the midline of the face, sound arrives at the right ear 40 microseconds before it reaches the left ear.

Moiseff and I anesthetized an owl, sutured small rings into the owl's ear openings, and fitted small earphones into the rings. After the anesthesia wore off, we broadcast sounds to each earphone independently. We found that if we played a sound on one earphone a few microseconds before we played it on the other, the owl would turn its face to a predictable position. For example, if we played the noise in the right ear 40 microseconds before we played it in the left ear, the owl would face 20° to the right of the midline—just as if the sound had been coming from that direction. We proved that the ability to perceive and process these split-second cues was critical to the owl's ability to pinpoint the horizontal location of sounds.

Earlier, Knudsen and I had studied which neurons are devoted to sound impulses. Now Pettigrew and I were trying to determine which neurons are devoted to locating sound. When these cells are stimulated by a sound they emit electrical charges that can be picked up with an electrode and displayed on an oscilloscope screen.

To locate and track these neurons in an owl, we anesthetized the bird and inserted a tiny electrode into its brain. We dressed the owl in a tiny leather jacket to keep it from flapping its wings and injuring itself. We then positioned it under the speaker track and began the tedious process of placing the microelectrode on a neuron, moving the speaker through a series of positions, and broadcasting sounds at each position until the neuron fired. We found that each neuron responded only to sound emanating from a very small area in space. We identified many neurons by the position of the sound source to which they responded.

Next, we wanted to see how a neuron responded to a sound emanating from the corresponding area in space when one ear was partially plugged. We inserted the microelectrode on a neuron, positioned the speaker in the corresponding area, and broadcast the sound. The neuron fired. But when we plugged one of the owl's ears, the neuron no longer fired. We had to shift the speaker in order to stimulate the neuron. When the left ear was plugged, we had to move the speaker below and to the left of its original position. When the right ear was plugged, we had to move the speaker above and to the right. The owl's brain made the same mistake in these experiments as its head made in the earlier research.

This test told us how the cues to the elevation of a sound registered in the owl's brain, but we also wanted to know how the cues to the horizontal location were processed. We placed the microelectrode on a neuron that we had previously located — the neuron we knew responded to sounds 20° to the right of the midline — and inserted the tiny earphones in the owl's ears. Then, as before, we played sounds in one ear a few microseconds before they were played in the other ear. The neuron fired only when the sounds were played 40 microseconds apart. This substantiated our earlier findings that the owl judges the horizontal location of the sound by the interval between the time it reaches the first ear and the time it reaches the second. It also explained why a neuron responds only to sound coming from a very restricted area in space — it has to respond to cues from two dimensions — the sound's horizontal location as well as its elevation.

As Knudsen and I continued to chart neurons according to the location of the sounds they registered, we were plotting a map that showed the relationship between the locations of neurons in the brain and the locations of corresponding sound sources. As we expected, the neurons that registered sounds emanating from sources near each other are located in the same region of the brain.

Our work with the barn owl has enabled us to learn much about the intricate relationship between the sounds we hear and the way we perceive them. Although the owl can pinpoint the elevation of most sounds better than humans can, its ability to locate a sound on the horizontal plane is much the same as ours. Thus, our research with the owl may provide us with insights into binaural sound localization in humans and perhaps a better understanding of such subjects as architectural acoustics and stereo technology.

Plants that Eat Animals

By Anne Simon Moffat

Studies of carnivorous plants are revealing that these highly developed forms of botanical life function in some ways like the insects they devour

A small blue-green housefly circles a New Jersey peat bog, looking for a suitable spot to land and feed. It alights on a bulbous stalk that is studded with rosy filaments and appears to be bathed in a heavy dew. But as the fly touches down, it becomes evident that it has made a disastrous choice. The "dew" is actually a sticky secretion and the fly is instantly mired. The insect struggles to cross the stalk, picking up more glue with each step. As it nears the edge, its path is blocked by red filaments laden with the same deadly syrup.

The fly thrashes against the filaments in a vain attempt to free itself. The tentacles respond to these blows by bending forward and thrusting the fly ahead. The fly abandons its struggle as the stalk slowly curves over it. Within a few hours, the insect has disappeared within the plant's clutches. The housefly has met its doom.

This type of scene—a predator devouring its prey—is played out every day in nature. However, in this case, the prey is an animal, and the predator is a plant, *Drosera intermedia.*

Drosera is the botanical name of the sundew, a carnivorous or meat-eating plant. Although the sundew's diet is composed of insects, its larger carnivorous cousins can consume small mammals and even tiny birds. Such unseemly appetites made carnivorous plants the subject of folklore and scientific curiosity long before 1875 when British naturalist Charles R. Darwin published detailed proof of their existence in his classic volume, *Insectivorous Plants.*

The study of carnivorous plants is less organized and advanced than fields such as viruses or nuclear physics. Yet it has evolved into a unique body of knowledge in which observations made with the naked eye are as important as those made with the electron microscope. In fact, many of its most valuable contributions have come from amateurs who have joined taxonomists and plant physiologists in identifying carnivorous plants and describing how they feed.

This has been no simple task. There are more than 400 varieties of carnivorous plants. Some, like the *Pinguicula* or butterworts, sport delicate flowers that rival African violets in their fragile beauty. Others, such as the *Sarracenia flava*, a pitcher plant, have yellow trumpets. Growing in stands across a meadow, they may be mistaken for hosts of golden daffodils. Some, like *Cephalotis follicularis*, the Albany pitcher plant, have bristly forms that seem to have been created for another world. Others, such as *Darlingtonia californica*, the cobra plant, are downright frightening with a snakelike appearance. But all have one characteristic in common — the ability to trap animals and digest the nutrients from their carcasses.

Carnivorous plants, like all other plants, make food through photosynthesis, a process that takes place in small bodies called chloroplasts located in leaf and stem cells. In photosynthesis, water drawn up through the plant's roots and carbon dioxide absorbed from the air through leaf pores are combined to form complex sugars and carbohydrates. The energy to power this process is supplied by sunlight absorbed by the chloroplasts.

In addition to carbon dioxide and water, plants also need certain other nutrients, principally nitrogen and phosphorus, which are usually supplied by the soils in which they grow. However, carnivorous plants obtain these necessary nutrients by digesting animals. This ability enables them to survive in the impoverished soils of acid peat bogs, sandy marshes, and rocky slopes that cannot support other forms of plant life. In richer environments, they might be crowded out by faster-growing competitors.

While carnivorous plants are united in their ability to derive nutrients from animals, they are divided into two categories by the manner in which they trap these nutrients. Plants with passive traps use alluring colors, scents, or textures to attract insects. They imprison and digest their victims while remaining immobile. However, plants with active traps move to trap and digest their prey.

There are two types of passive traps. The simplest is the pitcher plant — named for the structure of its leaves, tubelike with a lip at the top. Beads of nectar on this lip lure an insect to the leaf's slippery edge. If the insect is sure-footed, it will descend into the tube on a one-way path of hairs down to a pool of collected rain water at the base. If it loses its footing, it will plunge directly into the stagnant bath. In either case, the sharp, downward-pointing hairs surrounding the pool make escape impossible.

The author:
Anne Simon Moffat is a free-lance writer who specializes in botanical subjects.

A cartoonist's depiction of a "man-eating" plant illustrates a common misconception. Even the largest of carnivorous plants limits its dinner to daintier morsels: insects, tree frogs, and small rodents.

The sun pitcher, *Heliamphora nutans*, a primitive form of pitcher plant found only on a few remote mountains of South America, relies upon bacteria in this rain-water pool to decompose its prey. A more sophisticated form, *Nepenthes*, a denizen of the Asian and African tropics, appears to secrete digestive juices powerful enough to consume insects within hours. Certain species of this plant, described by the English botanist Joseph Dalton Hooker in 1859, have made it a subject of lore about the "man-eating" appetites of some plants. Such stories were based upon the discovery of skeletons of small birds inside the tubes of the larger representatives of the species.

The passive flypaper plants comprise the other type of passive traps. There are only two species of passive flypapers: *Byblis*, the Australian rainbow plant, and *Drosophyllum*, the Portuguese sundew. Both plants sport narrow tapering leaves studded with beads of a botanical glue secreted by leaf glands to trap insects.

When an insect first alights on a rainbow plant or Portuguese sundew, it is held lightly. But, as it struggles to release itself, it becomes bound in the glue. The glue obstructs the insect's airways, and it eventually suffocates. A second set of leaf glands secretes enzymes to digest the meal.

Plants in the second category of carnivorous plants—those with active traps—are subdivided according to the way in which they

Plants that trap and digest insects come in a variety of forms. Cobra plants, *opposite page, left,* bear a disconcerting resemblance to their reptilian namesakes. Leaves of the Albany pitcher plant, *opposite page, below,* look like tiny elfin boots. Stands of yellow pitcher plants, *below,* light up a pine barren with their radiance. The butterwort's showy flower, *left,* provides an elegant foil for its fleshy, insect-trapping leaves.

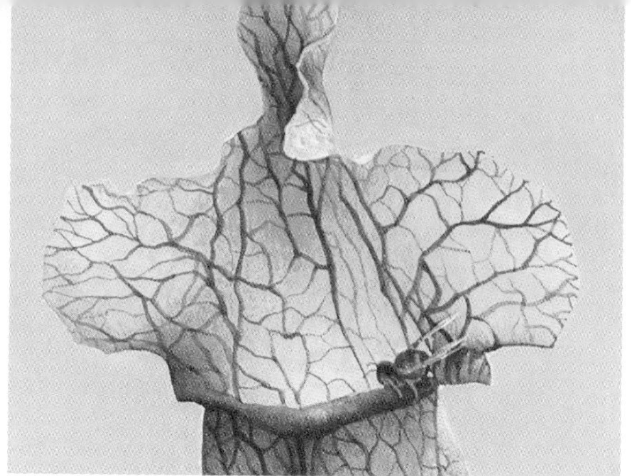

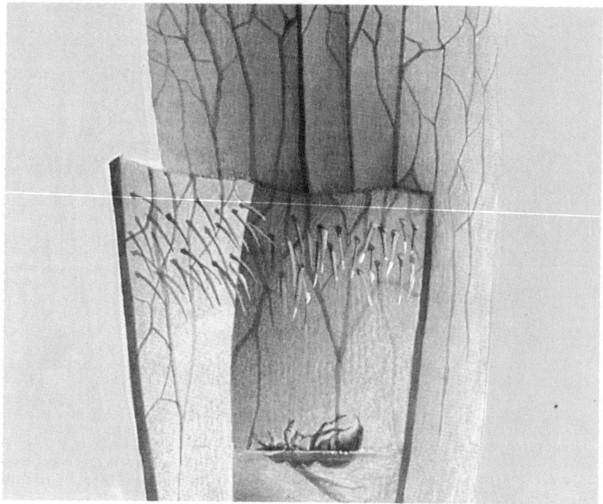

The pitcher plant, *above,* like all passive traps, catches its prey without moving. Sharp hairs block the escape of an insect that has ventured inside, *above right,* and guide it down to an enzyme pool, *right,* where it will be digested.

capture their prey. Their traps fall into three types — active flypaper, trap door, and steel trap.

The active flypapers, like their passive counterparts, secure their prey with a glue secreted from leaf glands. However, while the passive flypapers remain motionless as their dinner is consumed and digested, the active flypapers go into action as soon as the prey is secured. Their leaves slowly roll over the prey, enveloping the victim completely within a matter of hours. This deadly embrace is actually a matter of economy — it brings the digestive juices secreted by a second set of leaf glands into closer contact with the prey. The insect is efficiently bathed in these acid secretions, and its nutrients are absorbed by the plant within a few days. When the leaves reopen, only the undigested wings and tough external skeleton remain.

Trap doors are found in the *Utricularia* or bladderwort. There are many species of *Utricularia*, several of which are rootless, underwater plants with fine, feathery branches that bear hollow, bulbous leaves about the size of a pinhead. Between meals, these leaves look like tiny deflated balloons, because glands on the leaf walls take some of the water from inside the leaf, creating a vacuum. Each leaf has a small opening surrounded by thin sensitive hairs and covered with

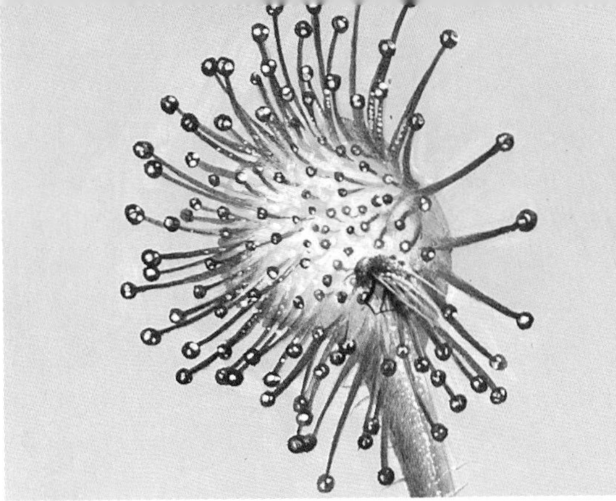

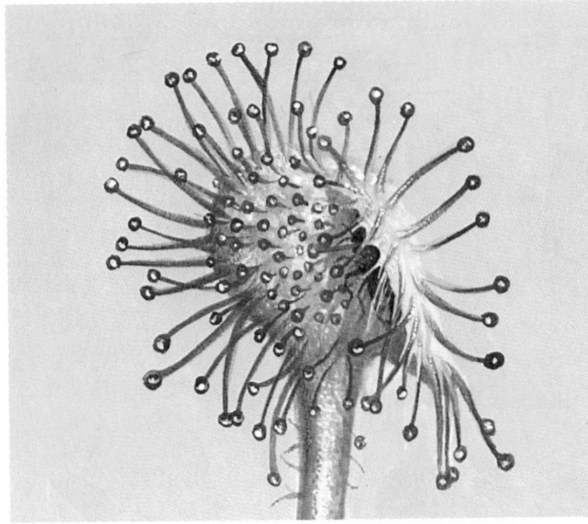

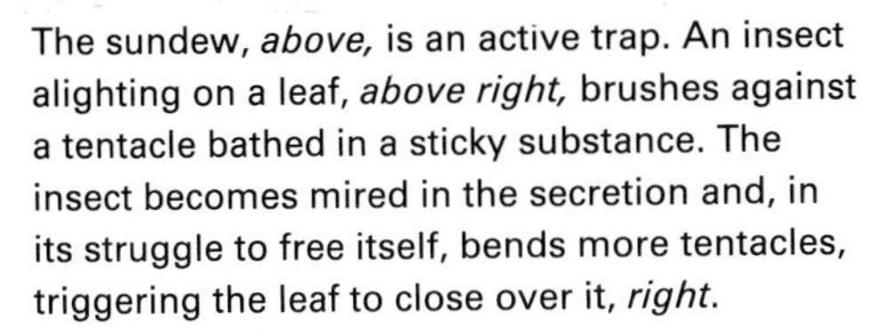

The sundew, *above,* is an active trap. An insect alighting on a leaf, *above right,* brushes against a tentacle bathed in a sticky substance. The insect becomes mired in the secretion and, in its struggle to free itself, bends more tentacles, triggering the leaf to close over it, *right.*

a trap door hinged at the top. When a microscopic water creature such as a rotifer, mosquito larva, or newly hatched tadpole brushes against one of these hairs, the trap opens. A vacuum inside the leaf sucks in the water carrying the creature. The trap door then snaps shut. The entire process takes a fraction of a second.

Dionaea, or Venus's flytrap, employs a steel trap. Its trap consists of two crescent-shaped leaf lobes attached to a midrib. Each lobe is ringed with about 10 to 25 spiny teeth, which lock together when the trap shuts. The underside of each lobe has three or more trigger hairs. If one is touched two or more times, or if at least two hairs are touched within seconds, the trap slams shut.

When the flytrap is open, each leaf curves outward like an upturned saucer, but after it closes, the leaves curve down to form a loose cage that holds the prey. The walls of its leafy prison allow the insect enough room to struggle in an attempt to escape. As it does so, it brushes against the trigger hairs, and each contact causes the trap to close ever more tightly. Stimulating the hairs also causes the release of an extremely acidic digestive solution, which kills the prey. As digestion progresses, the leaf lobes become increasingly flatter. In about five days, when the nutrients are completely absorbed, the

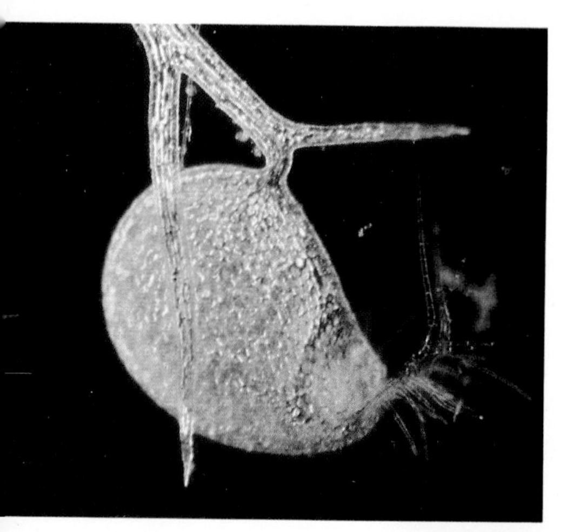

A hollow leaf of the aquatic butterwort is flat, *above,* until hairs that trigger a small trap door in the tip are brushed by an insect larva. The larva's tail is sucked in through the trap, *above right*. The larva continues to trigger the trap as it wriggles, and is sucked further into the leaf in stages, *right,* until only its head is still free, *below right*.

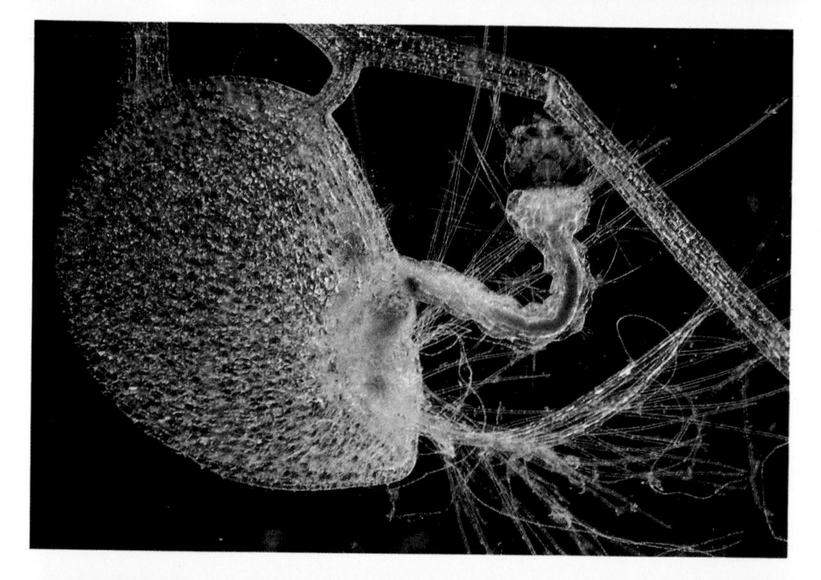

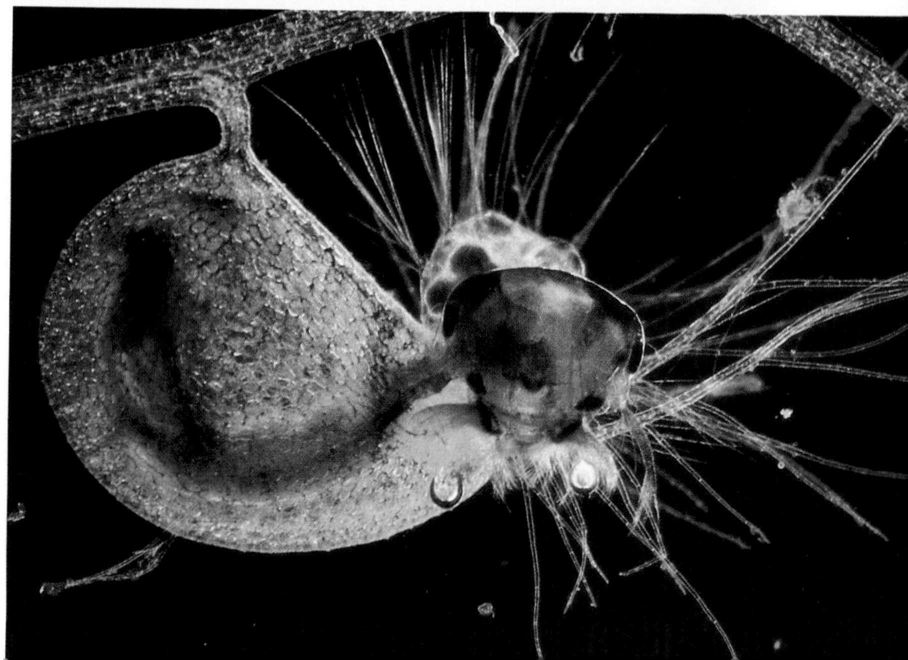

A fly alighting on a Venus's flytrap, *above,* stimulates trigger hairs on the leaf surface, causing the leaf to snap shut, *right*. As the fly struggles inside its leafy prison, it continues to brush the trigger hairs, and the leaf closes even more tightly about it to seal its fate, *below*.

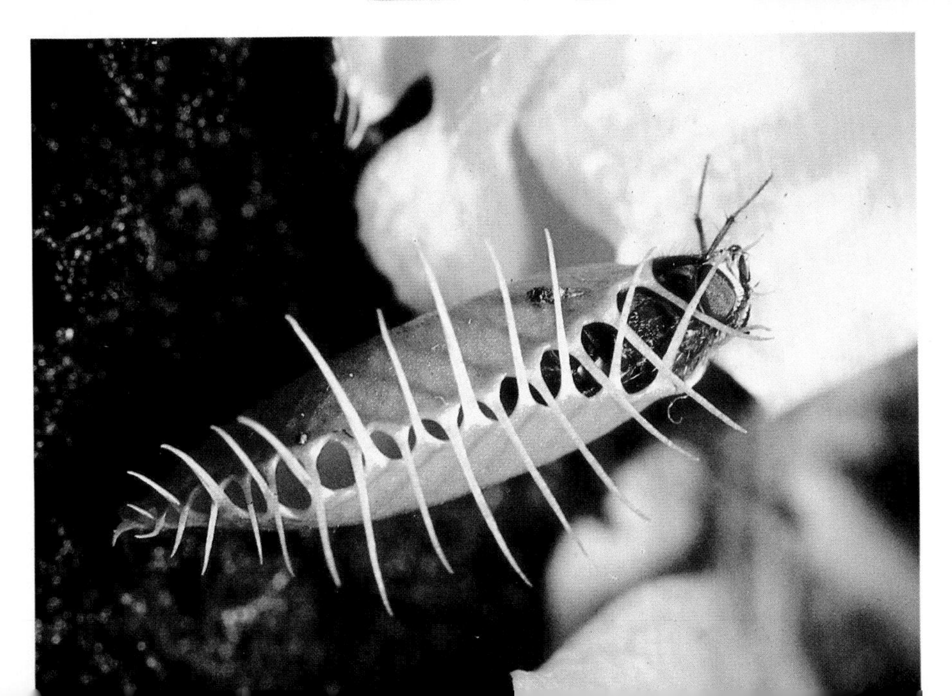

Plant physiologist Stephen E. Williams studies a chart of action potentials generated by stimulating the tentacles of a sundew. The charges were registered by electrodes connected to a voltmeter.

leaves reopen. Only the undigested wings and external skeleton remain to be cleaned away by wind or rain, leaving the flytrap a fresh palate for its next meal.

The Venus's flytrap is the best known and most widely studied of all carnivorous plants. Darwin referred to the flytrap as "the most wonderful plant in the world." He chose it as the subject of the research that he undertook with his friend, physiologist John S. Burdon-Sanderson of University College in London, in the 1870s.

Darwin and Burdon-Sanderson made some remarkable discoveries about the flytrap, and scientists working a century later with more highly sophisticated equipment have neither repudiated nor significantly improved upon their findings. Darwin had noticed that, in both the flytrap and the sundew, the section of the leaf that began to move was often some distance away from the hair that was stimulated, and that it took about a second for this motion to begin. He theorized that some "nerve impulse" must pass from the hair to the area that moved and suggested that Burdon-Sanderson, who had been studying nerve impulses in animals, investigate this.

Burdon-Sanderson used a galvanometer — an instrument that detects and measures an electrical current — to determine the effect of stimulating the flytrap's trigger hairs. He attached a thin wire from the galvanometer near the base of a trigger hair and another wire close to the stalk of the leaf. He brushed the hair twice with a bristle and found that the galvanometer registered a faint electrical current.

Next Burdon-Sanderson set out to track that current, employing a technique similar to the one he used to study nerve responses in animals. He developed an instrument that he called the capillary electrometer, which could be connected to the leaf with wires hooked to wicks soaked with a conducting solution. Using this instrument, Burdon-Sanderson detected changes in the electrical charges of the membranes of cells radiating from the base of the trigger hair to the outer areas of the leaf. These membrane changes, which result in electrical signals that travel through the plant, are called action potentials and are known as nerve impulses when they occur in animals. These action potentials traveled through the leaf at a rate of 20 millimeters (0.78 inch) per second.

Burdon-Sanderson's work also illustrated that one stimulation of a single hair would not close the trap. He was not able to detect any significant movement when he stimulated a single hair once, even though an action potential occurred. But when the second stimulus produced an action potential, the leaf responded. Moreover, the strength of the lobe movement increased with each successive stimulation. The first stimulation had only primed the pump for the second, which set off the process that closed the trap, even though every time he bent a trigger hair, there was an action potential that spread over the trap. The response to each action potential depends on the number and frequency of the action potentials.

Burdon-Sanderson published his discovery of the action potential in *Proceedings of the Royal Society*, Great Britain's most prominent scientific journal, in 1876. But his work was largely overlooked, and it was not until 1965 that a major refinement of his theory was published. That year, animal physiologist Stuart L. Jacobson of Carleton College in Ottawa, Canada, discovered another stage in the process—a single electrical signal called a receptor potential that transformed the mechanical stimulus into an action potential. Jacobson and animal physiologist Robert M. Benolken of the University of Texas at Austin pinpointed the source of this potential in 1970, by taking successive slices of tissue from the trigger hair, stimulating the hair, and measuring its ability to generate an action potential.

The action potential disappeared when the scientists removed a layer of cells at the base of the hair inside a notch that enables it to bend easily. These cells, now classified as sensory cells, were identified as the site of the first receptor potential recorded in plants. They have similarities to cells in insect antennae.

Darwin suggested to Burdon-Sanderson that he repeat his action potential studies in the sundew. He never did. Thus, almost 100 years later, Stephen E. Williams of Lebanon Valley College in Annville, Pa., and Barbara G. Pickard of Washington University in St. Louis became the first plant physiologists to track the action potentials triggered by stimulating sundew tentacles.

Williams and Pickard found that, as in the flytrap, the action potential resulted from a receptor potential that occurred in sensory cells at or near the base of the head of each tentacle. However, in the sundew, these action potentials did not spread throughout the leaf but were confined to the stimulated tentacle. As a result, only

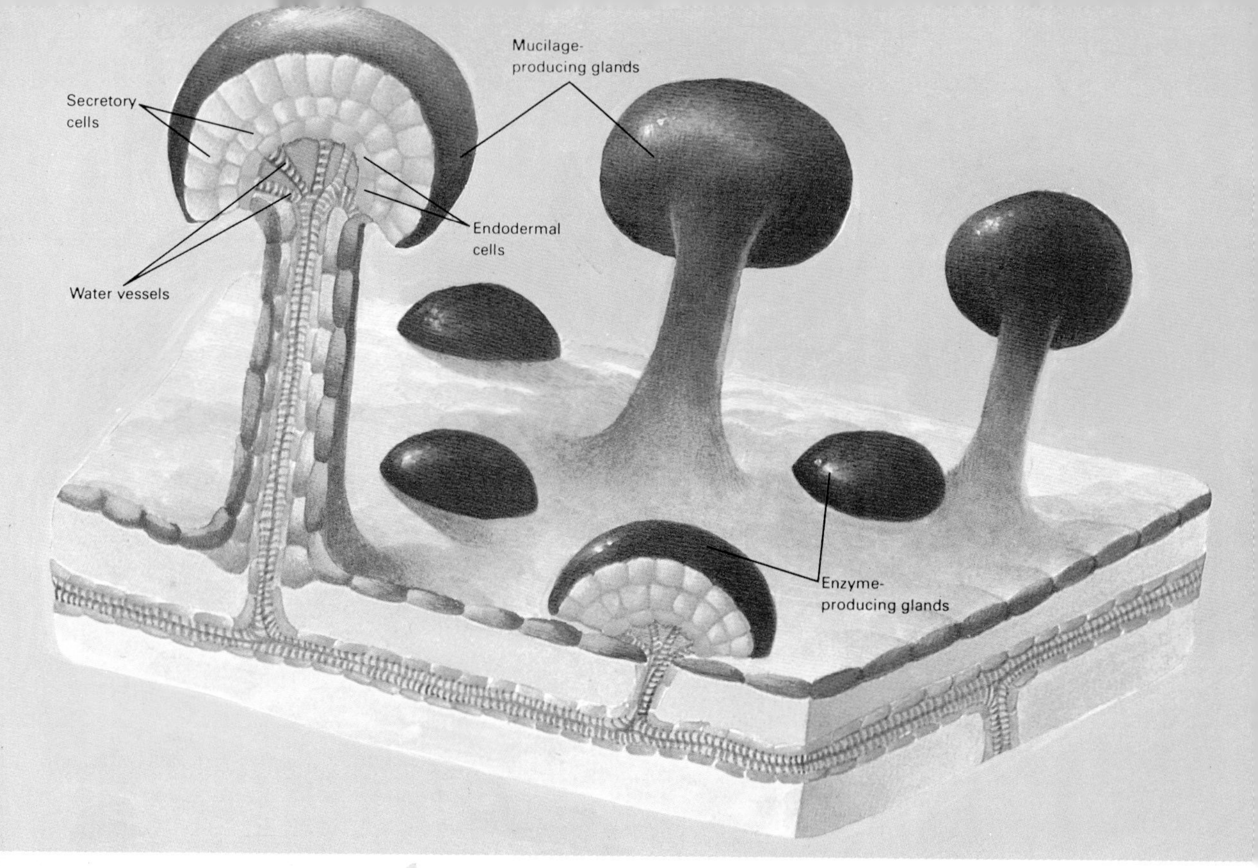

The Glands of the Predator
The rosy tentacles of the sundew, *left,* glisten with a mucilage that holds prey fast. The mucilage is the product of glands like those of the dewy pine, *above,* some of which secrete enzymes to digest prey. Mucilage and enzymes are produced and stored in secretory cells at the top of the gland, and carried to the surface by water that has passed from vessels and epidermal cells. In a scanning electron micrograph, magnified about 125 times, *below,* mucilage glands look like mushrooms rising above buttonlike enzyme glands on the leaf's surface.

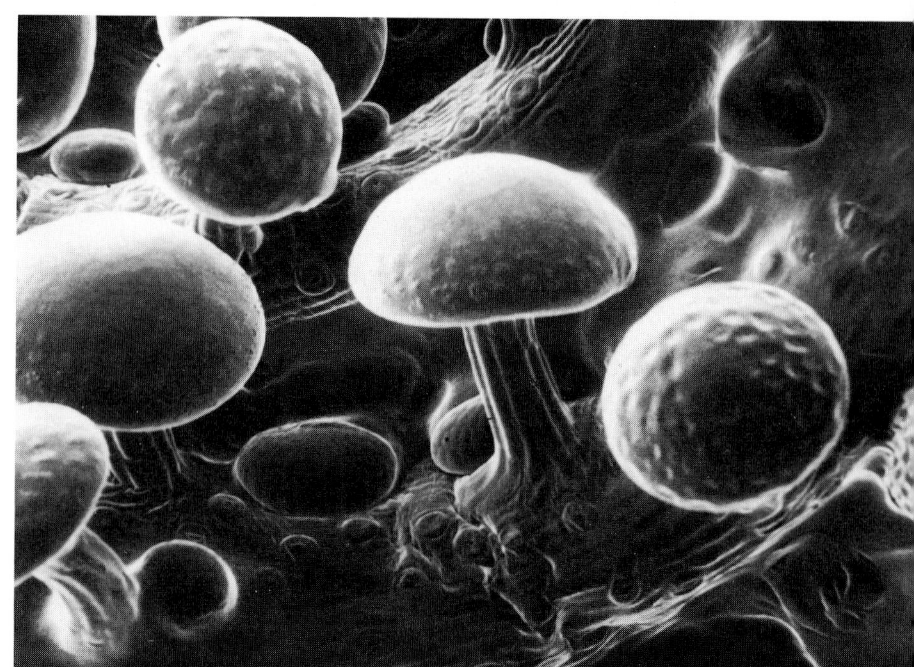

the stimulated tentacle moved. They also reported that the action potential moved more slowly in the sundew than in the flytrap, traveling only 1.67 millimeters (0.07 inch) per second. But they noted that each receptor potential was capable of generating several action potentials to perpetuate the motion of the tentacle.

Although recent research into trapping motions may have served only to support or embellish Darwin's theories, modern investigations into the motion in plants after they have captured their prey have yielded some unexpected results. Darwin had correctly attributed the continued tightening of a closed trap to continued stimulation of the trigger hairs or tentacles as the insect struggled to escape. However, he had no explanation for the fact that the trap continued to close even after the insect had died.

Williams and Pickard in 1972 proposed an explanation. They postulated that there are two types of movements in carnivorous plants—the rapid movement of entrapment and the slower movement of digestion. Research had shown that rapid movement was initiated by a mechanical stimulation and transmitted by an action potential. They suggested that slow movement was triggered by chemicals from the decaying prey and transmitted by hormones.

Williams, working with Frank T. Lichtner, then an undergraduate at Lebanon Valley College, bathed partially closed flytraps with solutions of sodium and ammonium in concentrations similar to those that would be released by decomposing insects. They found that the traps had narrowed by about 40 per cent after eight hours.

Martin Bopp, a plant physiologist, and Inge Weber, an undergraduate student at the Botanical Institute of the University of Heidelberg in West Germany, reported similar results with the sundew in 1982. They placed a small ball of cheese on a sundew leaf and noted that, 24 hours later, the leaf had curved upward at an angle of 132 degrees. Glass balls the same size placed on other sundew leaves elicited no response whatsoever.

A second part of Bopp and Weber's experiment supported Pickard and Williams' hypothesis that this movement was the result of hormonal action. They repeated the experiment with the cheese and added a few drops of triodobenzoic acid, a chemical that blocks the transport of the plant growth hormone auxin. The leaf curvature was reduced by 50 per cent. The results of the experiment seem to indicate that auxin may play an important role in the sundew leaves' ability to bend around their prey.

Future research is expected to shed more light on another fascinating aspect of carnivorous plants—digestion. Most carnivorous plants have specialized glands that secrete the enzymes to break down prey into nutrients that the plant can absorb. Some glands, such as those in the pitcher plants and others with passive traps, secrete digestive enzymes constantly. Others, like those in the flytrap, secrete the enzymes only after they are stimulated by the trig-

Caring for the Carnivore

An overfed Venus's flytrap suffers the indignity of indigestion. A black spot on the upper left lobe indicates that it is rotting in its own digestive juices—the result of overstimulated enzyme glands.

A collection of carnivorous plants can be a source of continuing entertainment for people who enjoy seeing one of nature's most unusual dramas enacted right in their own homes. However, growing carnivorous plants is not for everyone. Only a few species adapt easily to life in captivity, and they require very exacting care and feeding.

The easiest species to acquire and grow are those native to North America—*Dionaea*, Venus's flytrap; *Sarracenia*, the pitcher plant; *Darlingtonia*, the cobra plant; and *Drosera*, the sundew. These plants should be bought or ordered from commercial growers rather than collected from their natural habitats because many varieties are in danger of becoming extinct. Also, wild plants are more likely to be infected with disease and less acclimated to indoor conditions than their cultivated counterparts.

Each of the four species mentioned requires approximately the same care, so it is possible to combine several varieties in one indoor garden. They should be planted in well-drained pots in a loose, porous soil. Live green sphagnum moss, the chief component of the bogs where most of these plants grow, is the first choice, but it may be difficult to obtain. A good alternative is a mix composed of one part silica sand, one part peat moss, and one part perlite. Either medium should be kept moist, but not soggy.

Because these plants are native to bogs and swamps, they require a high level of humidity—usually more than the average home provides. This problem can sometimes be solved by growing them in a bathroom (provided that there is enough natural light), using a small portable humidifier near a grouping of pots, or placing the pots in a glass container or terrarium.

These sun-loving plants require high levels of light—preferably natural light from a sunny window. If the plants are growing in a covered container, however, direct sunlight will raise the temperature to extremely high levels and they will die rapidly, as if from heatstroke. Plants under glass should be grown in a north-facing window or under fluorescent light. They do best in daytime temperatures of up to 30°C (86°F.) with temperatures as much as 10°C (18°F.) lower at night.

The plants should be placed outdoors when weather conditions are favorable, to give them a chance to catch insects. They should never be fed large insects or chunks of meat or cheese. Such feedings overstimulate the digestive glands and cause the plants to rot in their own secretions. However, they may be given a "snack" of a small sliver of corned beef or cheese occasionally.

Ironically, even carnivorous plants can be prey to some of the same insects that plague other houseplants. They are particularly susceptible to attack by mealybugs—small insect colonies that look like bits of white cotton—and scale—which appear to be tiny turtleshells ranging in color from tan to dark brown.

Both types of insects can be eradicated with a light spraying of malathion diluted according to the manufacturer's instructions. Mealybugs will die upon contact with malathion; scale will not drop off the plant until a few days later. Because malathion does not harm eggs, it should be reapplied within two weeks to take care of any insects that may have hatched since the first insecticide treatment.

Even if carnivorous plants shed leaves or develop black, rotten-looking foliage as the sunlight grows weaker in the autumn, this should not be a cause for alarm—it is merely a signal that the plants are going into a period of dormancy.

At this point, the plants should be watered sparingly, so that the soil is only slightly moist, and should be placed in an area where the temperature is lower, such as a porch or basement. They may also be stored in plastic bags in the refrigerator, but should not be allowed to freeze. Plants growing under fluorescent tubes should have their "daylight" hours reduced to approximate those in nature. Like the insects that they feed upon in the wilds, the plants will remain dormant until the next spring. [Anne Simon Moffat] gering mechanism. It was not until the development of the electron microscope in the late 1960s that scientists were able to get a close view of these minuscule glands studding the leaf surfaces. Yolande Heslop-Harrison, a plant physiologist at University College in Wales, has used the electron microscope to determine that all carnivorous plant digestive glands share common structural elements. The secretory cells, which produce digestive enzymes, form an outer cap that lies over a second layer, the endodermis, which is in contact with vessels that transport water through the plant.

Water from the vessels floods the endodermis and seeps into the secretory cells where it picks up the digestive enzymes. The digestive fluid then oozes through the secretory cells to the surface of the gland and spills onto the leaf. There the pool of secreted fluids extends and deepens to cover the prey. After digestion, the pool is reabsorbed within an hour. If the prey is exceptionally large, the glands may continue to secrete digestive fluid for hours, and reabsorption does not take place quickly enough. The leaf, bathed in its own digestive juices, begins to rot, suffering a glutton's indigestion.

Heslop-Harrison and her colleague, plant physiologist Bruce Knox, traced digestion in a butterwort by tagging a small amount of protein with the radioactive isotope carbon 14. They placed the radiotagged protein on the leaf and tracked its progress through autoradiography — a process that illuminates the path of radioactive particles on photographic film. As the digestive enzymes secreted by the plant dissolved the radiotagged protein, the scientists traced its progress through the secretory cells into the endodermal cells and into the vessels. After eight hours, the nutrients in the protein had been distributed throughout much of the leaf.

In her studies of the structures within the secretory cells, Heslop-Harrison found similarities to structures in animal cells. The vacuoles of secretory cells that store digestive enzymes are comparable to lysosomes, cellular structures that break down proteins, in animal cells. The nuclei of secretory cells contain more genetic material than other plant cells — a condition that also exists in the salivary glands of fruit flies. In addition, the cells involved in secretion have many Golgi bodies — just as do some animal secretory cells.

In spite of these similarities — and those of action potentials to animal nerve impulses — plant physiologists do not see carnivorous plants as a bridge between the plant and animal kingdoms. However, they do see these plants as excellent models for the study of vital processes in other plants. The study of trap and digestive movements may prove valuable in understanding the leaf movements of other types of plants. Learning the mechanics of entrapment may help scientists to stimulate the development of similar insecticidal qualities in agricultural crops. The study of carnivorous plants — a science that lay dormant for almost a century — is alive with possibilities for the future.

The Hairy Stars

By Michael J. S. Belton

Astronomers anticipating the return of Halley's Comet are mounting a worldwide effort to learn more of the secrets of this special family of celestial objects

Gently falling through the heavens, seemingly headed directly for the Sun, the icy nucleus of Edmund Halley's famous comet is about to rekindle interest in a celestial visitor. This lump of ice and dust in early 1982 was at the edge of explored space, just outside the orbit of Saturn. It is traveling on a path that will bring it once again to the world's attention.

Astronomers in particular eagerly await their first chance to really study the best-known comet close up. As it passes through the inner solar system in November 1985, the comet may be encountered first by the National Aeronautics and Space Administration's (NASA) spacecraft *Galileo* on its way to Jupiter. Moving in opposite directions, Halley's Comet and *Galileo* will careen past each other at nearly 240,000 kilometers per hour (kph) (150,000 miles per hour (mph)), and at least 48 million kilometers (30 million miles) apart. The spacecraft will have only a limited time to inspect the comet.

The comet will hurtle on, thrusting northward through the plane of Earth's orbit, reaching a speed of 198,000 kph (123,000 mph) at its closest point to the Sun, about halfway between the orbits of Mercury and Venus, on Feb. 9, 1986. By that time, it will find itself transformed from a cosmic triviality into the most enormous phenomenon in the solar system and, briefly, a thing of rare beauty.

Halley's Comet was named for the 18th-century English astronomer Edmund Halley. He accurately predicted, from a study of past observations, that a particular comet would reappear on a definite path around the Sun in 1759 and would recur about every 77 years thereafter. Most people until then had thought comets appeared by chance and traveled through space at random. The advent of such spectacular and unexplainable objects in the sky awed people, and they attributed mysterious properties and powers to comets. For example, the great 14th-century Italian painter Giotto in 1304 depicted a comet blazing over a manger as if to herald the birth of

Christ. This was Halley's Comet, in fact, which Giotto had observed during its appearance in 1301.

Most comets, the "hairy stars" (*astera cometes* in Latin) of the ancient Romans, are found by amateurs. The Japanese are credited with the greatest number of discoveries over the past 25 years. In the United States, Leslie C. Peltier of Delphos, Ohio, began looking for comets in 1918 and has discovered 13 so far. Australian William Bradfield has found 10 comets, all in the Southern Hemisphere. See THE SECULAR STARGAZERS, *Science Year*, 1981.

We know that a comet we see streaking across the sky is a three-part object, consisting of nucleus, coma, and tail. Its water-ice and dust nucleus, the body, will average 10 kilometers (6 miles) in diameter. This is surrounded by a mostly hydrogen coma, or atmosphere, as much as 10 million kilometers (6 million miles) across. The coma is formed as the Sun's heat evaporates the outer layers of the nucleus. Gas molecules and dust particles are swept back from the coma by the pressure of sunlight and by the solar wind—a wild expansion of gases boiling off the Sun's corona and flowing into space. These cause the comet to form one or more tails, which may extend for 150 million kilometers (91 million miles) into space. A comet's brightness comes mainly from sunlight reflected by its coma.

In its 1986 appearance, Halley's Comet will reach its brightest and most active phase when its orbit takes it close to the opposite side of the Sun from Earth. Thus the beauty of the comet may be lost to Earth-based observers in the Sun's blinding glare.

It is from space that we may gain our best view. In March 1986, soon after the comet swings past the Sun and passes back through Earth's orbital plane, five more spacecraft will approach it.

Leading the pack will be two Russian *Venera-Halley* spacecraft returning from Venus. They will fly through the comet's coma at a distance of about 9,700 kilometers (6,000 miles) from the nucleus while their television cameras return the glorious view to Earth. Next will come the *Planet-A* mission, two spacecraft making the first Japanese interplanetary probe. The remaining spacecraft—the European Space Agency's armor-clad *Giotto*—will approach the comet relentlessly. Collision seems unavoidable. *Giotto* will pugnaciously rip its way into the heart of the comet, analyzing and communicating information back to Earth even as it destroys itself.

If all goes according to plan, the United States will have a space shuttle in orbit to study Halley's Comet in March 1986. It will point special telescopes and cameras toward the comet in concert with others at ground-based observatories throughout the world. Coordinating this unprecedented effort will be the NASA-backed International Halley Watch. The project, begun in 1981, is under the joint direction of astronomers Ray L. Newburn, Jr., of the California Institute of Technology's Jet Propulsion Laboratory (JPL) in Pasadena and Jurgen Rähe of the University of Erlangen-Nuremberg in

The author:
Michael J. S. Belton, an astronomer at Kitt Peak National Observatory near Tucson, Ariz., is leader of the imaging science team for NASA's *Galileo* mission.

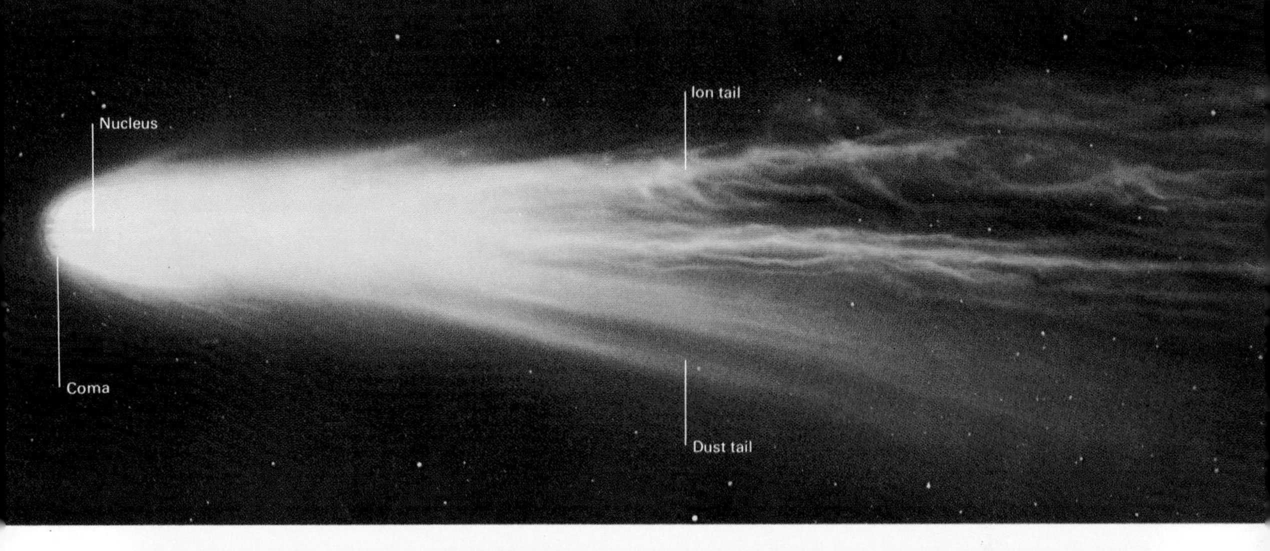

Blazing across the sky, *top,* a comet consists of a tiny ice and dust nucleus surrounded by a huge coma, made up mainly of hydrogen and swept backward into one or more brilliant tails. When Halley's Comet flashed over Flagstaff, Ariz., on May 13, 1910, *above,* it far outshone both the bright planet Venus and the city's lights (at lower left).

Erlangen, West Germany. The predictability of the return of Halley's Comet allows scientists to make detailed plans for gathering data. Everyone participating in the International Halley Watch will spend many days in a great effort to grasp the knowledge we believe a study of the comet can yield — knowledge of the origin of comets and planets, of their chemistry and physical processes, and, possibly, of the origin of materials essential to the development of life.

Comets are infrequent visitors. Thus, we can study one for only a short time on its rare journey in toward the Sun from the farthest point of its orbit. Data about the other objects in the solar system — the planets and their moons; asteroids, or minor planets; and meteoroids, or interplanetary rocks — have accumulated over centuries of much more leisurely study. Details of the physical structure and chemistry of a cometary nucleus remain a secret of nature. The properties of the nucleus of Halley's Comet, for example, are barely

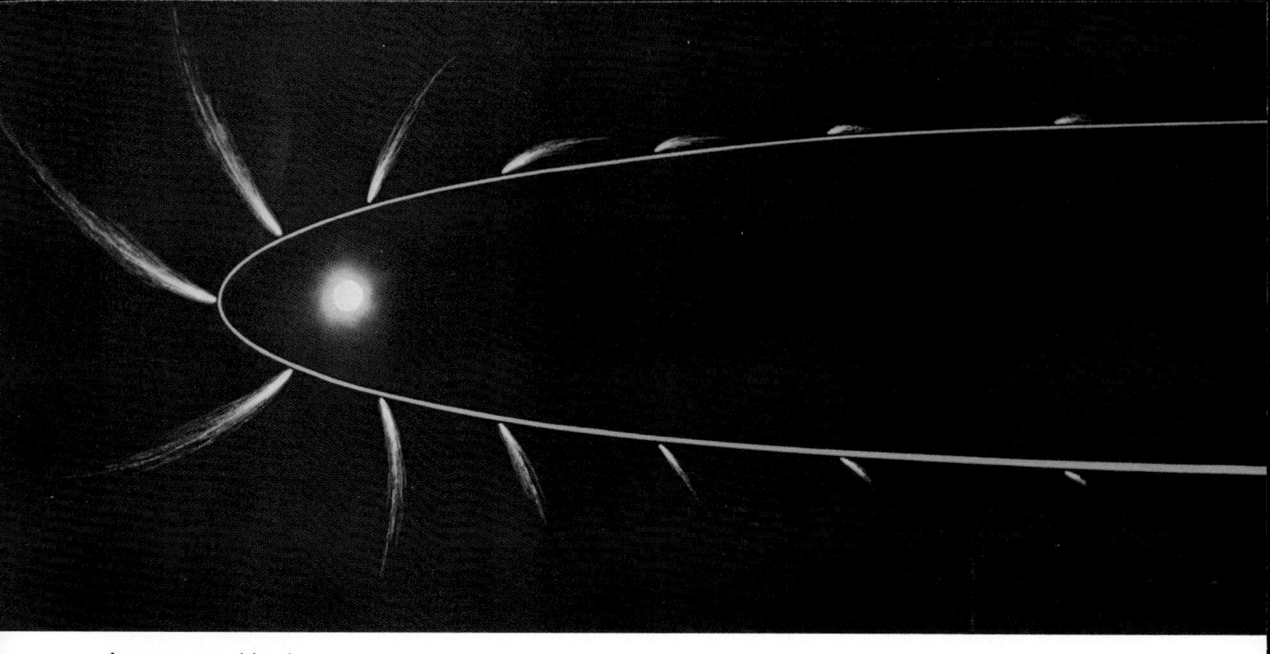

As a comet orbits the Sun, the solar wind – a stream of electrically charged particles – causes its tail to alter in shape but always to point away from the Sun, *above,* acting like a "solar-wind sock." Observations of the tail of Halley's Comet, made over seven weeks in 1910, *opposite page,* provide a record of how the tail grows and recedes as it nears and leaves the Sun.

discernible through a fog of uncertain evidence. Nevertheless, by focusing on three main areas, we can draw a crude sketch of what the body of Halley's Comet is like.

First, we can determine the maximum brightness of the nucleus. Since 1977, a few other astronomers and I have been making a personally exciting, but nevertheless unsuccessful, effort to find the comet. We have been using two of the world's most powerful telescopes — one at Mauna Kea in Hawaii and one at Kitt Peak National Observatory near Tucson, Ariz. By early 1982, we still had found no trace of it. The comet was too faint to see because the nucleus is either smaller or darker than we thought.

Second, we have measurements of the motion of Halley's Comet made during several of its many earlier returns to the Sun. According to calculations by astronomer David W. Hughes of the University of Sheffield in England, the 1986 appearance will be the comet's 41st since it was first noted in connection with a battle featuring a certain King Wu in ancient China in 1058 B.C.

While the early historical observations are not accurate, those of the past five visits, dating from 1531, are quite precise. Astronomer Donald K. Yeomans of JPL showed in 1977 that, throughout history, certain forces have consistently slowed down the time it takes the comet to pass through the inner solar system. These forces are called nongravitational because they are the extra forces required to explain our observations of the comet's motion after we have accounted for all the normal gravitational attractions of the Sun and the planets. We think they are due to the "rocket effect" of more gases escaping from the sunlit surface of the nucleus than from the unlit surface. Yeomans' work tells us that even though some of these forces are extremely weak — equivalent to only about one-millionth of the acceleration felt by the driver of a car making a normal start from a stop sign — they are still very effective. Combining the results of Yeomans' work with some known laws of physics allows us to estimate the mass of Halley's Comet and to make an educated guess about how it rotates.

For the third factor in describing Halley's Comet, we have the record of the brightness of its coma and tail when it last appeared. The brightness is the result of an enormous amount of dust particles and gas molecules — especially the molecule C_2 (two carbon atoms joined together) — being vaporized from the nucleus as the comet moves around the Sun. The more material that is heated up and blown off the surface of the nucleus, the brighter the comet appears.

Scientists have combined the record of the visual brightness of Halley's Comet in 1910 with recent spacecraft and rocket observations of the hydrogen coma of similar comets. From these calculations, we can make a reasonably accurate estimate of the rate at which water vapor was released from the surface of the nucleus of Halley's Comet. This is significant because we believe that water is the prime volatile, or easily vaporized, component of all cometary nuclei. We can gain a more precise idea of some of the properties of the nucleus, such as size and weight, from knowing its vaporization rate.

JPL's Newburn in 1980 provided what I believe to be a convincing estimate of the water-production rate of Halley's Comet at various distances from the Sun. When Halley is as far from the Sun as Earth is, Newburn found, its nucleus throws off about 6 metric tons (6.6 short tons) of water molecules — and probably a similar amount of dust particles — into space every second.

By combining this evidence, and using what we know of other comets, we now have a basic idea of what the nucleus of Halley's Comet is like. We believe it is a compact, probably irregular, but nearly spherical ball made of equal parts of water-ice and fluffy, black carbonaceous dust, plus a small amount of other matter. In spite of its icy nature, the surface of the nucleus, barely 4 kilometers (2.5 miles) across, is quite dark. It reflects less than 20 per cent of the light that falls on it because the black dust is so thoroughly mixed

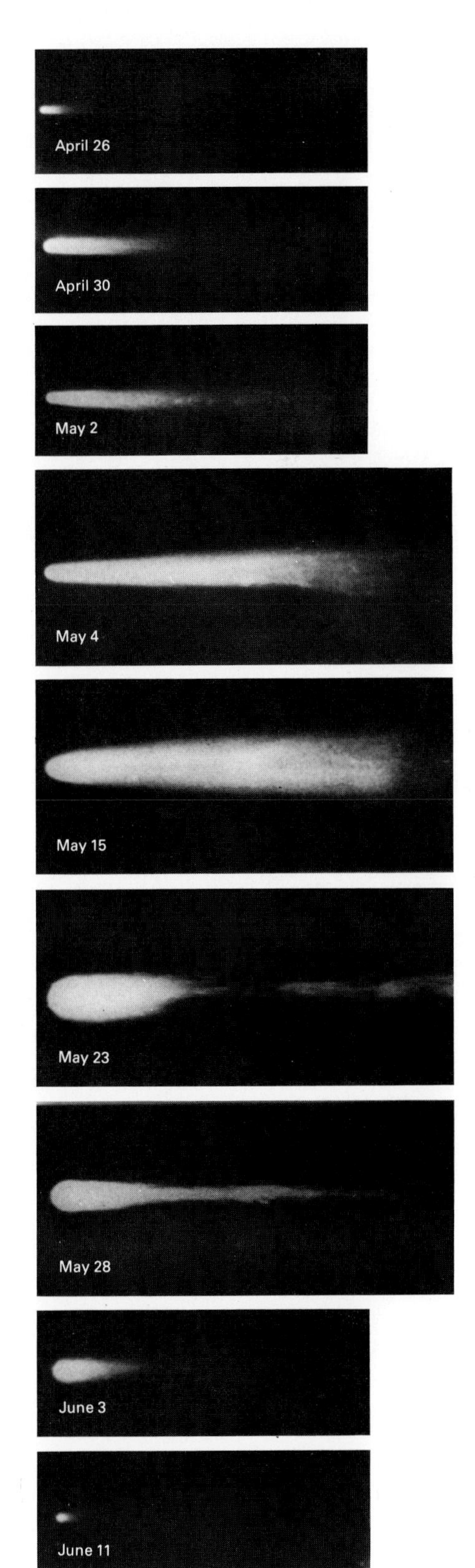

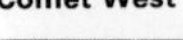

Comet West

Comet Morehouse

Comet Arend-Roland

Comet Mrkos

Seven comets that visited the vicinity of the Sun during this century displayed their dazzling and distinctive forms of heavenly beauty.

with the ice. Most of the surface of the nucleus is chemically active while the comet is close to the Sun. Some regions, from time to time, produce jetlike eruptions of gases more volatile than water vapor.

The nucleus rotates relatively quickly, turning once around its axis in about one-half an Earth day. Its mass is about 34 billion metric tons (37 billion short tons), of which it loses about 100 million metric tons (110 million short tons) to space each time it passes the Sun. To put it another way, the entire surface of the comet is stripped of material to a depth of about 4 meters (13 feet) on each orbit. We cannot expect Halley's Comet to last for more than another 340 appearances — about another 26,000 years.

At the end of its last visit, Halley's Comet disappeared from view after June 15, 1911. Since then it has traveled on its great looping path out to a point far away from the Sun, just outside Neptune's orbit, but high above the plane of the planets and back to its present position some 1.8 billion kilometers (1 billion miles) from the Sun.

We had expected that the comet might be bright enough to be seen again by Christmas of 1981. Comets are capricious phenomena and can brighten or fade very suddenly. I, along with astronomer Harvey Butcher, decided to try to take advantage of any unpredictable behavior Halley's Comet might indulge in. Therefore, when we began our 1977 program to find the comet, we used an ultrasensitive electronic camera on the 400-centimeter (158-inch) Mayall telescope at Kitt Peak. Our aim was to spot the comet at the greatest possible distance in order to have the best chance of finding it in a dormant state. If we could measure the light the comet gave off before it was

Comet Kohoutek

Comet Ikea-Seki

Comet Brooks

heated by the Sun, we could be sure that it came from the surface of the nucleus rather than from the coma. Analysis of the light's properties could give us direct evidence of the physical characteristics of the nucleus. For example, measuring its brightness tells us about its size. Then, if we found that the brightness varied periodically over time, we could learn something about the rate at which the nucleus spins and, perhaps, something about its shape. Finally, if the nucleus were bright enough we would use a special telescopic device to study its electromagnetic spectrum for clues to the comet's chemical composition.

The task of spotting Halley's Comet when it had reached only the brightness Yeomans and Newburn predicted for it during 1981 and 1982 turned out to be far from trivial. Because the comet is so much nearer to us than the background stars are, it appears to move rapidly back and forth across the sky in the course of a year. But the actual motion of Halley's Comet along its orbital path in 1982 is still very small—it is Earth that is moving.

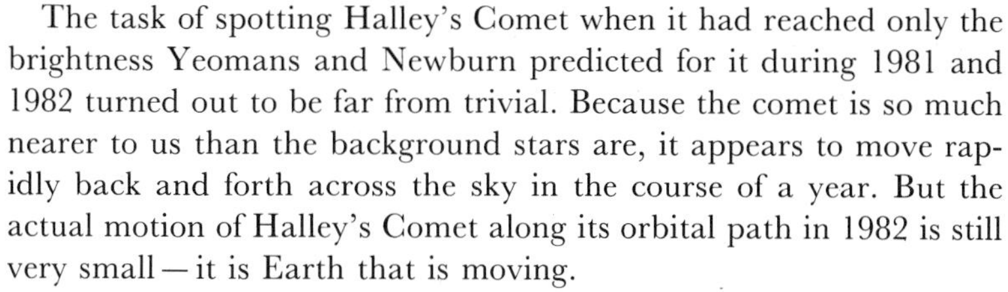

To have our telescope's electronic camera register the image of the comet, we have to move the telescope carefully and precisely during an exposure to follow the comet's predicted path. That causes the images of faint stars in the picture to be smeared into long and rather broad trails. If there were only a few stars as bright as the comet, this would be a minor problem. But unfortunately, the position of Halley's Comet in early 1982 is near the bright star Procyon in the constellation Canis Minor—just a few degrees from the plane of the Milky Way. As a result, the sky is filled with stars as far as we can see through a telescope, and the star trails on the photograph can easily blot out any sign of the comet. Thus, we must select the day and time of observation that minimizes the effects of those myriads of stars.

After much work and experimentation, we found that — out of the six months that Halley's Comet would be in the night sky during the entire 1981-1982 observing season — there were only three nights when we might stand a good chance of finding it. The best of these turned out to be Dec. 25, 1981 — and the observatory is always closed on Christmas Day. Another promising night produced no results because of bad weather and high winds. On the third promising night, we were able to conduct a search, although only for three hours. We did not see the comet, but that fact itself was important because it showed us that Halley's Comet must be much fainter than we thought. Assuming the most advantageous of situations, I believe now that it could be found as early as September 1982. On the other hand, if we are unlucky and its surface reflectivity is quite low, we might not find it until the end of 1984.

Our search for Halley's Comet is a very deliberate one, but one of the most fascinating discoveries of comets was an accidental one. It was made in October 1981 by solar physicists Donald J. Michels, Neil R. Sheeley, Jr., Russell H. Howard, and Marten J. Koomen of the United States Naval Research Laboratory (NRL) in Washington, D.C. Michels and his colleagues did not even know they had found a comet until two years after it no longer existed. The scientists are conducting a study of the solar corona, a part of the Sun's atmosphere, using a U.S. Air Force research satellite. Instruments on the satellite block out the bright disk of the Sun, creating the effect of a permanent solar eclipse, while cameras automatically record what is happening within the corona. On Aug. 30, 1979, the scientists took a routine series of pictures of the corona. Various delays kept the NRL team from seeing the data for two years. When they looked at the pictures, they saw a remarkable record of the last 139 minutes in the life of a bright comet before it plunged into the Sun's atmosphere.

The event is of considerable scientific interest because when the NRL team reconstructed the comet's orbit from the pictures, they found it to be related to a well-known group of nine bright comets called sungrazers. The orbital characteristics of the sungrazers tell us something about how cometary nuclei can evolve. Astronomer Brian G. Marsden of the Harvard-Smithsonian Center for Astrophysics in Cambridge, Mass., showed in 1967 that the orbits of these comets fall naturally into two subgroups. He inferred that all of them probably were once a single comet that long ago split into several parts. During their many subsequent passes of the Sun, only two of the largest fragments survived. Recently, Marsden believes, each of these again broke into a number of smaller sungrazers.

This idea of cometary evolution underscores an important property of cometary nuclei—they seem to be quite fragile, evolving partially by catastrophic disintegration, or fragmentation. Astronomers might have been tempted to think that because they approach the Sun so closely, sungrazers are simply unable to withstand the strong tidal forces it raises in them. But observation of many comets has shown that fragmentation is rather common. Astronomers have observed it occurring as far as 800 million kilometers (500 million miles) from the Sun, where tidal forces are almost nonexistent.

Research on comets took a giant step forward starting in 1968 when astronomers used the second Orbiting Astronomical Observatory to initiate studies of comets from Earth orbit. This—together with a great stimulus from efforts to observe the otherwise disappointing Comet Kohoutek in 1973, and a substantial, but unfulfilled, planning effort made by U.S. scientists and engineers for a Halley's Comet space mission—has greatly increased our understanding. Numerous scientists working in many areas have contributed substantially. For example, some astronomers sent rockets bearing imaging spectrographs above Earth's atmosphere to study comets' light in the ultraviolet region of the spectrum. They showed that all comets have the same basic chemical composition, though they may differ greatly in the ratio of gaseous to dusty material. Other recent observations seem to prove the long-standing hypothesis that comets are composed primarily of water-ice. An exciting new discovery was that they also contain a mixture of a great variety of molecular compounds. Astronomers using ground-based microwave radio telescopes have detected carbon-bearing organic molecules being liberated from a cometary nucleus. Other ground-based studies are yielding a variety of additional information. Radio astronomers are using radar echoes they have received from a few comets to learn more about the size and nature of the surface of a nucleus. Improved optical telescopes have yielded new facts about the processes involved in the formation—and occasional complete detachment—of ion and dust tails. Observations

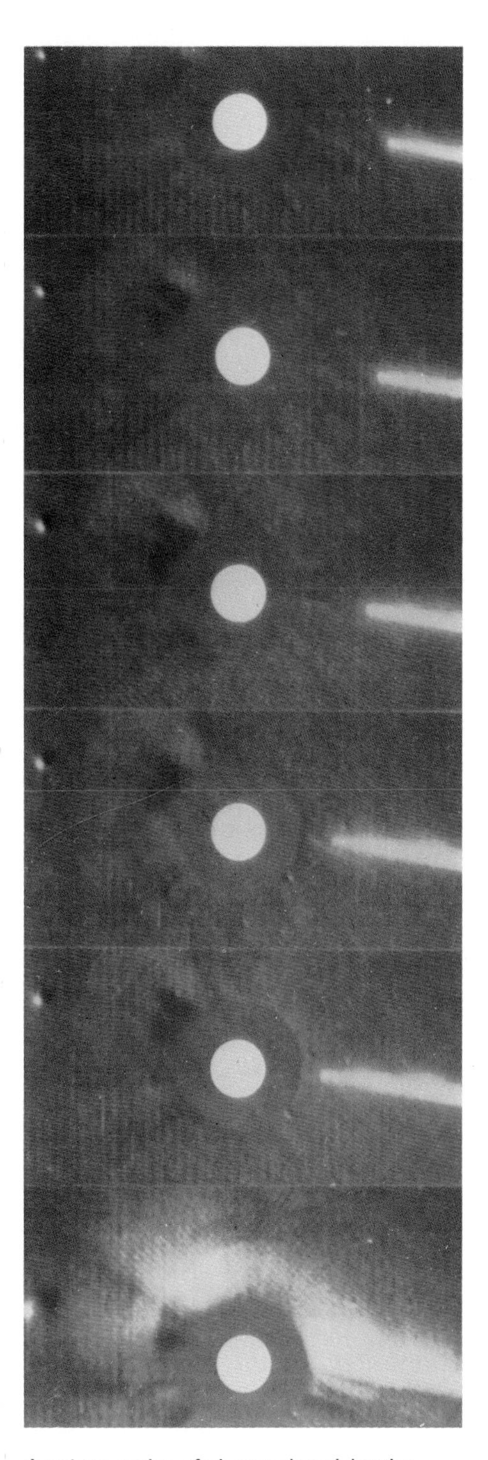

A unique series of photos chronicles the collision of a comet with the Sun on Aug. 30, 1979. From 4 million miles away (top), to fiery annihilation (bottom) took 11 hours.

at infrared wavelengths have revealed that siliceous, almost sandy, material makes up most of the dust in the tails. Observers using large optical telescopes with ultrasensitive detectors have gathered new information on the properties of comets at great distances.

Although there is much more we want to learn about comets, we certainly have a better idea of their nature now than people did when they saw them as special omens. Most astronomers believe comets were formed about 4½ billion years ago, at the same time as the giant outer planets—Jupiter, Saturn, Uranus, and Neptune. Some scientists think comets might even predate the formation of the Sun and planets—that they were ancient occupants of the large interstellar cloud from which the solar nebula fragmented. On March 13, 1980, astronomer Edward Bowell of the Lowell Observatory in Flagstaff, Ariz., discovered an object that may be a not fully compacted cometary nucleus. Comet Bowell, seems to be surrounded by what could be particles of the original solar nebula.

A few astronomers view comets as having formed more recently. They characterize them as minor creations that somehow originated within the giant planets and broke free, perhaps through massive explosions or after a planet disintegrated near the asteroid belt.

However comets originated, we know that most of them, perhaps as many as several tens of billions, remain in a vast spherical cloud surrounding the solar system. This cloud, called the Oort comet cloud for Dutch astronomer Jan H. Oort who suggested its existence in 1950, extends to the limits of the Sun's gravitational attraction. A few comets, perhaps 1,000 or so, have been trapped by the gravitational attraction of Jupiter, and to some extent by Saturn and Uranus, into short and predictable orbits around the Sun, some of which pass near Earth. Many astronomers think this may be how Halley's Comet came to make such regular reappearances. A final and seemingly incontrovertible fact about comets is that their composition, except for hydrogen and the rare gases, reflects the cosmic mix of the part of our Milky Way galaxy nearest the Sun.

These facts make it impossible for us to think of comets as cosmic trivia. Instead, they offer us a wondrous opportunity for learning about the natural processes involved in the origin of our world.

Because comets are small and are usually inhabitants of deep space far from the Sun, their bodies must be uncompressed and unheated. Therefore, they must be basically unchanged from the state in which they were formed. The record of their creation should still be hidden in their structure. As a comet falls into the vicinity of the Sun and begins gently to throw off material into space for us to examine, it is in a sense reversing the arrow of time. If we can observe this process in a suitable way in a bright, fresh comet, the data may tell us how and where comets were created.

Some scientists think that comets may hold the key to understanding the genesis of complex organic molecules that are known to be

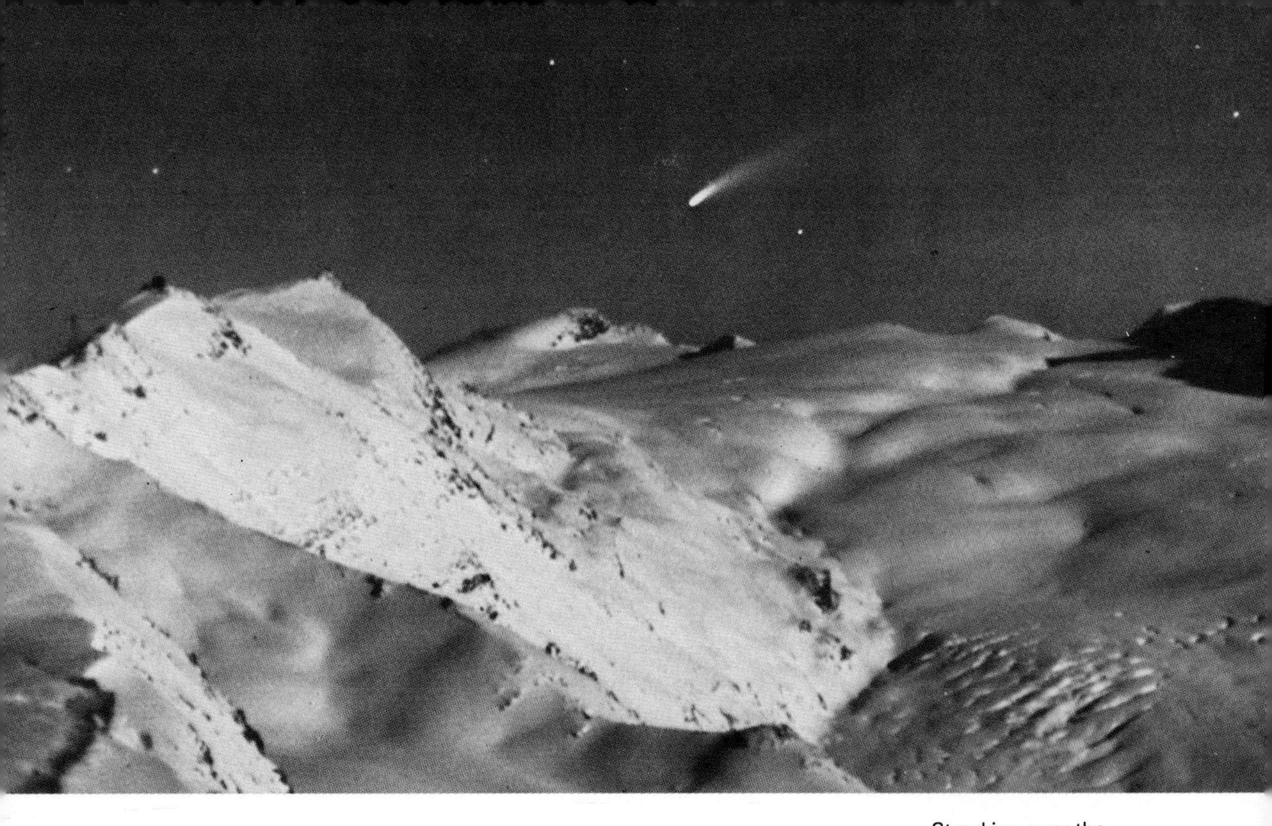

Streaking over the snowy Alps in 1970, Comet Bennett was one of many such visitors since eons past, some of which perhaps brought seeds of life to Earth.

essential to the chemistry of life. English astrophysicist Sir Fred Hoyle and his associate, astrophysicist Chandra Wickramasinghe, have called our general view of the origin of life "pre-Copernican." In earlier scientific reports and in their book *Lifecloud* (1978), they note that most people, scientists included, assume that life must have originated on Earth as the result of some special sequence of remarkable events.

They equate this idea with the notion people once had that Earth was the center of the universe. Polish astronomer Nicolaus Copernicus overturned that notion and radically altered the course of scientific thinking in 1543, when he demonstrated that Earth and the other planets revolve around the Sun. The two modern astronomers think the idea that life must have been created on Earth is as outdated as the idea of an Earth-centered universe.

Astronomers believe that the Earth formed amid much upheaval and great heat. Hoyle and Wickramasinghe believe that none of the chemical materials needed for the reactions necessary for life could have survived that. Nor do they believe that given the age of the Earth, there was time enough for these reactions to have occurred spontaneously. They say that some heavenly body whose history was calmer and cooler must have provided the chemical progenitors of life to the Earth. Comets seem to be the natural reservoirs of such material because of their age, their "cold" creation, and lack of subsequent change. Thus, the nuclei of comets may be the only place to find the chemical beginnings of life on Earth.

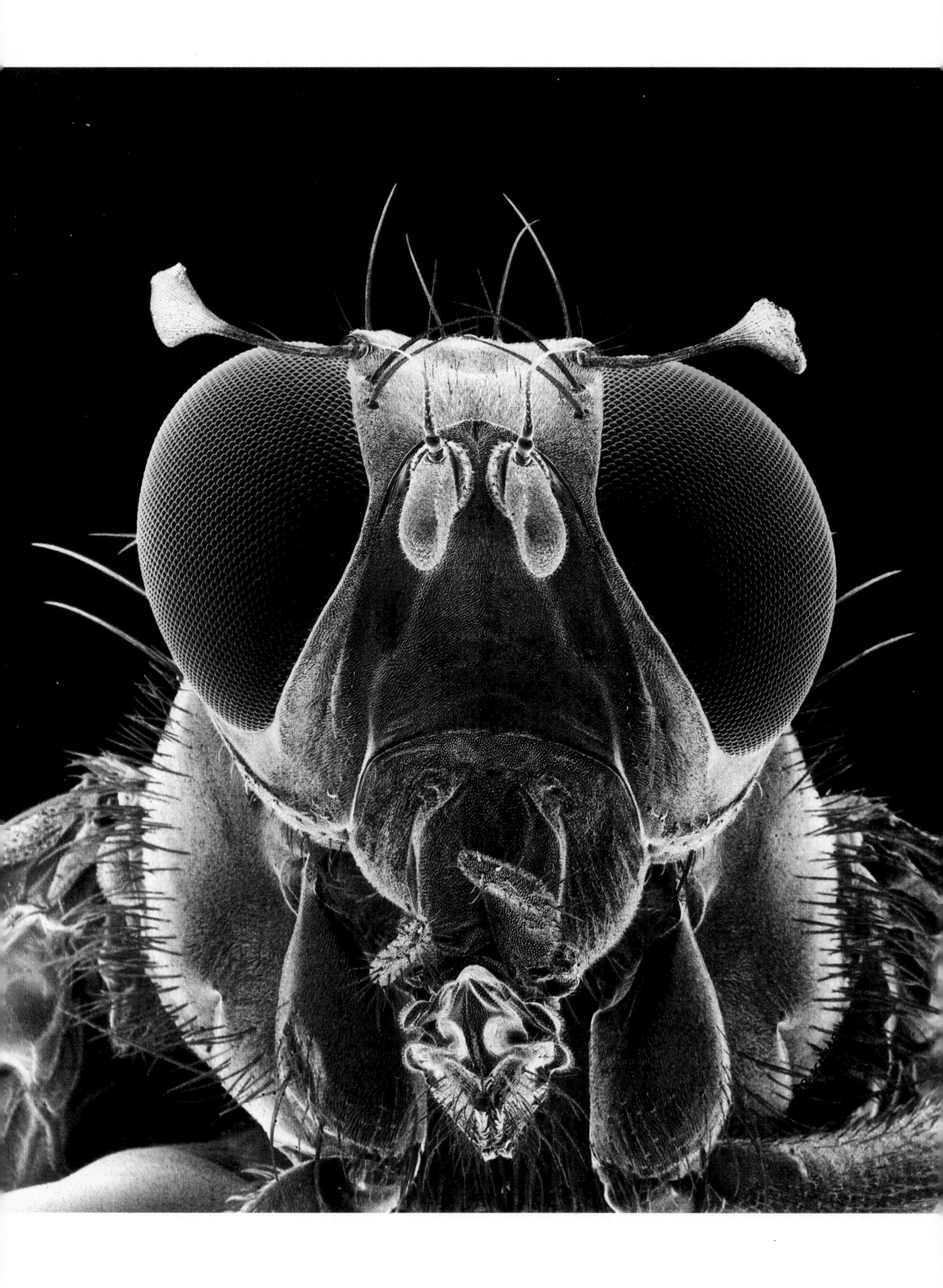

Stalking the Medfly

By Ben Patrusky

What went wrong in the battle against a voracious insect when scientific decisions had to be made before all the science was known

Californians living in Medfly-infested areas protest plans for aerial spraying of insecticide, *above*. The center of the storm was the dreaded Medfly, magnified 93 times, *opposite page*.

On June 5, 1980, a state entomologist on a routine inspection tour in San Jose, Calif., found two suspicious-looking insects in a flytrap hanging on a citrus tree in a backyard. Specimens in hand, the entomologist drove to the nearby office of the Santa Clara County agricultural commissioner. Telling no one about his discovery, he put the insects in a vial of alcohol to preserve them and dropped the package into the mail.

The mails proved exceptionally slow. The package arrived at the California Department of Food and Agriculture (CDFA) entomology laboratory in Sacramento, less than 100 miles away, nearly two weeks later. Only then were the pests positively identified and the alarm sounded. The much-dreaded, crop-ravaging Mediterranean fruit fly had invaded northern California.

Its arrival was to set in motion the biggest urban pest-management program ever launched in California. And the delay in discovering its arrival was a harbinger of the tactical blunders, false optimism, bureaucratic bumbling, scientific misunderstanding, and bad luck that consistently bedeviled the effort to eradicate the insects.

With California's $14-billion agricultural industry in jeopardy, the war on the fruit fly caused a fierce political battle, pitting farmers and politicians with strong agricultural constituencies against environmental activists and local officials representing urban residents.

An initial campaign to quash the infestation by spraying the ground with insecticide failed. The state's agribusiness leaders then demanded low-level aerial spraying to kill the bugs that threatened at least 50 commercially grown crops. Fearing the health hazards posed by insecticide "bombing," people living in the pesticide line of fire loudly resisted.

By the spring of 1982, nearly two years later, the controversy was still raging. Federal and state agencies had spent nearly $100 million on an eradication campaign, but there was still no telling whether the battle had been won. Officials admitted to only a guarded optimism—their caution stemming from the bitter memory of June 1981, when claims of victory proved to be unfounded.

The cause of all the fuss is a blue-eyed, droopy-winged creature about two-thirds the size of a housefly. The insect, whose scientific name is *Ceratitis capitata*, is known to Californians, in no way affectionately, as the Medfly. The most voracious fruit fly in the world, it has an appetite for as many as 250 kinds of soft-skinned fruit and vegetables. But orchard crops, such as peaches, apricots, and citrus fruits, are its favorites.

The adult female Medfly pierces the skin of the fruit with a needlelike appendage called an ovipositor and drops from 1 to 10 eggs into the hole. It then visits another fruit and repeats the process, laying up to 40 eggs a day or 800 in a lifetime.

The time required for the Medfly to pass through its four stages of development depends on temperature. For example, at an average summer temperature of 26°C (79°F.), the tiny eggs, a millimeter or less in length, hatch into larvae, or maggots, in two to three days. Tireless eating machines, the small, cream-colored larvae feed voraciously on the flesh of the fruit. Bacteria in the larvae's waste contribute to the destruction. Usually, the rotten fruit drops from the tree prematurely. The larvae then abandon the fruit and burrow into the soil to depths of up to 8 centimeters (3 inches). If the fruit remains on the tree, however, the larvae bore through the skin, fall to earth, then burrow into the ground.

In the soil, the insects enter their third stage—pupa. In preparation, they spin cocoons around their bodies until they are covered with a hard shell and look like grains of rice.

After 6 to 15 days, adult flies emerge from the cocoons and push their way up through the soil. Adults do not feed on fruit, preferring instead a diet of honeydew, a nectarlike liquid produced by aphids, or plant lice; mealy bugs; and soft-scaled insects. The flies lap up the honeydew as it comes from the insects' bodies. Copulation takes place about a week after the flies emerge from their cocoon. It may last for an hour or more, during which the females generally collect enough sperm in a special sac to last their egg-laying lifetime.

The Medfly's life cycle is shorter in warmer climates; longer in cooler climates. In Honolulu, Hawaii, for example, where the

The author:
Ben Patrusky is a free-lance science writer and a media consultant to several scientific institutions.

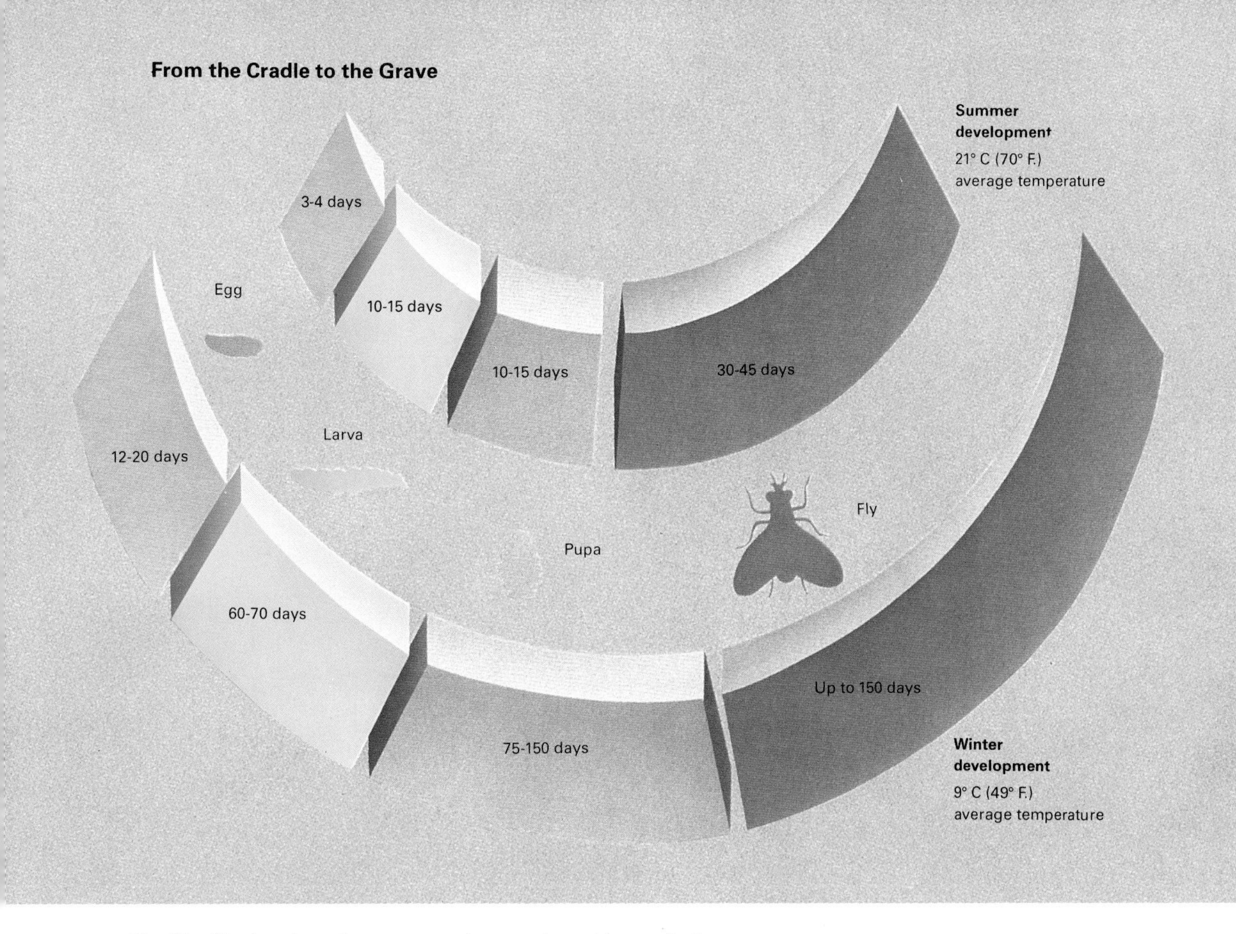

The Medfly develops from an egg into a winged insect in four stages.
The length of each stage varies according to the temperature.
The insect develops more quickly in warmer climates.

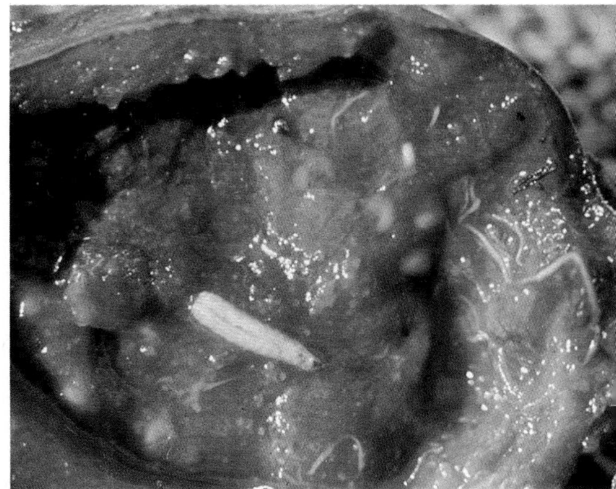

A female Medfly, *left,* prepares to pierce the skin of an orange and deposit her eggs in the fruit. Larvae, *above,* feed voraciously on the flesh of a fruit.

Medfly thrives, 10 to 13 generations are spawned each year. In Rome, Italy, which has cooler average temperatures, there are six to seven. And, as the 1980 infestation was to reveal, Santa Clara County's even cooler climate allows about three generations annually.

C. capitata originated in West Africa and spread throughout the Mediterranean in the mid-1800s. Since then, the Medfly has taken up permanent residence in many parts of the world, including Australia, in 1893; South America, 1901; Hawaii, 1907; Costa Rica, 1955; and Mexico, 1972. It also appears periodically in other areas, including the United States mainland. Yet despite its nomadic history, the Medfly is not a traveler by nature. The adult fly rarely strays more than a mile from the spot where it emerges from its pupal stage. Instead, the Medfly makes its far-flung excursions as a stowaway. And the agents of transit are generally human travelers bearing egg- or larvae-ridden fruit from Medfly-infested regions.

The first infestation in the United States, in 1929, cut a costly swath through the orange groves of central Florida. In a $7-million assault, 6,000 workers stripped fruit trees covering 487 square kilometers (188 square miles) and sprayed them from the ground with

A pest-control worker checks a trap set out to snare Medflies. Each trapped insect indicates the likelihood of 1,000 more in the area.

a honeydewlike bait laced with arsenic. The stripping disposed of already infested produce and deprived fertile females of nests for their eggs. The spraying killed adults that fed on the lethal mix. Victory was declared two years later, but not before 70 per cent of Florida's citrus crop had been destroyed.

In 1956, the Medfly infiltrated Florida again, in the Miami area. This time, the battle was fought from the air. Specially rigged B-17 bombers sprayed the then-new insecticide malathion, mixed in a bait solution, over a 2,600-square-kilometer (1,000-square-mile) area. Malathion became the chief weapon in subsequent fights against the Medfly—in 1962 in Florida and 1966 in Texas. In 1980, it became a center of controversy.

In 1975, the Medfly paid its first visit to California. A small infestation was discovered in Venice in Los Angeles County. Pest-control officials knew that they would encounter heavy opposition from the state's powerful environmental groups if they advocated aerial spraying over the densely populated urban area. Instead, they introduced an attack strategy that combined chemical and biological methods. They flooded the infested area with 100 sterile Medflies for

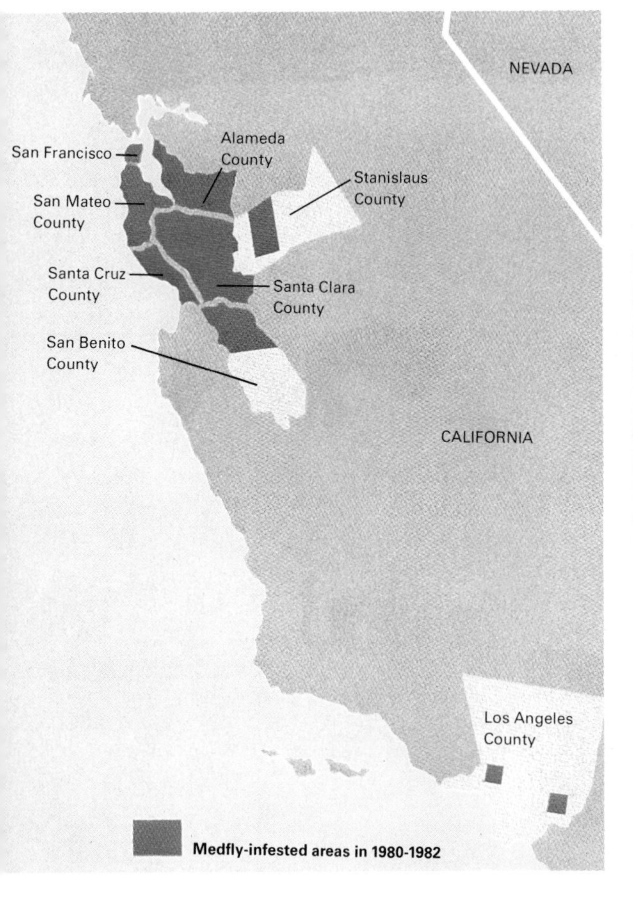

Five California counties and parts of three others, *left,* were infested by the Medfly from 1980 to 1982. A quarantine sign, *above,* symbolizes attempts to confine the pest to those areas.

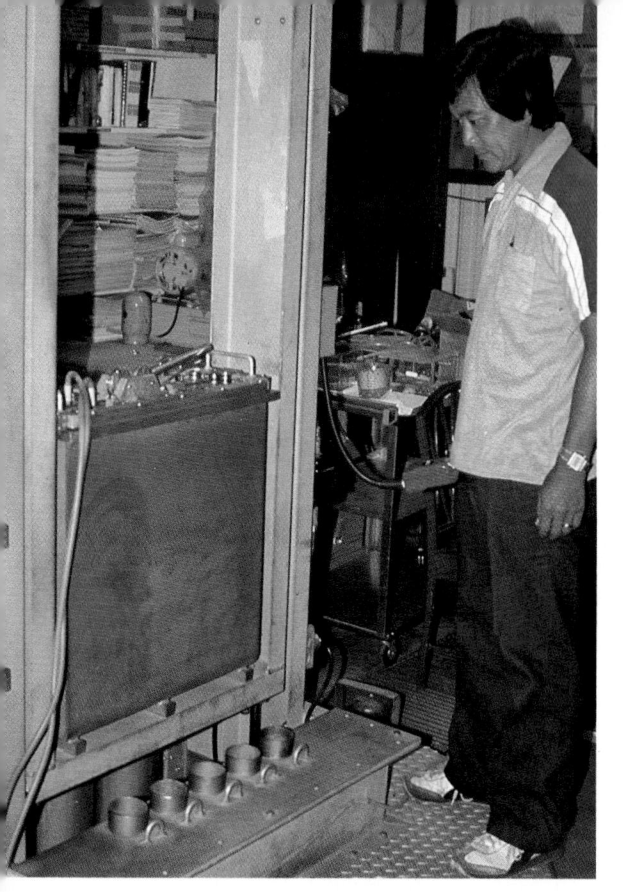

After Medfly pupae are sterilized by radiation equipment, *left,* they are dyed, *above,* so the adults can be distinguished from wild fertile flies. The sterile adults are then released by the thousands from a moving truck, *below*.

every 1 wild fertile male, enough to overwhelm the wild population. With sterile males monopolizing mating, most females would lay defective, unhatchable eggs. Pest-control officials backed up the release of the sterile flies with some fruit-stripping and selective ground-spraying of malathion-laced bait around infested trees as well as neighboring uninfested trees.

The sterile male fly technique was developed in the 1950s to suppress a Texas infestation of screwworm, which feeds off the flesh of livestock and other warm-blooded animals. The process involves exposing pupae in the late stages of development, when the reproductive system is forming, to doses of radiation strong enough to sterilize but not wholly destroy sexual function. For the technique to be effective, the sterile males must be able to pass the fluid that would ordinarily contain sperm to the wild females. Otherwise, the females seek fertile mates. Both male and female Medflies are sterilized be-

A worker drenches the soil beneath an infested tree with insecticide to kill Medfly pupae burrowing into the ground and adult flies pushing their way to the surface.

cause it is nearly impossible to determine the sex of a pupa. And both are released because it is too time-consuming to distinguish between adult males and females. Only adult sterile males, however, are needed to make the process work.

When the Medfly hit California in 1975, the U.S. Department of Agriculture's (USDA) research laboratory in Hawaii had just completed a two-year pilot study on the value of using sterile flies to control Medfly populations. As a result, a rearing facility to supply the flies required in Los Angeles was already in place. About 20-million irradiated pupae were shipped weekly and the newly emerged adults released into the combat zone. After a $1.5-million, seven-month campaign involving fewer than 50 workers — and about 500 million sterile Medflies — officials declared the infestation eradicated. So when the Medfly showed up again in 1980, federal and state pest-control specialists decided to use the same strategy. This time, however, things didn't work out nearly so well.

The Medfly actually made two appearances in 1980. On June 5 — the day the two suspicious-looking pests were discovered in San Jose — an adult Medfly turned up in a trap 640 kilometers (400 miles) to the south in Baldwin Park, a suburb of Los Angeles. The suburb is about 50 kilometers (30 miles) east of the site of the 1975 infestation. Los Angeles County did not delay. Within days, pest-control teams were hanging more traps in and around the infestation site. As "census takers," the traps helped pest fighters establish the extent of the infestation. The traps, which look like miniature pup tents, were baited with a chemical that attracts Medflies. Drawn to the bait, the flies were snared by a gummy substance on the tent floor. Pest specialists estimated that for each Medfly trapped, at least another thousand were in the immediate vicinity. In areas where flies were found, fruit was collected and checked for larvae. Initial findings indicated that this Medfly outbreak was even more limited than the small invasion in 1975.

As officials of the CDFA gathered in Los Angeles in mid-June to draw up the final blueprint for the eradication effort in Baldwin Park, word arrived about the Medfly's appearance to the north in Santa Clara County. On the assumption that the northern California infestation was also small-scale, the group recommended the same plan for both sites: sterile fly release; fruit-stripping; spraying of larvae-infested trees with malathion-laced bait; and drenching the soil beneath infested trees with fenthion, a pesticide that is more powerful and lasts longer than malathion. The fenthion treatment was designed to kill the larvae as they entered the soil to pupate or to destroy the flies as they pushed their way back to the surface. Once again the strategy worked splendidly in Los Angeles. By December, southern California was declared Medfly-free. A state-imposed quarantine that prevented the export of fruits that might carry Medfly larvae from the infested area was lifted.

To control the spread of the Medfly in an already infested area, members of a pest-control team bag fruit stripped from trees still free of the pest, *above left*. To prevent the Medfly from invading areas outside an infestation zone, an inspection officer confiscates fruit from motorists leaving the area, *above*.

In northern California, the story was quite different. The unfortunate two-week delay in identifying the Medfly was followed immediately by another equally damaging mistake. On June 19, the Santa Clara County Board of Supervisors denied a $50,000 request from the agriculture commissioner to buy more traps. The CDFA eventually stepped in to buy them, but crucial days had been lost. As more traps were set out, more flies were found, and officials realized that the area of infestation was considerably larger than anyone had imagined.

Few traps had been set out in Santa Clara County because scientists never thought the Medfly would threaten northern California. Their assumption, based on studies conducted in the 1950s in Hawaii by entomologist Powers Messenger, was that the fly could not survive the relatively cold northern California winter climate.

By the middle of August, 1,200 square kilometers (450 square miles) in Santa Clara County had been quarantined. The quarantine zone consisted mainly of private houses with backyard fruit trees. But there were also some commercial orchards in the zone and growers were beginning to feel the pinch. All fruit shipped from those orchards had to be fumigated or refrigerated for long periods.

As the infestation area grew, the eradication effort was complicated by an enormous logistical problem — where to get a sufficient number of sterile male flies. The plan called for 1 million flies to be released within each square mile of infestation in order to create the optimum ratio of 100 sterile males to 1 wild or fertile male. Officials

How Malathion Works

Malathion kills by disrupting the transmission of nerve impulses.

Nerve impulses travel along nerve cell extensions called axons and dendrites. These extensions do not connect but are separated by an extremely narrow space called the synaptic cleft. Chemicals called neurotransmitters carry impulses from the axons across the cleft to the dendrites. Acetylcholine is one of the chief neurotransmitters.

After dendrites receive the impulse, their surfaces must be cleared to receive new signals. This is done by molecules of a biochemical called cholinesterase. These molecules attach themselves to the acetylcholine molecules, carry them away from the dendrites, and chemically break them down, freeing the dendrites to receive new impulses.

Malathion disrupts this process. Malathion molecules attach themselves to cholinesterase molecules and prevent them from removing the acetylcholine. As acetylcholine builds up, the dendrites transmit impulses continuously. This eventually exhausts the nerve and transmission stops, resulting in the death of the insect. [B. P.]

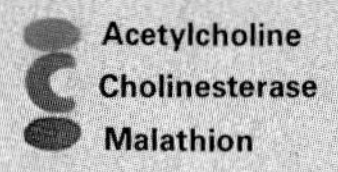

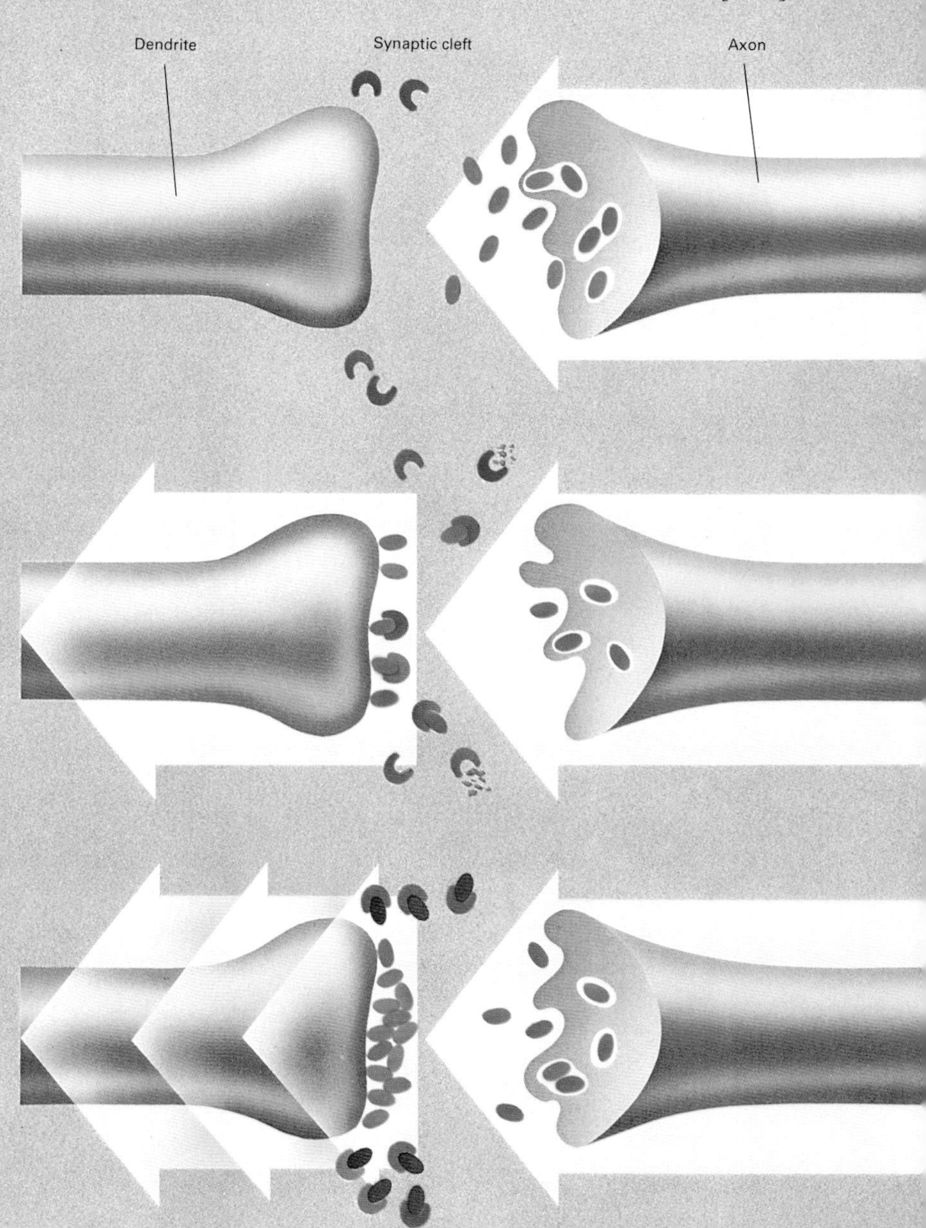

Acetylcholine molecules carry nerve impulses across the synaptic cleft that separates nerve terminals. Signals then continue along the second nerve.

Cholinesterase molecules attach themselves to the acetylcholine molecules at the second nerve ending, carry them away, and break them down. The terminal is then free to receive new signals.

Malathion molecules lock onto cholinesterase molecules. The second nerve transmits impulses continuously as acetylcholine builds up on the nerve ending.

also needed to create a "buffer zone" to keep stray fertile females from extending beyond the infestation area.

At the outset of the 1980 outbreak, the rearing facility in Hawaii—the sole U.S. provider of sterile flies—could produce only 20 million steriles per week, which was not enough to meet the weekly demand. So flies were brought in weekly from facilities in Costa Rica, Mexico, and Peru. By November, however, trap data told a grim story—as few as 26 sterile males to each wild male, far below the ratio needed to check the infestation.

Other aspects of the ground-based effort—fruit-stripping and spraying—were hardly faring better. One major stumbling block was the need to obtain a homeowner's permission to treat infested trees on the property. With many working couples in the area, often no one was at home to give pest-control teams permission to treat their yard. Between June and December, only about 55 per cent of yards judged in need of stripping and spraying had actually been treated. There was also difficulty in integrating the various phases of the pest-management program. Often, for example, soon after pest-control workers discharged sterile flies, the pesticide crews would come along and spray the area, killing many of the flies.

On November 20, with the situation going from bad to worse, USDA representatives urged the Medfly Project's Technical Advisory Committee to recommend aerial spraying "as soon as possible." The committee, made up of federal, state, and local pest-control officials, responded by advising postponing aerial spraying at least until the spring, and to concentrate instead on stepping up ground-spraying and fruit-stripping. Despite this, the CDFA and USDA on December 1 jointly announced plans to begin immediate aerial spraying with malathion.

The announcement drew strong opposition from people living in the area. Scientists from Stanford University in Palo Alto, in the heart of the infestation zone, and from the nearby Berkeley campus of the University of California joined in. If Messenger's suggestion that the Medfly could not last the winter in Santa Clara was correct, aerial spray would serve no purpose. If it was wrong, then nothing would be lost anyway. Winter spraying would kill few flies, the scientists argued, since most were probably beneath the soil in a state of pupal dormancy and well beyond the reach of air-dropped pesticide. In the end, the aerial-spray plan was scotched on a regulatory quirk. To spray effectively, aircraft would have to fly at top altitudes of 152 meters (500 feet), and such low-altitude flights required the approval of local governments, as many as 14 in the proposed spray zone. These governments denied permission.

Forced to back off, the CDFA, with the grudging consent of the USDA, moved to beef up the integrated ground-based program. The Medfly Eradication Project was reorganized and a new director appointed. On Christmas Eve in 1980, California's Governor Edmund

G. (Jerry) Brown, Jr., declared a Medfly state of emergency, which enabled the project to mobilize 2,000 workers from the California Conservation Corps, the National Guard, and other groups for a full-scale ground assault.

Beginning in January 1981, all fruit in the 130-square-kilometer (50-square-mile) infestation zone, was stripped, bagged, and dumped. Behind the strippers came the ground-sprayers. Meanwhile, 100 million sterile flies were being released each week. In all, 620,000 backyards were sprayed six times each between January and May, and 4 billion sterile flies were released. By June, all spraying had stopped, but the release of sterile flies continued.

The intensified integrated program, the largest ever attempted in the world, appeared to be successful. The Medfly warriors drew up plans for a huge post-battle celebration.

Then the roof fell in. On June 26, larvae were discovered in a 15-square-kilometer (6-square-mile) region known as Mountain View Gap in the core infestation area. The discovery was proof positive that a new round of breeding had begun. The next day, project headquarters was alerted to three more finds. By June 29, the larval count jumped to 27 infestation sites — all in the Gap. Why this sudden reproductive explosion? And why in the Gap?

When a yellow-dyed female Medfly laden with eggs turned up in a trap in early July, blame quickly fell on a batch of "sterile" flies from the rearing facility in Peru. Officials suspected that the flies had been improperly irradiated.

They knew the female was Peruvian because it was dyed yellow. When officials began importing steriles from several breeding facilities, they assigned each facility a different color. When sterile pupae arrived at the Medfly Project's California headquarters, they were dusted with a fluorescent dye. This distinguished the sterile adults from the wild flies. As the adult flies pushed out of their cocoons, the dye stuck to the body and to a balloonlike organ called the ptilinum, which retracts into the head once the fly has emerged completely. If the dye came off, lab technicians could still identify the sterile flies by puncturing the head and looking for dye marks.

Field inspectors visited trap sites weekly and delivered the catches to headquarters for screening. Suspect fertile flies — those which did not fluoresce under ultraviolet light — were sped to the CDFA's entomological lab in Sacramento for dissection.

When, on July 7, the lab found a large batch of eggs — presumably incontrovertible proof of fertility — in the yellow-dyed female, Medfly project leader Jerry Scribner and the technical committee were certain they had their proof. If this Peruvian-shipped female was fertile, then many of the emerging males were probably fertile too. Also, in checking fly release records, officials discovered that a large number of Peruvian steriles had been released in Mountain View Gap on June 14. If these steriles were indeed fertile then, given the warm

Sunlight glinting off their whirling rotor blades, a squadron of helicopters trails streamers of malathion in the battle against the tenacious Medfly.

weather, larvae would have appeared at the end of June—exactly when they were first discovered.

Later, Scribner came to doubt this explanation for the Mountain View Gap flare-up. He learned, for example, that irradiated females, even though infertile, often continue to produce eggs. So the discovery of eggs in a female was not incontrovertible proof of fertility. The infestation also may have been due to an entirely different cause—a case of mistaken identity. Originally, sterile flies from Hawaii had been dyed blue. But the technical advisory committee ordered a switch to pale green to make identification easier. Under ultraviolet light, however, the pale green proved to be very similar to the Medfly's natural color. For this reason, checkers at the Los Gatos field laboratory may have mistaken wild flies for sterile ones. So the outbreak in the Gap could have been the result of workers seriously underestimating the true extent of the infestation and failing to undertake sufficiently vigorous eradication measures.

In February 1981, the committee had laid contingency plans for spraying by helicopter. The "trigger" for the spraying, the committee decided, would be the discovery of at least three separate infestation sites. The 27 finds in the Mountain View area more than met this criterion. Because of the governor's December 1980 declaration of emergency, local officials did not need to approve low-level flights. But the CDFA and USDA decided to delay aerial spraying until the technical committee, scheduled to meet on July 7, had a chance to make an official recommendation. By the day of the meeting, the infestation area had expanded to 155 square kilometers (60 square miles), far beyond Mountain View Gap.

The committee deliberated in an open-air forum attended by several hundred citizens waving placards protesting aerial spraying. Late in the day, after having heard from a long parade of speakers, most of whom opposed aerial spraying, the committee prepared to vote formally. But a last-minute telephone request from the governor persuaded the committee to postpone its decision until it met with Brown in Sacramento the following day.

The next day, Brown asked the committee to support another ground-based campaign. The committee refused and immediately voted unanimously for aerial spraying with malathion.

At this point, Brown, a candidate for the United States Senate, took one of the biggest political gambles of his career. He ordered the CDFA to abstain from aerial spraying, a move that infuriated California's politically powerful agricultural industry. He called instead for one massive, last-ditch ground operation. In announcing his decision to the press on July 8, Brown said: "Subjecting 500,000 people — including pregnant women, infants, and children — to aerial application of a toxic pesticide is not an acceptable alternative to a safer, effective ground-spray operation."

Brown's assessment of the malathion peril seemed to contradict that of a state-appointed, blue-ribbon health advisory committee charged with evaluating all known scientific literature related to the pesticide's health effects. The panel, composed of 24 eminent physicians and scientists — including several who had once strongly opposed aerial spraying — concluded in June that the pesticide was one of the safest insect killers known. The panel said there was no indication that human exposure to malathion, at the low concentrations planned for the aerial effort, would cause acute illness or long-term problems such as birth defects, genetic damage, and cancer. People are protected from malathion poisoning, at least to some degree, by liver enzymes, which insects lack. Pest-control officials favor its use because it breaks down within a few days and washes off with water. Also, malathion sprayed aerially is mixed with a Medfly bait that has the consistency of molasses and so cannot be easily inhaled.

In the end, Brown's call for another vigorous ground campaign came to naught. Within 48 hours, he was forced to reverse himself when United States Secretary of Agriculture John R. Block threatened to quarantine all California produce unless aerial spraying began. The aerial campaign began at midnight on July 14, as a lone helicopter rose from a secret base to make the first flight.

Throughout the summer, a growing squadron of helicopters flew more and more malathion spray missions as the zone of infestation grew. At its peak, the spray area encompassed a total of 3,400 square kilometers (1,300 square miles). Then, gradually, the size of the spray zone began to diminish. By early 1982 it was down to 480 square kilometers (184 square miles), with the last aerial spraying scheduled for late spring.

The eradication effort then became a waiting game to see if any fresh finds would appear. If they did, officials believed they would be detected quickly by the much-improved trapping system. Over 30,000 traps dotted the Santa Clara Valley, compared with 80 in early June 1980. But Medfly fighters did not expect to find much. If they did, helicopters would begin another round of spraying.

That attitude worries environmentalists. They are concerned that the apparent failure of the ground-based effort will be misconstrued as evidence that a combination biological and chemical approach to pest control does not work. They fear that aerial spraying will become the automatic response for all future infestations.

Many scientists have been critical of the science used for many decisions made during the Medfly eradication campaign. Much of the trouble in Santa Clara, for instance, derived from a poor early-warning detection network, the result of erroneous assumptions based on one 30-year-old study conducted on lab-reared Hawaiian Medflies. Nor was anything done to ensure that the sterile flies released in northern California were hardy enough to compete with the wild population. As Stanford University biologist Paul Ehrlich puts it: "For all practical purposes there has been zero science—zilch—practiced on the [Medfly] problem."

Ehrlich noted that the Medfly Project was doing "the largest marked [fly] release experiment in the history of the universe," and would have provided an "ideal way to get basic information on dispersal and survival in the wild. But no scientist was in place nor any effort made to get this kind of data from the traps." Ehrlich reported that when he asked a USDA official why such studies were not being done, he was told: "We do not have the luxury of doing research in the midst of an eradication program."

To Ehrlich and his colleagues, this lack of appreciation for the value of basic research stems from what has been called the "spray-now-ask-questions-later school of pest control" or the "nozzlehead mentality" that, they believe, has long pervaded agricultural agencies on both the federal and state level.

It is almost certain that the Medfly will show up again sooner or later. Will every new visitation mean another aerial bombardment with malathion? And what if one such visit brings a malathion-resistant Medfly, leaving pest fighters with an empty arsenal?

Not long after the aerial spray campaign began, CDFA Director Richard E. Rominger said, "It is difficult to translate scientific data into public policy. When the science is absent, it is more difficult. In the Santa Clara Valley Medfly War, the needed basic facts were not available. An extensive research project about the sex life of Medflies in San Jose will receive top priority. No one will ever again make fun of research about the sex life of an insect."

Time Bombs in the Blood

By Thomas H. Maugh II

Now haunted by fear of painful crises set off by their deformed red cells, sickle cell victims look to a new generation of drugs for relief

Nine-year-old Phil loves to play baseball, but he could not finish the Little League season with his team this year. Shortly before the season ended, Phil came down with a cold. He developed a high fever and severe pain in his muscles and abdomen, "Like a toothache all over my body," he said. His parents recognized the symptoms; they had been through this before. They rushed Phil to the hospital—for the fourth time in his young life—where doctors gave him painkillers, large amounts of liquids, and oxygen.

The pain went away within 48 hours, but the recurrent crises have begun to take their toll on Phil's body, and his doctor wants him to give up his beloved sport. Already, Phil's heart shows signs of enlargement and his spleen, liver, and kidneys have been damaged. As he grows older, Phil will probably begin to lose his eyesight. The odds are that he will die of an infection before he reaches the age of 30. Phil has sickle cell disease.

Sickle cell disease is an inherited disease that occurs mainly among black people. It affects the red cells in blood. Red blood cells are the vehicles that carry oxygen from the lungs, through the arteries, and into the network of tiny blood vessels, or capillaries, that deliver blood to the body's organs and tissues. Normal red blood cells are shaped somewhat like doughnuts. They are very flexible, because they have to squeeze through capillaries smaller than their diameter.

In sickle cell disease, red cells can become rigid and deformed, often twisted into a hooked, or sickle, shape. These tend to stick in the capillaries and block blood flow, preventing oxygen and other nutrients carried by blood from reaching tissues and organs.

Many victims of sickle cell disease lead reasonably normal lives for long periods with only occasional crises. Doctors are not certain what sets off a crisis, but they tend to occur at night and in persons experiencing physical stress, such as exposure to cold or infections. A sickle cell crisis can be mild or severe, and the symptoms vary according to which organs are most affected. Eventually, the recurrent blocking of oxygen and nutrients produces irreversible damage to the organs, and they cease functioning. Sickle cell victims die young either from organ failure or from severe infections.

Sickle cell disease is caused by an abnormal type of hemoglobin, one of the main ingredients of red blood cells. There are about 270 million hemoglobin molecules in each cell. These molecules pick up oxygen molecules when the blood passes through the lungs and carries the oxygen through the bloodstream.

Sickle cell disease is inherited through genes like all physical characteristics, such as eye color, hair color, and even the ability to curl one's tongue. In sickle cell disease, a child receives one hemoglobin gene from each parent.

If a child receives genes from both parents for the abnormal hemoglobin, known as hemoglobin S (for sickle), the child's red blood cells will be made up almost entirely of hemoglobin S, and the child will have sickle cell disease. A child who receives one normal hemoglobin gene and one abnormal hemoglobin gene will have what scientists call sickle cell trait. About 40 per cent of the hemoglobin in the blood cells will be abnormal. Persons with sickle cell trait do not suffer from the crises of sickle cell disease. The abnormal hemoglobin is detected through special blood tests.

Hundreds of thousands of persons, mostly black, of African or Mediterranean descent carry genes for the abnormal hemoglobin S. About 1 in every 10 American blacks has sickle cell trait. But in some areas of Africa the proportion of individuals with sickle cell trait is as high as 3 in every 10. Scientists estimate that about 1 in 600 American blacks has sickle cell disease, a total of about 50,000. While there are no reliable statistics, researchers are certain the proportion is much higher in Africa.

Normally, a gene that causes a problem of such magnitude would be bred out of the population over a period of time because the victims would die before having children. But apparently the sickle cell gene has survived for two related reasons. First, it helps protect those who bear it from malaria, a sometimes fatal disease that is common in tropical areas. Malaria causes periodic fevers, chills, and sweating and is the result of a parasite that invades the liver and the red blood cells. Secondly, persons with sickle cell trait benefit from its malaria-fighting properties but do not suffer the life-threatening crises. They survive and pass on the gene to their children.

The author:
Thomas H. Maugh II
is senior staff writer
for *Science* magazine.

Although there is still much to learn about it, sickle cell disease is one of the best understood of all human diseases. Scientists believe

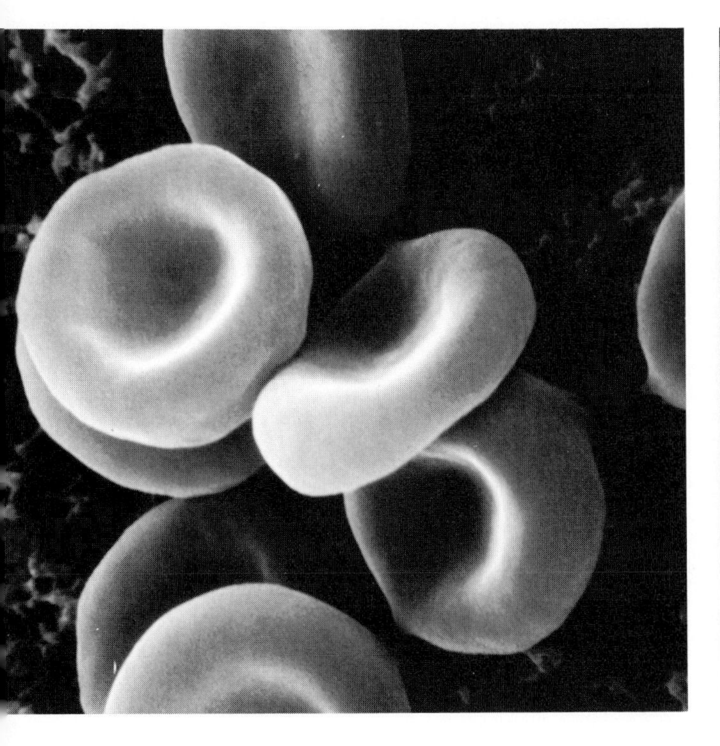

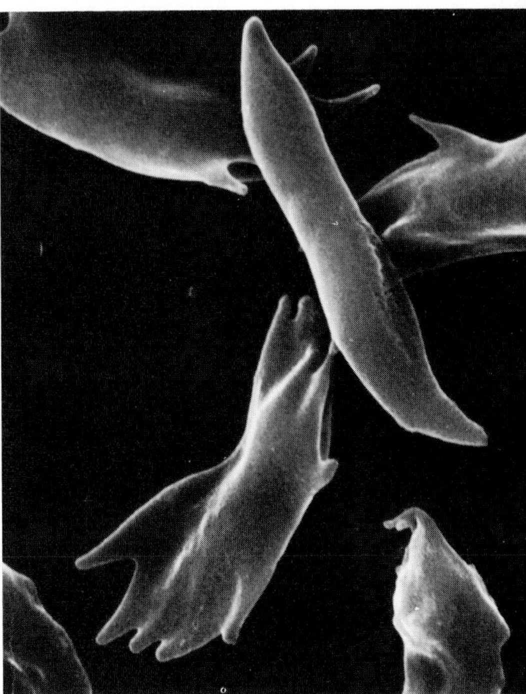

Normal red blood cells (magnified 8,000 times), *above left,* are round and resemble doughnuts. Sickle cells, *above,* are twisted into odd shapes, some of which curve like a sickle (magnified 5,000 times).

they know where sickle cell disease arose, why it protects against malaria, and exactly what causes it—down to the individual atoms in the hemoglobin molecules. This knowledge may enable researchers to design revolutionary new drugs that can be targeted to specific points on the hemoglobin S molecule to treat sickle cell disease.

Sickle cell symptoms were first described in 1910 by U.S. cardiologist James B. Herrick. Other investigators later discovered that the disease affects red blood cells and that the cells become distorted after they have released their oxygen. The first important breakthrough in understanding the disease occurred in 1949, when Nobel-Prizewinning chemist Linus C. Pauling and his colleagues at the California Institute of Technology in Pasadena found that the sickling is caused by an abnormal hemoglobin molecule.

Hemoglobin is made up of iron and a very complex protein. Like all proteins, it is created from amino acids. There are 20 common amino acids that can be linked together in various combinations, like beads in a necklace, to produce the proteins that make up body tissues and carry out most of the body's functions. There are two kinds of these chains of amino acids, called alpha and beta chains, in the hemoglobin molecule. Two alpha and two beta chains combine to form the hemoglobin molecule, which can carry four molecules of oxygen, one on each of the chains.

Many amino acids have an electrical charge, either positive or negative, determined by the number of electrons that orbit the nuclei of their atoms. Pauling discovered that a hemoglobin S molecule

How Sickling Slows Circulation

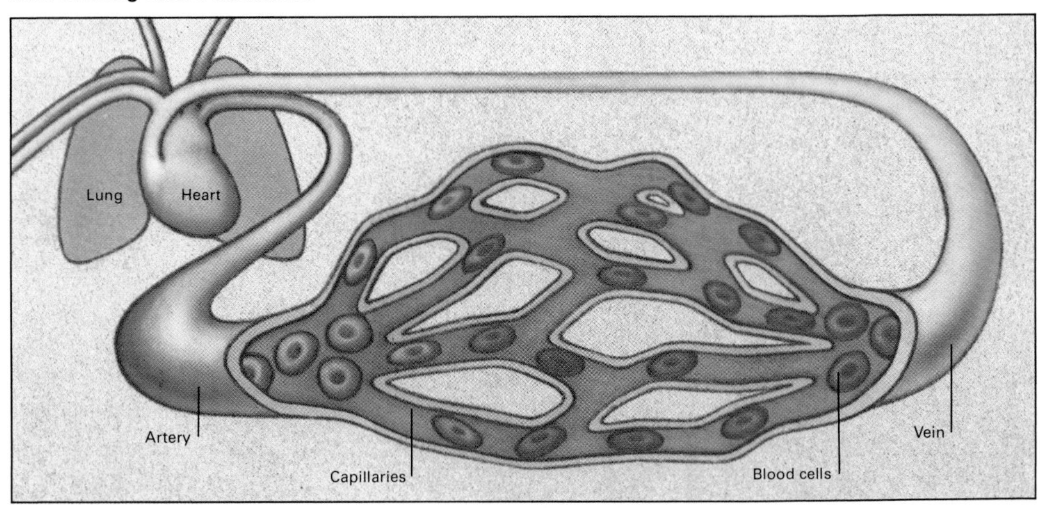

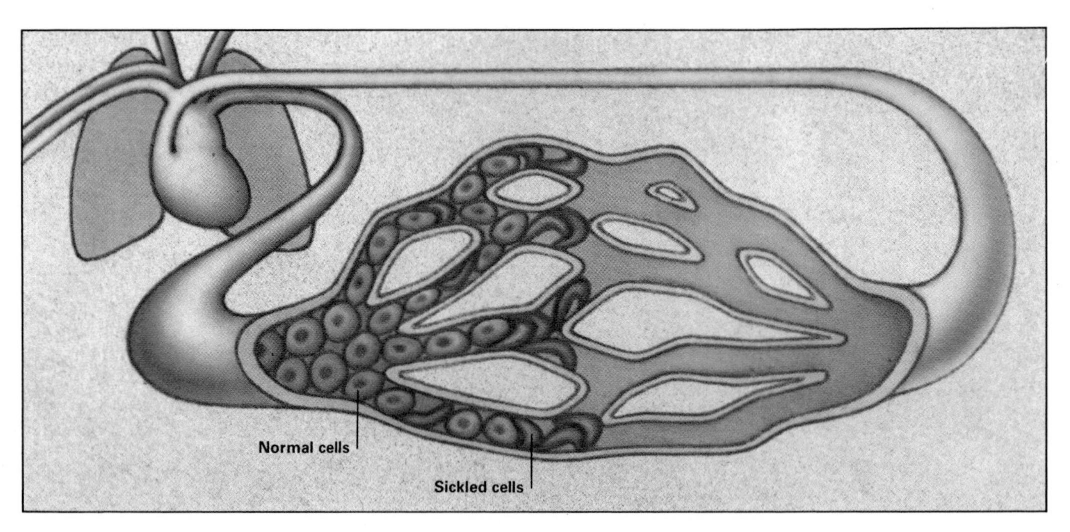

Normal red blood cells delivering oxygen from the lungs are flexible enough to squeeze through capillaries, *top,* and return to the heart and lungs through the veins. But sickle cells, after giving up oxygen, get stuck in the tiny blood vessels, *above,* cutting off the vital flow of oxygen and nutrients.

carries two fewer electrons, or units of negative charge, than does a normal hemoglobin molecule. Sickle cell disease thus became the first disease whose cause could be so specifically related to an inherited defect in a protein molecule.

The precise point of the defect in the hemoglobin molecule was located in 1956. Biochemist Vernon M. Ingram of the Massachusetts Institute of Technology in Cambridge found that one amino acid substitutes for another at a particular site on the beta chain. This substitution results in the loss of one negative charge per beta chain, or two negative charges per hemoglobin molecule, just as Pauling had found.

In 1977, molecular biologists Sherman Weissman, Bernard G. Forget, and their colleagues at Yale University in New Haven, Conn., showed that this amino acid substitution could be traced to a specific change, or mutation, in the gene that codes for hemoglobin. Most scientists are now convinced that this mutation is the sole cause of sickle cell disease. Since the mutation protected against malaria, people carrying one sickle cell gene survived the onslaught of the parasitic disease while many with normal hemoglobin did not. These survivors produced children, spreading the sickle cell gene.

Such a mutation apparently occurred in at least two places in the world. Molecular biologists Yuet Wai Kan and Andree M. Dozy of the University of California at San Francisco used genetic engineering techniques in the early 1980s to identify subtle differences in what they believe are two distinct variations of the sickle gene. They apparently arose independently in malaria-prone areas. One gene appeared in West Africa and spread through North Africa into Mediterranean populations. It is prevalent in persons living in these areas. The second gene seems to have originated in East Africa and spread to the Middle East and Asia. Most American blacks with sickle cell disease or sickle cell trait have the gene that arose in West Africa because their ancestors came from there.

In the mid-1960s, scientists began using high-powered electron microscopes to study the structure of hemoglobin molecules. They found that hemoglobin S molecules bearing oxygen are scattered randomly throughout a red blood cell, as are normal hemoglobin molecules. But when the hemoglobin S molecules give up their oxygen, something very unusual happens. They join to form long chains known as polymers, tens of thousands of hemoglobin molecules long. Each sickled blood cell contains thousands of these polymers.

While the electron microscopists were puzzling over these chains of hemoglobin molecules, X-ray crystallographers were beginning to get their first look at the atomic structure of this abnormal hemoglobin by beaming X rays through crystals of hemoglobin S. When a substance is in a crystal state, each molecule is rigidly locked into a specific place. X rays passing through the molecules of the crystal are deflected when they strike an atom. The deflected X rays produce characteristic patterns on photographic film. Scientists can interpret these patterns to deduce the precise location of each atom in the molecules of which the crystal is composed.

In 1972, X-ray crystallographers Barry C. Wishner and Warner E. Love of Johns Hopkins University in Baltimore succeeded for the first time in growing high-quality crystals of hemoglobin S molecules that were not bound to oxygen. X-ray studies of these crystals have shown that the abnormal hemoglobin S polymer is a double-stranded structure. The abnormal amino acid of each hemoglobin molecule in one chain bonds to a specific spot on a hemoglobin S molecule in the other chain. When the hemoglobin S molecules take up oxygen again, they change shape slightly. This disrupts the bond and the polymers break up.

Even though scientists have learned much about hemoglobin S, they are still not certain how the hemoglobin polymers cause red blood cells to sickle. The simplest explanation is that the growing polymers distort the shape of the cell and hold the cell membrane in a rigid position just as the material of a tent is stretched taut between tent poles. But changes also occur in the membrane of the cell during sickling. Scientists disagree about whether these changes simply reflect the stretching of the membrane by the polymers or whether other biological effects are involved.

The changes in the membrane allow calcium and potassium to flow through the membrane more freely. The concentration of potassium in a red blood cell is normally higher than its concentration in blood plasma, the clear liquid part of the blood; the concentration of calcium is normally lower. In sickled cells, the concentrations of both these elements inside the cell become much closer to the concentrations in plasma. Scientists believe that this, along with the spearlike polymers, may play a role in protecting against malaria.

The first indication of a relationship between malaria and sickled cells had been noted in 1954, when epidemiologist Anthony C. Allison of the Medical Research Council in London found that children with sickle cell trait had much less severe cases of malaria than did those with normal hemoglobin. For more than 20 years, scientists were mystified about the possible connection.

Understanding the connection began in 1976, when parasitologists William Trager and James B. Jensen of Rockefeller University in New York City and J. David Haynes and his colleagues at the Walter Reed Army Research Institute in Washington, D.C., independently developed techniques for growing the microscopic malarial parasite *Plasmodium falciparum* in test tubes. *P. falciparum* is the para-

Disorders such as skin ulcers, *below,* or an enlarged heart, *right,* result when body tissues are deprived of oxygen by a sickle cell crisis.

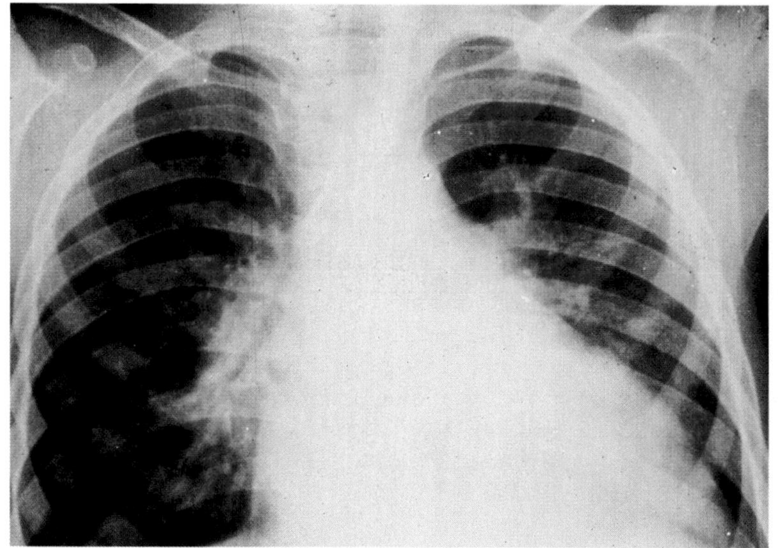

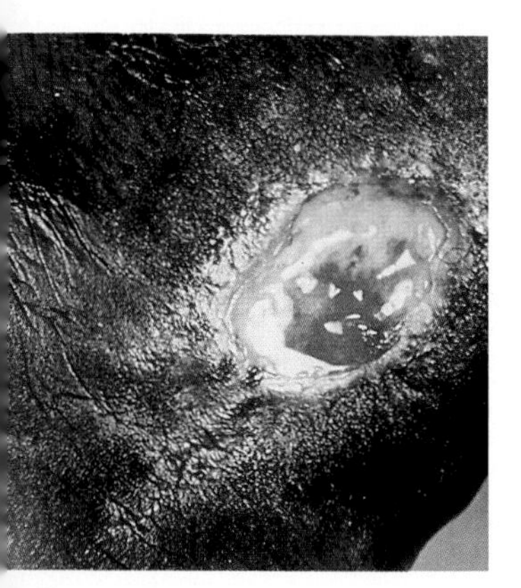

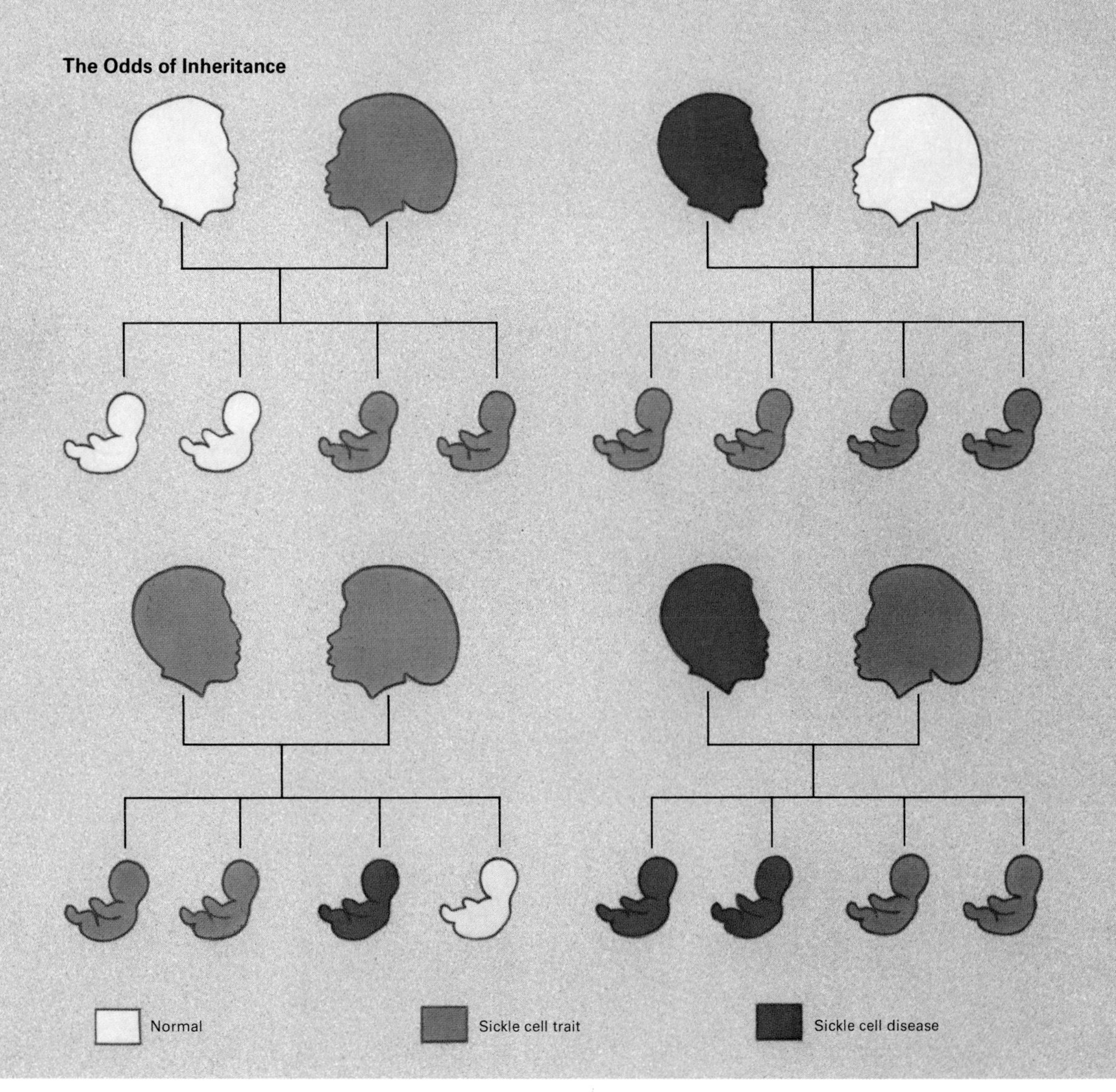

The odds of a couple producing children with sickle cell disease range from zero for one normal parent and one with sickle cell trait to 50/50 for one parent with sickle cell trait and the other with sickle cell disease.

site responsible for the most severe and often fatal form of malaria. The parasite is transmitted to humans through the bite of the female *Anopheles* mosquito. A key step in the parasite's complex reproductive cycle takes place in red blood cells. Parasitologist Milton J. Friedman of the University of California at San Francisco, who was then working in Trager's laboratory, found that the parasite grows well in red blood cells containing hemoglobin S as long as the blood cells have plenty of oxygen.

Friedman grew cultures of red cells from persons with sickle cell disease and with sickle cell trait. When he and his colleagues removed oxygen from the cultures of sickle cell disease blood cells, all the parasites died within a day. The scientists examined the cells under a microscope and found that the needlelike polymers that

Where Sickle Cells Arose

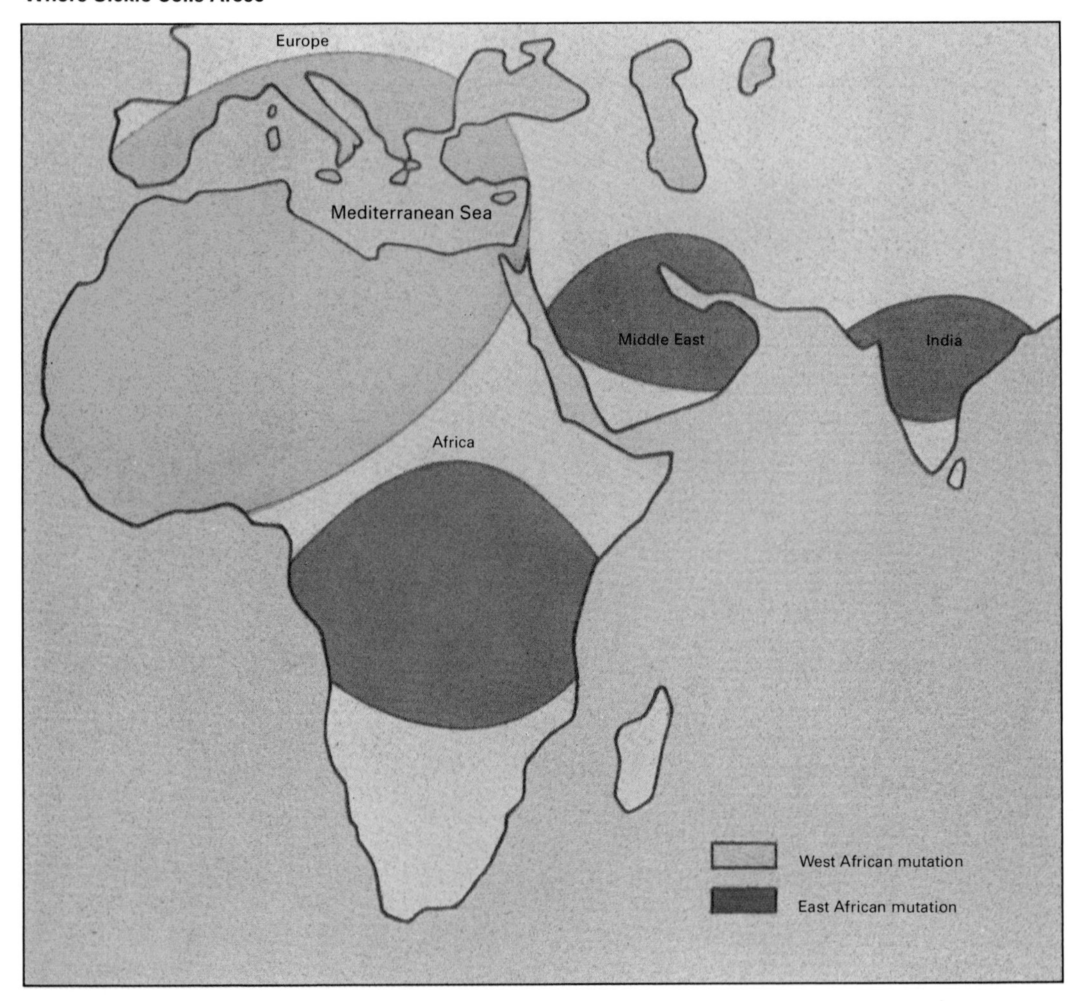

A mutation in the hemoglobin gene that conferred protection against malaria but also caused sickle cell disease occurred in West Africa and spread throughout the Mediterranean area. A similar mutation occurred in East Africa and spread to India and the Middle East.

formed had pierced the parasites, killing them. The scientists did the same experiment on red cells from persons with sickle cell trait. Many of the parasites died within two days, but not from stabbing; they appeared to have died from chemical changes in the cell. Earlier research had shown that the malarial parasite requires a high concentration of potassium in order to grow. Trager and Friedman proved that the loss of potassium from the cell due to changes in the membrane when it sickled killed the parasites.

Even though it contains some abnormal hemoglobin, a sickle trait cell in the human body does not normally sickle. Why do they sickle when infected with the parasite? Trager and Friedman knew that any red blood cell, normal or abnormal, when infected by the parasite develops sticky knobs on its surface that impede its passage through the narrow capillaries. After releasing oxygen, the cell can be stuck in the capillary for many hours, unable to return to the lungs for more oxygen. Furthermore, infection by the parasite makes the interior of the normal or abnormal red blood cells more acidic than usual. In the normal cells, the parasite reproduces and bursts out to infect other red blood cells.

But something quite different happens in red cells of persons with sickle cell trait. The high acidity and lack of oxygen cause sickling in about 40 per cent of their infected red cells, according to Trager and Friedman. The sickling causes the cells to lose potassium, thus killing the parasite. This naturally reduces the number of parasites that can reproduce. Presumably this gives the body's immune system additional time to mount its defenses and thereby decreases the severity of the malaria symptoms.

Research in 1979 by biochemists William A. Eaton, James Hofrichter, and Philip D. Ross of the National Institute of Arthritis, Diabetes, and Digestive and Kidney Diseases (NIADDK) in Bethesda, Md., helped explain why sickle cell crises occur only periodically. They found that the hemoglobin S molecule behaves differently under various conditions. By experimenting with this hemoglobin in test tubes, Eaton and his colleagues found that there is a variable delay period between the time the hemoglobin S molecule gives up oxygen and when it begins to form polymers. They believe that the delay period reflects the length of time needed for enough of the abnormal hemoglobin S molecules to come together, so that they can begin growing into long polymers.

In test tubes, the delay period varied from a few thousandths of a second to days, depending upon such things as temperature, the concentration of the hemoglobin S, the amount of oxygen present, and the acidity in the cell. The researchers created conditions in the test tube similar to those found in the body. They removed the oxygen and observed that the delay period for formation of polymers in the test tube is just about the same as the time required for red blood cells to pass through the capillaries.

Further experiments by Eaton's group indicated that this delay period occurs in red blood cells of patients with sickle cell disease. Under normal conditions, most red blood cells do not sickle until after they have left the capillaries, and they regain their normal flexibility when they take up new oxygen in the lungs. Under conditions of stress, however, the red blood cells release oxygen more rapidly and hemoglobin S polymers form while the cells are still in the capillaries, setting off a sickle cell crisis.

According to Eaton and Hofrichter, this delay period is the most important factor in determining the severity of the symptoms of sickle cell disease. They claim that conditions that shorten the delay period in the test tube are the same conditions that touch off sickle cell crises in humans. These include higher acidity caused by infections, increased concentrations of hemoglobin S because of dehydration, and higher temperatures due to fever. On the other hand, treatment that could lengthen the delay period could reduce the severity of the symptoms. These include diluted concentrations of hemoglobin S, increased binding of oxygen to hemoglobin S, and increased concentrations of normal hemoglobin.

Studies by Eaton's group showed that methods that could increase the delay period in the test tube 10 to 100 times would alleviate symptoms only slightly. Greatly alleviated symptoms require methods or drugs that could increase the delay period 1,000 to 10,000 times. Treatment that could increase the delay period a million times or more would produce a "cure."

Although a great deal is known about the biochemistry of sickle cell disease, relatively little is known about the course of the disease in human beings. The symptoms are complex and can easily be mistaken for other diseases, particularly when treated in hospital emergency rooms. Also, sickle cell victims often die young, sometimes before the disease has been correctly diagnosed.

For this reason, the National Heart, Lung and Blood Institute in Bethesda set up a program in the late 1970s to follow the course of the disease in known sickle cell patients. This study will provide valuable information about risk factors and complications. It will also provide an index of degrees of severity that will help scientists determine the effectiveness of the drugs to be tested.

There are presently no drugs used regularly to treat sickle cell disease. Many have been studied in the hope that they would shorten sickle crises. Scientists have generally experimented with chemicals that are known to disrupt the type of bonding responsible for polymer formation.

Scientists once thought, for example, that urea—a simple organic compound—would be good for this purpose. But a large trial in human beings in the early 1970s showed that it was not effective. Eaton's research has since explained why. The concentration of urea used in the therapy only doubled the delay period from the time the hemoglobin S gave up oxygen until it formed polymers. This did not buy enough time to reduce symptoms.

More powerful drugs present other problems. For example, the amino acid phenylalanine is much more effective at delaying polymer formation than is urea. But it produces toxic side effects.

Doctors have also experimented with cyanate in treating sickle cell patients. For a large trial of cyanate in the early 1970s, they used concentrations that increased the delay period for polymer formation from 7 to 30 times. This produced some reduction in the severity of symptoms, but not a great one. In any event, the trials had to be stopped because cyanate also produces toxic side effects.

Researchers at the University of Kansas and Ohio State University are experimenting with cyanate treatment on blood that has been removed from patients. Their blood must be treated every 7 to 14 days. This process is performed with a device, similar to the blood-cleansing kidney dialysis machine, developed by biomedical engineer Albert L. Babb of the University of Washington Medical School. Because this process is so costly and complex, it is used only for those patients who have the most severe crises.

The precise identification of the bonding sites on the hemoglobin S molecule, however, has opened the door to the development of drugs designed specifically to act on those sites. The leading researchers in this area are biochemists Alan N. Schechter and Constance T. Noguchi along with their colleagues at NIADDK and a team headed by biochemists Alexander Rich of the Massachusetts Institute of Technology and Marian Gorecki of the Weizmann Institute in Rehovot, Israel.

Both groups are attempting to design short chains of amino acids, called peptides, that will attach to the surface of the hemoglobin S molecule at the site where bonding occurs. This will prevent the abnormal molecules from coming together to form polymers. A major advantage of the use of peptides is that the amino acids of which they are composed are naturally present in the body, so there should be very few side effects.

Both groups have obtained promising results with peptides containing the amino acids phenylalanine and tryptophan. Rich and

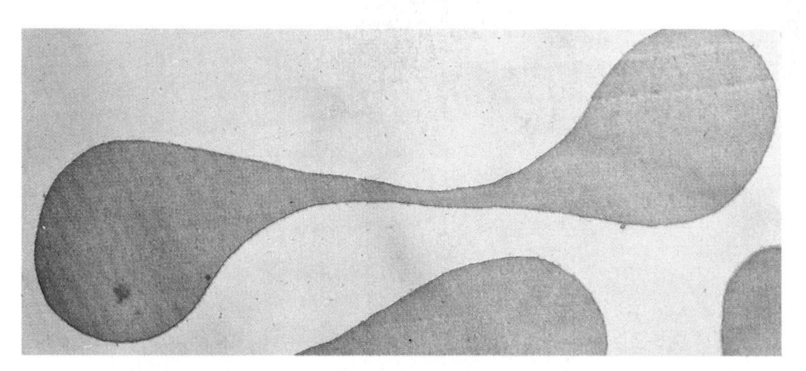

Normal hemoglobin molecules, *left,* revealed through an electron microscope (magnified 146,000 times), are distributed evenly in a grainy pattern throughout the interior of red blood cells. Polymers of abnormal hemoglobin, *below left,* look like crystals inside the rigid and deformed sickle cell (magnified 124,000 times).

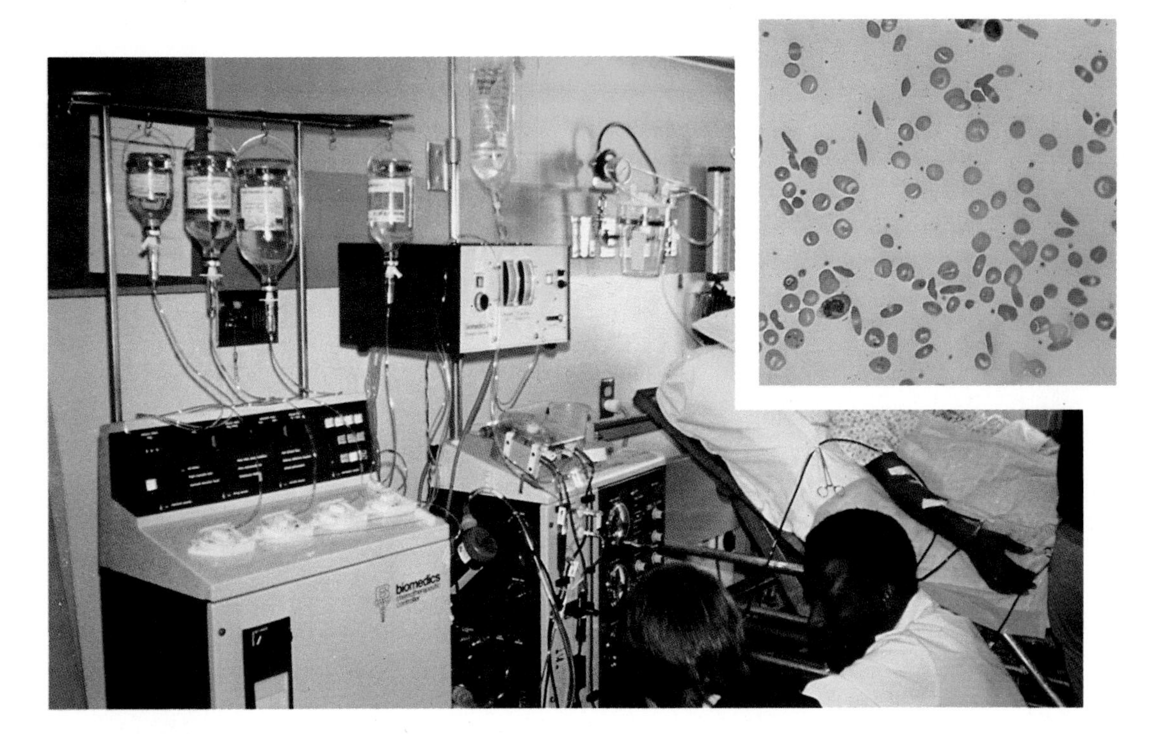

To avoid the harmful side effects of highly toxic drugs, blood is removed from the arm of a sickle cell victim, treated, then cleansed before it is returned to the body. This is an experimental program to prevent sickle cells, *inset,* from forming in the bloodstream.

Gorecki hope to begin studies in humans sometime in 1982. These potential drugs would be taken daily to prevent sickle crises, but probably would have little value in easing the symptoms of an existing sickle cell crisis.

Another potential way to prevent polymers from forming is to lock hemoglobin S into the shape it assumes when it is bound to oxygen. The hemoglobin molecules then cannot fit together to form chains after the oxygen is released. This might be achieved with a drug that would bind permanently to two specific sites on the hemoglobin S molecule. Hematologists Bertram Lubin of the Children's Hospital Medical Center in Oakland, Calif., and William Mentzer of the University of California at San Francisco have experimented with one such drug, dimethyl adipimidate, in the test tube. They found that it completely prevents red blood cells from sickling, even when they have given up all their oxygen.

But the drug would have a serious drawback if used in humans. It can react adversely with proteins in other cells throughout the body. So the scientists will have to withdraw the patient's blood, treat it, and remove the excess drug with one of Babb's machines before the blood can be returned to the patient.

Chemist Irving M. Klotz of Northwestern University in Chicago and biochemists Joseph A. Walder and Arthur Arnone of the University of Iowa College of Medicine in Iowa City have synthesized a family of drugs, called substituted fumarates. These bind permanently to two different sites on hemoglobin S—much like dimethyl adipimidate — making it harder for the molecule to release oxygen. Since sickling occurs after oxygen is released, the blood cell has a better chance of escaping into a larger blood vessel if it releases oxygen just before leaving the capillary. Fumarates may produce fewer side effects because they are more likely to react only with hemoglobin S than is dimethyl adipimidate. Fumarates also seem promising because, in the test tube, they produce the greatest delay period so far observed for any potential drug.

Another way to prevent polymers from forming is to keep hemoglobin S molecules away from one another. Scientists in 1980 showed that this can be done by increasing the volume of each red blood cell, which decreases the concentration of the molecules. A team headed by hematologist H. Franklin Bunn of Harvard University Medical School and nephrologist Robert M. Rosa of Beth Israel Hospital in Boston caused red blood cells to swell, and thus increase their volume, by creating low concentrations of sodium in the blood. They did this by having sickle cell patients drink large quantities of fluids and limit salt in their diets. The doctors also gave them a hormone that restricts the formation of urine. This treatment reduced the number of severe sickle cell crises in some of the patients. But this is an extreme form of therapy that the scientists use only in the most severely afflicted patients.

For the long run, perhaps the most promising way to help sickle cell patients lies in genetic engineering. Since bone marrow is the source of all hemoglobin, scientists may one day be able to insert genes that code for normal hemoglobin into the bone marrow of sickle cell patients. These genes would then produce a higher ratio of normal hemoglobin to abnormal. Such an approach would represent a cure of sickle cell disease. But these genetic engineering techniques have not yet been developed, so it will probably be many years before scientists can attempt this kind of treatment.

Scientists are also investigating drugs that act on the red blood cell membrane. One such drug is Cetiedil. Preliminary studies on patients in Africa have shown that Cetiedil reduces the severity of sickle crises. Biochemist Charles M. Peterson of Rockefeller University has found that the drug enters the red blood cell membrane and stays there for many hours, but no one yet knows what it does there. Nevertheless, Peterson in 1981 began his own trials to test its effectiveness in humans.

The scientists studying sickle cell disease believe that within the next five years there will be drugs available to help afflicted children and adults lead a longer, more productive life. Such drugs would have to be taken by sickle cell victims every day for the rest of their lives. So the scientists are proceeding with caution, trying to be sure these drugs are safe and will not produce harmful side effects. But sickle cell victims can now hope for relief from the pain that comes in the middle of the night.

KONICA
The Face of Madness
Hugh W. Diamond
AND THE
Photography

Bringing Images to Mind

By Brian Zakem

Psychotherapists are discovering how photographs can help troubled people understand and deal with their problems

Like many young people just starting out, Ann, a bright and attractive 20-year-old, lives with her parents. She has been highly praised by her employers for her work with retarded adults and is considering college.

But Ann is anything but a typical 20-year-old. Six years ago, she was living on the streets of Chicago, heavily involved with drugs and alcohol. An emotionally deprived, physically abused child, she dropped out of high school at 14 and ran away from home. Before she was 20, she had four abortions.

Although Ann moved back home when she was 17, probably in an attempt to get the nurturing she was denied as a child, she continued to feel a deep anger toward her parents. She often expressed that anger by impulsively lashing out at her friends or by turning her rage inward against herself. She also used her anger to create an emotional barrier between herself and others.

Ann entered outpatient psychotherapy with me about a year ago. During her years on the street, Ann's safety and survival had depended to a great extent on keeping a sharp eye on her surroundings. For this reason, and because she often talked enthusiastically about movies she had seen, I asked her to bring snapshots of her family to our sessions. Discussing those photographs and the thoughts and memories they evoked has helped Ann understand why she feels so dependent on the family toward whom she is hostile. They have also helped her to learn to deal with those feelings of hostility and anger.

Since the early 1970s, more and more psychologists and other mental health practitioners have begun to use photographic images to diagnose mental problems and help patients to cope with them. Phototherapy is based on the knowledge that visual images can accurately convey messages about how a person thinks and feels—messages that could be overlooked in verbal communication.

In general, psychotherapy aims to help people, like Ann, with emotional and behavioral problems to learn more about themselves. It also helps people to develop better ways of dealing with stress and increase their feelings of self-worth. To accomplish these goals, psychotherapy patients, or clients, discuss their feelings and problems with a trained therapist. During these sessions, therapists help patients understand the nature and causes of their problems and learn how to cope with them. The therapist may use a variety of techniques to help patients communicate more freely. Phototherapy can provide some of these techniques.

Photographic images can be effective psychotherapeutic tools because thoughts often are experienced as visual images before they are translated into words. Thus, photographs can provide a unique point of entry into the memory and the emotions associated with past events, as well as into current problems of living that the patient cannot cope with. Instead of relying on a patient to recollect a past event by just thinking or talking about it, a therapist can use a picture as a memory jogger. While looking at the photographs with the patient, the therapist asks such questions as: "Who are the people in this photograph? When was the photo taken? What were you thinking about at the time? How were you feeling? What does the photo make you think about now?" In addition, the photographs themselves can become a way of communicating without words. Through them, patients often reveal to the therapist information they find difficult to put into words.

Finally, photographs are useful in psychotherapy because they are so accessible. Most people have an extensive collection of personal and family photographs taken over time. In addition, today's easy-to-operate cameras make picture-taking something nearly everyone can do with at least a modest degree of success.

Phototherapy draws on a wide range of photographic forms, including still photographs; motion pictures, including animation; and videotape or videodisc recordings. Eventually, sophisticated holographic or three-dimensional images, now used experimentally, may be used regularly.

In 1979, psychologist J. Douglas Stewart, a contemporary pioneer in phototherapy, identified three basic uses for photographic images in psychotherapy. He called them projective images, historical documents, and self-statement photographs.

The author:
Brian Zakem is a therapist and consultant in private practice. He is director of the International Phototherapy Institute and founder-editor of *Phototherapy* magazine.

Ann's family snapshots help her to understand her past. Her old house, *left,* reminded Ann of the times she hid in her room after being beaten by her parents. Ann said her great-aunt, *below left,* was the "only person who really loved me." She called her dog, John Tom, *below right,* her "son."

Ann and the author discuss the family photographs at a therapy session.

Ann's father, *above,* now treats her like the adult she wants to be. Ann said her mother, *left,* who often abuses her verbally, is more pleasant while reading comfortably in the den.

Projective Images are either easily recognizable photographs of people, scenes, and everyday objects or abstract photos that therapists use to generate reactions in patients. The photos may trigger feelings ranging from emptiness, confusion, and fright to calm, warmth, and intimacy. Therapists use the responses to help them learn more about patients' problems.

TURKISH

Historical Documents are family snapshots and other personal photographs that can help patients recall past experiences and the memories associated with them. A wedding portrait, *right,* can remind patients of a time when they felt hopeful and happy; when family relations were harmonious.

A photo of Wilma (center) with her sisters at a church dinner honoring her for her effective volunteer work reminded Wilma that she had accomplished something worthwhile. This realization helped her to recover from her depression and sense of worthlessness.

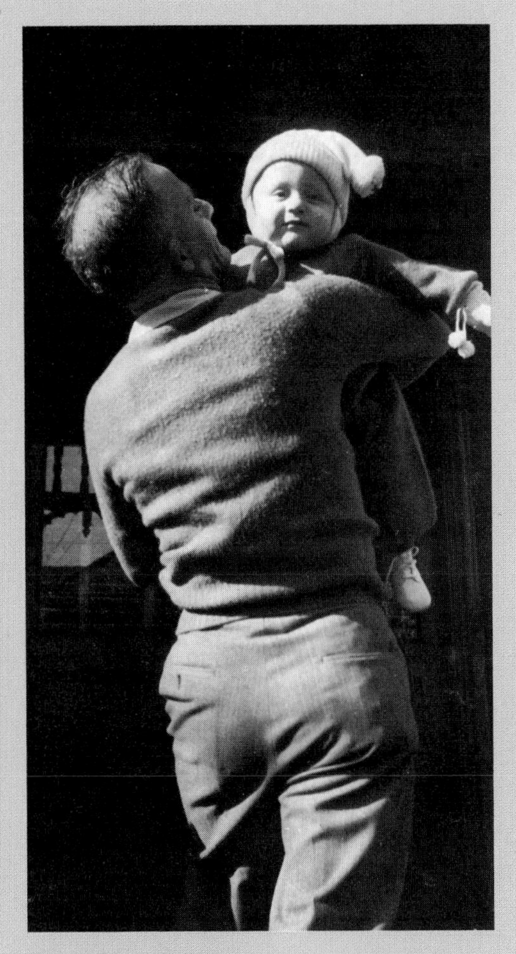

A photo of Alan at age 2 with his father helped him remember his feelings of rage and abandonment when his father, uncle, and grandfather died soon afterward. Discussing these feelings helped Alan accept the deaths of these men he had loved and to realize that they did not die because they were angry with him. It also helped him to understand why at age 32 he was extremely attached to his mother and unable to move from her home.

Looking at this snapshot of herself and her older sister as children encouraged Janice to discuss the jealousy and inferiority she felt toward the sister, whom she considered prettier and brighter than she.

Projective images can be abstract, artlike photographs or easily recognizable photos of people, places, and objects. Used by the therapist as diagnostic tools, projective images can sometimes elicit powerful responses from the patient. By analyzing these responses, the therapist can discover more about the patient's feelings and problems and use that information when devising an appropriate psychotherapy treatment program.

Historical documents consist of family snapshots or other personal photos, such as those found in family albums. Therapists probably use historical photographs more than any other type of photo in phototherapy. Such photos are used to establish a valuable link in the patient's mind between the past and the present. Not only can such photos help a patient recollect past experiences, even those from childhood, but they can also trigger emotional memories. By evoking the emotions associated with a moment frozen on film, a photo can help the patient and therapist uncover repressed feelings or unresolved conflicts. Such photographs document significant events in the patients' lives, such as weddings, vacations, and family get-togethers. Thus, they can stimulate more generalized thoughts about the others in the photo or about the patients themselves. Historical photographs may also reveal something about the emotional interactions that are occurring or have occurred among all the people in the picture.

People generally avoid photographing stressful events, such as funerals or even a family gathering that may have become unpleasant. Thus the absence of photographs of an important occasion may also be significant.

At times, therapists use historical photographs to confront patients who have persistent and unrealistic or inaccurate beliefs about themselves. For example, Jim, a chronically depressed young man, was convinced that he had always been unhappy and that his life had been uniformly hopeless. But by looking at pictures of himself smiling and having a good time, Jim realized that there were times in the past when he had been happy and that perhaps in the future he could be happy again.

Stewart's third use of photos in phototherapy — self-statement photographs — are usually taken by the patients. They represent the patients' inner feelings and their views of themselves, others, and their world. As inner representations, such photographs are particularly useful in stimulating discussion between therapist and patient. In addition, taken over a period of time, a series of such self-statement photographs can help the therapist evaluate the patient's progress during psychotherapy.

Therapists also use photographs to increase patients' awareness of their feelings and behavior. For example, therapists might instruct patients to take photographs of their families at a time when they feel happy, or frustrated, or anxious. In order to complete the as-

Self-Statement Photographs, made or chosen by the patients themselves, can reveal their inner feelings and thoughts. A patient poses with masks representing different aspects of her personality.

A dilapidated truck was seen by one chronic mental patient recovering from his third mental breakdown as symbolizing the emptiness and loneliness of his life.

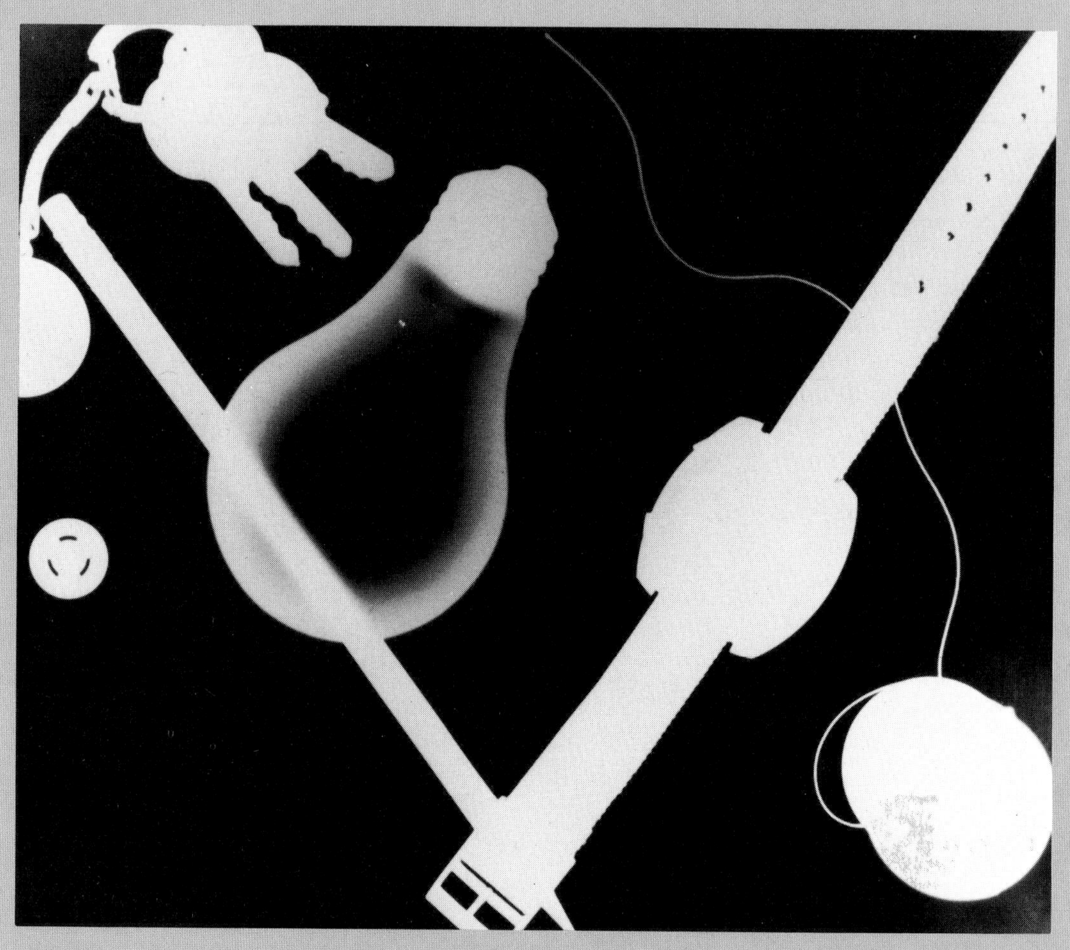

A therapist shows her patients, *right,* how to develop photograms – photographic images made by exposing to light an object placed on sensitized paper. A photogram may be a group effort, *above,* where each patient chooses an object to include in the picture.

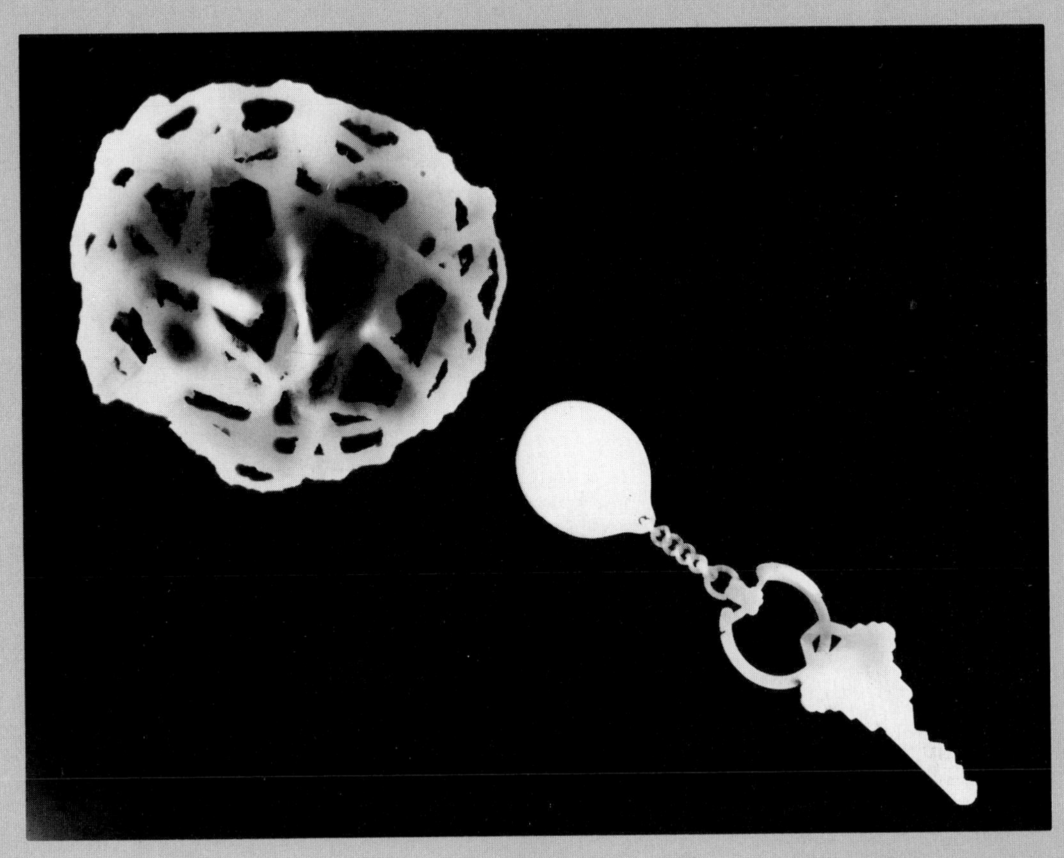

A key traveling through space represents the wish of a chronic mental patient to escape from the mother with whom he lived.

An unworldly photogram symbolizes a 28-year-old divorced father's desire to be alone on another planet.

Patients participate in group phototherapy projects using different forms of photography, *above right.* Some patients videotape or film other patients acting as performers. Others take photographs of the proceedings. The results of these activities can document how socially withdrawn patients increase their interactions with other group members, *above.*

signment, a patient must recognize when he or she is feeling that particular emotion. Later discussions of the photograph with the therapist may help the patient discover what triggered that emotion at that specific time.

Phototherapy often appeals to psychotherapy patients because taking pictures is fun. In many cases, just learning to operate a camera benefits the patient. The creativity involved in mastering even basic photographic skills can be enormously gratifying and often increases a patient's self-esteem. These feelings of creativity and enjoyment can become valuable therapeutic devices for psychotherapists in the course of treating patients who are depressed or socially or emotionally withdrawn.

Therapists involved with phototherapy work with groups as well as with individuals. Generally, the techniques are the same, although group members often work together to create photographic images. In group therapy, patients share experiences and learn from one another. The group also provides social and emotional support to members in times of stress.

Therapists working with groups sometimes invite members to bring in still photos of themselves and their families for discussion. Working together in small groups, members also may compose photograms — photographic images made by exposing to light an image placed on sensitized paper. Members also may participate in group video or film projects.

In a typical group phototherapy project that I conducted, a group of 20 patients was divided into four smaller groups. One group, acting as performers, staged a talk-show program. The second group videotaped the program, while the third group recorded the proceedings with still photographs. The last group filmed the other groups in action.

Allowing patients to choose which group they preferred gave them the opportunity to participate as much or as little as they wished. As filming progressed, however, even those patients who had chosen only to take still photographs became enthusiastically involved in the project. Members often switched groups, a development that increased the interactions within the larger group. As a result, many members of the group became less socially and emotionally isolated and more supportive of one another, and thus, the group as a whole became more cohesive.

Therapists themselves often use videotape recordings as a training tool. By observing the recordings with a supervisor, they can learn to eliminate those mannerisms that detract from their therapeutic relationship with their patients. Viewing videotape recordings can also help therapists, who are generally very verbally oriented, become more adept at recognizing and understanding the visual messages their patients send.

Phototherapy as a treatment option in psychotherapy is a fairly recent development, but its roots stretch back to the mid-1800s. Photographs were first used in the treatment of psychiatric and psychological disorders in 1848 when a British physician named Hugh W. Diamond photographed chronic mental patients in a London asylum. Although Diamond intended to use the photographs to document the physical changes that took place in his patients during treatment, he discovered that his patients reacted, sometimes strongly, to the photos.

In his book, *The Faces of Madness,* Diamond wrote, "The photographer needs in many cases no aid from any language of his own, but prefers rather to listen, with the picture before him, to the silent but telling language of nature . . . the picture speaks for itself with the most marked precision. . . ."

Diamond did not use the photographs in any systematic way, however, and his work and its possible implications were largely ignored by mental health practitioners until the late 1940s. At that time, researchers began using videotape recordings to confront patients with distorted self-images. The use of photographic images as therapeutic tools, however, remained limited. Finally, in the early 1970s, more therapists and researchers discovered the use of phototherapy techniques in mental health treatment.

The current frontier in phototherapy is rigorous research to determine under what conditions and for which type of patient phototherapy is most effective — and why. As psychotherapy gains a more solid scientific foundation and photographic equipment becomes more technologically sophisticated, phototherapy will, I believe, become an increasingly useful and widespread tool for the treatment of mental disorders.

Superdome
Claiborne Ave
NEXT RIGHT
Minolta
TAKANO
ヨドバシ
カメラ

Warmer, Wetter Weather Ahead?

By W. Lawrence Gates

The burning of fossil fuels may unbalance a natural chemical cycle, heating the earth and redistributing precipitation — perhaps even causing the seas to rise

"Now you two Iowa desert rats be careful when you get to Boston," Mrs. Henderson told her sons Mark and Dave through the open window of the high-speed intercontinental tube train. "We want you just to look at the canals, not fall into them."

"That's right," their father agreed. "And be sure to go to the exhibit in City Hall that shows what the town was like before the ocean rose."

"Aw, Dad," Mark protested, "you know we aren't interested in that historical stuff."

"I hope the engineer gets this train going pretty soon," said Dave. "Otherwise, we may be in store for Dad's lecture about how our hot, dry ranch used to be a cornfield."

Mr. Henderson laughed. "Yep," he said, "back in your great-grandfather Henderson's day, this part of Iowa was covered with cornfields. Seems hard to believe."

Of course, in 1982, there are no dusty ranches in the middle of Iowa and you don't need a boat to get around in Boston. However, if current trends in the use of fuels and the clearing of forests continue, the grandchildren of today's high school students may see many sights that you would find hard to believe.

Many meteorologists, scientists who study the weather, believe that the burning of fossil fuels, such as coal, natural gas, and petroleum, along with massive cutting of forests, may bring about such changes. They would do so by altering the greenhouse effect that keeps the heat of the earth and the atmosphere in balance.

When a fossil fuel burns, carbon in the fuel combines with oxygen in the air to form carbon dioxide (CO_2) gas. This gas, released through chimneys and exhaust pipes, eventually becomes part of the atmosphere. There, it mingles with CO_2 that has entered the atmosphere through natural processes, such as the decay of trees and other plant life.

CO_2 in the atmosphere allows most sunlight to pass through it and strike the earth. But it absorbs energy that radiates upward from the earth and then reradiates part of this energy back to the surface. In this way, some of the earth's radiation is trapped, warming the atmosphere.

This warming action is similar to the heating process in a greenhouse. The glass roof and walls of a greenhouse admit sunlight, which heats the plants and other objects inside. However, the glass prevents the heat inside the greenhouse from escaping until the objects reach a higher temperature.

The earth and the atmosphere do not become hotter and hotter as a result of the greenhouse effect because they cool themselves by radiating energy into space. This maintains relatively steady average temperatures year after year. However, if the burning of fossil fuels adds too much carbon dioxide to the air, the earth and the atmosphere might not be able to cool themselves rapidly enough to shed their excess energy. They would thus become warmer.

A severe greenhouse effect might melt the gigantic ice sheet that covers West Antarctica. As this ice melted, the earth's oceans would rise, flooding port cities, such as Boston.

Temperature changes in the upper atmosphere would also change rainfall patterns, drenching many of today's deserts. On the edge of northern Africa's Sahara, now the world's largest desert, children might grow up on farms. In Western Australia, heavy rainfall would fill dry lake beds, opening that arid state to large-scale agriculture.

But the change in the weather that brought beneficial effects to some areas would also transform what is now lush farm country into dry grassland fit only for grazing cattle. Changes in the ability of the

The author:
W. Lawrence Gates is a professor and chairman of the Department of Atmospheric Sciences at Oregon State University in Corvallis.

land to provide a particular kind of crop might occur so quickly that farmers would not be able to adapt to them.

Scientists who are concerned about this possibility are trying to determine how various rates of fossil fuel use would affect the climate. Among the thousands of measurements they make each day from weather stations, balloons, ships, and satellites, one may outweigh all the others in its importance for the future. It is the measurement of CO_2 in the atmosphere at a weather station on the 4,169-meter (13,667-foot) Mauna Loa volcano on the island of Hawaii. There, an instrument draws in outside air at the rate of about 0.50 liter (0.53 quart) per minute. Every 20 minutes, the device automatically determines the concentration of certain gases.

The amounts of nitrogen and oxygen, which make up about 99 per cent of the atmosphere, have been nearly constant since Charles D. Keeling of Scripps Institution of Oceanography in San Diego began the observations at Mauna Loa in 1958. However, the average concentration of CO_2 has increased every year. In 1981, the atmosphere contained 7 per cent more of this gas than in 1958. Meteorologists have found the same rate of increase at other sampling stations both closer to and farther from the equator. Furthermore, researchers estimate that the 1981 figure is 17 per cent higher than the value for the 1860s, shortly after the Industrial Revolution began to spread from Great Britain to continental Europe and North America. The rates of increase of fossil fuel use and of the worldwide concentration of atmospheric CO_2 are virtually identical, so the CO_2 build-up is almost certainly the result of the increase in the burning of fossil fuels.

This build-up of CO_2 in the atmosphere is part of a larger process of carbon exchange known as the carbon cycle. This exchange takes place between sources of the gas and *sinks*—processes that take the gas out of the air. Fossil fuel combustion and the decay of vegetation are major sources, while a process known as photosynthesis is a principal sink. In photosynthesis, plants combine energy from sunlight with water and CO_2 to make their own food. Plants also release oxygen during this process.

You take part in the carbon cycle—as a very minor source of CO_2—every time you breathe. When you inhale, you take in oxygen from the atmosphere. Your body combines the oxygen with carbon from your food, forming CO_2 which you then exhale. Chemically, respiration is the same process as burning. Plants also respire, although they consume much less oxygen by respiration than they produce by photosynthesis.

The oceans are major sources as well as sinks of atmospheric CO_2. The gas readily dissolves in water. However, warm water cannot dissolve as much CO_2 as cooler water can. Therefore, the warm surface waters of the equatorial and tropical oceans do not hold as much CO_2 as does the water closer to the poles. And when changes in the wind blowing over warm surface water raise the surface temperature a few degrees, CO_2 bubbles out of the ocean and into the atmosphere. On the other hand, when low-latitude waters cool, they soak up CO_2. On the average, however, they release more gas than they absorb, so they are a net source of CO_2 for the atmosphere.

The opposite is true of the cold surface waters in high latitudes—more than 60° latitude from the equator. These waters absorb more CO_2 from the atmosphere than they release into it, so they are a net sink for atmospheric CO_2.

The amounts of carbon that take part in the cycle are extremely large. Scientists measure them in gigatons (Gt). One Gt equals 1-billion metric tons (1.1 billion short tons). The atmosphere contains about 690 Gt of carbon in the form of CO_2. Every year, the atmosphere exchanges more than 150 Gt of carbon with the CO_2 sources and sinks.

Photosynthesis removes about 63 Gt per year from the atmosphere, and meteorologists presume that an equal amount of carbon returns to the air as organic carbon from decaying soil and humus. However, the large-scale clearing of forests may upset this balance by removing the photosynthesis sink that the trees would have provided. This also adds two CO_2 sources—the decay or burning of the trees and the destruction of underlying vegetation that has died but not decayed.

The atmosphere and the ocean exchange about 90 Gt of carbon per year. At the same time, fossil fuel combustion adds about 6 Gt of carbon to the atmosphere per year. However, only about 56 per cent of the CO_2 produced in this way between 1959 and 1979 stayed in the atmosphere. Apparently, the ocean and plant life absorbed the rest.

Meteorologists estimate that since the Industrial Revolution began the seas have absorbed only about 35 per cent of the carbon released into the atmosphere by burning fossil fuels. The ocean's ability to absorb more CO_2 from the atmosphere depends upon sedimentation—mud and the shells of dead animals that filter down to the sea floor. Calcium carbonate in the shells dissolves slowly to form carbonate, which consists of carbon and oxygen. The carbonate combines with water and dissolved CO_2 to form bicarbonate, thus taking CO_2 out of the water. As a result, the ocean is able to absorb more CO_2 from the atmosphere. The newly absorbed CO_2 also combines with water and carbonate and the process continues.

Variations in the carbon cycle show up in the Mauna Loa record. For example, the recorded amount of atmospheric CO_2 is at its highest level around May, when the surface waters of the oceans in the Northern Hemisphere warm up most rapidly, releasing the gas. The amount drops in September and October, when the seas cool.

The Mauna Loa record also shows longer-term variations that occur over periods of several years. Researchers have related these

The Greenhouse Effect

The greenhouse effect plays a major role in the warming of the earth and the surrounding air. This effect is a result of the flow of energy between the earth and the atmosphere.

The flow begins at the sun, which sends out vibrating waves of energy. These waves include visible light as well as radio waves, microwaves, infrared rays, ultraviolet rays, X rays, and gamma rays. Various objects can absorb various waves and take their energy. Our eyes, for example, absorb waves of visible light.

Whether a certain object absorbs a particular ray depends upon that ray's wavelength—the distance the ray travels as it vibrates through one cycle. Our eyes absorb light rays whose wavelengths range from 0.0004 to 0.0007 millimeter.

Carbon dioxide (CO_2) and water vapor, two of the main ingredients of the atmosphere, absorb infrared rays whose wavelengths range from 0.012 to 0.018 millimeter. Therefore, nearly all solar rays that have other wavelengths can pass through the atmosphere and strike the earth. The earth absorbs energy from these rays and so becomes warmer.

But every object that becomes warmer in this way can also cool itself by sending out waves of energy. However, the wavelengths of the new rays may differ from those of the absorbed rays. The earth sends out rays whose wavelengths are concentrated in the infrared range. Many of these rays pass through the atmosphere to outer space. However, a large amount of energy leaving the earth as infrared rays is in the range of 0.012 to 0.018 millimeter. This is absorbed by CO_2 in the atmosphere and water vapor.

The gases, in turn, cool themselves by sending out waves of infrared energy. Some of this energy goes into space but the earth absorbs a large part of it. As a result, the earth and the atmosphere are warmer than they would be if the atmosphere contained no CO_2 or water vapor. However, if the atmosphere contained more of these two gases, the earth's surface and the atmosphere would be even warmer than they are now.

These gases function like the glass panes in a greenhouse. Sunlight passes through the panes and heats objects inside the greenhouse. These objects emit rays that cannot return through glass until the objects become warmer. [W. L. G.]

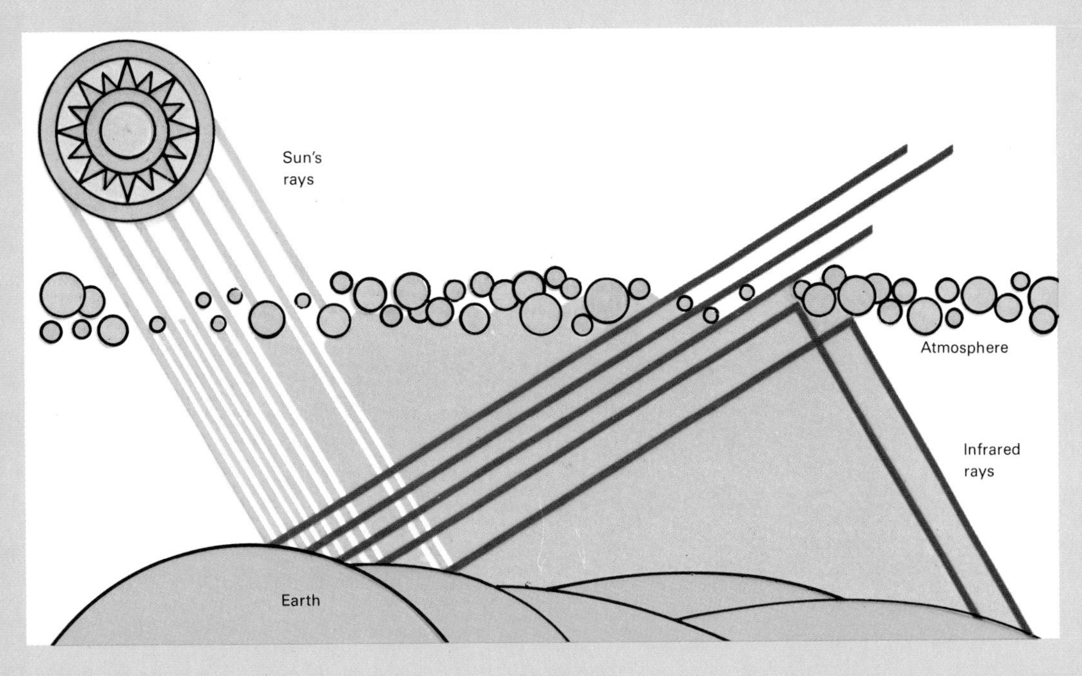

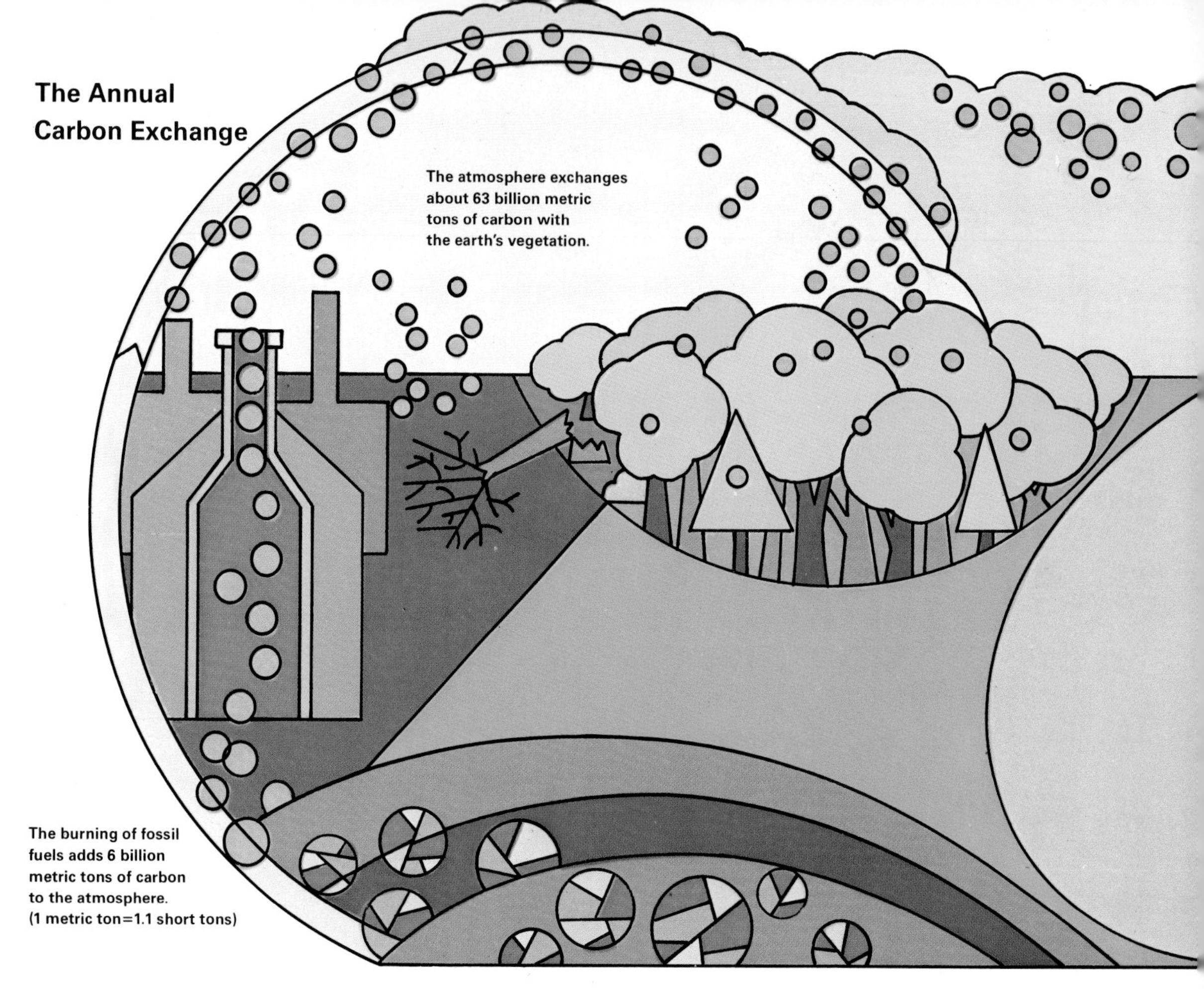

Natural cycles add about as much carbon to the atmosphere as they take from it, but the burning of fossil fuels puts extra carbon into the air. The oceans remove only a small part of this carbon. The rest apparently accumulates in the atmosphere.

variations to large-scale changes that take place in the sea-surface temperature in the equatorial Pacific over periods of two to four years. The cold, deep waters upwell, or rise to the surface, periodically. Upwelling cools the surface waters, increasing their ability to absorb CO_2.

Meteorologists have discovered evidence of even longer-term variations in the amount of atmospheric CO_2 during the past 30,000 years. In 1980, for example, geochemist Hans Oeschger of the University of Bern in Switzerland and his colleagues examined samples of ancient ice that had been drilled out of ice deposits buried far beneath the surface at Camp Century Station in Greenland and Byrd Station in Antarctica. The scientists analyzed the air trapped in small bubbles within the ice to determine the amount of CO_2 in the atmosphere when the ice formed. They found that CO_2 concentrations were lower during periods of extensive ice cover.

Such periods occur regularly. Meteorologists suspect that they are set in motion by changes in the tilt of the earth's axis of rotation and in the shape of the earth's orbit. These changes decrease the amount of sunlight reaching the earth during the summer, so the earth and its oceans become cooler.

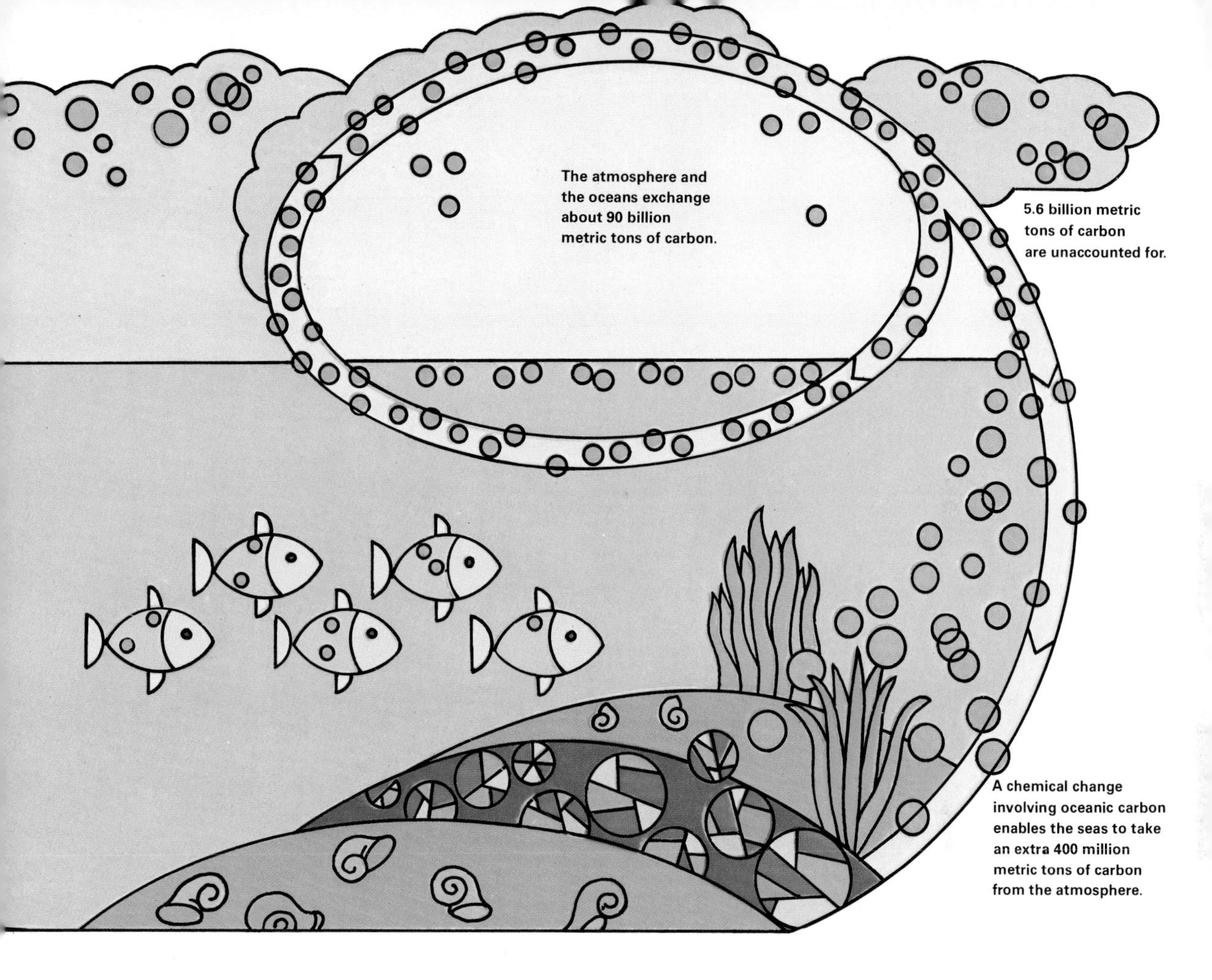

Oeschger and his colleagues reasoned that the cooler oceans would have absorbed more CO_2 from the atmosphere. In turn, lower concentrations of atmospheric CO_2 would have allowed a greater amount of heat to escape from the earth via a reduced greenhouse effect. The oceans would therefore have become even cooler and able to absorb even more CO_2.

The scientists found that concentrations were lowest during the most severe period of the last Ice Age, about 18,000 years ago. However, this drop in concentration is only partly accounted for by the fact that the sea-surface temperature was about 2.3°C (4.1°F.) below its present value. Researchers suspect that changes in oceanic circulation caused upwelling of cold water, allowing the ocean to dissolve even more CO_2.

Future concentrations of CO_2 in the atmosphere will depend upon the rate of fossil fuel combustion and the response of the carbon cycle. We cannot make precise predictions, but we can determine a range of probable concentrations.

The burning of fossil fuels adds about 6 Gt of carbon to the atmosphere each year. The clearing of forests lowers the ability of the earth's vegetation to absorb carbon by photosynthesis by 1.2 Gt

A researcher measures the carbon dioxide in a spherical tank filled with air taken from a sampling station. This analysis is part of a worldwide program that began in the 1950s.

per year. As the world's population continues to increase and industrialization continues to spread, these numbers will grow.

Meteorologists estimate that they may grow so slowly that the CO_2 concentration will increase by only 50 per cent by the year 2100. On the other hand, the CO_2 increase may be so rapid that in 80 years the atmosphere will contain up to six times as much of the gas as it does now.

Future production of CO_2 probably will lie somewhere between these values. Scientists believe it is most likely that the concentration will reach twice its present amount between 2035 and 2050. All estimates of the effect of such an increase indicate that the atmosphere will become warmer. This temperature increase will result from changes in the greenhouse effect and in the ability of the ocean to hold carbon dioxide.

The earth's climate is so complex that meteorologists cannot calculate precisely how an increase in atmospheric CO_2 would affect the temperature of the atmosphere and the earth's surface. Instead, they must make estimates of temperature changes based on computer calculations with simplified mathematical models that represent the earth and the atmosphere.

Meteorologists who are studying the effects of an increase in atmospheric CO_2 have developed many such models of varying complexity. Constructing a meteorological model is difficult and time-consuming. First, the researchers decide what phenomena to include in the model. Then they develop a computer program based on mathematical relationships among these phenomena. Next, the researchers program the computer and feed in data from certain observations — CO_2 concentration, for example. The computer then calculates the values of related phenomena such as ocean temperature and the researchers compare the calculations with observations. If the results do not match, the meteorologists must modify the program and use the computer again. This process continues until the researchers feel confident enough in the results to make projections

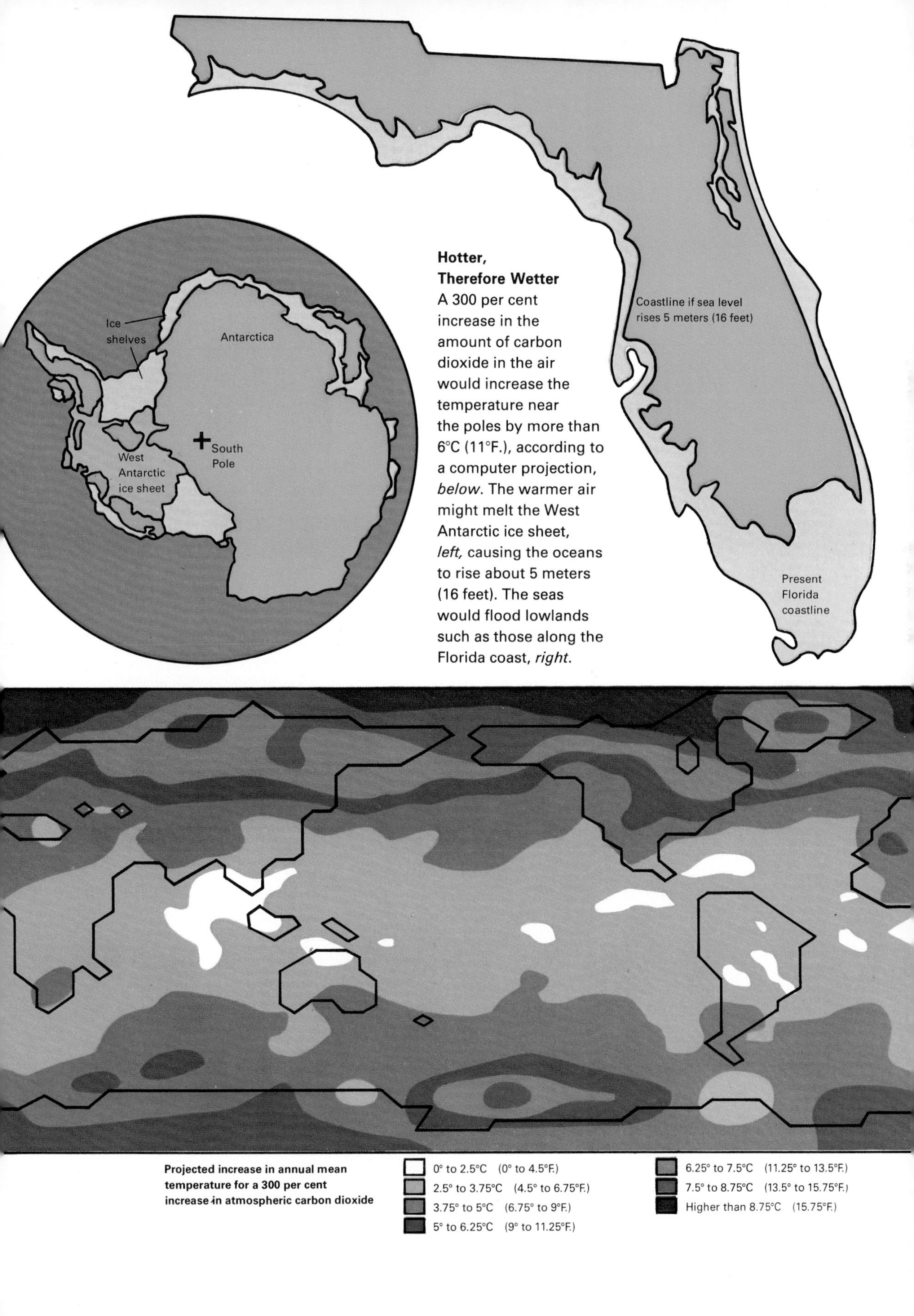

Hotter, Therefore Wetter
A 300 per cent increase in the amount of carbon dioxide in the air would increase the temperature near the poles by more than 6°C (11°F.), according to a computer projection, *below*. The warmer air might melt the West Antarctic ice sheet, *left,* causing the oceans to rise about 5 meters (16 feet). The seas would flood lowlands such as those along the Florida coast, *right*.

Projected increase in annual mean temperature for a 300 per cent increase in atmospheric carbon dioxide

A drilling rig in Greenland, *above,* extracts a cylindrical sample of ice, *opposite page,* that formed thousands of years ago. An analysis of the ice reveals details of the carbon dioxide concentration in the ancient atmosphere.

and to use the model as a stepping stone to a more complex model.

The simplest mathematical model consists of an imaginary atmosphere in which only the amount of CO_2 changes. Doubling the atmospheric CO_2, according to this model, raises the temperature at the bottom of the atmosphere — corresponding to the surface of the earth — by about 1°C (1.8°F.).

A more complex model that includes the effects of cloudiness and humidity predicts an average surface warming of about 2°C (3.6°F.) for a doubling of atmospheric CO_2. In this model, an initial increase in temperature permits the air to hold more moisture, and may increase the amount of evaporation. The additional water vapor in the atmosphere absorbs more heat from the earth, and so the atmosphere becomes even warmer.

In an even more complex model, ice and snow may melt away to expose the underlying surface. This melting would decrease the earth's ability to reflect sunlight. The earth would therefore absorb more energy from the sun, and the temperature would increase accordingly. This model predicts that doubling the CO_2 concentration would warm the earth's surface by 1.3°C (2.3°F.).

The most widely quoted modeling study was made in 1975 by meteorologists Syukuro Manabe and Richard T. Wetherald of the National Oceanic and Atmospheric Administration's Geophysical Fluid Dynamics Laboratory (GFDL) in Princeton, N.J. They used a so-called general circulation model (GCM) that includes the effects of sunlight, airflow, and precipitation.

However, Manabe and Wetherald did not include in their model complexities that result from the ocean's depth. For example, the model does not account for currents that cause upwelling nor the sea's storage of heat.

The two scientists calculated the ocean's surface temperature as though the ocean had no depth—as if changes in the temperature of the air next to the ocean warmed or cooled the ocean instantaneously. They found that doubling the amount of carbon dioxide would warm the earth's surface by an average of 2.9°C (5.2°F.). The temperature of the lower atmosphere would rise by an average of about 2.0°C (3.6°F.) at all latitudes. At the surface, however, the amount of warming would increase with distance from the equator, reaching a value of about 6°C (11°F.) near the North Pole.

Manabe and Ronald Stouffer of the GFDL showed in 1980 that representing the ocean by a layer of water 68 meters (223 feet) deep led to an average warming of about 2°C at the surface. The maximum warming, amounting to about 7°C (13°F.), would take place over the high-latitude oceans during the early winter. This is probably the best estimate available.

However, even Manabe and Stouffer's shallow model of the ocean does not include all details. For example, in the model, the heat that the ocean surface receives from the atmosphere is distributed uniformly to a certain depth. But in the real ocean, the depth to which effective distribution occurs varies from place to place. The model also neglects currents that cause upwelling. The absorption of heat by the ocean may delay a warming of the atmosphere by as much as 20 years.

Manabe and Stouffer's model also provided information about the exchange of moisture between the atmosphere and the earth. According to the model, precipitation and evaporation would be about 7 per cent greater during most seasons than at present.

Manabe, Stouffer, and other meteorologists who are studying the problem of CO_2 build-up are trying to develop a model that they can use to determine local changes in temperature and precipitation. One major step would be to represent the interactions among the various layers of water in the ocean.

Meteorologists would also like to develop models that would show how the earth's vegetation responds to changes in surface climate and vice versa. And they need a model that would explain how CO_2 concentrations vary with time and location in the atmosphere. Models that represented these changes and the activities of at least the surface layers of the ocean would help determine how various patterns of fossil fuel use would affect the climate year by year.

The model that scientists want would show them where to expect the first noticeable effects of an increasing concentration of CO_2. So far, meteorologists have detected no signal, but we may not be looking for the right effects in the right places.

James Hansen and his colleagues at the National Aeronautics and Space Administration's Institute for Space Studies in New York City suggested in 1981 that the 0.4°C (0.7°F.) rise in the average temperature of the earth's surface since 1880 may be such a signal. Their model includes the effects of volcanic dust and changes in the sun's radiation that have occurred since that year. These effects account for much of the observed variation in the temperature, but the remaining gradual increase seems to be a result of the CO_2 build-up. In 1982, Hansen and his colleagues related this warming to the 12-centimeter (4.7-inch) rise in the global sea level observed since 1880. Hansen suspects that the temperature will rise so much by the year 2000 that scientists will have no doubt about the cause.

Perhaps the first noticeable effects of a changed climate would be in agriculture. Some of these effects would be beneficial, while others might decrease crop yields.

The present-day climate zones that are favorable to agriculture, especially those in the middle and higher latitudes — 30° latitude and more from the equator — probably would shift toward the poles. Thus, farmers in the Northern Hemisphere would be able to raise crops that require relatively high average temperatures farther north than they presently can, provided the precipitation and the quality of the soil were suitable. Siberia might become prime cropland and Canada's wheat belt might expand northward.

On the other hand, the semiarid subtropical regions of both north and south hemispheres — areas that are now within 30° latitude of the equator—might move either toward or away from the poles. Then the already marginal use of these lands for grazing and crops could be seriously disrupted.

If the summer temperature in the middle latitudes increased while the precipitation decreased, yields of both corn and wheat probably would decline. Cornfields in Iowa might eventually become useful only for grazing. However, an increase in both temperature and rainfall would favor an increased production of rice in Arkansas, Louisiana, and Texas.

A greater concentration of CO_2 in the air would increase the efficiency of photosynthesis in all climates. However, an increase in the air temperature would probably increase the rate of plant respiration at the expense of plant growth. Furthermore, an increase in the cloudiness in areas that became wetter would reduce the sunshine available for plant growth.

The most serious threat of a change in climate is the possibility that it might make the oceans rise. The best estimates now available from both observations and model studies indicate that a warming of 6° to 10°C (11° to 18°F.) in the polar regions would melt the polar sea ice in the summer. However, this ice is floating on the ocean, so its melting would not affect the level of the sea. The oceans would rise only if the massive ice sheets that cover most of Greenland and Antarctica melted. But an ice sheet responds slowly to changes in the annual accumulation of snow and ice at its surface, so meteorologists expect little or no melting in Greenland and Antarctica.

An exception to this may be the West Antarctic ice sheet, part of the huge ice formation that covers the area around the South Pole. The ice sheet rests on a surface that is about 2 kilometers (1.2 miles) below sea level. If the sheet broke up, the part of the sheet that is above sea level would fall into the water, raising the oceans by about 5 meters (15 feet) over a period of about 100 years, perhaps sooner. This would flood parts of the Eastern Seaboard of the United States and much of northwestern Europe.

If world temperatures are already on the upswing, as Hansen suspects, we can expect warmer weather in the late 1980s and 1990s. As temperatures increased, there would be a slow but steady shift in the seasonal patterns of energy use, clothing, and recreation. People who, like the Hendersons, lived in the more northern climates would experience the greatest changes. We would expect gradual shifts in the patterns of world trade and tourism, along with adjustments in global economics and even social systems.

But if the change is sudden, society may have trouble adjusting to it. Some scientists say that the risk of a sudden rise in temperature is too high and we should cut back our use of fossil fuels now. Others maintain that we should wait for clear evidence that the burning of fossil fuels is warming the atmosphere.

Meanwhile, they continue to monitor CO_2.

North
STOP
cancel

The Promise of Videodiscs

By Arthur Fisher

This new technology has great potential for home and industry — if it can survive incompatible systems and a reluctant market

You place a record on a special player connected to your television set and press a button. A picture of Fifth Avenue and 34th Street in New York City appears on the screen, with the Empire State Building in the background. Working the controls, you move the scenery and seem to enter it.

You can travel up Fifth Avenue to Central Park and watch the seals in the pool at the zoo. Or make a left turn and go over to Broadway; then take a right to Times Square and the theater district. You can even ride the Empire State Building's high-speed elevators to the 86th-floor observation deck for a breathtaking view of the city. As you progress, the image on the screen changes to reflect your surroundings, just as if you were on a real tour.

By simply changing records, you could similarly explore London, Paris, Rome, Moscow, or anywhere else.

You cannot do this in your home yet. But at the Massachusetts Institute of Technology's (MIT) Architecture Machine Group, you can tour the pleasant resort town of Aspen, Colo., in just this way. Such electronic trips, and much more, are made possible by a new piece of technology called the videodisc.

A videodisc is a means of storing pictures and sounds on a disc that looks like a long-playing phonograph record (LP). Like an LP, the disc is played on a machine that has a turntable. But there the similarities end. The videodisc is a means of storing both pictures and sound. And the videodisc player transmits the pictures and sound over a television set to which it is connected.

At its most basic level, a videodisc system can be used to watch movies, in much the same way you would watch a movie on TV. Or you can put on a videodisc of your favorite rock group in concert and sit back and enjoy the music.

But videodisc players also have a number of interactive features that enable you to do much more. You can play games, solve puzzles, learn a foreign language—all at your own pace; sort through thousands of items in the Sears Roebuck catalog; teach yourself to play tennis, perform gymnastics, or make paper airplanes. At the touch of a button on a handheld control panel, you can make whatever you are watching proceed in slow motion, reverse, or one step at a time. You can stop the action, or almost instantly get to any point on the program. You can even choose which of two different sound tracks to listen to.

Not all of these options are available with each kind of videodisc, however. There were two disc-player systems on the market in the spring of 1982, with a third system that was still to be introduced. None of the systems plays discs manufactured for the others. Each system has advantages and disadvantages—in price, flexibility, and freedom from mechanical wear.

Some experts think that the videodisc format for home entertainment may not survive, partly because of the competition brought about by conflicting systems, and partly because of competition from videotape recorders (VTRs). A videodisc player can play only prerecorded discs. VTRs have a distinct advantage in that they can record television programs as well as play them back. And with an optional videotape camera, you can tape your own programs, including home movies of the family.

The author:
Arthur Fisher is group editor of science and engineering at *Popular Science* magazine.

The videodisc was born, in very crude form, around 1926. Its inventor, a Scottish engineer named John Logie Baird, was a television pioneer—the first man to transmit genuine TV pictures of moving objects. Baird's videodiscs were grooved wax records, sold in London shops under the brand name "Major Radiovision." They were played on an elaborate electronic machine called Phonovision, which used a stylus, or needle, to trace the grooves. The pictures, accompanied by sound, appeared on a television set. Sales of the discs were disappointing, however, and Baird abandoned the project.

Today's videodiscs differ radically from Baird's — as well as from one another. The most sophisticated is the optical disc, or laser disc. The player for optical discs is the first home product to incorporate a laser, a device that produces focused, single wavelength beams of light. The optical-disc system was developed by the Dutch electronics firm N. V. Philips Corporation and the U. S. entertainment giant MCA, Incorporated. The first optical-disc player was introduced in the United States in 1978 by Pioneer Electronic Corporation.

Take an optical disc from its sleeve and you notice that the silvery, grooveless, intensely reflecting surface shimmers with ever-shifting rainbow colors as you turn it in the light. You can handle the mirrorlike disc any way you like, because a clear plastic coating protects it from dust, oily fingerprints, and scratching. Underneath that plastic armor lies a series of microscopic pits, some 26 billion of them, etched into the aluminum-coated, reflective surface of the disc. The pits represent a "map" of the originally recorded signal. When the player is started, a beam of laser light is aimed at the revolving disc through a system of prisms, mirrors, and lens. The light reflects off the surface of the disc and strikes a photodetector. The arrangement of the pits causes changes in the pattern of the reflection, and the photodetector converts this information into electrical signals. The signals are then decoded and the original program is reproduced on a TV set. Because there are no grooves to guide the laser

John Logie Baird, a Scottish engineer, invented the videodisc in the mid-1920s. He played the discs on a crude but elaborate Phonovision machine.

pickup across the disc, the entire laser assembly is moved outward from the center of the disc to the edge along a slide, guided by special circuits. The laser pickup plays the record from underneath.

The sophisticated guidance system and the gas laser of the optical-disc players make these machines the most expensive of the three systems — about $750 as of spring 1982. In addition, the sensitivity of the laser system has created problems in the manufacture of the discs. For example, a single speck of dust wafted onto the disc before it is protectively coated could obliterate dozens of pits.

However, the highly complex optical-disc system has many advantages. Because there is no stylus touching the disc, the disc cannot wear out. The laser itself has a life of at least 10,000 hours. The laser beam is precisely focused on pits that lie beneath the disc's surface coating, so dust and grease cannot interfere with playback.

The optical-disc system is also highly flexible. Most of the discs

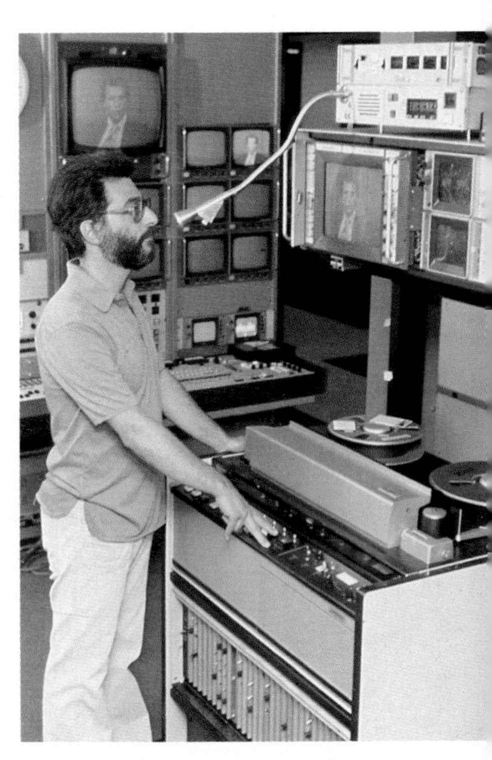

Actors, directors, and technicians produce a program for an optical disc, *above left,* as an engineer records the action on videotape, *above.* A computerized editing machine, *left,* then puts the tape, along with slides, films, and other media, onto a master tape that is used in making videodiscs.

play for half an hour per side; the disc turns at 1,800 revolutions per minute (rpm) — 30 times a second. One revolution of the disc is equivalent to one frame of a television broadcast. (Data near the center of the disc are more compressed than data near the rim.) Therefore, if the laser beam is kept from moving across the disc, it keeps reading the same image as the disc turns, and you get "freeze frame" or stop motion, without loss of clarity.

In addition, optical discs can store an incredible amount of information. If the program consisted only of still pictures, such as pages from books, the disc could store 54,000 frames on each side. This is more than enough to display all 22 volumes of THE WORLD BOOK ENCYCLOPEDIA.

Because the laser pickup is unrestrained by a groove, the optical-disc system offers true random access — the laser beam can get to any point on the disc almost instantly. Every frame on the disc is

A machine operator examines a disc for flaws, *above left,* before it is coated with aluminum and etched with pits. The electron micrograph, *above,* shows some of the 26 billion pits. They represent a "map" of the originally recorded signal. A worker cleans the coated surface of the finished disc, *left,* before putting it into a sleeve.

How Videodisc Systems Work

All videodisc systems convert information from discs into TV signals. Differences in technology make the systems incompatible.

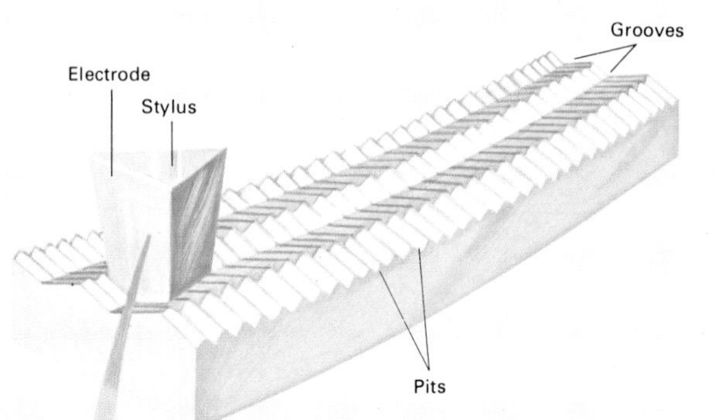

A capacitance electronic disc system uses a disc that has grooves of varying depths. The differences in depth determine the signals picked up by the electrode on the stylus.

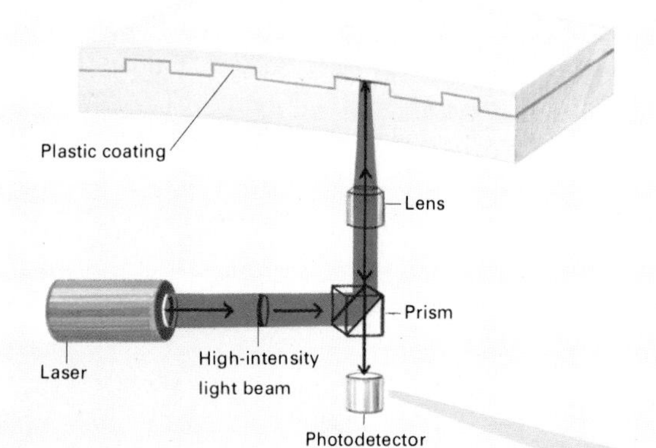

An optical-disc system aims a laser beam at a disc that has been etched with pits. A photodetector picks up signals in the form of changes in the reflection of the beam off the disc.

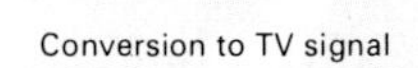

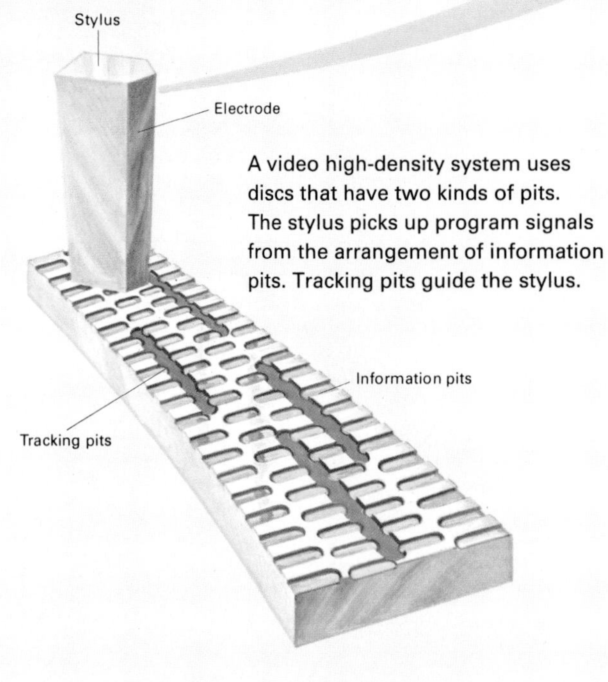

A video high-density system uses discs that have two kinds of pits. The stylus picks up program signals from the arrangement of information pits. Tracking pits guide the stylus.

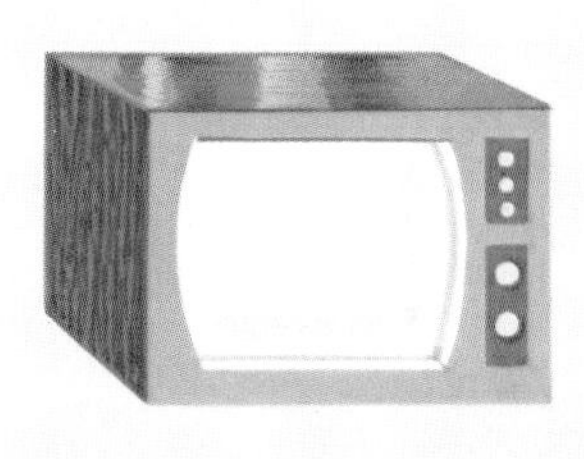

electronically encoded with a number. Enter the number on a control panel, push the "search" button, and the player will display any one of the 54,000 frames on that side and then, if you wish, go on playing from there.

There are also optical discs that play for one hour on each side. These discs, which are used for movies, have more than one TV frame per revolution. As a result, the freeze-frame pictures are not as clear and the random access is not as quick.

The optical-disc system's only present rival was introduced by RCA Corporation in 1981. RCA's capacitance electronic disc (CED) system is much simpler than the optical-disc system.

The CED disc, like an ordinary phonograph record, has grooves cut into its vinyl surface. But these grooves are so small — only one ten-thousandth of an inch wide — that about 40 of them would fit inside one groove of a conventional LP. And the spiral they make up is some 19 kilometers (12 miles) long.

Anything that small is extremely delicate. For protection, the disc is enclosed in an envelope called a caddy that shields it from dust, fingerprints, and scratches. Without the caddy, the discs would quickly deteriorate, giving poor reproduction of the sound and pictures. To play the disc, you slip the caddy into a slot on the side of the player. When you withdraw the caddy, the disc stays inside. You insert the caddy to retrieve the disc

At the bottom of the CED disc's grooves lies the audio-video information, not in the form of a pit code, but as up-and-down variations in the surface. These variations conform to the changing electronic signals from the program that was recorded.

A stylus designed to track these minuscule undulations would quickly erode them. So engineers invented a stylus consisting of a tiny diamond with a metal electrode on one face. The tip of the diamond is just large enough to ride along the sides of the grooves and always stay at the same height. But as the wavy bottom of the grooves spins by at 450 rpm, there is a constantly changing vertical distance between the bottom of the groove and the metal electrode. You can visualize it as the bottom of the groove rising and falling under the stylus.

In the CED system, the disc and the metal electrode serve as electrically charged conductors. The stored energy, or capacitance, between the conductors varies with the distance between them. As the space between the disc and the metal electrode fluctuates in exact correspondence with the undulating bottom of the grooves, this minute change in capacitance is translated into electronic signals that reconstruct the original sounds and pictures.

Because this system is less complex than the optical-disc system, CED players are considerably less expensive — selling for about $300 as of spring 1982. However, they are not as versatile. For example, there is no true freeze frame. You can make the stylus play over the same groove repeatedly, but each groove consists of four different frames. As a result, the image is often jittery.

And because the stylus is confined to a groove, you cannot zip all over the disc to almost instantly locate a specific frame, as you can with optical discs. You can search for a scene, but the stylus must track forward or backward through the grooves. The basic RCA player has two fast-forward and two reverse speeds. At the fastest speed — 120 times normal — you cannot see a picture. Instead, a digital display appears on the TV screen to show you how many minutes of playing time have elapsed. Once you are near the desired segment, you can use a slow-speed search — 16 times normal — to watch the picture and zero in on what you want.

Another disadvantage of the CED player is that the contact between the disc and the stylus will eventually wear out the stylus as well as the disc. RCA rates the stylus as good for 1,000 hours. The stylus can be easily replaced for about $70. Each disc should last for at least 100 plays before showing any signs of wear.

The third type of videodisc system, which combines some of the features of both the optical-disc and CED approaches, is called the video high-density (VHD) system. It will attempt to achieve the advantages of the other systems without their handicaps. The VHD system was developed by Victor Company of Japan (JVC) — an affiliate of Matsushita Electric Industrial Company.

Like the CED system, the VHD player has a diamond stylus with a metal electrode to sense changes in capacitance between the stylus and an electrically conductive disc. The disc spins at 900 rpm. But instead of undulations in a groove, the information signal is encoded

Type of Player

Features	Tape	CED	Optical-disc: 30-minute side	Optical-disc: 60-minute side	VHD
No disc or stylus wear			✓	✓	
Stereo sound	✓	✓	✓	✓	✓
Two-hour playback	✓	✓		✓	✓
Multiple speeds for forward and reverse	✓	✓	✓	✓	✓
Freeze frame	✓	✓	✓		✓
Random frame access			✓		✓
Recording capability	✓				

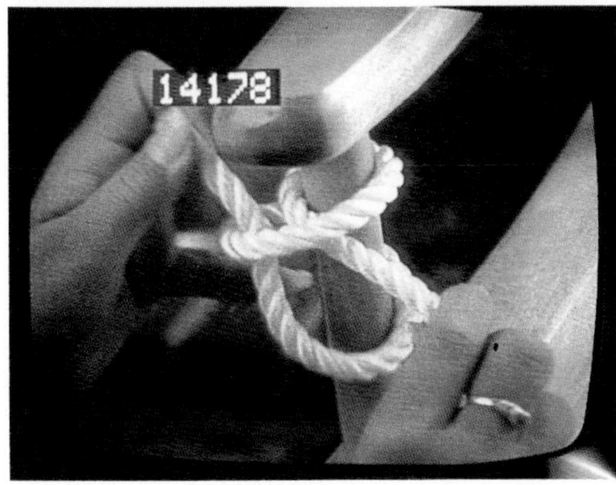

A young viewer learns sign language from "The First National Kidisc," which calls for the full use of the optical-disc system's interactive features. The disc also enables youngsters to learn knot tying, rock dancing, and other skills at their own pace. Each frame of the disc is encoded with a number. By entering the number on a control panel, the viewer can get to any point on the disc and stop the action.

in about 25 billion pits arranged in a spiral, similar to an optical disc. The disc also has a series of tracking pits—elongated depressions—on either side of the information pits. The tracking signals guide the stylus by sending current to a coil-magnet combination in an arm that holds the stylus. The part of the stylus that contacts the disc is flat and smooth, and much wider than the tracking signals and the information pits. The VHD stylus causes less friction than the stylus of a CED system. The manufacturer claims that the stylus has a lifetime of 2,000 hours, and that each disc can be played at least 10,000 times before there is any noticeable deterioration. Like CED discs, VHD discs must be kept in a protective caddy.

Because the VHD disc has no grooves, the system offers quick random access to any point on the program. However, the discs contain two TV frames per revolution. In the freeze-frame mode, two frames appear alternately. If there is any change from one frame to the other, the "still" picture will flicker. The VHD player is expected to be priced between the optical-disc and CED systems.

As far as picture quality goes, all the videodisc systems produce clear, sharp images, although the optical-disc system appears to hold a slight edge. There is no question that any videodisc player yields

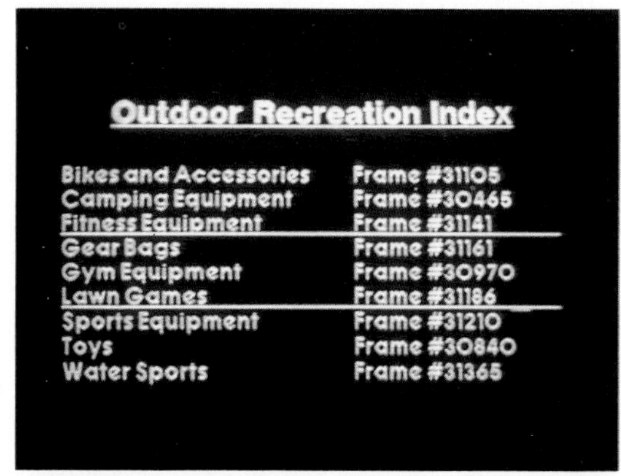

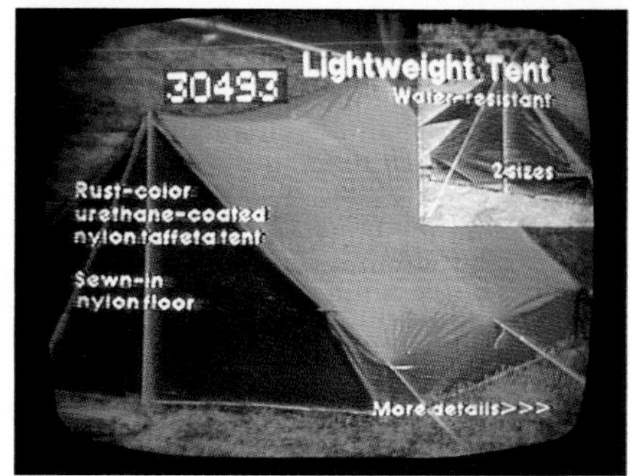

A home shopper views a live-action fashion show, *above,* from the Sears Roebuck and Company summer catalog for 1981, which was put on an optical disc as an experiment in electronic shopping. The disc also has an index, *top right,* still pictures and descriptions of thousands of items, *bottom right,* and ordering information.

a better picture than a videotape recorder. A large variety of program material is available in both optical-disc and CED formats, including movies — both classics and modern blockbusters; dramatic events, such as plays, concerts, and ballets; and sports programs.

If you want more than passive entertainment, videodiscs enable you to instruct yourself in a multitude of activities. It is here that the interactive potential of the optical-disc system really shines.

For example, "The First National Kidisc," produced by Optical Programming Associates, calls for the full use of the optical-disc system's features — freeze frame, step viewing, random access, and dual sound track. It allows children to actively participate in the program, rather than just observe it. The program is divided into 26 chapters and is not necessarily meant to be absorbed at one viewing, or in any particular order. Among the activities that Kidisc viewers can pursue are: making paper airplanes; learning sign language; creating a musical instrument; touring a movie studio and a zoo; learning to perform magic tricks; and making a secret-code device.

There is also a disc on "How To Watch Pro Football," in which seven National Football League coaches guide the uninitiated through the intricacies of the game. Again, this disc uses the inter-

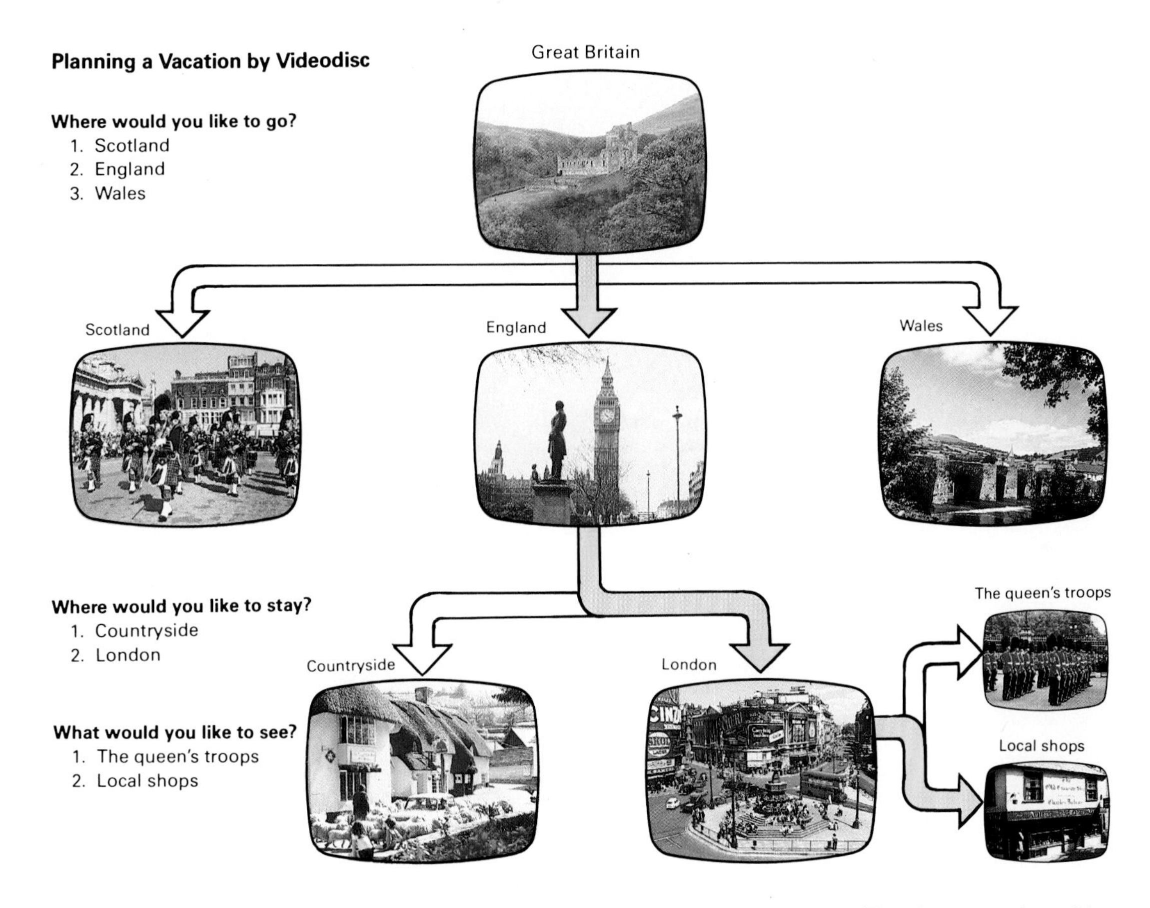

Planning a vacation with an optical videodisc permits you to tour a place in words and pictures before deciding whether to go there. Once you have chosen Great Britain, for example, you can pick which country to visit and then narrow your choices of where to stay and what to see.

active features of the optical-disc system to permit learning the ins and outs of football at your own pace. For example, you can choose which type of play to watch, then stop the action or slow it down.

If you want to be a gourmet cook—or at least a better one—an optical disc called "The Master Cooking Course" presents Craig Claiborne and Pierre Franey, two of the world's best-known cooking authorities, in a step-by-step guide to sophisticated cuisine. They prepare four meals, demonstrating more than 100 techniques. The two audio tracks are put to full use. The first track describes the cooking procedures and the second gives background information about the meals. You can listen to either track while watching the meals being prepared. At the end of each side of the disc are the recipes for all the dishes and a glossary of terms, which you can read with the freeze-frame control, just as if you were reading a cookbook. Each side has an alphabetical index, listing the exact frame number where specific topics, dishes, and techniques can be found.

Other interactive optical discs can teach you how to belly-dance, exercise to jazz, and appreciate wine.

Instructional material can also be found on CED discs, but their flexibility is limited compared with the optical-disc system. RCA, for

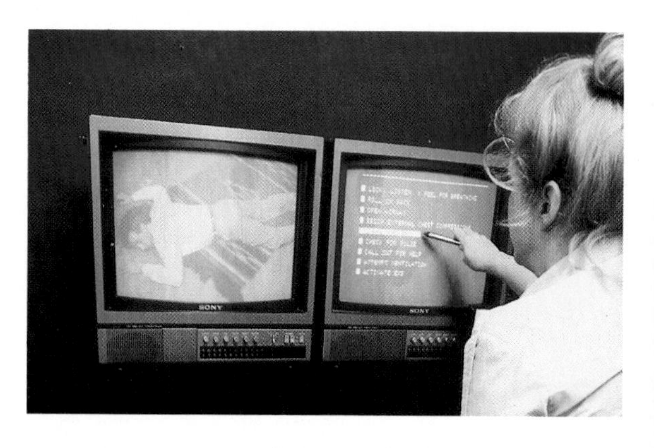

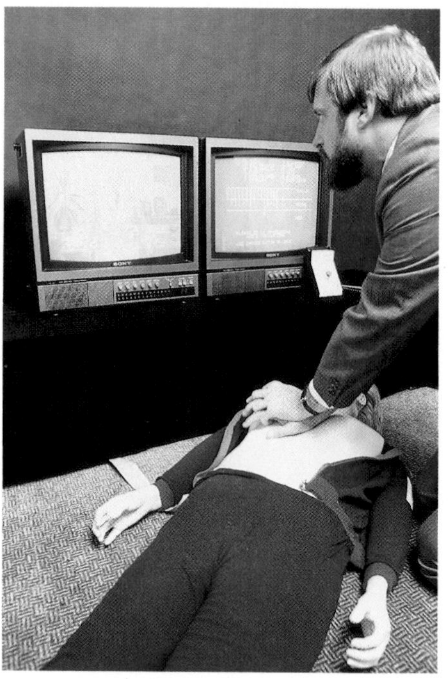

In learning cardiopulmonary resuscitation(CPR), students use an optical-disc system connected to a computer. One TV screen shows a heart attack victim and the other screen asks the student what she should do. The student chooses a response by touching the screen with a light-pen, *above.* Another student practices CPR on a dummy, *right,* as one screen provides continuous instruction and the other rates the student's performance.

example, presents Julia Child in her "French Chef" TV programs, Dr. Benjamin Spock on caring for the newborn, and "Complete Tennis from the Pros" with Arthur Ashe and other stars. But these discs are meant to be watched much like a TV show. RCA says that programs like "Complete Tennis" incorporate slow-motion or still frames in the original material, so the viewer doesn't need those controls on the player. "We could supply stop action and random access with the CED system if the need really existed," says Jack K. Sauter of RCA. But providing those features by electronic means presumably would increase the player's price considerably. Sauter agrees that, for some purposes, the optical-disc system is the better choice.

The optical-disc system is already being used in industry. Both the Ford Motor Company and General Motors Corporation (GM) use optical players to help train employees. Between them, they have some 14,000 players using interactive programs. GM's disc has an index allowing the trainee to choose instructions on how to fix an automobile exhaust system, for example. At the end of the lesson, the trainee answers questions by punching the appropriate buttons on a control panel. After a correct answer, the screen flashes the next question. A wrong answer brings the trainee back to the beginning of the lesson.

GM has also placed more than 10,000 videodisc players in its showrooms, enabling customers to watch a sales film displaying GM cars. When they have singled out a particular car model, they can learn what options are available for it.

Sears, Roebuck and Company put its 236-page summer catalog for 1981 on a videodisc to provide customers with electronic shopping. The disc has live-action fashion shows and demonstrations, still pictures and descriptions of some 18,000 items, plus a table of contents and ordering information. The discs and players were installed in a number of Sears catalog stores. The discs were also distributed on a trial basis to 1,000 homes that have videodisc players.

But the real advantage—and the full potential—of videodiscs may not be seen until their voluminous capacity for storing visual images is combined with a computer's artificial intelligence. One of the possibilities is the user-controlled "tour" like that of New York City. MIT's sophisticated computer program enables you to turn a corner in Aspen simply by pushing a button on a control panel. The computer interprets the command, searches for the correct "around-the-corner" image on the disc, and commands its display. The tour could just as easily be a trip through the solar system as a trip through Aspen.

Another disc and computer project at MIT teaches bike repair. You touch an image of the bike on the TV screen with a light-pen, pinpointing the component you want to learn about. The computer automatically selects frames on the disc that display that part, and the tools and techniques needed to deal with it.

Meanwhile, videodiscs have a long way to go before they become a commercial success in the home market. Consumers are confused by the new technology of videodiscs and by the incompatibility of the different systems. The same problem of incompatible systems delayed the introduction of long-playing records and color television sets in their early years. For each of those products, only one system survived the competition of the market place. Consumers are afraid that the same thing will happen with videodiscs, and that the system they buy may soon become obsolete.

But videodiscs face another problem. Consumers have yet to be convinced of the advantages of videodiscs over videotape. Videotape recorders, with the capability of making recordings as well as playing them back, offer potent competition, even though they are considerably more expensive and do not have the interactive features of videodiscs. The least expensive VTR sells for about twice the price of the least expensive videodisc player.

One company, Sony Corporation, abandoned the home videodisc technology in the 1970s. Sony concentrates on the production of videotape recorders for the home, and makes videodisc players only for industry. However, as of the spring of 1982, other companies were not ready to give up on home videodisc players. These firms note that phonographs and audiotape players exist side by side in millions of homes. They hope that, someday soon, videodisc players and videotape recorders will likewise be a part of the same home entertainment center. The fate of the videodisc may depend on this.

Energy for the Eons

By Dale M. Meade

Science is nearly ready to harness forces that power the stars to provide the world with a virtually limitless supply of energy

Physicists and engineers throughout the world are shooting tremendous bolts of energy into huge electromagnets and ripping atoms apart with surges of heat in an effort to duplicate the cosmic fire that lights the sun and the other stars. These scientists hope to build miniature "stars" on earth from which they can take energy to meet humanity's needs.

People have depended almost entirely on the sun as their source of energy throughout history. We use sunlight to grow crops that give our bodies energy and we burn "stored sunlight" in the form of fossil fuels such as coal, natural gas, and petroleum to heat our bodies and our homes and to do useful work.

But our appetite for energy has increased rapidly. Energy consumption has increased by 550 per cent since 1920, even though the population has increased by only 150 per cent since then. Furthermore, energy experts expect annual consumption to grow from the present 10 trillion watts to 100 trillion watts by the year 2050. As a result, petroleum may become scarce in the early 2000s, and natural gas may last only 40 more years. There is enough coal to last for hundreds of years, but burning large amounts of any fossil fuel increases the amount of carbon dioxide (CO_2) in

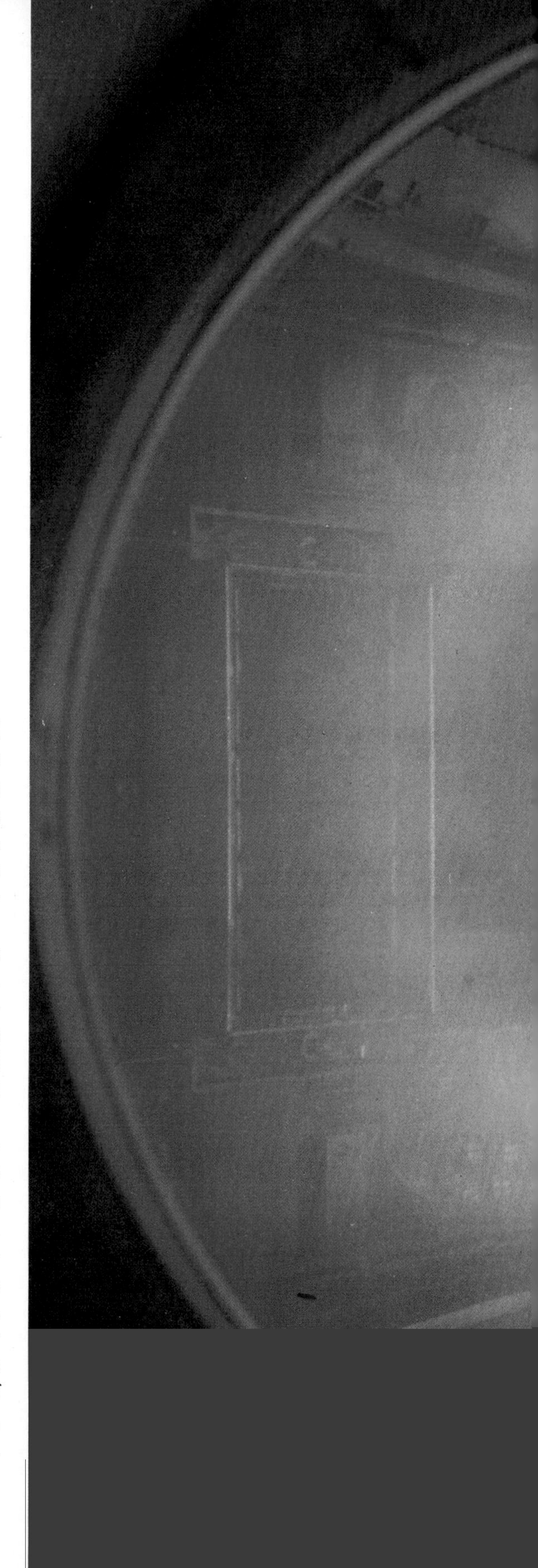

the atmosphere. Scientists suspect that a major build-up in CO_2 would increase the atmosphere's ability to hold in heat from the sun, thus boosting the temperature of the earth's surface, with potentially serious effects on the weather (see WARMER, WETTER WEATHER AHEAD?).

Researchers are therefore working on alternatives to petroleum and natural gas. They are experimenting with geothermal turbines that use energy from hot water and rocks beneath the earth's surface; generators that run on high water brought in by the tides; windmills; machines that use the energy of movement of ocean waves; and various devices that collect large amounts of solar radiation. Of these, only large solar collectors could meet the needs of the next century. Solar devices work best where the sun shines brightly on large areas for long periods of time. But many of the world's population centers are in northern areas that are overcast much of the time. These therefore would still need other energy forms.

One energy candidate already in use is nuclear power, which supplied only about 1 per cent of the energy that we consumed in 1982. Nuclear power comes from energy stored in the nuclei of atoms. Atoms consist of one or more electrons orbiting a central core, or nucleus. The nucleus is made up of at least one proton and one or more neutrons, except for the most common form of hydrogen, whose nucleus consists of a single proton.

Most nuclei on earth have the same composition today as they had when they formed billions of years ago. However, some nuclei have changed in an unusual way. When a neutron strikes such a nucleus, it fissions, or splits, into two approximately equal parts and emits two or more neutrons in the process. The mass of the fragments and the two neutrons is less than the mass of the original nucleus and neutron. The lost mass is converted to energy—mainly heat. Nuclear reactors can use this heat to convert water into steam which, in turn, drives electrical generators.

The world's supply of fission reactor fuel, a uranium isotope called U-235, would last about 100 years if nuclear power replaced coal immediately. And an experimental machine called a breeder reactor runs on even more plentiful materials. This machine converts the element thorium or the uranium isotope U-238 to reactor fuel as it produces power. Full-sized commercial breeder reactors would be able to produce 500 times as much energy as the world's coal reserves contain.

However, the fuel that breeders make can also be used in nuclear weapons, which concerns some people. Many people also feel that nuclear reactors that work by fission are unsafe. They are concerned that an accident in an ordinary U-235 reactor might release reactor fuel into the environment or allow a large amount of radioactive gas or water to escape. There are also some questions about the storage of radioactive waste from nuclear reactors.

The author:
Dale M. Meade is head of the Experimental Division of the Plasma Physics Laboratory at Princeton University in New Jersey.

An advanced type of nuclear reactor that is still under development might produce more energy than fission. In fact, it could provide a steady supply of virtually unlimited energy with virtually none of the potential dangers. This reactor is the miniature "star"—a fusion reactor.

The fuel in experimental fusion devices consists of two isotopes or forms of hydrogen. One is tritium, whose nucleus is made up of one proton and two neutrons. The other is deuterium, which has one proton and one neutron in its nucleus. Tritium is extremely rare in nature, so it would have to be manufactured. Fission reactors can produce tritium for experimental fusion reactors, while a commercial fusion reactor would breed its own.

Nature's supply of deuterium is extremely plentiful. At current rates of energy use, the water in the oceans can provide enough deuterium to last for 100 million years. If a reactor consumed the deuterium available in just 1 liter (0.26 gallon) of seawater, it would produce the same amount of energy that burning 300 liters (79 gallons) of gasoline would provide.

Furthermore, fusion reactors would be inherently safe. If the hot fuel were to get out of control, it would strike a reactor wall, which would cool it immediately, causing fusion reactions to stop. Furthermore, if the cooling system were to malfunction, the temperature of the reactor would rise by no more than 50° to 100°C (90° to 180°F.) Thus the reactor would not melt down.

However, the reactor would be slightly radioactive. Some neutrons produced in fusion reactions would strike the metal structure of the reactor, making a small number of its atoms radioactive. But the quantity of radioactive material in a fusion reactor would be about 100 times smaller than that of a fission-type reactor that produced the same amount of power.

Tritium itself is slightly radioactive. However, the radioactivity of the tritium in a fusion reactor would be about 1,000 times smaller than the radioactivity in the rest of the machine.

For these reasons, the United States, Russia, Japan, and a group of European nations in 1982 were spending a total of $2 billion per year on fusion research. The effort to develop a fusion reactor began about 1950, but scientists are only now nearing completion of the first phase—building an experimental reactor that will produce more energy than it consumes.

Fusion is the opposite of fission. When a tritium nucleus and a deuterium nucleus get close enough to each other, they join or fuse to form a helium nucleus—made up of two protons and two neutrons—and emit a neutron. As in fission, the total mass of the protons and neutrons that take part in a fusion reaction decreases during the reaction. Most of the lost mass is converted to heat energy in the helium nuclei and the emitted neutrons. The reactor would use the neutrons' heat energy to produce electricity.

Glossary

Deuterium: A form of hydrogen whose nucleus has one proton and one neutron. The nucleus of an ordinary hydrogen atom consists of a single proton.

Electromagnetic coil: A length of insulated wire wrapped around a piece of metal, usually iron, that magnetizes easily. Passing current through the wire turns this metal into a magnet.

Field line: An imaginary line used to describe the strength and shape of a magnetic field.

Inertial confinement: The holding of a plasma in position by its own inertia – its tendency to remain still – so that nuclear fusion can occur within it.

Ion: In a plasma, an atom stripped of its electrons, thus giving it a positive charge.

Magnetic confinement: The holding of a plasma in position by a magnetic field so that nuclear fusion can occur in it.

Magnetic field: The space around a magnet in which the magnet's powers of attraction and repulsion are effective.

Magnetic mirror: A linear magnetic field that repels plasma particles from its two ends somewhat as mirrors in this configuration would reflect rays of light.

Nuclear fission: The splitting of an atomic nucleus into two nearly equal parts.

Nuclear fusion: The combining of two atomic nuclei to form a nucleus that is more massive than either of them.

Nuclear reactor: A device in which nuclear fission or nuclear fusion takes place.

Plasma: An extremely hot mixture of ions and free electrons.

Tokamak: A fusion-type nuclear reactor that is shaped like a doughnut.

Tritium: A form of hydrogen whose nucleus has one proton and two neutrons.

Fission reaction

Fusion reaction

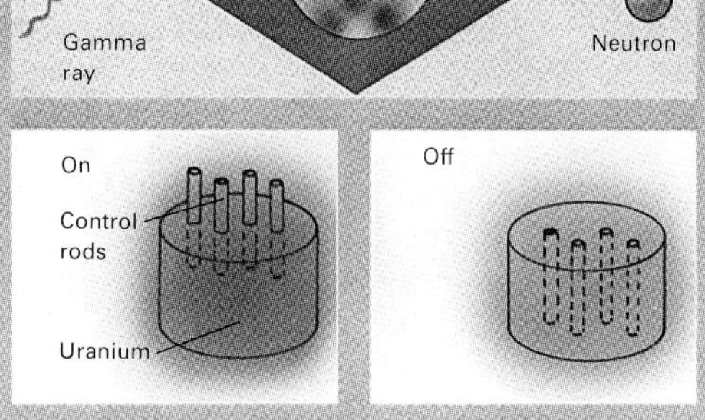

Turning Reactors Off
In fission, *top,* a neutron hits a uranium nucleus, which splits, emitting gamma rays and neutrons. As neutrons strike other nuclei, *above left,* fission continues. Rods that absorb neutrons control fission but do not stop it completely, even during shutdown, *above right.*

In fusion, *top,* heat fuses tritium and deuterium nuclei, forming a helium nucleus and liberating a neutron. But when hot nuclei and electrons (the plasma), *above left,* go out of control and hit the wall, they cool immediately into a thin gas, *above right.* Fusion immediately ceases.

Fusion is the power behind the sun and the other stars. In fact, stars are raging fusion furnaces in which successive reactions of light elements produce heavier and heavier nuclei up to the element iron, which is 56 times as massive as the most common form of hydrogen. All nuclei have a positive electrical charge and therefore tend to repel one another. But at extremely high temperatures, such as the 15 million°C (27 million°F.) at the center of the sun, nuclei move so rapidly that they overcome this repulsion and get close enough to fuse.

On the much cooler earth, however, scientists must find a way to heat tritium and deuterium to tremendous temperatures and also find a way to contain this hot fuel so that nuclei will fuse. They must design a system in which energetic helium nuclei would remain in a container, heating the fuel to higher temperatures, while the energetic neutrons would escape from the container and deposit their energy in the reactor walls to provide the heat for a steam generator.

The major problem that designers face is the fact that raising the fuel to high temperatures makes it very difficult to channel. At high temperatures, tritium and deuterium atoms lose their electrons, forming a plasma — a swarm of negative electrons and positive nuclei called ions. As the electrons move around the plasma container, they emit X rays, just as electrons bouncing back and forth in a radio antenna radiate radio waves. These X rays leave the plasma, taking energy with them.

In order to make up for this energy loss, the reactor must raise the plasma temperature, causing more fusions that produce more energy. The temperature of a perfectly contained plasma would have to reach 50 million°C (90 million°F.) — three times the temperature of the sun's center — for the plasma to produce more energy than it consumes. The fusion of nuclei in this plasma would then continue even if the supply of heating energy from outside the reactor were shut off. The plasma would then be *ignited.*

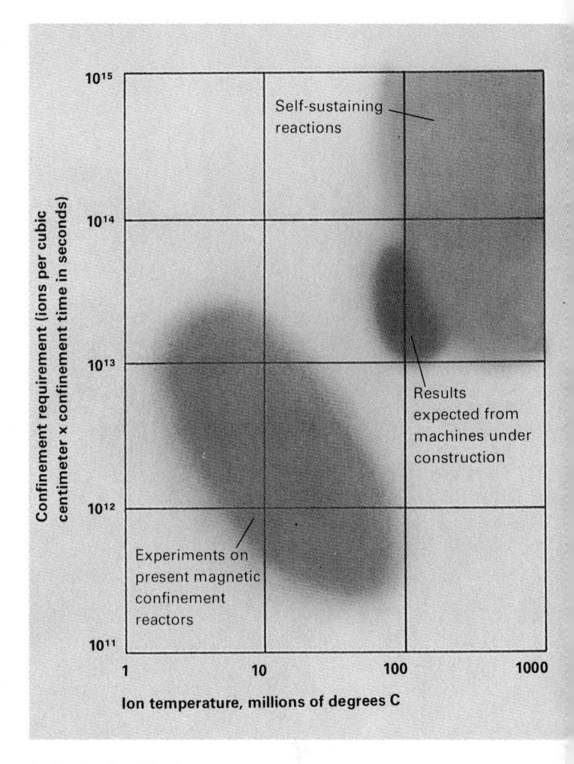

Criteria for Fusion
Experimental magnetic confinement devices have not yet heated a dense enough group of ions to high enough temperatures for a long enough period of time to produce a fusion reaction that continues under its own power. However, machines now under construction may reach this goal.

However, no one has been able to design a reactor that can contain a plasma perfectly. Plasma particles — ions as well as electrons — leak from the containers of experimental reactors, taking energy with them. More fusion has to occur to make up for these losses. The ability of a plasma to ignite in a working reactor depends upon three things — plasma temperature, plasma density, and the length of time the reactor's container holds the plasma. In 1955, physicist John D. Lawson of the Atomic Energy Research Establishment in Harwell, England, calculated that a tritium-deuterium plasma in a reactor will ignite if its temperature is at least 100 million°C (180 million°F.). At the same time, the fuel density — in ions per cubic centimeter — times the length of time the fuel is confined — in seconds — must be greater than 200 trillion. Physicists call this number the confinement parameter.

The problem of confining the hot plasma is extremely difficult to solve because it would melt a container made of any material substance. Scientists are working on two solutions to this problem.

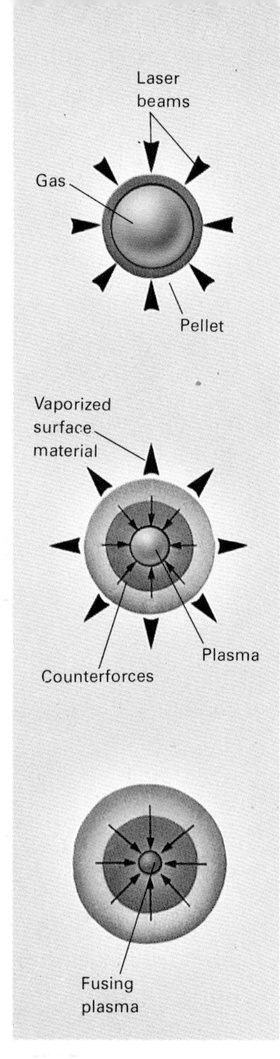

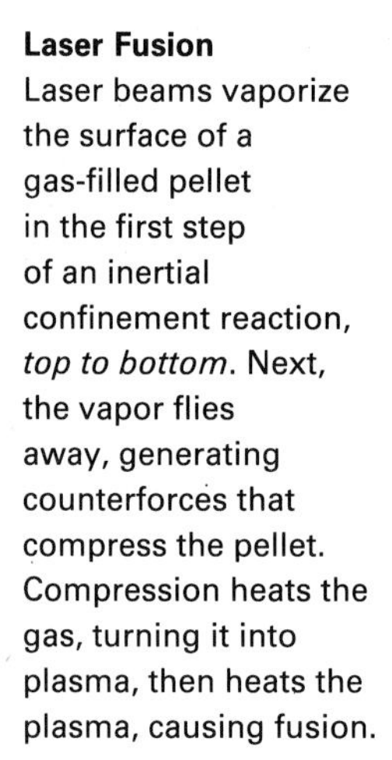

Laser Fusion
Laser beams vaporize the surface of a gas-filled pellet in the first step of an inertial confinement reaction, *top to bottom*. Next, the vapor flies away, generating counterforces that compress the pellet. Compression heats the gas, turning it into plasma, then heats the plasma, causing fusion.

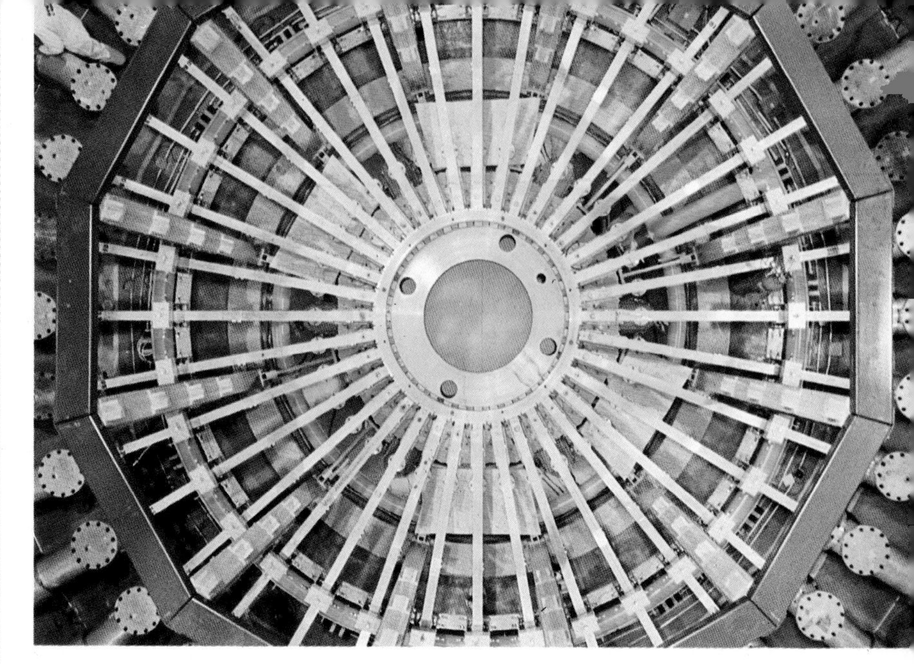

The first solution, inertial confinement, uses the deuterium-tritium fuel's inertia — its tendency to remain at rest — to prevent the plasma from escaping before fusion occurs. The other solution, magnetic confinement, employs a magnetic bottle, a container made up of magnetic fields. A magnetic bottle can contain plasma particles because they are electrically charged.

Scientists want to design an inertial confinement reactor that uses powerful beams such as laser beams to heat a dense body of fuel extremely rapidly. The fuel for this ideal reactor is a deuterium and tritium gas in a hollow glass ball or pellet about 0.5 centimeter (0.2 inch) in diameter. The ball is mounted in the center of a large number of long lasers, arranged like the spokes of a wheel, that shoot intense bursts of light at the pellet. When the beams strike the pellet, they transfer up to 10 million billion watts per square centimeter (0.155 square inch) to its surface, evaporating the surface rapidly. The vapor flies away from the surface like a rocket leaving a launching pad. The force of reaction to the flight, like the reaction force that a rocket exhaust exerts on its launching pad, drives the pellet inward, compressing it. This compression heats the inside of the pellet to fusion temperatures. Fusion reactions take place rapidly in an explosion that liberates energy equivalent to the explosion of about 0.5 kilogram (1 pound) of TNT. The pellet then expands in one-billionth of a second, cooling the plasma and ending the reactions.

So far, no inertial confinement device has transferred energy to a pellet rapidly enough to ignite plasma. At Lawrence Livermore National Laboratory (LLNL) in California, a system of 20 lasers, called Shiva, has compressed pellets to 100 times the density of liquid deuterium and tritium, about 10 per cent of the compression that would ignite plasma. The laser system fills a building 70 meters (230 feet) long, and 30 meters (98 feet) wide, and 30 meters high. Shiva has bombarded 0.5-millimeter (0.02-inch) pellets with 26 trillion watts of power for one ten-billionth of a second. LLNL plans to build a laser system called Nova by the late 1980s that will have 10 times the power of Shiva. Physicists expect Nova to produce as much fusion energy as the energy in the laser beams.

Lasers are effective power sources for fusion reactors because their light is easy to focus on a small pellet. However, a laser consumes almost 20 watts for every watt of power it produces. In other words, a laser is 5 per cent efficient. On the other hand, a high-powered electron or ion beam can be 25 per cent efficient.

Physicists Glenn W. Kuswa and Gerald Yonas of Sandia National Laboratories in Albuquerque, N. Mex., have built a device that delivers 30-trillion-watt pulses of proton beams. But these beams are not powerful enough to ignite plasma. Kuswa and Yonas therefore propose to build a 72-beam device that would deliver 100 trillion watts to a pellet 0.5 centimeter (0.2 inch) in diameter. This device may ignite plasma by the late 1980s.

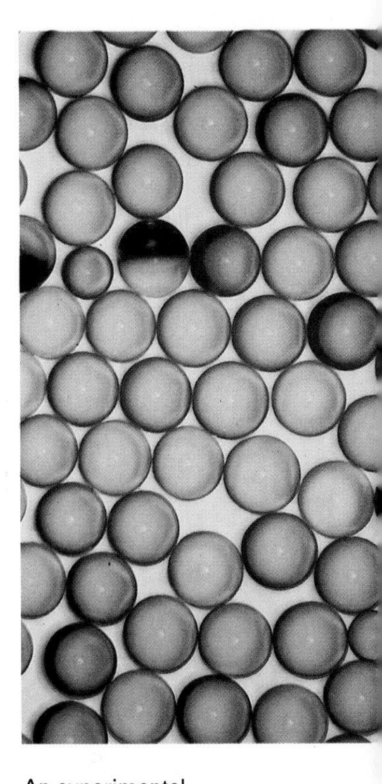

An experimental inertial confinement device, *opposite page,* has 36 electrical transmission lines that deliver 30 trillion watts of power to the target area in the center of the machine. This power causes the nuclei of gases in tiny glass targets, *above,* to fuse.

For the other major fusion system — magnetic confinement — theoreticians determined in the late 1940s that two types of magnetic "bottles" might be able to contain plasma. One bottle looks like a short pencil sharpened at both ends, while the other is shaped like a doughnut.

In the early 1950s, LLNL physicist Richard F. Post developed the magnetic mirror, a confinement device that formed the first kind of bottle. The device was made up of a long tube with a ring-shaped electromagnet at each end. Sending electricity through the electromagnets formed the magnetic bottle inside of the tube. Then, an electrical arc at one end of the tube ionized atoms of hydrogen, creating a plasma. Finally, machines called neutral beam injectors shot energetic beams of atoms at the bottle. Because these atoms were neutral, they could penetrate the bottle. When they did, they heated the plasma.

The bottle confined plasma fairly well. The magnetic field was strong at the ends of the bottle, so plasma particles that approached the ends tended to bounce back toward the middle of the cylinder as if they were reflected by a mirror.

However, many particles still escaped through the ends and also through the sides of the bottle. Russian physicist M. S. Ioffe solved this problem in 1961 with a reactor whose fields increased in strength with increasing distance from the center of the plasma. Thus, plasma particles met increasing magnetic resistance as they drifted away from the center.

This so-called magnetic well concept was incorporated into a device called 2XIIB, built at LLNL in 1974. This machine used an electromagnet shaped like the seam of a baseball. Turning on the electromagnet formed a bottle shaped like a bow tie with one end twisted at a right angle to the other. The two ends of the bottle

A 340-metric-ton (375-short-ton) superconducting electromagnet, made up of two coils shaped like the letter C, is tested at Lawrence Livermore National Laboratory in California, where it will play a major part in experiments on magnetic confinement.

extended beyond the openings in the electromagnet. This bottle confined most of the plasma in "the knot of the tie." However, a large number of ions still escaped from the ends.

Electrons are lighter than positive ions, so they moved more rapidly and therefore escaped more quickly. But as electrons escaped, they pulled many of the oppositely charged ions out through the mirror with them. So many nuclei escaped from the 2XIIB that the researchers concluded that a simple magnetic mirror could not provide the confinement needed for plasma ignition.

Physicists G. I. Dimov of the Institute of Nuclear Physics in Novosibirsk, Russia, and Thomas K. Fowler and B. Grant Logan of LLNL solved this leakage problem by suggesting the so-called tandem mirror arrangement in 1976. This kind of reactor would have two baseball magnets—one at each end of a long cylinder. Circular electromagnets would be arranged around the cylinder like rings on a finger. Turning on the electromagnets would form a magnetic bottle that looked like a cylinder with one end of a bow tie sticking out of each end.

Neutral beams would heat a dense plasma confined to the "bow ties" to extremely high temperatures. Hot electrons would leak out the ends much more rapidly than ions would, so the end plasmas would become positively charged. These plasmas therefore would repel the positive ions that come near the ends from the plasma in the cylinder. Neutral beams would also heat the plasma in the cylinder to fusion temperatures.

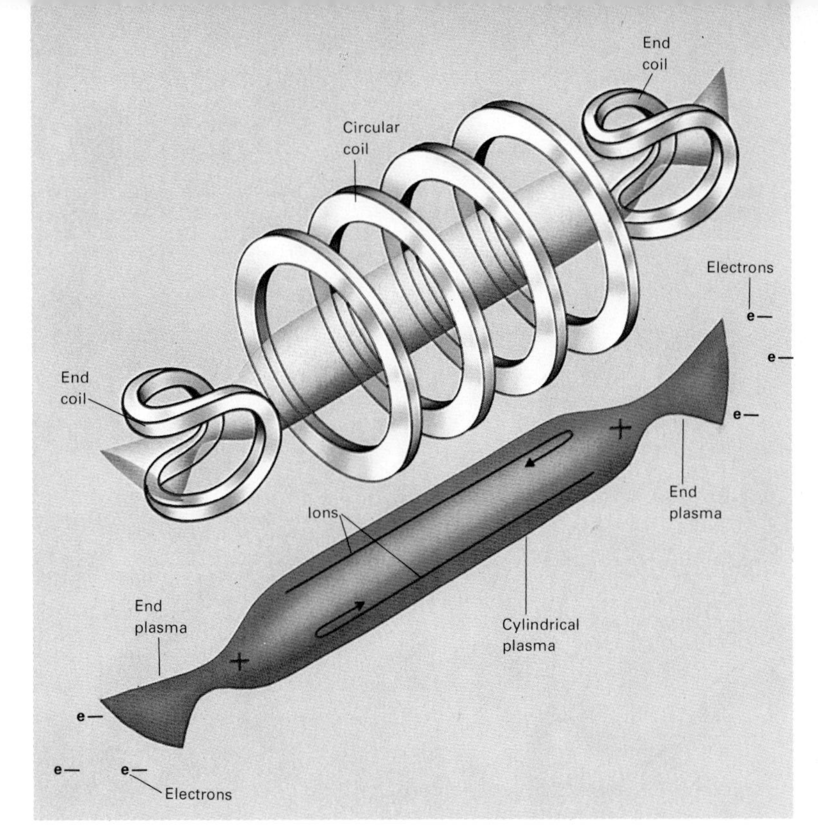

Bouncing Plasma
Twisted electromagnetic coils trap plasma in the ends of a mirror-type reactor. But electrons escape from the ends, making the end plasmas positive. These plasmas then act as mirrors, reflecting positive ions back into the cylindrical plasma, where fusion occurs. Circular coils set up magnetic fields that keep the ions from escaping out the sides.

Physicist Thomas C. Simonen and his colleagues at LLNL tested an experimental tandem mirror in 1980. Their results show that a tandem magnetic mirror can achieve a confinement parameter nine times as large as that of a simple magnetic mirror.

LLNL is building an advanced tandem mirror device called the Mirror Fusion Test Facility (MFTF) that has even more complex electromagnets to deal with problems of end leakage. LLNL scientists expect the MFTF to achieve a confinement parameter of 50-trillion at temperatures of at least 100 million°C by 1985. The MFTF will be 60 meters (197 feet) long.

Doughnut-shaped, or toroidal, bottles have no problem of end leakage, because they have no ends. The field lines — imaginary lines that describe magnetic fields — go all the way around the doughnut or torus. The bottle forms entirely within the reactor walls. Plasma particles circulate around the inside of the bottle, spiraling around field lines that are circular and parallel. However, particles can also move sideways. For example, in a process called diffusion, two ions collide and jump from one field line to another. An ion that undergoes successive collisions can gradually migrate out of the bottle and hit the wall of the torus.

The major type of toroidal reactor is the tokamak, conceived of by Russian physicists and Nobel laureates Andrei D. Sakharov and Igor Y. Tamm in the early 1950s. The tokamak has a set of vertical electromagnetic coils that fit around the torus like rings on a finger and horizontal coils extending the long way around the machine.

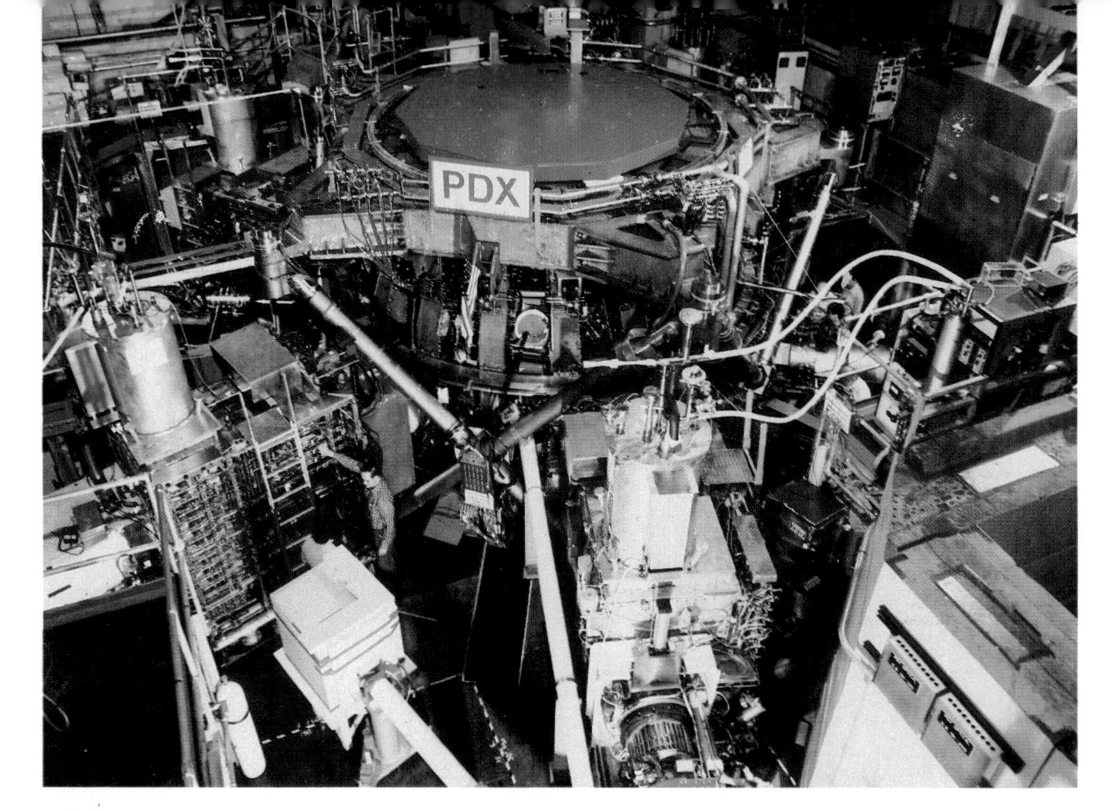

The Poloidal Divertor Experiment, a doughnut-shaped fusion device at Princeton University, is surrounded by machines that monitor tests of plasma heating and magnetic confinement.

A typical experiment on a tokamak begins with the removal of air from the toroidal chamber. Next, current flows through the vertical coils, setting up a *toroidal* (horizontal) magnetic field that goes all the way around the inside of the machine. This field is about 100,000 times as strong as the earth's magnetic field. Then, pure hydrogen gas enters through a tube in the side of the chamber. A pulse of electrical current then surges through a set of horizontal coils, setting up an electrical field in the chamber. This field first pulls electrons from the hydrogen atoms, forming a plasma, and then drives an electrical current through this plasma. The plasma current rises to about 1 million amperes for one second, heating the plasma to almost 10 million°C (18 million°F.).

The plasma current also helps to confine the plasma by creating a *poloidal* (vertical) magnetic field. This field combines with the toroidal field to form the bottle that holds the plasma.

In 1969, Russian experimenters led by physicist Lev A. Artsimovich first heated plasma to 12 million°C (21.6 million°F.) in a toroidal system in Moscow. Research groups throughout the world soon began building tokamaks of increasing size and variety. The next major step occurred at the Massachusetts Institute of Technology in Cambridge in 1977, when physicist Ronald Parker and his colleagues used a tokamak known as Alcator to reach a confinement parameter of 30 trillion, still far from the 200 trillion required.

Scientists soon found that heating plasma using only the electrical current could not raise its temperature much higher than 10 million°C. So, in 1978, physicists Harold P. Eubank and Wolfgang Sto-

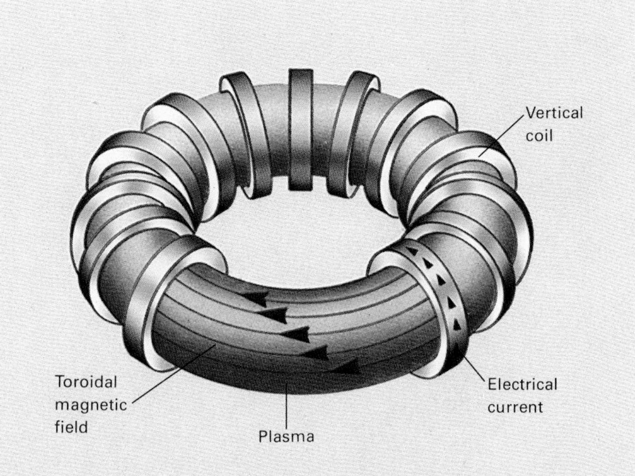

Two Fields in One
Electrical currents in electromagnetic coils set up magnetic fields that hold plasma in a doughnut-shaped reactor called a tokamak. First, current in the vertical coils forms a toroidal magnetic field around the reactor's center.

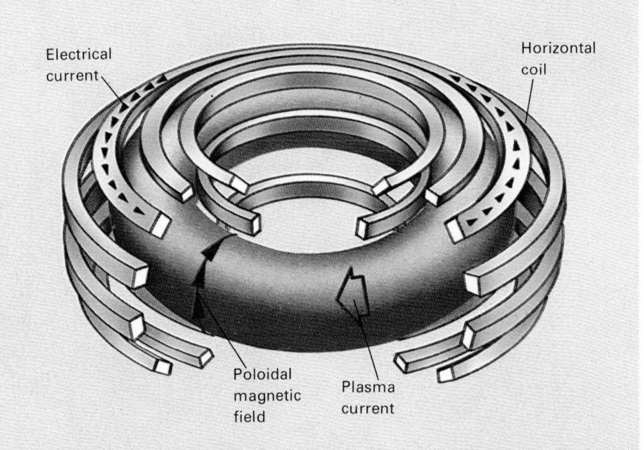

Then, current in the horizontal coils makes the plasma circulate around the tokamak's center. This flow sets up a poloidal magnetic field perpendicular to the horizontal coils.

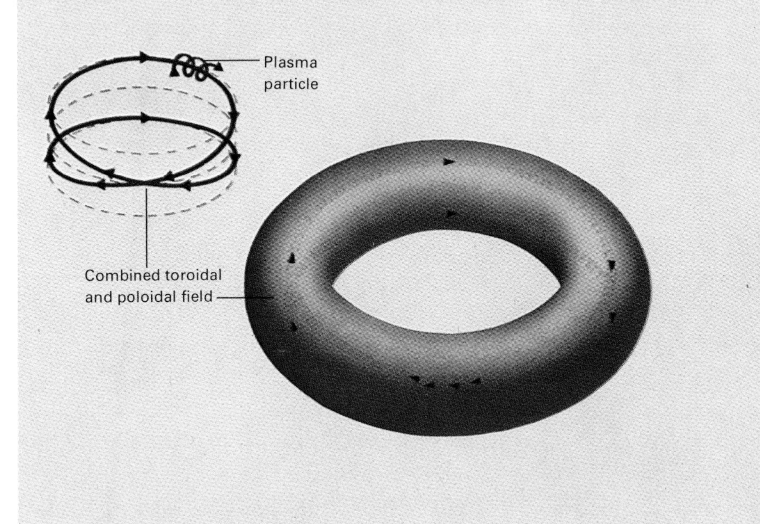

The two fields combine, forming a complex field around the center of the reactor. This field controls the paths of the circulating particles of plasma.

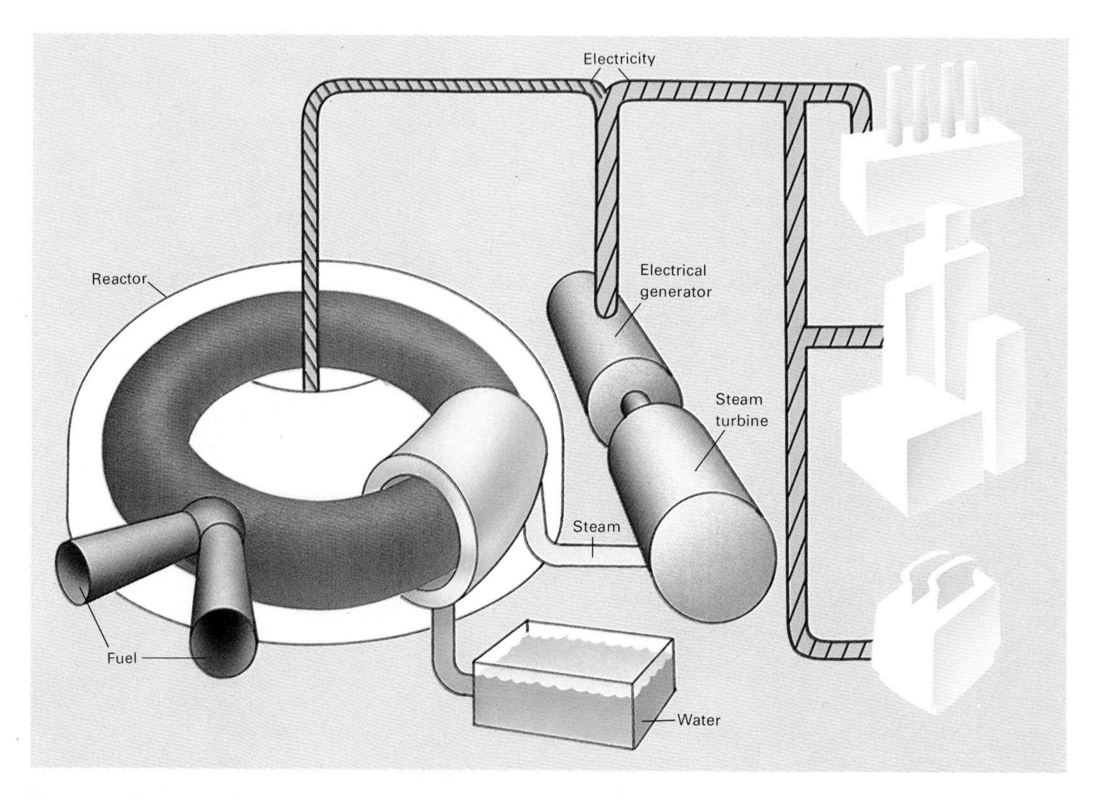

Power to Spare
The commercial reactor of the future may fuse cheap fuels, producing heat to boil water. The resulting steam would power turbines that drive electrical generators. The electricity produced would supply factories, offices, and homes, with energy left over to operate the reactor.

diek of the Princeton Plasma Physics Laboratory in New Jersey used a neutral beam injector to heat plasma to higher temperatures in the Princeton Large Torus (PLT), a tokamak that is 3 meters (10 feet) high and 6 meters (20 feet) across. The beams heated the plasma to 75 million°C (135 million°F.).

Present neutral beam injection systems are too inefficient to use in a commercial reactor. As a result, physicists are experimenting with radio frequency (RF) heating. In this technique, radio waves are transmitted into the plasma at frequencies that correspond to the frequencies at which particles spiral around field lines. When the radio wave's frequency matches a particle's frequency, the particle gets accelerated to higher energy, thereby heating the plasma.

Other tokamak experimenters are trying to replace the pulsing of electrical current through horizontal electromagnets that makes plasma electrons circulate around the torus. Tokamaks can force electrons to circulate for only a few seconds. Then the magnetic bottle falls apart, so the experimenters must reset the machine and start another cycle of confinement and heating. Operating the reactor in this way requires much more energy than the machine would need if the electrons flowed continuously. One way to provide steady flow is to use radio waves to drive the plasma electrons around the torus. Wave guide antennas near the outer edge of the plasma generate traveling radio waves that push the electrons along.

Still other experimenters have studied ways to increase tokamak efficiency. Physicists evaluate reactor efficiency according to the term *beta,* which represents the pressure that the hot plasma exerts divided by the pressure of the magnetic field that confines the plasma. The output power of a reactor is proportional to the square of the plasma pressure. Thus, if beta is doubled without increasing the magnetic field pressure, output power is quadrupled. The electromagnets that set up and maintain this field consume a great deal of energy. So researchers want to make beta as large as possible.

All these results have provided the basis for the next generation of tokamaks now under construction. The Tokamak Fusion Test Reactor (TFTR) at Princeton Plasma Physics Laboratory will be 6 meters (20 feet) high and 12 meters (40 feet) across and will cost almost $500 million. Scientists expect the TFTR to heat plasma to the break-even point in early 1986. Its neutral beam heaters will put 33-million watts of power into the plasma for one second. Plasma current — the flow of plasma electrons — will be 2.5 million amperes. The entire experiment will require almost 2 billion watts during its two-second pulse — enough power, if used continuously, to supply a city of 200,000 people. In this experiment, the deuterium neutral beam will heat a tritium plasma to reactor temperatures, and the fusion power produced will be approximately equal to the power required to heat the plasma.

Meanwhile, the European Community (Common Market) is building the Joint European Torus (JET) near Oxford, England. Plasma current will be 4 million amperes and the plasma will be heated with RF waves. Experiments will start in mid-1983.

The Japanese Atomic Energy Research Institute is building a $1-billion device called JT-60 that will be about the same size as the TFTR and expects to start operating it in 1985. The JT-60 will be capable of either high-power pulses for 10 seconds, or could operate continuously at 30 per cent of peak power. Russia's next tokamak, the T-15, will be between the PLT and the TFTR in size and will be ready to operate in 1984.

Experiments are continuing on two other types of toroidal reactors — the stellarator, which uses steady current through twisted electromagnets to help shape the field that confines the plasma; and the Elmo Bumpy Torus (EBT), which works like a combination mirror device and stellarator. About 20 vertical coils wound on the EBT's toroidal tube produce a toroidal field with a mirrorlike zone between adjacent coils.

Physicists are almost certain that some kind of reactor will ignite plasma before 1995. Scientists and engineers then will attack the technological and construction problems. If they succeed, shortly after the turn of the century, someone may push a button that sends a surge of power into a plasma deep inside a full-sized commercial fusion reactor, igniting the earth's first cosmic fire.

Diversifying Our Defenses

By Leroy E. Hood

Through an ingenious series of combinations and mutations, the body manipulates a limited number of genes to produce an infinite variety of antibodies

It was the Christmas season in 1891, and the happy songs of schoolchildren echoed through the streets of Berlin, Germany. One child, whom we shall call Anna, was not caroling with her classmates, however. She was in bed with a sore throat, fever, and aching muscles. Within a day, her condition had worsened. Her parents took her to a clinic where a doctor gravely delivered his diagnosis. Anna had diphtheria, a disease for which there was no cure.

The doctor summoned a young bacteriologist, Emil von Behring, who had been able to cure diphtheria in experimental animals, and Anna's parents gave Von Behring permission to try a daring new procedure on the girl. Von Behring had previously injected a sheep with the diphtheria bacterium, *Corynebacterium diphtheriae*. He removed some of the sheep's blood and injected this blood into Anna on Christmas night. By New Year's Day her condition had improved quite remarkably.

Anna's dramatic recovery was more than just a lucky break. It showed that the blood of the sheep had produced a substance that protected against diphtheria. This was the first demonstration of the important role that such substances, known as antibodies, play in the human body's defense system.

Antibodies are protein molecules produced in vertebrates—animals with backbones—by a certain type of white blood cell that originates in the bone marrow. Antibodies are Y-shaped, with a "tail" and two "arms." Each arm has a unique shape that enables it to chemically lock onto specific molecules on the surface of substances—such as viruses, bacteria, or chemicals—that have invaded the body. These invading molecules are called antigens. The lock between antibody and antigen triggers a sequence of events that destroys the antigen and eliminates it from the body. Thus, antibodies play a major role in protecting us against diseases such as colds, influenza, and measles.

Decades before scientists could see the antibody structure, they speculated about its form. They realized that antibody molecules were somehow able to recognize the specific structures of millions of different antigens. Was there one extremely versatile antibody or were there millions of different antibodies? Paul Ehrlich, a German bacteriologist, proposed the first explanation for how antibodies work. He described them as "magic bullets" that protected the body against antigens without harming its own tissues. He theorized that custom-tailored antibodies are fashioned to fit any type of antigen.

In the 1920s and 1930s, German immunologist Karl Landsteiner proved that Ehrlich's theory was correct. He injected a rabbit with a certain chemical, waited a short time, and extracted a sample of the animal's blood. Then he added the chemical to the blood sample in a laboratory dish and waited for a reaction. The blood cells formed "clumps" in the dish, indicating that antibodies in the blood had attached to the chemical molecules.

Landsteiner then changed the molecular structure of the chemical slightly and repeated the experiment. He found that the rabbit produced antibodies to the new chemical. As he repeated this procedure with different molecules, Landsteiner demonstrated that rabbits—and other vertebrates as well—could make antibodies to an extensive variety of antigens.

The author:
Leroy E. Hood is professor of biology and chairman of the Department of Biology at California Institute of Technology in Pasadena.

Once scientists had been confronted with proof that the body could make a huge number—possibly millions—of antibodies, they began to speculate as to how the body did this. The first reasonable theory was offered in the 1930s and 1940s by biochemists Felix Hurwitz and Linus Pauling. They proposed that the body had only one gene for all antibodies. A gene is a molecule of deoxyribonucleic acid (DNA) that contains the instructions for producing a body substance. Pauling and Hurwitz theorized that this antibody gene produced millions of "blank" antibody molecules that did not assume

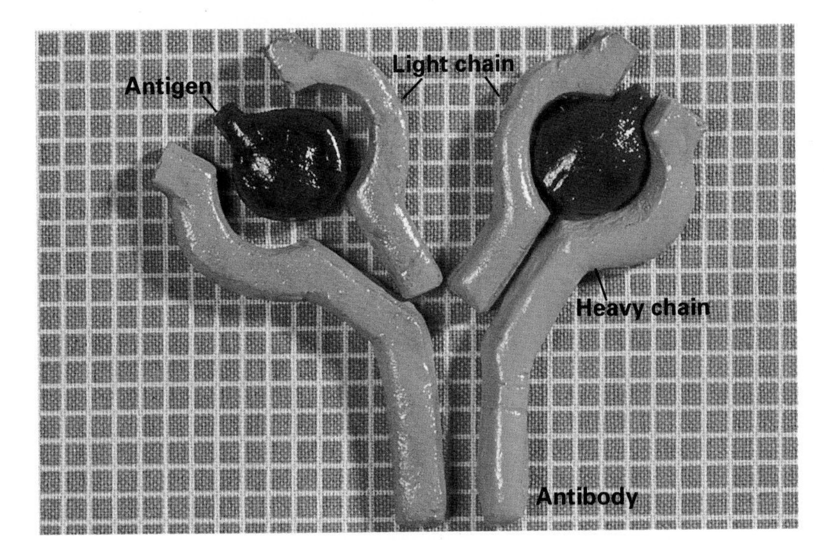

The Antibody Anatomy The Y-shaped antibody molecule is composed of two light chains and two heavy chains in a unique clawlike configuration that enables it to lock onto a particular antigen with exquisite precision.

their three-dimensional form until they came in contact with an antigen. The antibody then folded itself around a particular antigen.

This theory survived until the early 1960s when Edward Haber, a young immunologist at the National Institutes of Health (NIH) in Bethesda, Md., proved it wrong. Haber reasoned that if an antibody molecule to a particular antigen were unfolded it could not refold in the same way unless the corresponding antigen were present. However, when he unfolded an antibody through a chemical process in an antigen-free solution, he found that the antibody readily resumed its original shape. It did not rely on the antigen to give it form.

About the same time, immunologists Neils K. Jerne of Denmark, David W. Talmadge of the University of Denver, and Sir McFarlane Burnet of Australia proposed another idea—that each antibody-producing cell in the body made a distinct type of antibody molecule. They theorized that, because the body appeared to be capable of making millions of different types of antibodies, it must also be able to produce millions of different types of antibody-producing cells. The antigen wandered among these myriad cells until it chanced to hook up with its perfect antibody match protruding from the surface of one particular cell. The antigen-antibody connection stimulated that particular antibody-producing cell to reproduce, forming thousands of clones, or exact copies of itself, each with antibodies identical to the original.

This theory of antibody production is still widely accepted. However, it does not explain how the body stores and processes the plans to create 10 million types of antibody molecules. Such a task would seem to require the body's entire store of DNA, leaving none to program for blue eyes, brown hair, freckles, or other human traits.

In the mid-1960s, scientists began to search for an explanation. They were aided by the discovery of a type of tumor called a my-

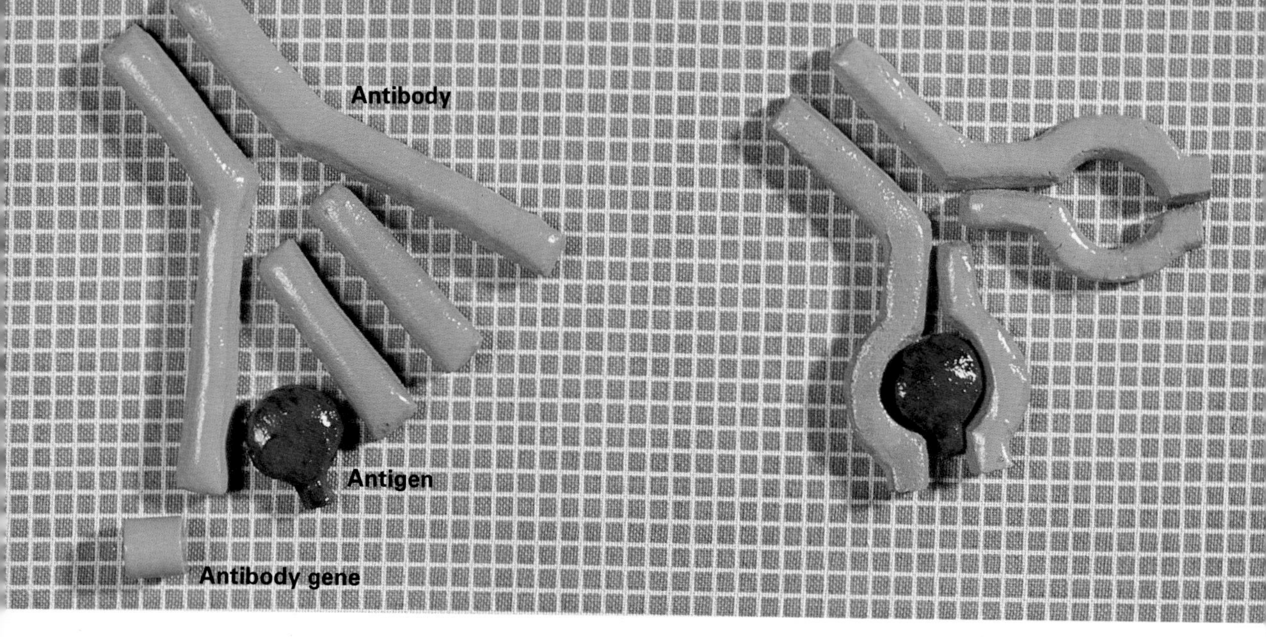

How Antibodies Adapt: Two Theories (Both Wrong)
An early theory of antibody diversity, *above,* held that all antibodies are coded by one gene and that each antibody is a "blank" until it comes in contact with an antigen. It derives its unique shape by forming itself around that antigen. A later theory, *opposite page,* stated that each antibody is coded by a separate gene and is produced in quantity only after it comes in contact with the antigen it matches.

eloma—a cancerous form of the human antibody-producing cell. These tumors could be implanted in mice, where they flourished—each producing large quantities of a specific antibody molecule.

This store of antibodies provided researchers with material for new types of analysis that would reveal the size, chemical charge, and other features of a protein molecule or determine the order of amino acids, or chemical building blocks, in the protein. Rodney Porter of Oxford University in England and Gerald M. Edelman of Rockefeller University in New York City carried out studies that revealed that each antibody molecule was made up of two distinct protein chains—a shorter chain, termed a light chain, and a longer chain, termed a heavy chain.

An analysis of the amino-acid sequence of the antibody by Frank Putnam of the University of Indiana in Bloomington and Norbert Hilschmann of The Rockefeller Institute revealed that each chain was divided into two sections. When they compared the structures of three antibody light chains, they found that one section of these chains had more or less the same sequence of amino acids. They called this section the constant region. However, they found that the composition of the other region of each chain varied from antibody to antibody. So they named that section the variable region. Moreover, the scientists soon realized that the antibody's form had a great deal to do with its function. The variable region, with its unique structure in each antibody, furnished a perfect lock for a particular antigen. The constant region, with its consistent chemical message, sounded a universal alarm to the rest of the immune system once the antibody had made contact with an antigen.

The discovery of the variable and constant regions gave rise to further speculation at research institutions around the world. At that time, in 1965, I was just beginning my graduate work with immunologists William J. Dreyer and J. Claude Bennett, who headed a

research team at California Institute of Technology (Caltech) in Pasadena. Dreyer and Bennett developed a revolutionary hypothesis. They suggested that two genes were required to code for each chain — one for the variable region and one for the constant region. Therefore not one, but four genes were required to code for each antibody. This theory was heretical because there was no evidence to indicate that an antibody — or any other protein — required more than one gene. Moreover, it was the first suggestion that at least some vertebrate genes are split, that is, that they have two or more coding regions separated by segments of DNA with no known function. However, research has since determined that most genes in eucaryotes—organisms whose cells have a definite nucleus—are split.

The Dreyer and Bennett hypothesis also suggested that the genes in eucaryotic cells are not stable, but that DNA sequences within them can be rearranged during differentiation — the stage when the cells of an embryo begin to take on their permanent designations as skin cells, bone cells, blood cells, or cells of other systems. All cells contain the body's entire genetic repertoire but, during differentiation, certain genes in each cell "turn on" to give that cell its particular character. Dreyer and Bennett proposed that the variable- and constant-region genes were widely separated in the DNA of the germ cells — the egg and sperm — but as antibody-producing cells developed, these two genes rearranged and moved closer together. They held that the genes' rearrangement was basic to the cell's ability to produce antibodies.

In the 10 years following the announcement of this hypothesis, my laboratory — initially at NIH and then at Caltech — and those of Donald Capra at the University of Texas Health Science Center in Dallas and Stuart Rudiboff of NIH continued to study the amino-acid sequences of antibody variable regions. These studies suggested that the antibodies were encoded by different families of genes for the heavy chains and light chains. The genes in these families code for similar, but not identical, proteins. When the gene for an entire antibody is put together in the antibody-producing cell, the genes for each chain are first formed separately. One light-chain-variable-region gene is chosen from its gene family — in much the same way that, in stringing a necklace, you might choose a bead from a collection that is similar in size and shape but different in pattern. The chosen variable-region gene then combines with a constant-region gene to form the composite light-chain gene. The composite heavy-chain gene forms similarly. The cell reads the genes to produce light chains and heavy chains which it joins to form antibodies.

These amino-acid studies also suggested that to create these different gene combinations, the cell must be using some fascinating methods of maneuvering DNA. We wanted to find out exactly what these DNA mechanisms were. Just as the myeloma tumors had provided scientists with an unlimited supply of antibodies to study, a new technique called genetic engineering that was developed in the mid-1970s promised to provide us with a seemingly endless supply of antibody genes for our research. Using genetic-engineering techniques, we were able to take a gene for a given antibody and splice it into a plasmid — a ring of bacterial DNA. The plasmids are added to bacteria cultures and are absorbed by the bacteria. As the bacteria reproduce, each clone also makes many copies of the antibody gene. Soon, large quantities are available for chemical analysis.

In the mid-1970s, Susumu Tonegawa of the Basel Institute for Immunology in Switzerland and Philip Leder of the NIH began to use genetic engineering to study light-chain composite genes. They discovered that the light-chain gene in the germ cell has three distinct coding sequences — for variable-, joining-, and constant-region genes — that are separated by sequences of DNA that have no apparent function.

Tonegawa and Leder discovered that, in the differentiated antibody-producing cell, this light-chain composite gene has been altered. The inactive DNA segment between the variable and joining gene is gone and the two are connected. However, the inactive DNA segment between the joining- and constant-region genes remains — to be taken out later when the antibody-producing cell transcribes the DNA instructions and puts the light chain of the antibody molecule together.

Our laboratory began to study heavy-chain composite genes in 1976. We found that heavy-chain genes are similar to the light-chain genes except for two features. The heavy-chain gene contains a third segment, called a diversity gene, that codes for part of the variable region of the chain. The variable, diversity, and joining regions in germ cells are separated by inactive DNA. The antibody-producing cell must cut these out and join the variable, diversity, and joining genes together to form a variable heavy-chain gene.

We also found that, while the light chain has only one constant-region gene, the heavy chain has five—these code for different classes of antibody molecules that operate in different parts of the body and carry out different functions. Initially, the cell produces only one of the five classes of antibody molecules. This one has a large, heavy tail that cannot squeeze through the lining of the blood vessels. When the body requires an antibody for a specific location, for example, the lining of the nose where an attack of cold germs is underway, the antibody-producing cell will provide a different class of antibody—perhaps one with a tail to permeate the mucous membranes in the nose. To do this, a different constant-region gene takes the place of the original in the composite gene and programs a new lighter tail for the antibody.

Once we knew the form antibody genes take, our next mission was to explore just how antibodies themselves acquire so many different forms. Dreyer, Talmadge, and I suggested that this diversity was present very early—in the germ cell. We thought that each different antibody variable region was coded for by a distinct gene in these cells, and that, as the antibody-producing cell developed, only one of these enormous numbers of genes was turned on. A team consisting of Melvin Cohn of the Salk Institute for Biological Studies in La Jolla, Calif., and Gerald M. Edelman and Oliver Smithies of the University of Wisconsin in Madison proposed another theory—that there were only a few antibody genes, but that they mutated as the organism developed. A third team—immunologist Elvin A. Kabat of Columbia University in New York City, Don Capra at Southwestern Medical School in Dallas, and Thomas Kindt at NIH—proposed a third theory. They suggested that in either chain, any variable gene might connect to any joining gene. Since there are about 250 genes in the variable-gene family and 4 genes in the joining-gene family, there are about 250 × 4 or 1,000 possible combinations of the two genes for the variable region.

Our research and that of other groups in the past 10 years has indicated that all three theories are correct, and that antibody diversity is a result of their synthesis. The germ cells indeed carry a large number of genes for antibody production, which combine as the cells of the organism differentiate. The composite heavy chain gene forms from a constant-region gene, a joining-region gene, a diversity-region gene, and a variable-region gene. Initially, there is only 1 possible constant-region gene, but there is a selection of 4 joining-region genes, 10 diversity-region genes, and 250 variable-region genes available for assembling the composite gene.

If you were stringing together a four-bead gene necklace from these four different types of genes, you could see at once how many different combinations you could assemble. Your first choice is limited because there is only one constant bead available. The second choice is broader, because you have to choose from four different

Antibody Assembly Line

The genes that program each chain of an antibody are actually composites assembled from a large selection of smaller genes. The heavy-chain composite gene forms from four gene segments – 1 of 250 variable-region genes, 1 of 10 diversity-region genes, 1 of 4 joining-region genes, and 1 constant-region gene. One of 4 additional constant-region genes may be substituted later. The light-chain composite gene forms from three genes – 1 of 250 variable-region genes, 1 of 4 joining-region genes, and 1 constant-region gene. The cell assembles the two chains separately according to instructions carried by each composite gene. The antibody is formed as the two chains unite.

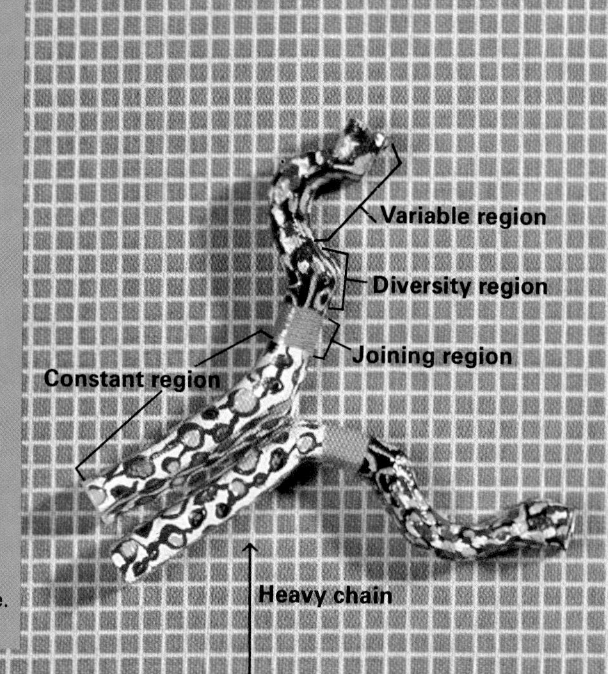

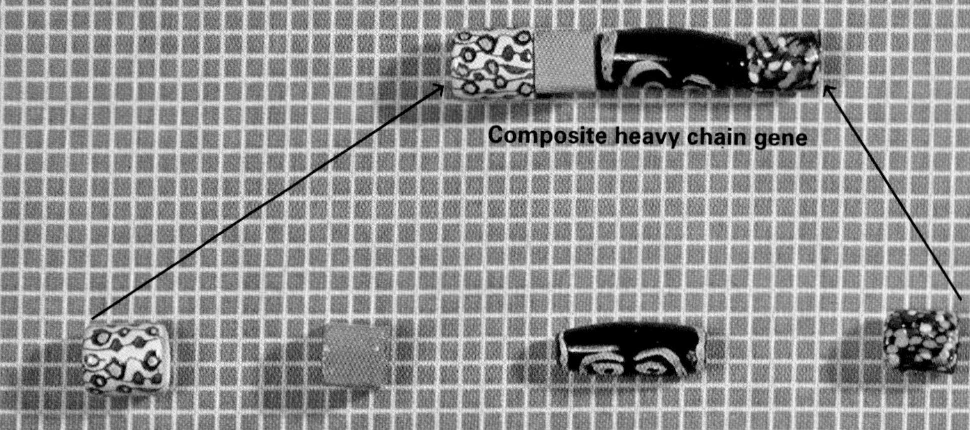

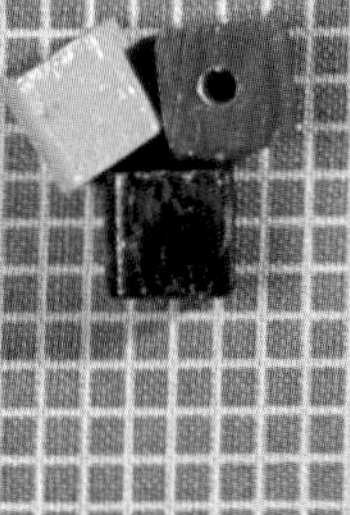

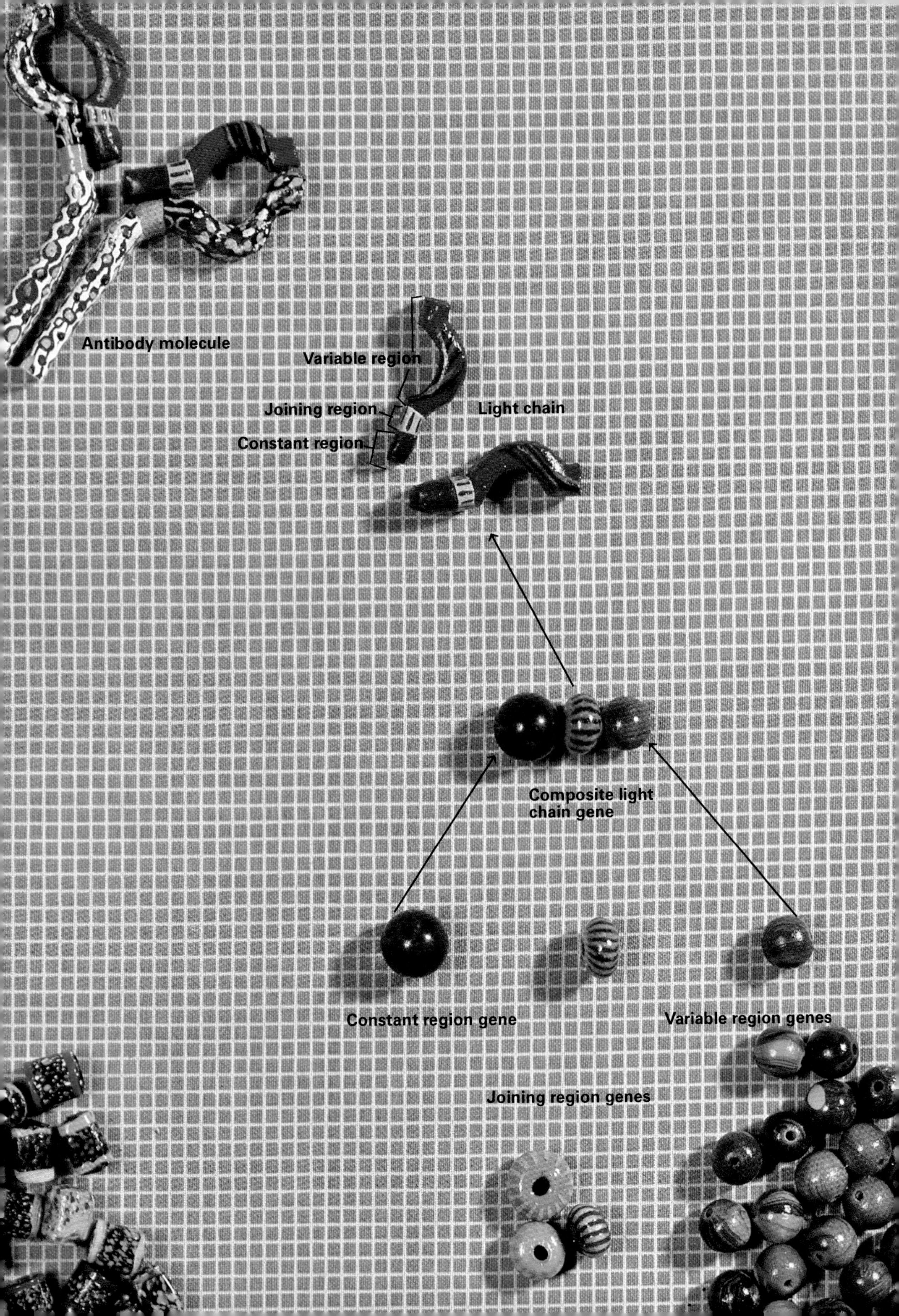
Antibody molecule
Variable region
Joining region
Light chain
Constant region
Composite light chain gene
Constant region gene
Variable region genes
Joining region genes

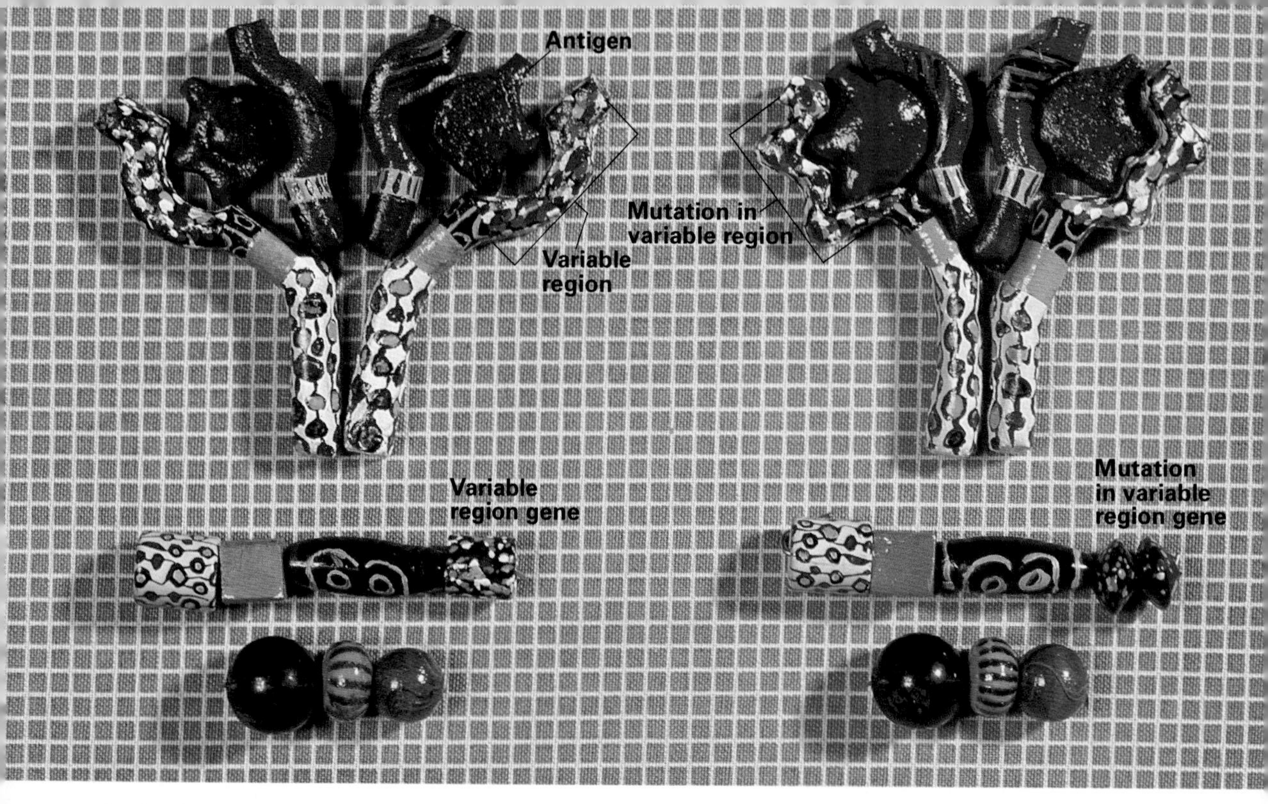

Further Fine-Tuning
A mutation in the variable-region gene may occur after the antibody has made contact with the antigen, thus altering that region to ensure a more precise fit.

joining-region beads. You make your choice from that group and add it to the strand beside the constant-region bead. Next, you select one of the 10 diversity-region beads and string it on after the other two. Your final selection offers a choice of 250 beads. You choose one bead from this enormous group and add it to the other three. You have completed your heavy-chain gene necklace, and it is unique. Your particular necklace is one of the 1 × 4 × 10 × 250 or 10,000 four-bead necklaces that you could have strung using that particular collection of beads. Similarly, there are 10,000 possible heavy-chain composite genes, enabling the body to produce 10,000 different heavy chains.

The light-chain gene assortment offers a similar, but more limited, choice — 1 constant-region gene, 4 joining-region genes, and 250 variable-region genes. If you were stringing a gene-bead necklace from this assortment, you could assemble 1 × 4 × 250 or 1,000 different 3-bead necklaces.

If you were to make a double-stranded choker with one 4-bead strand and one 3-bead strand, you would find that there are 1,000 × 10,000 or 10 million ways to do so. Thus, there are 10 million ways a cell can assemble an antibody from the possible light and heavy chains.

In 1979 Tonegawa, Leder, Martin Weigert of the Institute for Cancer Research in Fox Chase, Pa., and I demonstrated that antibodies can undergo one special type of mutation. It is called junctional diversification, because it occurs at the points connecting the variable and joining segments in the light-chain gene and the variable, diversity, and joining segments in the heavy-chain gene. During the joining process, the length of any of these genes may vary slightly. In assembling your gene-bead necklaces, for example, you might find that one of the beads was slightly longer than you had expected. To keep the necklace a uniform length, you would have to make the next bead slightly shorter.

When the cell goes about its business of converting the information in a composite gene containing such an irregularity, it changes the shape of the variable region of the antibody slightly. The antibody will then "fit" a slightly different type of antigen than before. This change in the gene takes place as the embryonic cell is being transformed into its antibody-producing form.

Tonegawa suggested in 1978 that a second type of mutation occurs. David Baltimore of MIT and I demonstrated in 1981 that this second type of mutation takes place much later in the cell's development—after it has completely assembled the antibody. The antibody has arrived at the cell surface and has made contact with a particular antigen. However, its grip on the antigen may be somewhat tenuous because it is not a perfect fit. The antibody gene in the nucleus changes and one of its variable segments is altered slightly. Thereafter, all antibodies will be produced according to this revised genetic plan and will hold the antigens fast.

Each time either of these mutations occurs, a new antibody is born. When we consider that a mutation may occur regularly in any of the 10 million genetically possible antibodies, the number of antibody molecules that the body can produce becomes truly staggering—if not infinite. Moreover, each antibody in this infinite assortment may change classes by taking on a new constant or tail region.

Thus we have discovered that the gene system employs several ingenious maneuvers in its quest to diversify. Gene segments can combine to produce thousands of different variable region genes; the resultant variable gene can ultimately join with any of five constant genes to form a heavy chain gene; and the particular heavy chain programmed by that gene can join with any of thousands of light chains to form an antibody.

Witnessing the antibody network's skill at forming combinations leads us to wonder if this ability extends to other body systems as well. At present we do not know. But it seems probable that, like the antibody genes, other multi-combinational families arose to handle the demand for very specialized systems as complicated organisms developed.

The search for such families in the brain is just beginning, but if they are found, they will provide fundamental insights into how the brain carries out its many complex functions. Future research may determine that our ability to reason, like our ability to fight disease, may reside in our genes' ability to amplify a limited amount of information into an infinite store of knowledge.

The Brightest Beacons

By Harding E. Smith

Mysterious and extremely powerful objects called quasars may reward radio and optical astronomers with answers to questions about the early universe

The "most distant object in the universe," according to the *Guinness Book of World Records*, is one of a class of celestial phenomena discovered only a little more than 20 years ago. The discovery of quasars opened up a whole new field of astronomical research. However, despite intensive study with many types of telescopes during the past 20 years, these baffling objects continue to pose more questions than astronomers have answers. Are they really the most distant and most luminous — and therefore the most energetic — objects in the entire universe? If so, what is the source of their tremendous energy output?

Radio signals emitted by quasars gave astronomers the first clue to their existence, but it took a long time to find that clue. Radio astronomy developed into an active astronomical discipline in the late 1940s and early 1950s. Early radio telescopes were not so precise as those we use now, and it was difficult to pinpoint the celestial sources of the radio noise they detected.

In 1960, astronomer Allan R. Sandage of California's Mount Wilson and Palomar Observatories, using the giant 5-meter (200-inch) telescope on Palomar Mountain, photographed the region of the sky where the radio source 3C48 had been discovered. (3C48 stands for the 48th radio source in the third list of sources compiled by radio astronomers at the University of Cambridge in England.)

To his surprise, Sandage found an inconspicuous blue, starlike object right at the position of the radio source. Shortly thereafter, a team of radio astronomers headed by Cyril Hazard, working at the Australian National Radio Observatory at Parkes in New South Wales, used their 64-meter (210-foot) radio telescope to obtain a precise position for the radio source 3C273. They noted that a somewhat more intense, but still faint, starlike object appeared at the position of 3C273. Although it is still the brightest quasar known, 3C273 is more than 250 times fainter than the faintest star our unaided eyes can see. If these objects are not stars, what are they? Astronomers coined the terms *quasi-star* or *quasi-stellar object*, which were shortened to quasar.

Astronomy is an observational science; astronomers cannot construct an experiment to test a physical theory as elementary particle physicists or molecular biologists do. We must be satisfied with analyzing the light coming from stars, galaxies, and quasars. One of the most powerful techniques available to observational astronomers, spectral analysis, breaks up the light from a distant object into its electromagnetic spectrum — a visual display of its component wavelengths. The shortest wavelengths in the visible part of the spectrum are at the blue end, and the longest are at the red end. Below the blue and above the red are, respectively, the ultraviolet and the infrared regions, which are also used in these analyses.

Atoms emit or absorb light in specific patterns at wavelengths that vary from element to element. For example, the pattern of oxygen atoms is different from that of carbon, which is different from that of hydrogen. The spectrum of light from a particular element is as characteristic of that element as a fingerprint is of an individual. By studying the spectrum of a star or galaxy, astronomers can determine which elements are present in it and in what amounts. They can also learn what conditions exist in that object, such as its temperature and density.

The author:
Harding E. Smith is an associate professor of physics at the Center for Astrophysics and Space Sciences of the University of California in San Diego.

When astronomers first analyzed the spectra of the quasars, they were perplexed. The spectra certainly were not like those of ordinary stars. The spectra of most stars show absorption features — dark lines in parts of the spectrum where light has been absorbed by atoms of elements in gaseous form in the outer atmosphere of the star. But the quasars' spectra show the opposite — strong, broad, bright features in emission. Moreover, their emission features do not appear at wavelengths corresponding to features produced in such abundant elements as hydrogen, carbon, and oxygen in the laboratory. Nor do the features appear at the same wavelengths in all of the known quasars.

In early 1963, astronomer Maarten Schmidt of the California Institute of Technology (Caltech) in Pasadena cracked the code of the quasars' emission features. Sitting in his office staring at a photograph of the spectrum of the quasar 3C273, Schmidt recognized a familiar pattern among the spectral features. It was the well-known pattern of light produced by hydrogen atoms — but the pattern was shifted in wavelength toward the red, or longer wavelength, end of the spectrum by 16 per cent.

Schmidt checked his result very carefully, realizing that if it was correct, he had made an extremely important discovery. After confirming his result, he excitedly hurried down the hall to the office of Jesse L. Greenstein, another Caltech astronomer then studying these mysterious objects. Together they examined a photograph Greenstein had obtained of the spectrum of 3C48. They quickly found that 3C48 had an even higher red shift — 37 per cent.

Schmidt was excited because the red shifts implied that quasars must be very distant objects. A red shift is produced in the spectrum if an object is receding, or moving away from us. As an object moves away, its velocity "stretches out" the light waves emitted by that object, shifting them toward longer wavelengths, toward the red. (Objects moving toward us show blue shifts.) The red shift of 16 per cent for 3C273 means that 3C273 is moving away from us with a velocity of 16 per cent of the speed of light.

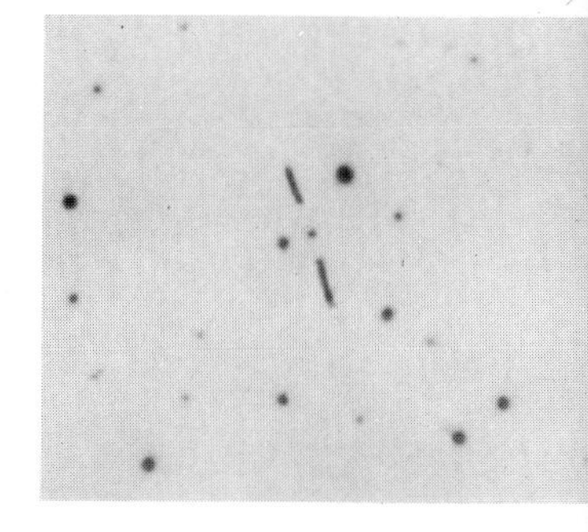

Quasar OQ172 (between the lines), the "most distant object in the universe" according to the 1982 *Guinness Book of World Records,* is moving away at a velocity over 90 per cent of the speed of light. Its detected light was emitted about 18 billion years ago.

Objects recede from us due to the expansion of the universe. Early in this century, astronomers discovered that galaxies in all directions are moving away from our Milky Way galaxy. The faster an object is moving away, the more distant it is. Such distances are called cosmological because they result directly from the expansive nature of the universe, or cosmos. The expansion is such that the distance of a galaxy is directly proportional to its velocity. The red shift of 3C273 implied an incredible distance of 3 billion light-years. (A light-year is the distance light travels in a year at a speed of 299,792 kilometers [186,282 miles] per second.)

Since Schmidt's discovery, many quasars with even higher red shifts have been found. The highest red shift recorded as of early 1982 is that of a quasar known as OQ172, discovered in 1972 by a team of astronomers headed by E. Margaret Burbidge and Joseph Wampler of the University of California, San Diego. OQ172 has a red shift of 3.53. This implies a velocity of more than 90 per cent of the speed of light, or a distance of about 18 billion light-years. When the velocity of an object is much less than the speed of light, as is the case with 3C273, the percentage of red shift is the same as the

Reading the Red Shift

In their efforts to learn about the universe, astronomers are restricted in large measure to analysis of the light coming from the distant objects they are studying. Fortunately, nature has provided several invaluable tools that aid us in deciphering the message in the light received.

One particularly important tool is the red shift. The motion of any body that is emitting waves of any kind causes a shift in the frequency or wavelength of those waves as detected by a stationary observer. Motion away from the observer stretches out the waves toward lower frequency or longer wavelength. Motion toward an observer compresses the waves, shortening the wavelength and increasing the frequency. Most of us have experienced this phenomenon with sound, which is called the Doppler effect, when standing near a railroad track as a passing train sounds its whistle. As the train approaches, the Doppler effect shifts the whistle sound to shorter wavelengths and it seems to have a higher pitch. When the train is moving away, the whistle sound is shifted to longer wavelengths and seems to have a lower pitch. As the train passes, we hear the whistle drop in pitch from the high approaching pitch to the lower receding pitch.

The same thing happens to light. Objects moving away from us have their light waves stretched out to longer wavelengths; objects moving toward us have their light waves compressed to shorter wavelengths. In the visible region of the electromagnetic spectrum, red is the longest wavelength light and blue or violet is the shortest wavelength. Therefore, we speak of objects moving away from us or toward us as having "red shifts" or "blue shifts," respectively. We detect these shifts because each element emits or absorbs light at certain characteristic wavelengths.

When we measure the light coming from an astronomical object, we identify the pattern of emission or absorption from the various elements, determine whether it is shifted toward the red or toward the blue, and thus deduce the object's direction of motion.

In the early 1900s, astronomers deduced that the universe is expanding. Galaxies in all directions are moving away from our galaxy.

Because they are moving away, their spectral features exhibit red shifts. Astronomer Edwin P. Hubble demonstrated in 1929 that the expansion of the universe is such that the distance of an object is directly proportional to its velocity, and thus to its red shift. This means that the objects moving the fastest are the farthest away. Therefore, by measuring the red shift of a galaxy, we can determine its distance. If quasars' red shifts are due to the expansion of the universe, then the amount of the red shift tells us the quasars' velocity and distance. The most-studied quasar, 3C273, with a red shift of 16 per cent, is moving away from us at about 16 per cent of the speed of light, or about 48,000 kilometers (29,800 miles) per second. This is a distance of 3 billion light-years. [Harding E. Smith]

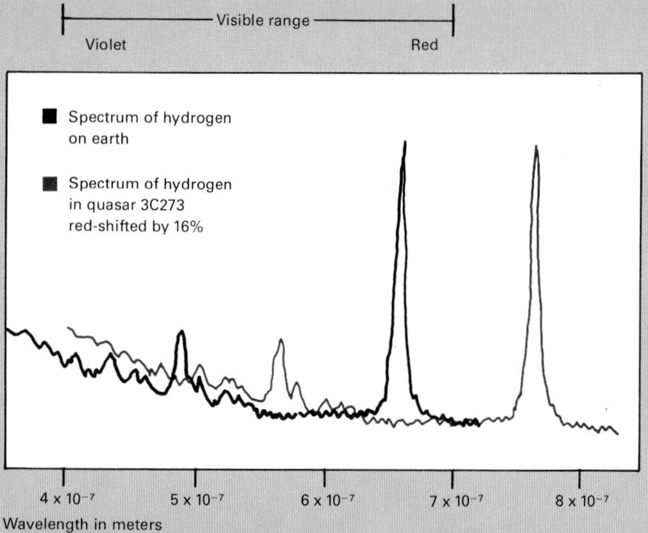

Comparing spectra of hydrogen in emission features from quasar 3C273 with hydrogen's known wavelength on the earth led to the discovery that the element's characteristic line was red-shifted in emission by 16 per cent. This indicated that 3C273 is moving away from the earth at 16 per cent of the speed of light.

percentage of the speed of light. However, when velocity approaches the speed of light, as in the remarkable OQ172, the percentage of red shift increases by a much greater amount than the percentage of the speed of light.

The fact that we can see quasars at great distances implies that they must be extremely luminous—that is, the total amount of light energy they expend per second is enormous. A galaxy of hundreds of billions of stars would appear a thousand times fainter than 3C273 at a distance of 3 billion light-years. The light from a galaxy as far from the earth as OQ172 would be undetectable even with the largest telescopes and most sensitive detector systems.

We also know that the quasars must be very small, because of the way in which their brightnesses vary with time. Nearly all quasars' visible-light output "flickers" over a time scale of a few months. Some quasars, however, become twice as bright or more in only a few weeks. Since its discovery in 1965, the quasar 3C279 has been noted for its variability. Astronomers Lola Eachus and William Liller of the Harvard-Smithsonian Center for Astrophysics in Cambridge, Mass., were interested in the history of 3C279. In 1975, they examined photographs of the area of the sky containing 3C279 that were taken long before the discovery of quasars. The astronomers discovered that in 1936, and again in 1937, 3C279 had undergone incredible outbursts, brightening by more than 25 times in less than one month.

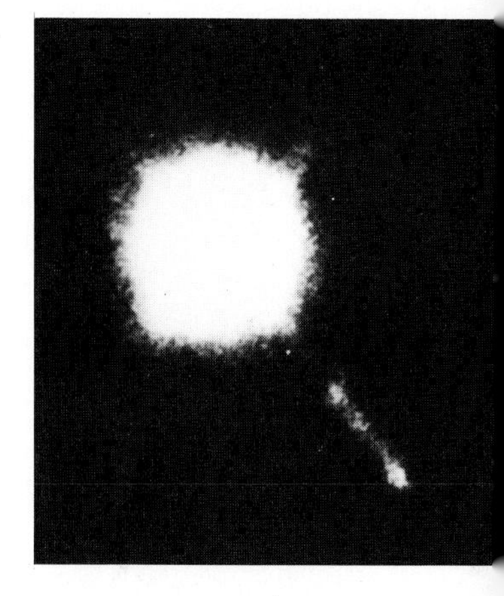

Matching radio emission from two regions of a stellar source with a photo showing a starlike object and its associated luminous jet in the same location provided an early clue that 3C273 was a quasar.

Because light travels at a definite speed, it takes a certain amount of time to travel across the source that emits it. An outburst of light emitted simultaneously at the front and back of a quasar's emitting region will reach an observer at different times, separated by the time it takes the light from the back to cross the source. An outburst will appear to occur during all the time it takes for the light from different regions to reach us. If 3C279's light is seen to vary over a few weeks, then the quasar must be smaller than a few light-weeks in size.

Since the early 1970s, astronomers have been using a technique called Very Long Baseline Interferometry (VLBI) to probe the centers of quasars. By linking a radio telescope from Goldstone in California with one in Bonn, West Germany—aided by as many as half a dozen telescopes in-between—astronomers synthesize a telescope that is equivalent in its ability to pinpoint radio sources to a radio telescope as big as the earth. Because of the difficulty of coordinating the use of these telescopes, and the complex nature of the observations, we can study only a few of the brightest radio quasars. When the array of telescopes is pointed at a quasar, we often find that the central region has a radio source consisting of two or more signals. In several cases, we have seen that in the months between one VLBI observation and another, the radio signals, and thus their source, appear to have moved. Knowing the distance of the quasar from its red shift, we can translate the change in position in the sky into the distance the source has moved. From the time it has taken, we can calculate the apparent velocity at which it is moving. This velocity often turns out to be greater than the speed of light — in apparent violation of physicist Albert Einstein's theories of relativity. In a 1981 study, Caltech radio astronomers reported that signals of 3C273's central radio sources are moving at a rate corresponding to a fantastically fast 9.6 times the speed of light.

Does this mean that Einstein was incorrect, that the speed-of-light "barrier" can be broken? Most astronomers and physicists think not. Einstein's theories of relativity have been extensively tested — on the earth in high-energy accelerators, by means of space probes in the solar system, and to some extent by observations outside the solar system. In all cases, the predictions have proved correct. There are theories that explain why some objects moving at close to the speed of light may appear to move faster than light, but no one has yet succeeded in developing a detailed theory for quasars. Until such a theory is worked out, this apparent superrelativistic, or faster-than-light, expansion will remain another unsolved part of the quasar puzzle.

Our idea that quasars are extremely bright and travel at a velocity apparently faster than light comes directly from our inference that they are very far away. If quasars were not so far away, many of the problems would be simplified. This possibility led astronomers to question whether the quasars' red shifts give us the correct distances. If the quasars' velocity is not due to the expansion of the universe, or if the red shift is produced by some other mechanism, then perhaps the quasars are much closer than we think.

Probably the leading proponent of the view that quasars are not as distant as they seem is astronomer Halton C. Arp of Hale Observatories in Pasadena, Calif. Since 1967, Arp has found a number of cases that seem to support his arguments. In one case, he found quasars with high red shifts that lie close to nearby galaxies with

Estimating Quasar Size
Because light travels at a constant speed, light from the front and back of an emitting region is seen at different times. If light emitted in one outburst from a quasar is observed to continue over a two-week period, light rays from the back of the quasar must have taken two weeks to reach the front. Therefore, the quasar must be no more than two light-weeks in size.

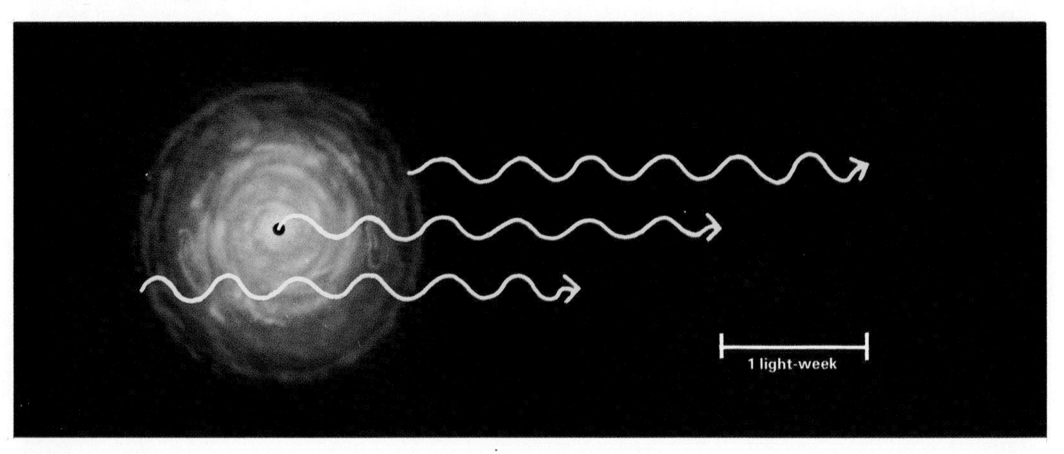

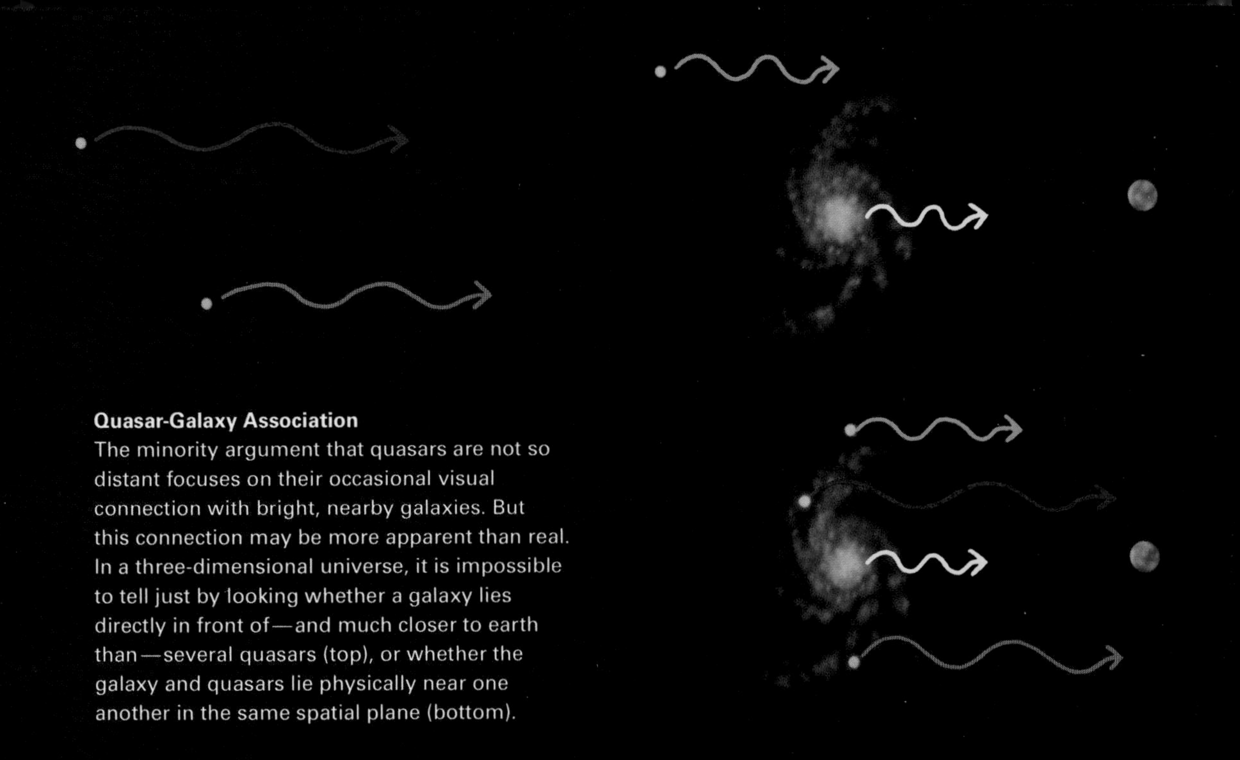

Quasar-Galaxy Association
The minority argument that quasars are not so distant focuses on their occasional visual connection with bright, nearby galaxies. But this connection may be more apparent than real. In a three-dimensional universe, it is impossible to tell just by looking whether a galaxy lies directly in front of—and much closer to earth than—several quasars (top), or whether the galaxy and quasars lie physically near one another in the same spatial plane (bottom).

lower red shifts; in another case, they appeared to actually lie within the spiral arms of a nearby galaxy; and in yet another case, a quasar appeared to be attached to a nearby galaxy by a bridge of luminous material. Arp argues that these cases are confirming evidence that quasars are relatively nearby objects. In any one case, it is quite difficult to prove that objects with different red shifts are physically associated. Still, the number of these cases that Arp has discovered is difficult to explain. If his ideas proved correct, the meaning of red shift would be changed completely.

Other astronomers maintain that these apparent associations are just coincidences, and insist that the quasars must be very distant. An important survey done in 1979 by astronomer Alan Stockton of the University of Hawaii in Honolulu showed that at least some quasars must be as far away as their red shifts imply. Stockton found that several low-red-shift quasars appear to be members of small groups of faint galaxies. He showed that, in nearly all cases, the galaxies have the same red shift as the quasar. This implies that the galaxies and quasar are associated, and that they lie at the distance determined by their common red shift.

The red-shift controversy originated in evidence from quasars' emission features. Absorption features in their spectra were subsequently found. Some quasars, particularly those with high red shifts, show regions in the spectrum where atoms of gas lying between us and the quasar have absorbed the light from the quasar. Many quasars have hundreds of such absorption features. Just as astrono-

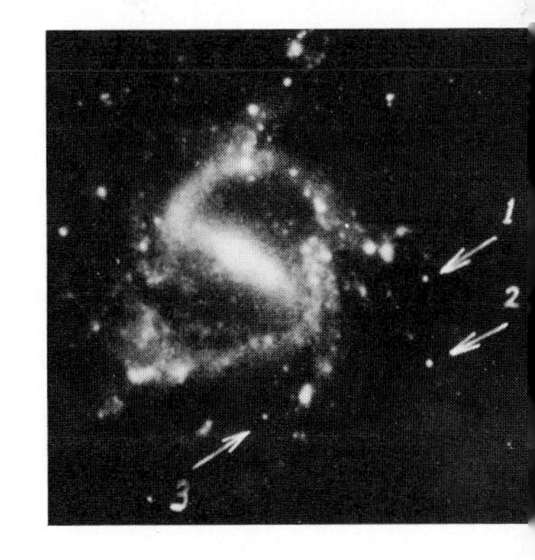

Three quasars that seem to be nestled in the arms of spiral galaxy NGC1073, only 75 million light-years away, have red shifts that place them more than 5 billion light-years away. Such juxtaposition of objects is cited as evidence that red shifts can be misleading by those who seek to prove that quasars are really close.

mers can recognize the characteristic patterns of a quasar's emission features and determine a red shift from them, they can also determine a red shift from the gas that is producing absorption. In nearly all cases, the red shifts found from the absorption features in the spectrum of a particular quasar are smaller than those found from the emission features of the quasar. Astronomers have suggested two possible origins for these absorption features.

One possibility is that the material is unrelated to the quasar, and just happens to be lying in a galaxy between us and the quasar. A galaxy that is closer to the earth than the quasar will have a red shift due to the expansion of the universe that is correspondingly smaller than the quasar's red shift. As the light from the quasar passes through the galaxy on its way to us, atoms in the galaxy will absorb light at their characteristic wavelengths.

We would then see these features at the red shift of the galaxy that produces the absorption. If this is in fact what is happening, it is very exciting because it means that studying the absorption features in the spectra of quasars can tell us something about galaxies that are too distant to be seen directly. Being so distant, those galaxies are very much younger than the nearer ones we have been able to study. Because all of the high-red-shift quasars that we know about have such absorption-line red-shift systems, this theory requires that galaxies cover enough of the sky so that the light from a quasar is certain to pass through a galaxy somewhere along its travels. We are not certain that galaxies can be so extensive.

The other theory is that the material producing the absorption comes from the quasar itself. This means that from the quasar's point of view, the absorbing material is moving toward us and away from the quasar. Such material must have been ejected from the quasar. The greater the difference between the emission red shift of the quasar and the absorption red shift, the greater the velocity with which the material must have been ejected. In some cases, this velocity approaches the speed of light. If this theory is correct, then quasars are even more fantastic than we had believed, because the energy required to eject such material at such great velocity would exceed even the quasars' luminous energy output.

Recent evidence suggests that perhaps both theories are correct. In a few cases, we have actually seen the galaxy that produces the absorption; in other cases, the properties of the absorbing material are so similar to those of the quasar that we are certain they must be associated. Many astronomers now believe that quasars are ejecting material, but only at a small fraction of the speed of light.

Oddly enough, although quasars were discovered by their emission of radio waves, most quasars are not strong radio sources. In early 1982, there were about 1,600 quasars cataloged. Many of them are radio sources, because it is easy to identify "radio loud" quasars. Astronomers estimate, however, that there are about 15 times as

A Quasar's Central Engine
The power source may be a massive black hole that continuously converts gravitational energy into other energy by unknown means as it sucks in hot swirling gas and simultaneously spews out streams of electrons traveling at speeds near that of light.

many "radio quiet" quasars. Two techniques have been used to find quasars without the clue of radio emissions.

When astronomers began to study quasars, they noted that one reason they look different from most normal stars is that they emit more light in the ultraviolet part of the spectrum than they do in the blue and yellow part. A special photographic technique makes use of this characteristic. Astronomers photograph areas of the sky through three separate filters—ultraviolet, blue, and yellow. Between each exposure they move the film slightly so that a triple image is recorded. Objects whose image appears brighter through the ultraviolet filter than through the blue and yellow filters are probably quasars. Astronomers check this by observing the red shift. Only

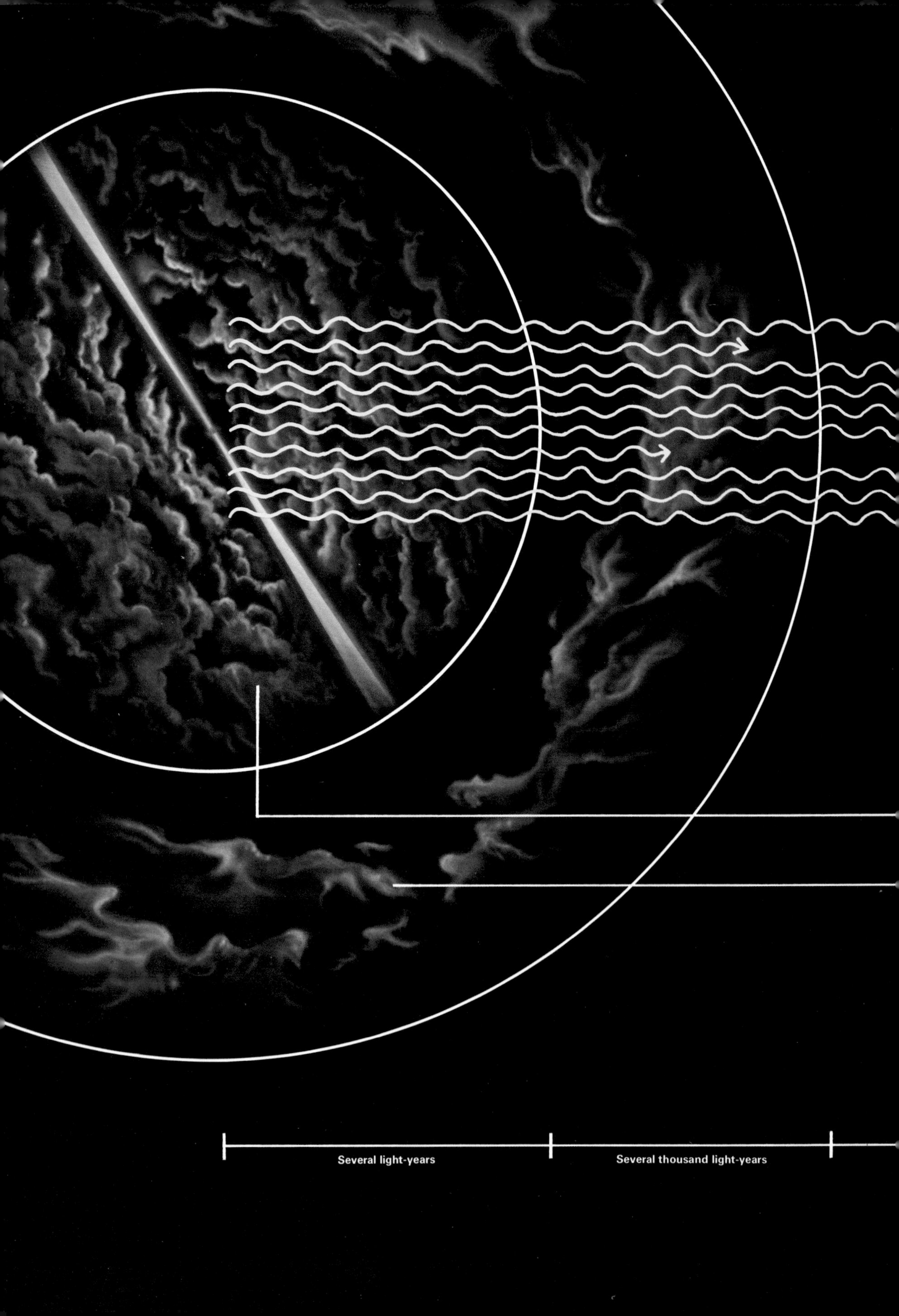
Several light-years
Several thousand light-years

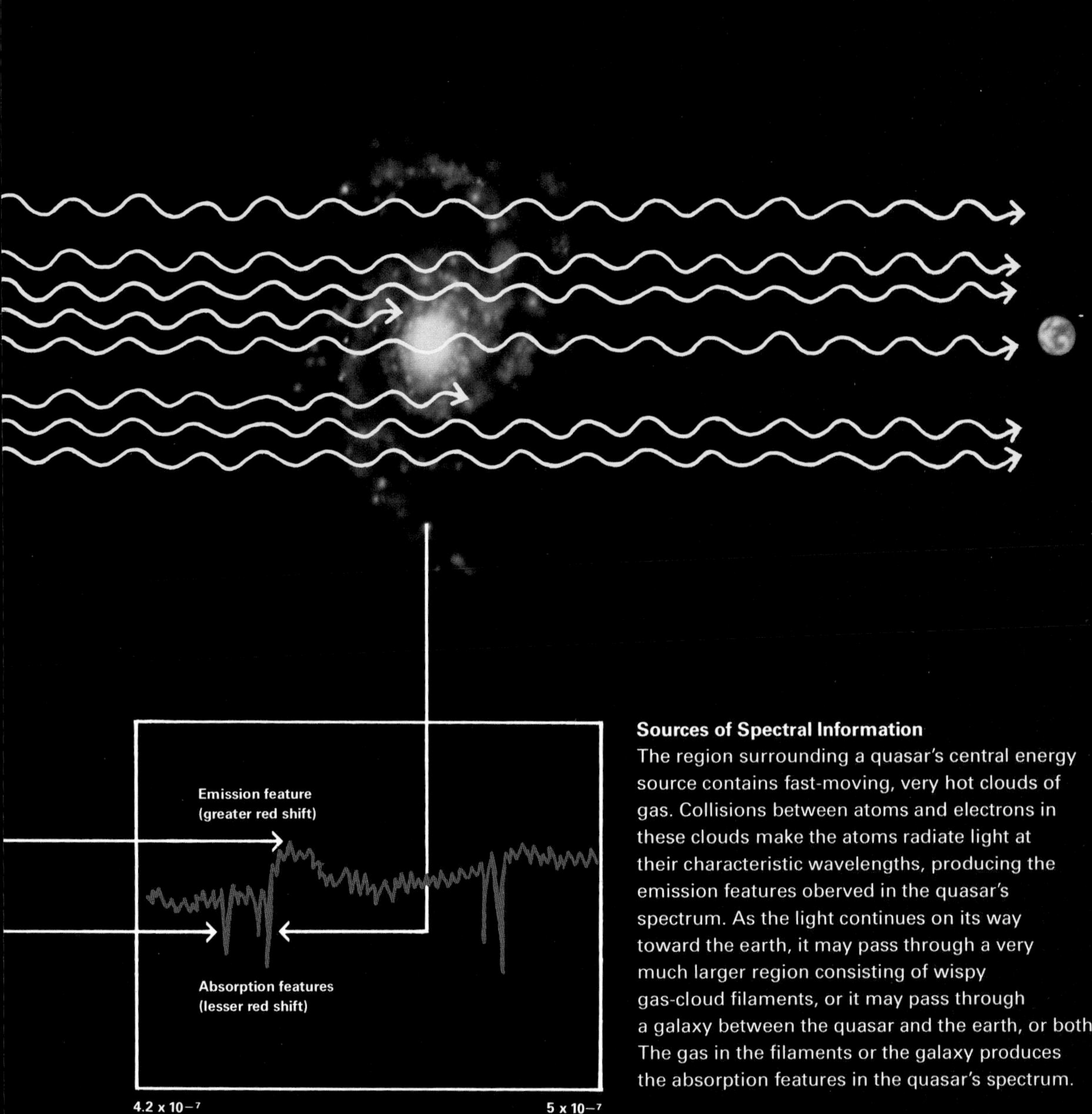

Sources of Spectral Information
The region surrounding a quasar's central energy source contains fast-moving, very hot clouds of gas. Collisions between atoms and electrons in these clouds make the atoms radiate light at their characteristic wavelengths, producing the emission features oberved in the quasar's spectrum. As the light continues on its way toward the earth, it may pass through a very much larger region consisting of wispy gas-cloud filaments, or it may pass through a galaxy between the quasar and the earth, or both The gas in the filaments or the galaxy produces the absorption features in the quasar's spectrum.

1 such object out of more than 100 is a quasar. (Most are hot stars in our own galaxy called white dwarf stars.) In 1981, astronomer Richard Green of Palomar Observatory, working with Maarten Schmidt, completed a survey using this technique. The survey revealed more than 100 new quasars whose appearance in the sky is bright enough to make them worthy of detailed study.

Another technique makes use of the quasars' strong emission features to identify the quasar and find its red shift at the same time. Astronomers using this method place a prism in front of the film when taking a photo of the sky. The prism spreads out the light from an object so that its spectrum—as well as its image—is recorded. The presence of strong emission features in the spectrum readily identifies a quasar, and their position tells us the quasar's red shift.

The results of such studies suggest that, over the whole sky, there are millions of quasars bright enough to be studied with the most powerful optical telescopes. The studies also revealed that there are many more high-red-shift quasars than low-red-shift quasars. If the high-red-shift quasars are very distant, then we see them as they were in the distant past, because of the time it takes for light to travel to us. This tells us that there must have been many more quasars in existence eons ago. Quasars appear to be a phenomenon of the early history of our universe.

What could quasars possibly be? If these objects truly are producing such tremendous energy from such a small region of space, where does this energy come from? Based upon our current understanding, we cannot answer these questions—we can only speculate. The largest aggregates of matter are the galaxies. We know that matter is highly concentrated near the centers of galaxies, and Einstein showed us that matter is equivalent to energy. Furthermore, our own Milky Way galaxy has violent central activity occurring on a small scale, and many other galaxies are known to have centers of activity almost as energetic as quasars. Perhaps, then, quasars are events occurring in the center of galaxies. It is reasonable because we know that there is a large potential for energy there, and we know that at least some quasars are associated with galaxies. There is even some evidence that supports this speculation. Many quasars show a faint structure that many astronomers believe is a galaxy underlying the bright quasar.

We also believe that as a massive galaxy is in the process of forming, a region of very high density may be formed at the center as the galaxy collapses under its own gravity. It may be that in the center of a massive galaxy, gravity is so strong that material will continue to collapse to a point of zero size and infinite density—a black hole. A black hole has such a strong gravitational attraction that any material passing too close to it will be sucked into it.

How can such a black hole, devouring or pulling in material around it, be responsible for the energy *output* of a quasar? As the tremendous gravitational force of a black hole pulls material toward it, gravitational energy is transformed to heat and light. Astronomers have speculated that the gravitational energy released by an amount of material a few times the mass of the sun falling into a massive black hole, then undergoing a process whose nature is a mystery to us, would release enough energy to power a quasar. No theory currently explains how the gravitational energy is transformed into the energy we see. The continuous emission we observe from quasars in the radio and visible regions of the spectrum is believed to be produced by synchrotron radiation — high-energy particles radiating as they spiral around lines of magnetic force. The magnetic field in a quasar is incredibly jumbled and chaotic.

The black hole theory is the most popular theory, but it is not the only one, and it certainly does not provide all the answers. Another theory suggests that massive stellar explosions called supernovae produce the quasar's energy. A supernova is the death gasp of a massive star. Such occurrences are rare — about once every 100 years in our galaxy — but it would require about 3,000 supernovae per year to account for the energy output of one of the most luminous quasars. Other theories involve objects called spinars — massive rapidly rotating stars with strong magnetic fields — or annihilation of large clouds of matter and antimatter. It is possible that no one has yet imagined the correct theory of quasars.

Although astronomers have little direct understanding of the "central engine," 20 years of studying quasars has not been entirely in vain. We know that the magnetic field region around the central power source must be smaller than a few light-weeks in size. Beyond this region are clouds of gas. These clouds move randomly through a region up to a few light-years in size with velocities of several thousand kilometers per second. They are heated by the synchrotron radiation to temperatures of approximately 10,000°C. Collisions between atoms and electrons in these clouds cause the atoms to radiate at their characteristic wavelengths, producing the emission features we observe. Surrounding these clouds is a hot, diffuse gas that extends out to about 100 light-years. Beyond that, at an uncertain distance, are other gas clouds that produce the absorption lines. Is all of this embedded in a galaxy of stars? Perhaps.

The problems posed by the quasars are fascinating in their own right, but the astronomer's interest goes beyond simply trying to understand these strange creatures in the astrophysical zoo. If it is true that quasars are the most distant and most luminous objects in the universe, then they are beacons illuminating the distant past. By understanding the quasars, we may probe the universe in its beginning. Comparing its past and its present may allow us to speculate about its future. A strong motivation behind astronomers' research is the hope of using quasars as candles to light up the dark corners of cosmology.

Our Most Mysterious Sense

By John N. Labows, Jr.

Scientists are discovering that smell plays a significant role in influencing human emotions and behavior

We smell the fragrance of freshly cut hay and picture in rich detail scenes from a country childhood. A hint of perfume reaches us and we clearly see the face of a loved one far away. For many people, smell is the most evocative sense. The trigger for some of our most vivid memories may be the impact of a few odor molecules on a membrane no larger than a postage stamp.

In many ways, smell is also our most mysterious sense. Most people find that while a smell helps to recall an event, it is nearly impossible to "remember" smells themselves the way we remember sights and sounds. Smell serves memory because our olfactory system is closely linked with the part of the brain concerned with memory and emotion, although we do not know how. Nor do we know precisely how we perceive odors, or how we are able to distinguish so many different ones.

Human beings and all other living creatures are constantly bombarded with signals from the environment. Our five external senses enable us to detect these signals. Special cells, called receptors, in the sense organs translate the signals into nerve impulses, which speed to the brain for analysis and interpretation. Different types of signals activate different types of receptors. For example, receptors in the eyes respond to light; those in the ears, to sound; and those in the skin, to pressure, heat, and cold. Smell and taste are called the chemical senses because their receptors respond to molecular signals. We taste when molecules in a liquid, such as the saliva in the mouth, activate receptors in taste buds on the tongue. We smell when airborne molecules strike olfactory receptors in the nose.

Although human beings and most animals have developed separate senses of taste and smell, the two remain closely related. In fact, for some substances, such as chloroform, what we think we are smelling we are really tasting. On the other hand, often what we refer to as the taste of a food is its smell. If you were blindfolded and your nose was stopped up, you probably could not distinguish potatoes from apples or red wine from coffee. If you hold your nose, you can block out about 80 per cent of the flavor of most foods. This is why people with a head cold usually have trouble tasting food.

Although our olfactory system is amazingly sensitive, human beings and other primates cannot smell nearly as well as most other kinds of animals. Some scientists think that our ancient ancestors lost their keen sense of smell when they left the ground for the trees. Since sharp eyesight was more important there, the balance of the senses shifted. In the process, noses changed shape and the size of the olfactory organs decreased. The sense of smell became less acute.

Odors are still one of the chief means of communication for many species of animals. And scientists are discovering that odors may be more important to human beings than we had thought. For example, researchers have learned that we can sometimes identify one another by smell and that odors affect our moods.

Odor is a pervasive part of our daily lives. In the United States, men and women spend $2 billion a year on scent. Products ranging from fabric softener to dishwashing liquid are scented to transmit signals like "clean" and "fresh." Consumers can even buy machines that waft fragrance through their homes.

The author:
John N. Labows, Jr., is an organic chemist at the Monell Chemical Senses Center in Philadelphia.

Research into the nature and uses of odors may enable us to expand the world's food supply by making unfamiliar or unpleasant-tasting food more appealing. It may provide an easy way to determine when a woman is fertile and a reliable method of diagnosing disease. Finally, of course, scientists — and perfume manufacturers — want to know whether odors affect human sexual behavior. Can we really fall in love at first whiff?

As a result, smell has become an exciting field for research. As an organic chemist, I first became interested in smell research while studying the chemicals used by insects to protect themselves. About six years ago, I joined the staff of the Monell Chemical Senses Center in Philadelphia to pursue research on human odors that result from bacteria acting on skin secretions. Several colleagues and I are currently investigating the odors produced by pathogenic, or disease-producing, bacteria. Our work may someday lead to the use of odors as a diagnostic technique.

To understand how we perceive odors, we can trace an aroma as it passes through the olfactory system. Normally, when we inhale, air flows into the nose and through the nasal cavity to the lungs. When we exhale, however, the nasal passages become partially blocked by three bony projections called turbinates. This blocking action stirs up the air and pushes the gas molecules that make up an odor onto the moist mucous membrane lining the nasal cavity. As a result, when we breathe normally, we smell more of an odor when we exhale than we do when we inhale. Of course, when we really want to smell something, we sniff. Sniffing forces more air and, thus, more odor molecules onto the olfactory membranes.

On the mucous membrane, the molecules are captured by hairlike projections called cilia. The movement of the cilia pushes the molecules over the mucous membrane and onto two small patches called the olfactory membranes, where our smell receptors are located.

About 5 square centimeters (1 square inch) in area each, the olfactory membranes lie behind and slightly above the bridge of the nose. Compared to the membranes of many animals, human membranes are quite small. Sheep dogs, for instance, have olfactory membranes of about 150 square centimeters (23 square inches).

Each human olfactory membrane consists of an estimated 10 million tightly packed, column-shaped receptor cells, which have extensions at either end. One extension is microscopic cilia, which project through the layer of mucus lining the surface of the membrane. The other connects with extensions of the olfactory nerve at the base of the membrane. Receptor cells are separated by cells that provide physical support and produce new receptors when they divide.

Molecules pass over the membrane and become attached to the cilia. This triggers nerve implpuses in the receptor cells. The impulses speed along the olfactory nerve to one of two football-shaped organs called the olfactory bulbs. These are located on the underside of the frontal lobe of the brain. Inside each bulb are glomeruli, tufts of nerve cells that resemble tree branches. The glomeruli collect the nerve impulses and relay them along the olfactory tract to the temporal lobe of the brain. There, the brain decodes the impulses and tells us what it is we have smelled.

Although the brain does most of the analytical work of the olfactory system, scientists believe some decoding of odor signals takes place in the olfactory bulb. For example, in experiments with animals, researchers have discovered that specific glomeruli repeatedly

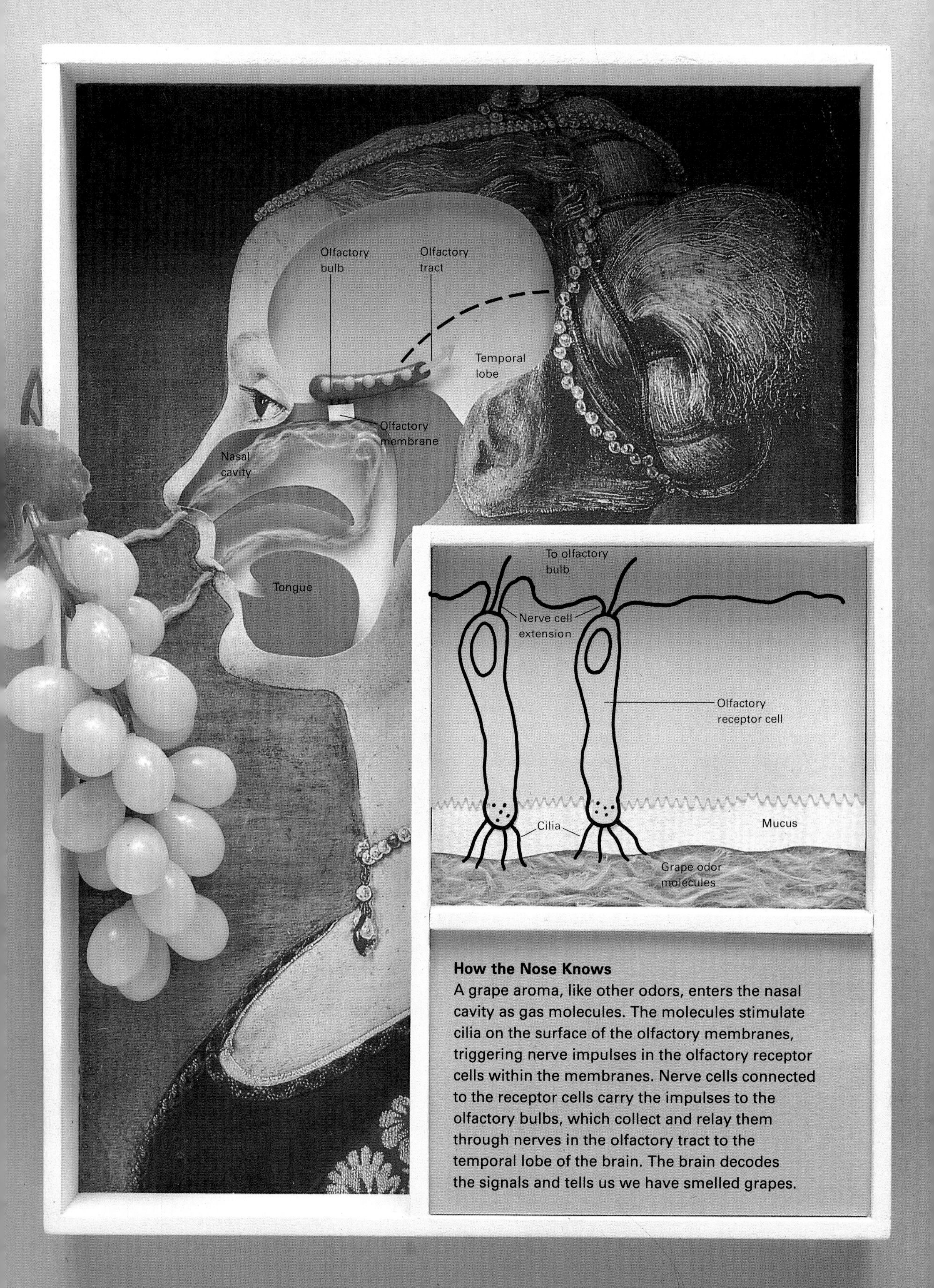

How the Nose Knows
A grape aroma, like other odors, enters the nasal cavity as gas molecules. The molecules stimulate cilia on the surface of the olfactory membranes, triggering nerve impulses in the olfactory receptor cells within the membranes. Nerve cells connected to the receptor cells carry the impulses to the olfactory bulbs, which collect and relay them through nerves in the olfactory tract to the temporal lobe of the brain. The brain decodes the signals and tells us we have smelled grapes.

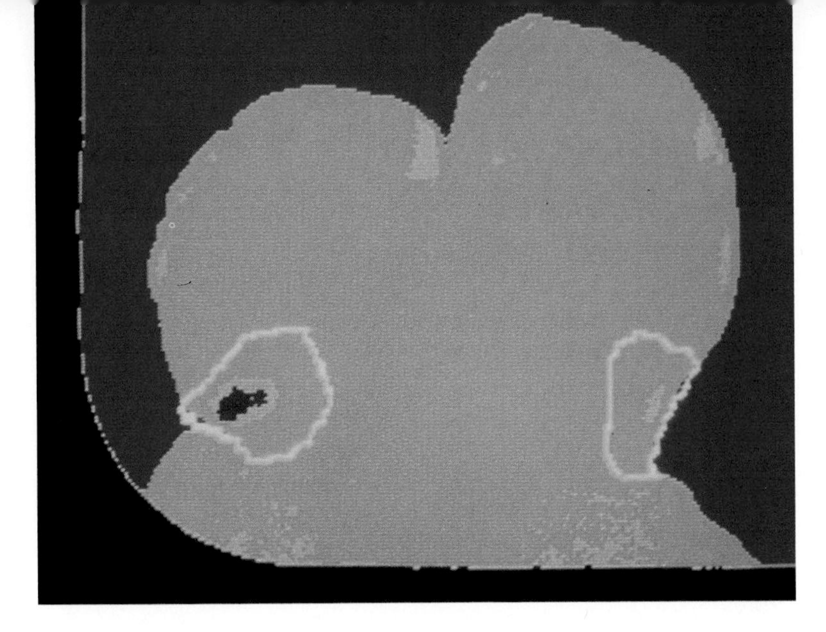

Specific glomeruli, shown in brown, in a radioimage of the olfactory bulbs of a male guinea pig respond to the odor of female urine.

respond to specific odors. Psychobiologists Charles J. Wysocki and Gary K. Beauchamp at Monell tested odor responses in the glomeruli of guinea pigs using 2-deoxy-D-glucose, a form of the simple sugar glucose, which accumulates in the cells.

Stimulated nerve cells absorb more glucose than those that are not stimulated. The researchers injected radioactive 2-deoxy-D-glucose into male guinea pigs that then were stimulated with the odor of female urine. By measuring the level of radioactivity in tissue samples of the olfactory bulb, the researchers discovered that certain groups of glomeruli had higher levels of glucose. They concluded that those glomeruli responded to odors in the urine. Gordon M. Shepherd, a neurobiologist at Yale University, found similar results in experiments in 1980 with the glomeruli of young rats stimulated with the odor of their mother's nipple.

Researchers also have conducted electrophysiological studies of the electrical responses generated in olfactory cells stimulated by an odor. For example, in the late 1970s, Shepherd placed electrodes in the glomeruli of tiger salamanders. His experiments revealed that certain groups of glomeruli repeatedly responded to nerve impulses carrying signals for such odors as camphor and banana oil. In 1979, physiologist David Moulton of the Veterans Administration Hospital in Philadelphia conducted similar experiments with receptor cells in the olfactory membrane of tiger salamanders.

Human beings and many types of animals have an extra sense of smell called the common chemical sense that enables them to feel odors. The common chemical sense registers the sensation of odors, such as the stinging sensation of ammonia or the cool sensation of menthol. Like other molecules, molecules of such substances interact with cilia on the olfactory membrane and trigger nerve impulses in the receptor cells. However, these molecules also trigger impulses in the trigeminal nerve, the major nerve in the face, which has branches at the base of the olfactory membrane. Some odorless gases, such as ozone and carbon dioxide, and dangerous chemicals such as benzene also activate the trigeminal nerve.

The Roman philosopher and poet Lucretius believed that pleasant smells were composed of smooth, round atoms, while bitter or harsh smells were made of hooked particles that tore their way into the nose. Our knowledge of the structure of molecules has grown considerably since Lucretius proposed his theory in 47 B.C., but scientists still have much to learn about how odor molecules interact with our smell receptors and how we can perceive so many different odors.

Odors may consist of a single chemical or hundreds of different compounds. But substances give off odors only if they are volatile—that is, if they change easily from a solid or liquid to a gas. Interestingly, some less volatile chemicals, such as those given off by bell peppers, have a stronger odor than some more volatile ones, such as alcohol. Within some compounds, such as salt and sugar, the electrostatic forces holding the molecules together are so strong that these substances do not vaporize easily and so are almost odorless.

Odor molecules trigger our sense of smell by becoming attached to large, complex molecules called receptor proteins located on the cilia. According to one theory, odor molecules can be grouped into a few basic classes and have a one-to-one relationship with receptor proteins. Like a lock with one key, each type of receptor protein binds only one class of odor molecules.

A second theory suggests that each molecule interacts with more than one receptor protein at the same time. Because each cilia has more than one type of receptor protein, odor molecules may bind with different proteins on the same cilia or different proteins on different cilia. Each receptor protein binds those parts of a molecule that it resembles in shape. Thus, only 24 to 30 receptor proteins acting in different combinations could transmit information about an almost infinite variety of odors.

Although we are remarkably good at detecting odors, we are remarkably bad at identifying them in the absence of visual cues. If we are asked to identify even a common odor, such as pine or chocolate, we often fail miserably. We may remember that we have smelled the odor before. We may be able to say whether the odor comes from an edible or inedible substance. But most people probably will not be able to say what the odor is. This is usually not the result of a medical or perceptual problem, but rather a cognitive or thought problem. This frustrating experience has been referred to as the "tip-of-the-tongue syndrome."

Sometimes, however, medical problems do interfere with our ability to detect odors. Flu, colds, sinus infections, and allergy attacks can block the nasal passages and dull our olfactory receptors. Generally, this type of anosmia, or loss of smell, is temporary.

As many as 15 million Americans, however, suffer from a permanent loss of smell. Total or severe anosmia may result from a case of flu, an allergy attack, or a blow to the head. This type of anosmia can be dangerous since it may interfere with the ability to detect toxic fumes. It can also lead to nutritional deficiencies since eating is no longer as pleasurable. Because the loss of smell is not as life-threatening nor as obvious as the loss of sight or hearing, many anosmics feel that their condition is not taken seriously and so suffer from psychological problems. At present, there is no cure for total or severe anosmia.

Even people with a seemingly normal sense of smell may have specific permanent anosmias. John E. Amoore, a biochemist at the University of California Medical Center in San Francisco, has studied specific anosmias related to human odors. In 1977, he discovered that 47 per cent of the population cannot smell androsterone, a chemical with a urinelike odor. Thirty-six per cent cannot detect malty smells, and 12 per cent cannot smell musky odors. Wysocki experimented with mice in 1977 and found that specific anosmias are inherited. Studies of human twins supported this theory.

Despite the problems we sometimes have with our olfactory systems, the human nose is usually better at detecting the presence of odors than any scientific instrument. Instruments are useful, how-

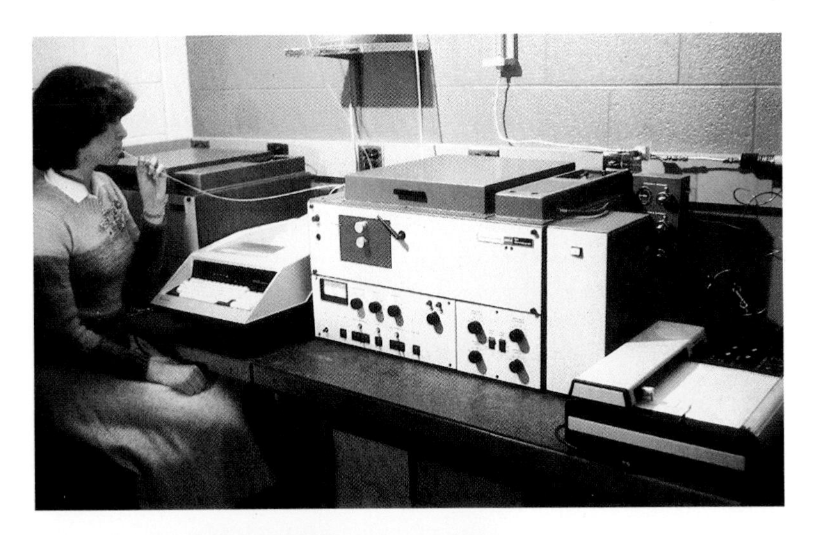

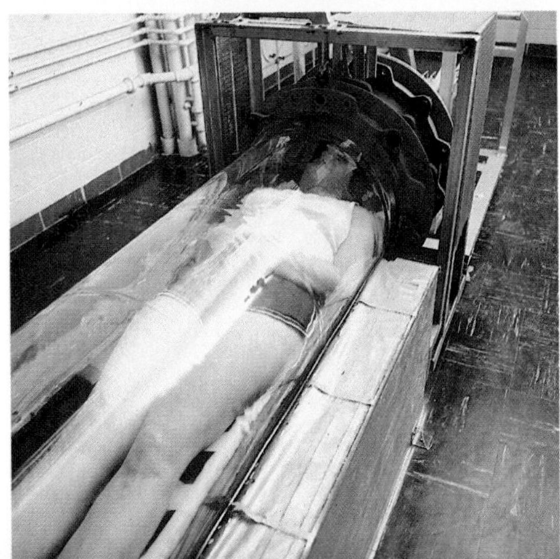

A woman breathes into a gas chromatograph in an experiment to determine how breath odors change during the menstrual cycle, *above*. An odor chamber, *left,* which collects odors from the entire human body, may someday be used to diagnose disease.

Hundreds of male red-sided garter snakes, *above,* are lured by the scented trail of a single female. A sow, *above right,* stands motionless after being sprayed with a synthetic version of a pheromone secreted by boars during mating. Pig breeders use the synthetic pheromone to keep sows from running away during artificial insemination.

ever, in analyzing what those odors are. Scientists generally use a gas chromatograph and a mass spectrometer in odor analysis. The gas chromatograph separates odors into their individual molecular components. The molecules are then fed into a mass spectrometer, which identifies those components.

Sometimes researchers use the human nose in combination with machines. Manufacturers of food flavorings, perfumes, and other scented products rely on human olfactory expertise and gas chromatography to isolate the essential components of odors they want to reproduce. For example, to reproduce the aroma of strawberries commercially, a technician uses the gas chromatograph to break the aroma down into its more than 100 molecular components. A specially trained researcher, appropriately called a "nose," smells the individual odors coming from the exit port of the gas chromatograph and identifies those three or four components that together represent the essence of strawberry. These chemicals can then be synthesized and combined in proper proportions to duplicate the natural aroma.

Odor analysis has many other uses. Operators of food storage facilities analyze the odors in storage bins to determine if the food has begun to spoil. Scientists test air samples to detect and identify hazardous vapors in industrial plants. Law enforcement officers analyze odors in luggage to detect concealed drugs or explosives.

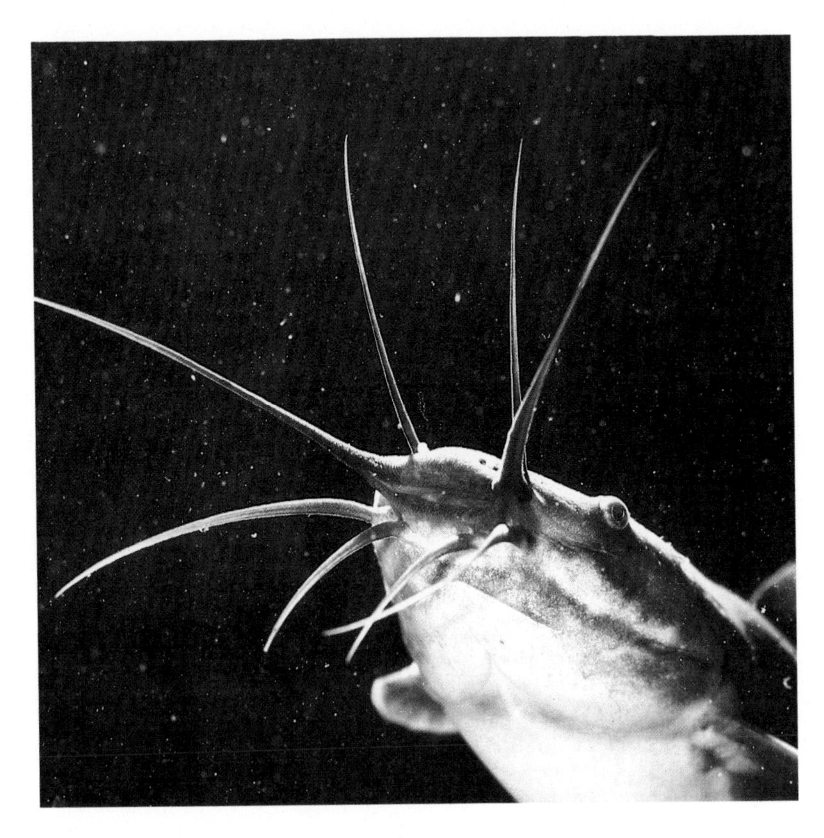

A catfish detects food odors through smell receptors on its barbels, or whiskers.

By analyzing odors given off by animals, scientists have learned much about the fascinating role those odors play in animal communication and the way smells affect behavior. In 1959, biochemists Adolph Butenandt and E. Hecker of the Max-Planck Institute of Biochemistry in Munich, West Germany, identified a chemical secreted by silkworms to attract mates. Since then, scientists have discovered that most insect species and many other types of animals produce these chemical messengers called pheromones. They have also discovered that pheromones convey a variety of signals.

Pheromones include odors from urine, specialized skin glands, vaginal secretions, and even saliva. Sometimes, animals use these signals to directly affect the behavior of other members of their species. For example, deer, mice, snails, and certain ants release alarm pheromones that warn of danger. Dogs, foxes, and coyotes use pheromones in urine to mark their territory and warn other animals away. Marmoset monkeys mark tree branches with a scent from a skin gland to communicate their rank within the group. A higher-ranking monkey may prove his dominance by placing his mark over that of a lower-ranking monkey.

Pheromones play their most important role in reproduction. Like the silkworm, many types of animals use pheromones to attract mates. But these odors have other uses as well. A pheromone re-

Products that mask unpleasant odors or generate pleasant ones are the basis of a billion-dollar industry.

leased by the queen bee keeps other females in the hive from becoming sexually mature. Odorous chemicals, called androgen steroids, in the saliva of boars cause sows to stand still in the mating position. However, the sows respond to these steroids most strongly when they are in estrus — in heat — implying that their hormones control either their perception of the boars' pheromone or their interpretation of its signal. Interestingly, it is the same chemicals that make sows such enthusiastic hunters of truffles — a type of fungi that grows on the roots of trees. In 1982, R. Claus and H. O. Hoppen of the Technical University of Munich and Heinrich Karg of the Lübeck School of Medicine in West Germany discovered that the highly prized delicacies contain concentrations of this boar pheromone.

In addition to triggering a specific form of behavior, pheromones may affect physiological processes, such as the estrus cycle, sexual development, and pregnancy, in some animals. Usually, these pheromones are urine odors, which act like primers to increase the production of certain hormones. For example, in 1969, animal behaviorist John G. Vandenbergh of North Carolina State University demonstrated that female rodents exposed to the urine odor of male rodents become sexually mature faster than females segregated from males. Sexually integrated females reached puberty in 40 days; sexually segregated females, in 55 days.

A trained olfactory expert called a "nose" may be able to identify hundreds of different odors.

Even more dramatic is the effect reported in 1959 by Hilda Bruce at the National Institute for Medical Research in London. She showed that newly pregnant mice will abort their litter if they are exposed to the urine odor of any male mouse other than their mate. Scientists believe these primer pheromones are nonvolatile — that is, they do not evaporate easily. But they have been unable to isolate specific molecules.

Recent studies indicate that animals that react to these primer pheromones may not perceive them through their olfactory system. Rather, they use an extra olfactory organ called the vomeronasal organ (VNO), found in the roof of the nasal cavity. When animals sniff the urine odor, they may bob their head or flick their tongue. These movements are thought to cause the primer to reach the VNO. An animal whose VNO has been surgically removed is still able to detect food odors through its olfactory system. However, such animals no longer bob their head or flick their tongue when exposed to urine odor.

Although some studies have suggested that some human beings also may have a vomeronasal system, the evidence is highly controversial. But VNO or not, we know that odors affect human behavior. Food odors make us salivate, and we seem to automatically avoid harmful substances, such as spoiled food and poisonous vapors, that are malodorous.

Michael Kirk-Smith, a psychologist at Warwick University in Great Britain, demonstrated in 1981 that odors can also affect mood. Human subjects were asked to complete a frustrating task and, at the same time, were exposed to an unfamiliar odor. When Kirk-Smith later exposed his subjects to that odor, he discovered that it evoked the negative emotions associated with the frustration they had experienced.

Generally, we humans rely on visual cues, such as facial features, to recognize each other. Researchers have discovered, though, that like many types of animals, we also can recognize people by smell. An experiment conducted in 1976 by Michael J. Russell, a researcher at the Brain Behavior Research Center at the University of California at Eldridge, suggests that human babies can recognize their mother's odor at a very early age. At 6 weeks of age, 6 of the

Odors encapsulated on special cards can help a physician diagnose some diseases that cause patients to give off a distinctive breath or body odor.

Odors Associated with Diseases or Conditions

Historical associations

Odor	Disease
Butcher shop	Yellow fever
Freshly baked brown bread	Typhoid
Fruit	Diabetic coma
Freshly plucked feathers	Rubella
Putrid	Scurvy
Rotten straw	Sweating sickness
Sour or musty bread	Pellagra
Stale beer	Scrofula
Sweetish	Diphtheria

Modern associations

Odor	Disease
Rotting apples	Diabetes
Fish	Uremia
Musty fish or raw liver	Liver failure
Maple syrup	Phenylketonuria
Bitter almonds	Cyanide poisoning
Garlic	Arsenic poisoning
Putrid	Lung abscess
Severe bad breath	Trench mouth
Cheesey	Chronic sweaty feet

From POSTGRADUATE MEDICINE

10 breast-fed infants tested responded to their mother's breast odor by making sucking movements. The infants did not respond at all or cried when exposed to the breast odor of a strange mother.

In another experiment, in 1982, psychologists Richard H. Porter and John D. Moore of the John F. Kennedy Center for Research at Vanderbilt University in Nashville, Tenn., asked 12 pairs of siblings to wear identical T-shirts for three consecutive nights while they slept. They discovered that 19 of the 24 children could later identify their sibling by sniffing the shirts. The researchers then repeated the experiment with parents. Of the 18 parents they asked to identify their child's T-shirt, 16 succeeded.

Of course, the big question is whether odors play a significant role in human reproduction and sexuality. Here, the evidence is tantalizingly inconclusive. Scientists have found odorous androgen steroids, androstenol and androsterone, in human underarm perspiration. Androstenol is the same steroid found in truffles and both are secreted by boars during mating. Experiments with androstenol, which has a musky odor, suggest intriguing possibilities. For example, in 1978, Kirk-Smith and other researchers at the University of Birmingham in England asked male and female volunteers to look at photographs of normally dressed women and judge their attractiveness. Some of the volunteers were exposed to androstenol at the same time. Researchers found that volunteers exposed to androstenol consistently gave the women in the photos higher marks for attractiveness than did those not exposed to androstenol.

Scientists also have discovered evidence that human odors may affect the timing of the menstrual cycle and may indicate when a woman is fertile. In 1971, Martha K. McClintock, a psychologist at the University of Chicago, observed that women living together in dormitories at Wellesley College in Massachusetts had closely timed menstrual cycles. In 1980, Russell investigated this effect in an experiment with 16 volunteers. Three times each week for four months, Russell dabbed the upper lip of each volunteer with a liquid. Half were dabbed with alcohol, half with a few drops of underarm perspiration from a woman unknown to the subjects. Russell reported at the end of his study that the menstrual cycles of the women in the first group were unchanged. However, the cycles of all but one woman in the second group had dramatically shifted to conform to the donor's cycle. He theorized that this menstrual synchrony may be the result of unnoticeable odors given off by some women.

Researchers also are investigating whether mouth odors can help women determine when they are fertile. In 1978, Joseph G. Tonzetich, an analytical chemist at the University of British Columbia in Canada, and George Preti, an analytical chemist at Monell, found that the concentration of sulfur compounds in a woman's mouth changes during her menstrual cycle. If these changes can be accurately charted, researchers may be able to develop a reliable method of pinpointing the time of ovulation.

Using odors to detect physiological changes is an ancient practice. Before the development of technologically sophisticated diagnostic tools, doctors often relied on their sense of smell to diagnose disease. Distinctive odors were associated with many diseases. Patients with typhoid smell like freshly baked brown bread. People with scrofula, a form of tuberculosis, give off the odor of stale beer.

Today, physicians are rediscovering the value of olfactory diagnosis. Odor is particularly useful, for instance, in diagnosing maple-syrup urine disease, a metabolic illness affecting very young infants. James G. Kostelc, an analytical organic chemist at Monell, found in 1980 that specific odors in saliva indicate gum disease. Some physicians are experimenting with encapsulated odors like the scratch-and-sniff tabs found in advertisements to help them diagnose disease. They compare the odor on the tab with that given off by the patient. Researchers also are studying the combination of odors given off by the human body with a long, tube-shaped instrument called an odor chamber. Subjects are placed inside and air is blown over them. Samples of the air are then collected and analyzed. Researchers are investigating the chamber's use as a diagnostic tool to detect disease, particularly diseases that affect metabolism.

Smell is more complex and probably more influential in our lives than we have suspected, and I think smell researchers are on the brink of many exciting discoveries. Some of these discoveries will have very tangible applications for our daily lives. But the greatest benefit will be a deeper understanding of the sometimes subtle ways in which people communicate through our most mysterious sense.

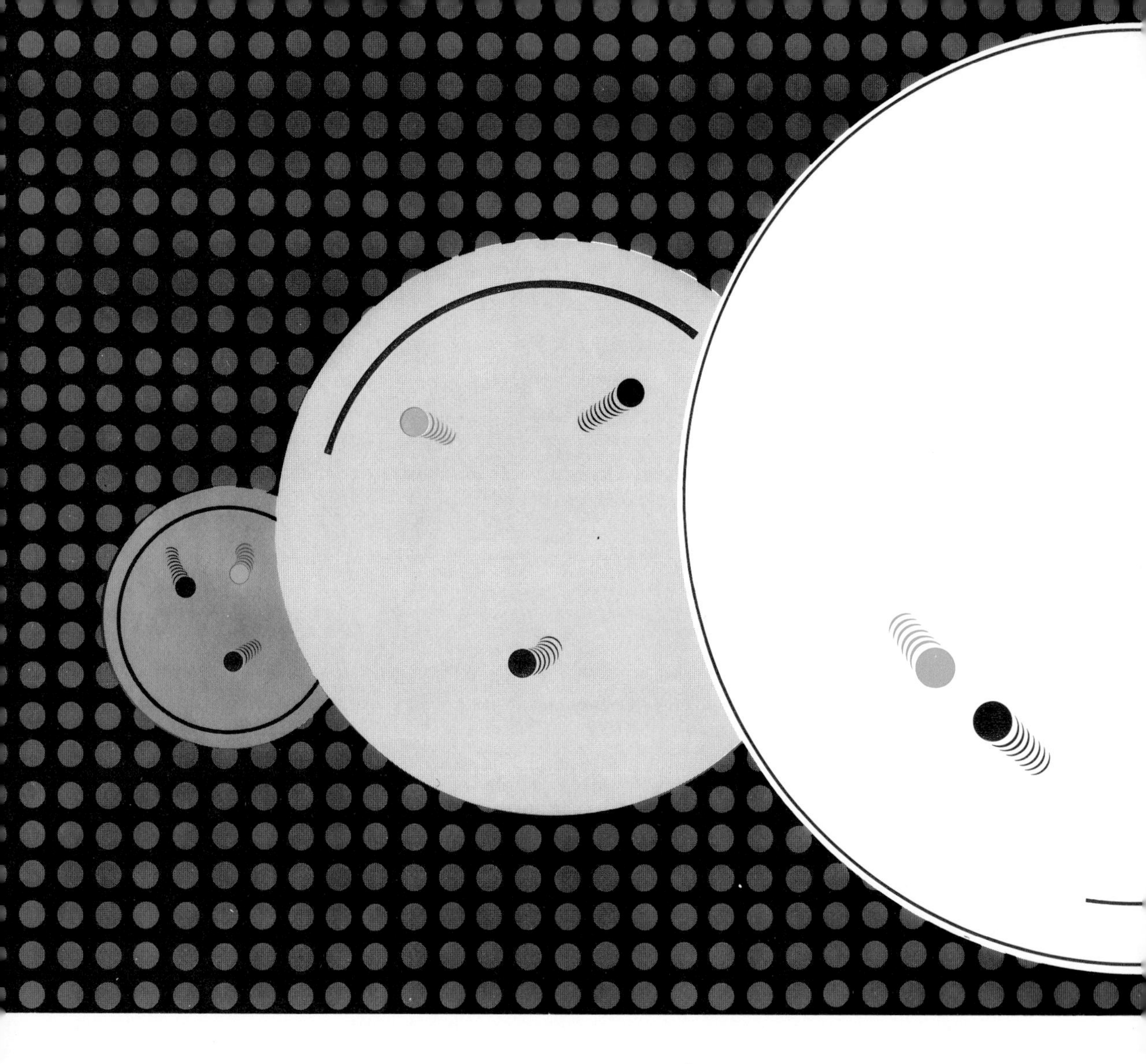

Catching Nature's Vanishing Act

By Robert H. March

Physicists are setting up huge but extremely sensitive detectors far underground to try to catch a proton or a neutron in the act of destroying itself

Beneath the tranquil ski slopes of Park City, Utah, lies an "underground city" of tunnels and caverns. They were dug for more than 100 years by miners in search of silver, using picks, shovels, and dynamite. Today, one of these caverns, part of the Silver King Mine, is the workplace of a different breed of miners. They are physicists searching for evidence that the matter that makes up all ordinary objects, such as the book you are reading, your body, and even the sun and the other stars, may be slowly disintegrating.

The focus of this modern hunt is a giant wooden tank that holds more than 760,000 liters (200,000 gallons) of water. The modern tools are 700 photomultipliers—electronic "eyes" that hang in the tank. The photomultipliers are there to record a particular pattern of light that would indicate the disappearance of a particle from one atom in the water.

More than 30 scientists and technicians from Harvard University in Cambridge, Mass.; Purdue University in West Lafayette, Ind.; and the University of Wisconsin in Madison worked for nearly three years to build and install this equipment. The evidence they seek would advance our understanding of the basic particles of matter enormously. It would reveal the basic unity of the forces that hold particles together and govern their movements.

Three kinds of particles — electrons, neutrons, and protons — make up atoms of matter. In an atom, one or more electrons orbit a central nucleus that is made up of protons and neutrons. In ordinary chemical reactions, nothing is altered beyond the movements of electrons from one atom to another and changes in the relative positions of atoms. The nuclei are unaffected.

However, in nuclear reactions such as radioactive decays, fission reactions, and fusion reactions, protons and neutrons can be rearranged or altered. For example, in one form of radioactive decay, a neutron is transformed into a proton by emitting an electron and a neutrino — an electrically neutral cousin of the electron. In a fission reaction, a nucleus splits into two parts and emits neutrons. In a fusion reaction, two nuclei combine. But in all of these cases, the number of nuclear particles — neutrons plus protons — is the same after the reaction as before. As a result, in both fission and fusion reactions, up to a few tenths of 1 per cent of the nuclear mass is converted to energy.

But the Silver King physicists are on the trail of a reaction that would convert all — or nearly all — the mass of a proton or neutron to energy. The proton or neutron would cease to exist as a particle.

Scientists who investigate theories of basic particles and forces have had great success in recent years. They have built huge, ring-shaped machines called accelerators that inject tremendous amounts of energy into particles, boosting their speeds to higher and higher levels. The machines then direct the particles to smash into one another. The scientists analyze the debris of the collisions to determine the nature of the forces that operate during these fleeting encounters.

Researchers have been building larger, more powerful machines that have probed deeper and deeper into the mysteries of nature. The largest particle accelerator on the drawing boards is a machine 27 kilometers (17 miles) in circumference that a group of European nations plan to build in the late 1980s.

But the theories that suggest matter is unstable also predict that an accelerator powerful enough to force a proton or neutron to disintegrate would have to be as large as our galaxy. Scientists cannot force a nuclear particle to disintegrate, so they must wait for a proton or neutron to decay by itself. However, the theories that predict such decay say that it is extremely rare. The half-life of a proton or neutron, the time in which half the protons or neutrons in a given group will decay, is about 10^{31} years. (The number 10^{31} is the same

The author:
Robert H. March is a professor of physics at the University of Wisconsin and the author of the Special Report "The Colorful World of the Atom" in the 1981 edition of *Science Year*.

as the numeral 1 followed by 31 zeros.) But a half-life of 10^{31} years also means that if scientists monitor 10^{31} nuclear particles for a year, they have a fifty-fifty chance of detecting one decay. This is the number of particles in about 17 metric tons (19 short tons) of matter. So, in order to see examples of disintegration, experimenters must monitor hundreds or even thousands of tons of matter. The water in the wooden tank in Utah weighs more than 750 metric tons (825 short tons), so the scientists at Silver King Mine hope to observe about 50 particle disintegrations per year.

If such a decay does occur, the disintegrating particle will emit a telltale pattern of light. The light rays will strike photomultipliers, which will send electrical signals to computers that will use the data to construct a picture of what happened inside the detector.

The detecting equipment is housed beneath more than 500 meters (1,640 feet) of rock to shield it from the cosmic rays that constantly bombard the earth. If the equipment were on the earth's surface, about 20 trillion cosmic ray particles would pass through the tank each year. Finding a few proton or neutron disintegrations in this hail of false signals would be impossible. However, only a few million cosmic rays will go through the tank in the mine each year. So the computers may be able to separate the pattern that indicates a decay from the cosmic ray signals.

Seven similar detection devices have been built in the United States, Europe, and Asia. The largest of these—in a mine near Cleveland owned by Morton Salt Company—resembles the Silver King detector and may well be the biggest scientific instrument ever constructed. It is housed in a hole measuring 18 by 24 meters (60 by 80 feet) on its surface and 21 meters (70 feet) deep, carved out of rock salt. This hole contains more than 4,000 photomultipliers monitoring nearly 10,000 metric tons (11,000 short tons) of water.

The detector is the brainchild of Frederick Reines of the University of California at Irvine and Maurice Goldhaber of Brookhaven National Laboratory on Long Island, N.Y. These two scientists built the last detector specifically designed for a search of this type in Los Alamos, N. Mex., in the 1950s. That apparatus weighed only a few hundred kilograms.

Two other devices are comparable in size to the one at Silver King. One is located in the Homestake Mine, a gold mine in South Dakota, and the other is under construction in a Japanese lead mine.

Four smaller detectors have a different design. Each of these consists of a sandwichlike arrangement of a heavy material, such as iron, interleaved with layers of particle counters. This arrangement packs more mass of material into a smaller volume and it can be placed in areas where space is limited. A team of Japanese and Indian scientists in 1980 installed such a detector in India's Kolar Gold Fields, 2,400 meters (8,000 feet) beneath the surface of the earth. Enlarging the chamber there would have been dangerous and

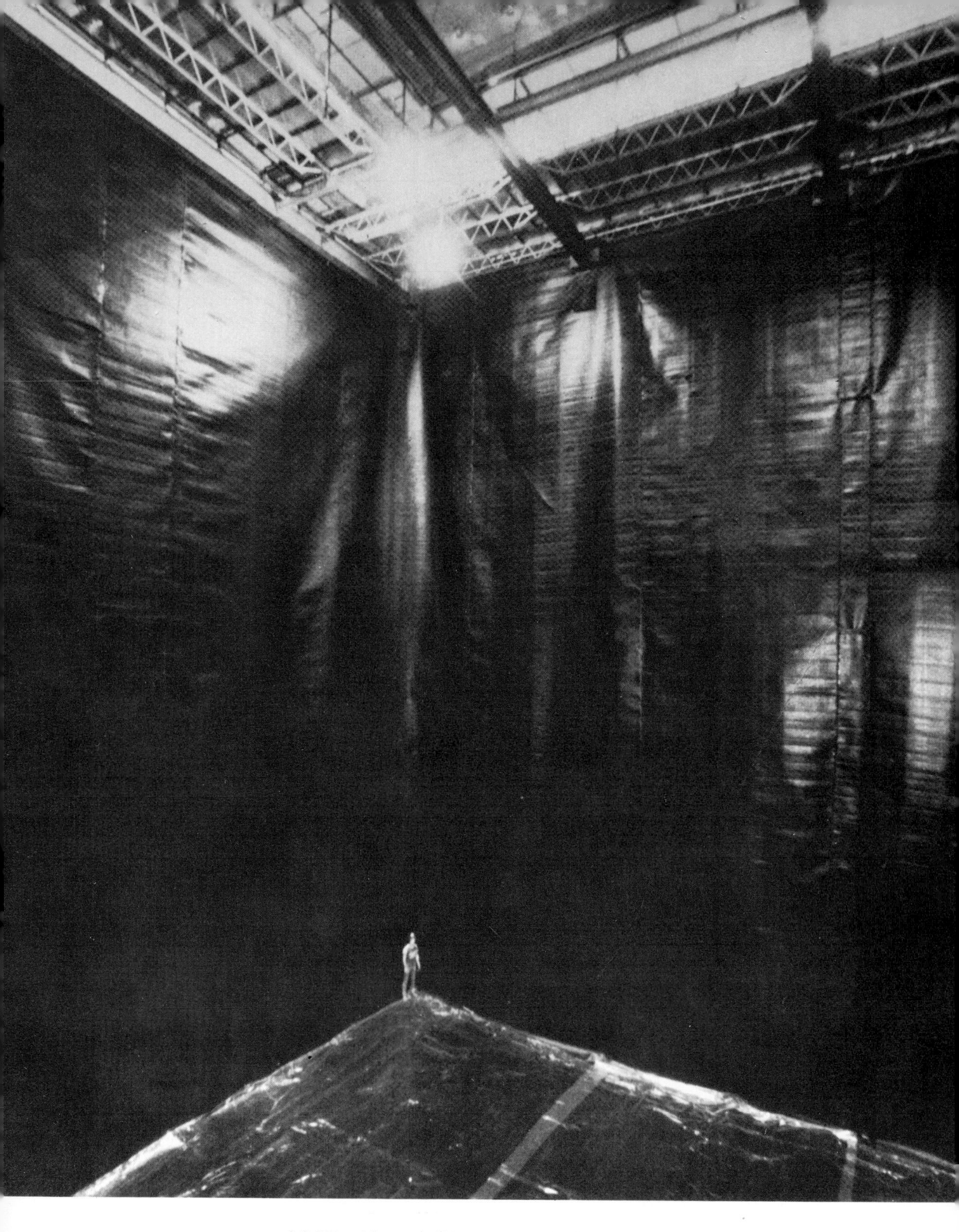

A 9,500-cubic-meter (336,000-cubic-foot) water tank carved out of a salt mine 594 meters (1,950 feet) underground near Cleveland may become the scene of the first detected act of proton self-destruction.

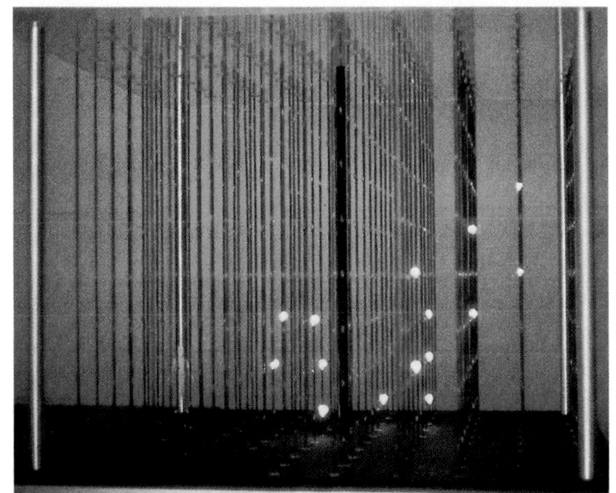

Sequence of flashes in a mock-up of a proton-decay detector, *left, from top to bottom,* shows how the self-destruction of a proton in the lower right portion of the device would generate a spreading pattern of light rays. Each light bulb represents a photomultiplier tube, *below,* which emits an electrical signal when light hits it.

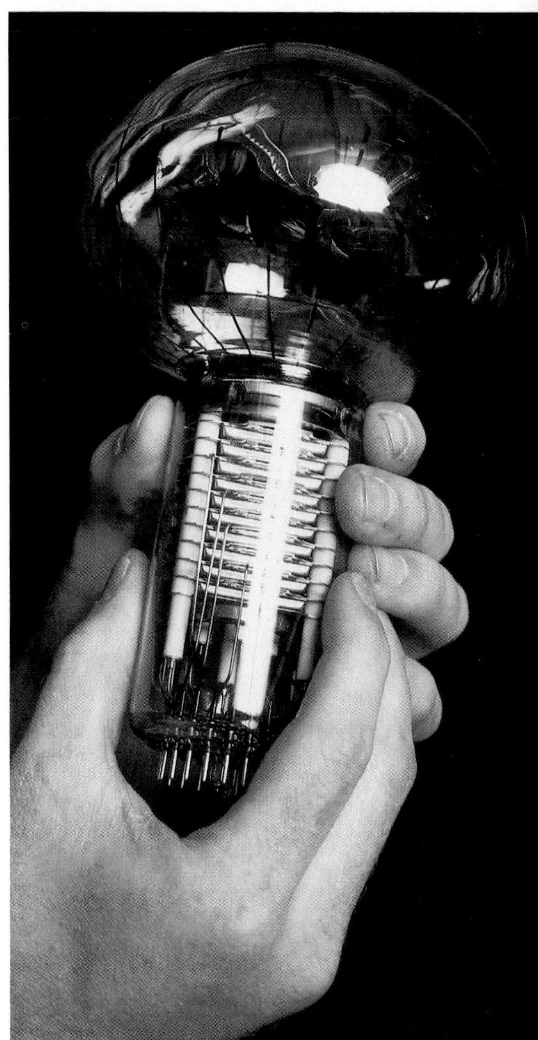

Field Particles and Their Forces

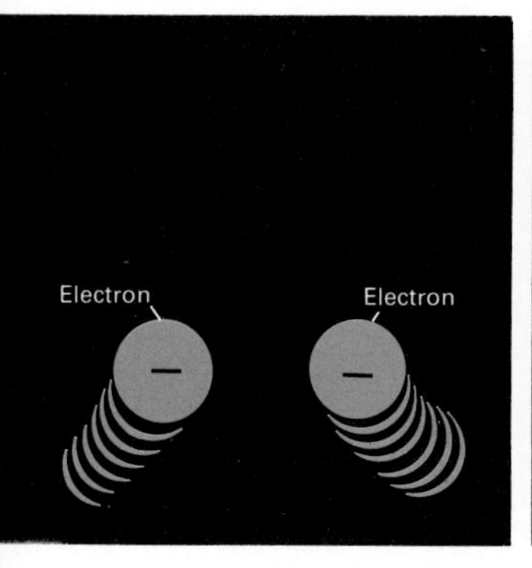

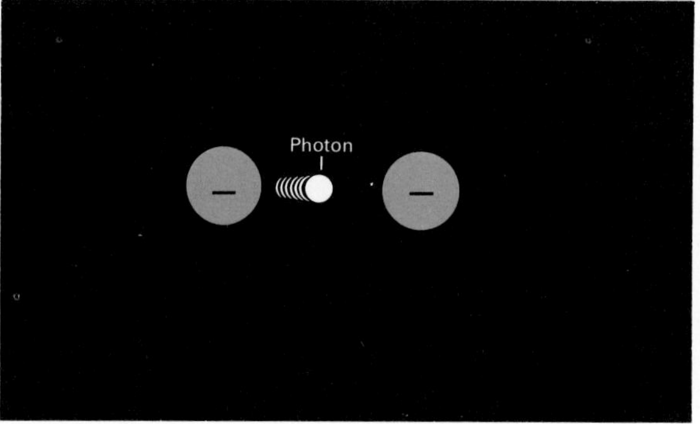

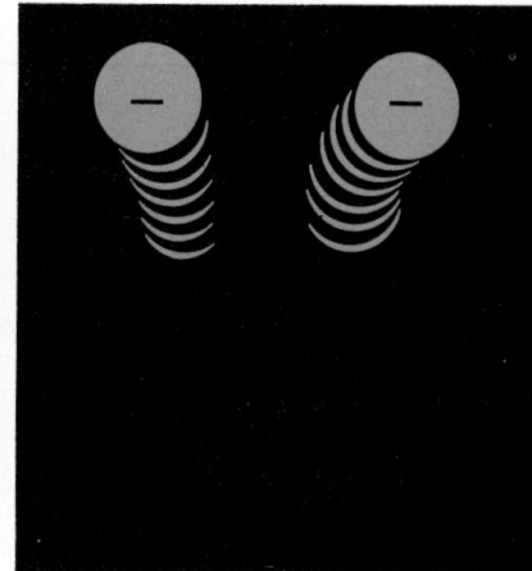

Approaching electrons exchange a field particle, a photon, then move away from each other. The photon carries the electromagnetic force with which objects that have the same electrical charge repel one another.

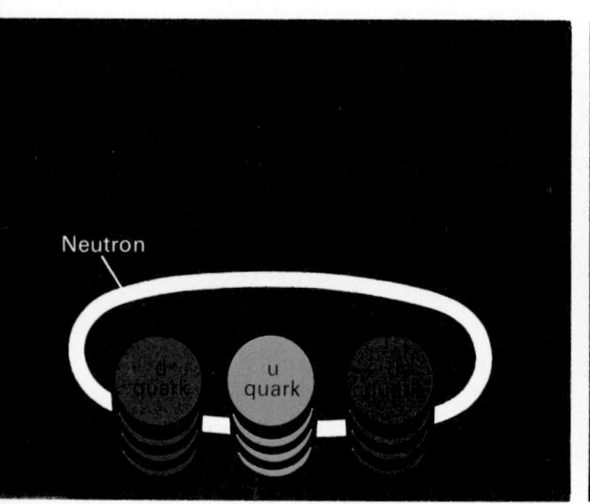

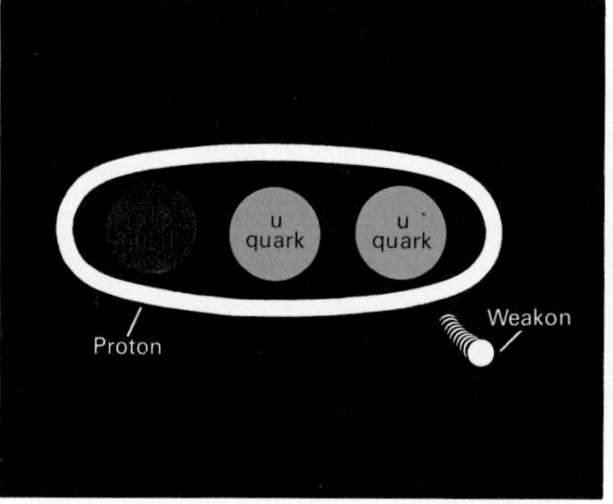

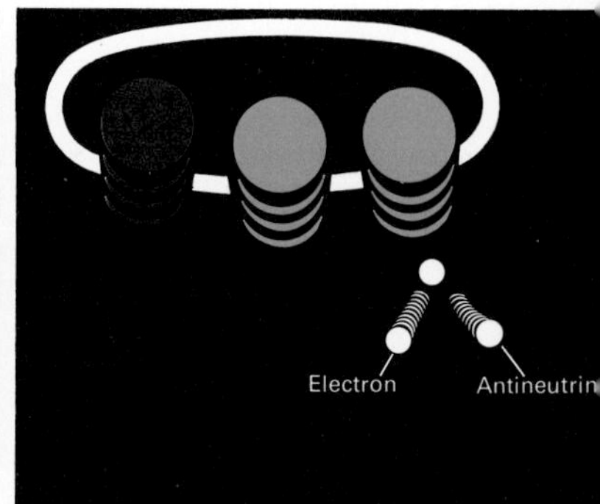

A neutron's d quark turns into a u quark as it emits a field particle, a weakon, which decays. The weakon carries the weak force that turns a neutron into a proton, while emitting an electron and an antineutrino.

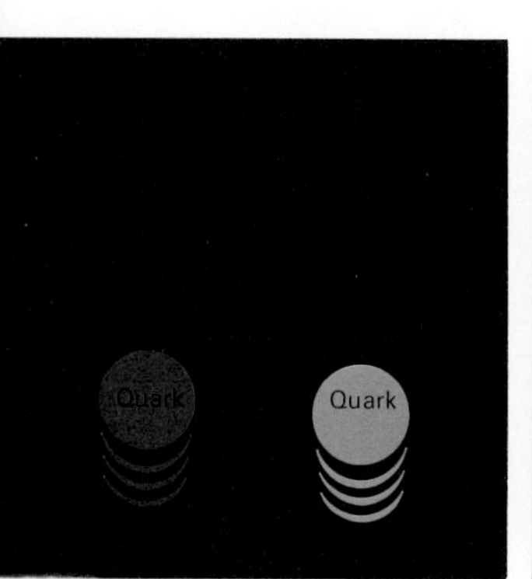

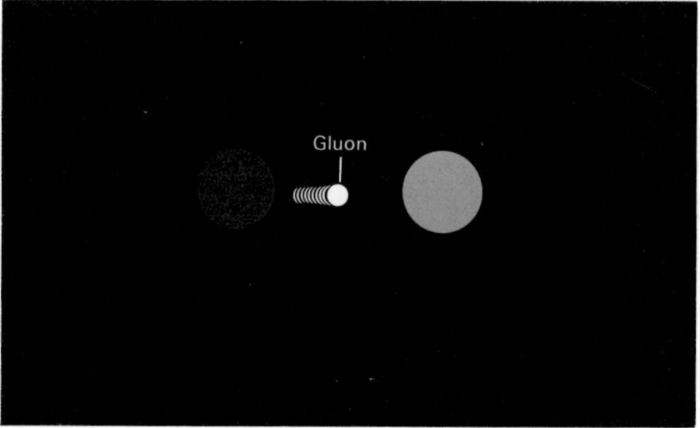

Two quarks exchange a field particle, a gluon. This exchange makes the quarks move toward each other. The gluon carries the strong force that binds quarks together in objects such as protons and neutrons.

expensive. A similar detector can be found in the Soudan iron mine in Minnesota, and more elaborate versions are under construction in two highway tunnels linking France and Italy.

In either type of detector, the distinctive pattern of nuclear particle decay would be the same. When a particle disintegrated, it would leave behind lighter particles to carry the energy away. We know of about 20 particles that are lighter than a proton or neutron. However, most of them are unstable, and will disintegrate within one-millionth of a second. Thus, soon after a proton or neutron disintegrates, only three kinds of particles would remain — electrons or positrons, their positive counterparts; neutrinos; and gamma rays, which are energetic packets of light.

The photomultipliers in the water-tank detectors would detect the light that is radiated as these particles pass through water. In the sandwich detectors, the emerging electrons, positrons, and unstable particles would directly trigger the counters that they passed through. In either case, scientists are waiting for a signal that originates inside the detector, with particles radiating from one point.

The energy released by the decay of a proton or neutron would be about 900 million electron volts. This is the energy equivalent of the mass of the nuclear particle. It is hundreds of times greater than the energy released by ordinary radioactivity. The light striking the photomultipliers in the water-tank detectors would provide a rough measure of this energy release, accurate to perhaps 10 per cent. The number of counters struck in the sandwich-type devices would provide a somewhat less precise estimate.

The key to the destruction of a nuclear particle is a phenomenon that scientists have understood since the 1930s — the annihilation of matter by antimatter. For every type of particle there is an object called an antiparticle. The antiparticle's mass equals that of the particle, but other properties of the antiparticle, such as electrical charge, are opposite to those of the particle. The positively charged positron, for example, is the antiparticle of the electron, which has a negative charge.

When particle meets antiparticle, they annihilate each other. But antiparticles are rare, so this process is infrequent. When it occurs, the mass of the particle and antiparticle are converted to mass and energy of lighter particles.

The idea that nuclear particles destroy themselves in this way is an outgrowth of the most important discovery in basic physics in the 1970s — that protons and neutrons are not really elementary bits of matter like electrons, but instead contain three smaller units called quarks. It takes two kinds of quarks, known as *u* and *d*, to build protons and neutrons. A proton is made up of the combination uud, while a neutron is ddu. To the limit of our present ability to measure, quarks, like electrons, have no size at all. The quarks inside a proton or neutron are in continual, rapid motion.

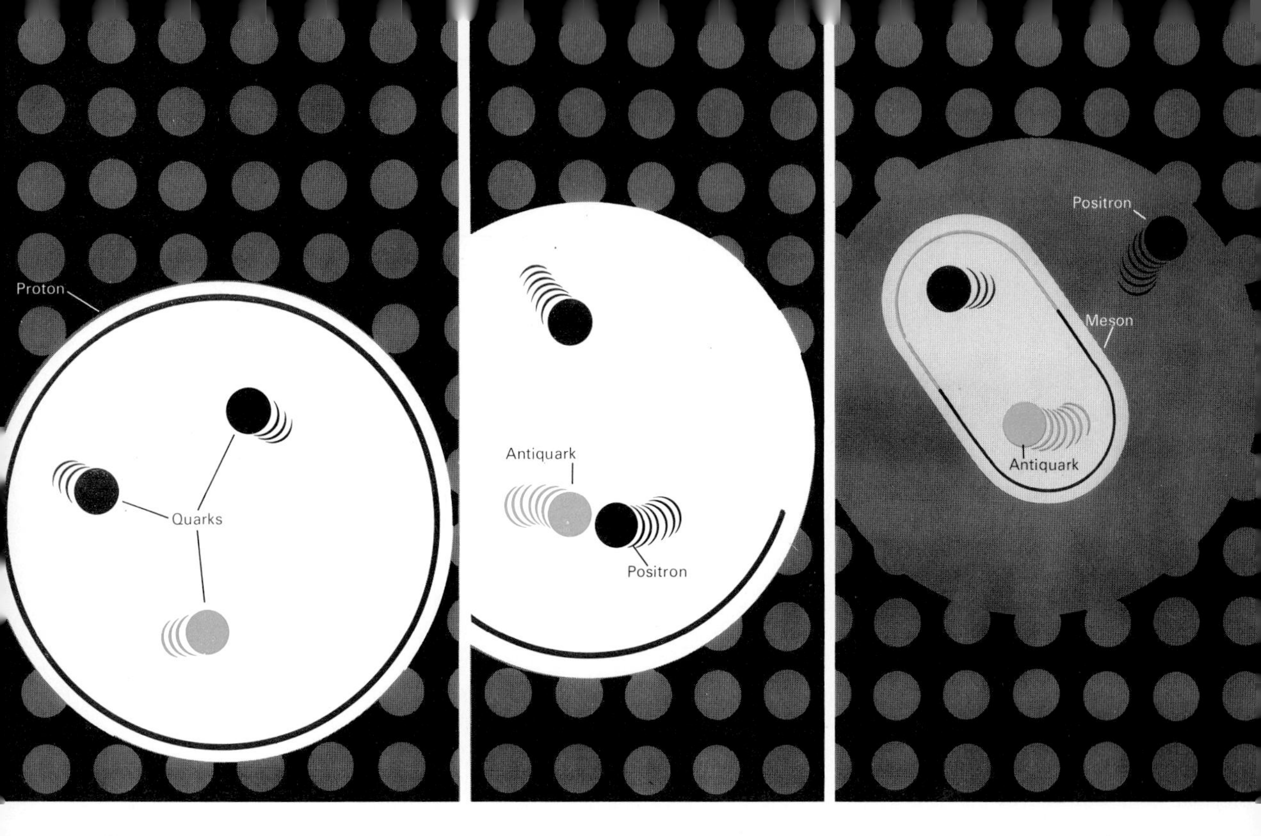

Death of a Proton
A proton may decay when two of its three parts called quarks get extremely close to each other. One quark becomes an antiquark while the other turns into a positron and flies away. The antiquark then joins the remaining quark to form an unstable meson that annihilates itself in a shower of light rays and particles.

Physicists now suspect that, under very special circumstances, a pair of quarks may be able to do something that has never been seen before—turn themselves into antimatter. This permits the proton or neutron of which they are a part to annihilate itself. But this cannot happen very often, because two quarks can do this only when they get extremely close to each other. The distance between them must be less than 10^{-29} centimeter. (The number is also written as a decimal point followed by 28 zeros and the numeral 1.) This is an incredibly small distance. Since a proton or neutron is mostly empty space, the chances of two quarks getting this close would be comparable to the chances of two grains of sand bumping into each other as they wandered throughout the solar system.

When two quarks get this close, they can convert themselves into an antiquark and a non-nuclear antiparticle. For example, the two u quarks in a proton could become a d antiquark and a positron. Several other combinations are possible, but the theories predict that this will be one of the most common. The positron will fly away, and will eventually meet an electron in the world of matter and be annihilated. The antiquark will join the third quark in a combination called a meson and head off in the opposite direction. However, we know that matter and antimatter cannot coexist for very long. The meson will self-destruct in less than one ten-millionth of a second. Finally, nothing will remain of the proton but some photons.

The theories that predict proton decay are based on accelerator experiments conducted during the 1970s. These experiments showed

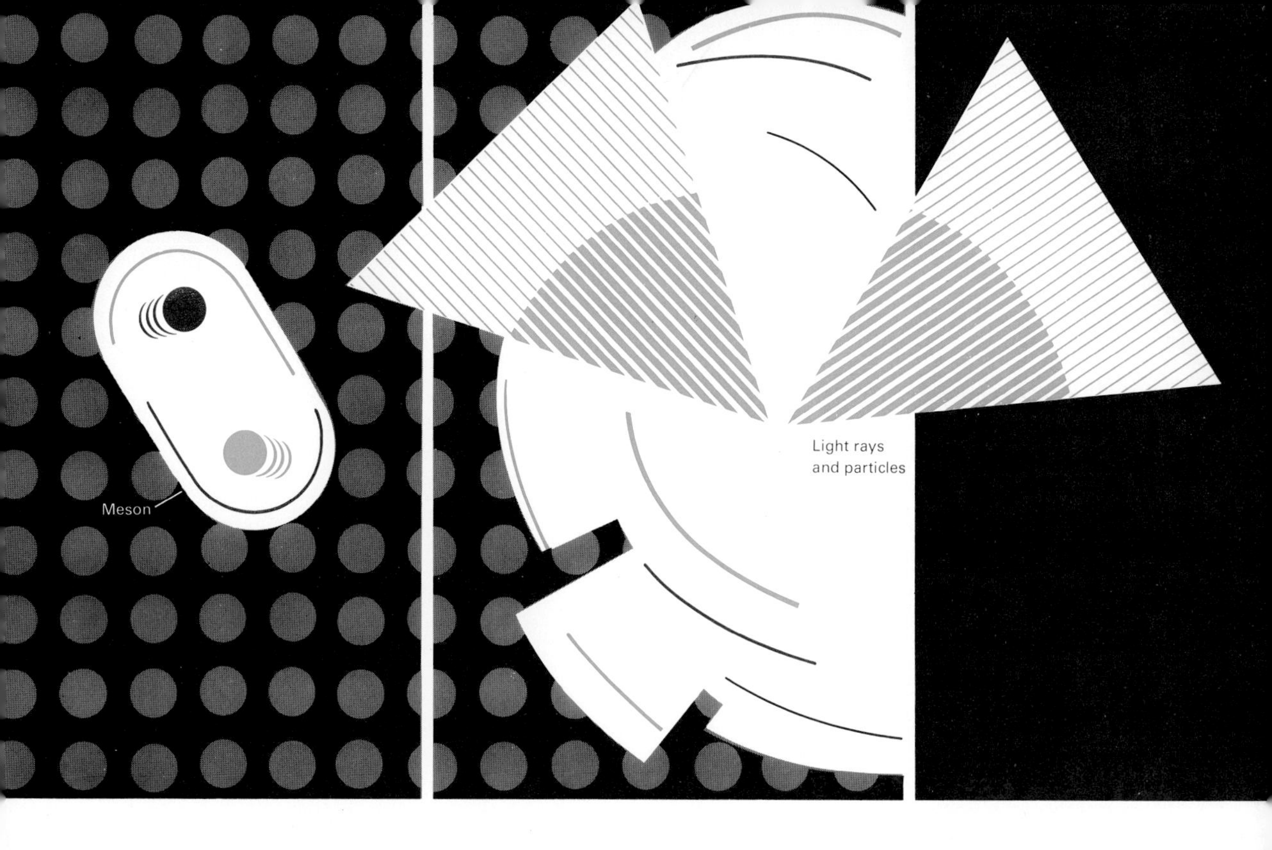

that a certain relationship between the strengths of two of the three basic forces of nature applies to particles as close as 10^{-16} centimeter to one another. Theoretical physicists now believe that this relationship governs a world 10 million million times smaller, controlling particles less than 10^{-29} centimeter apart.

One of the forces that the theories describe is the electromagnetic force, which makes electricity flow and causes magnets to attract each other. The second force is the so-called strong interaction that links the quarks of protons and neutrons.

The third basic force is gravity, which is too feeble to play a significant role in atoms. Until recently, physicists believed there was a fourth basic force, the weak force, but they now know that it is a form of electromagnetism.

Subatomic particles transmit forces by fields, which themselves consist of particles. For example, the electromagnetic force is carried by a field of photons. One electrically charged particle attracts or repels another by emitting a photon, which the other absorbs.

The strong force is carried in the same way by field particles called gluons, which greatly resemble photons. For example, both photons and gluons have no mass and move at the speed of light.

Fields not only hold combinations of particles together, but they also give these particles their identities. That is, subatomic particles differ only in their response to various field particles. Electrons, for example, can neither emit nor absorb gluons, so they are immune to the strong force. Particles that share this immunity are known as

Nature's Unifying Force
As two particles approach each other, the electromagnetic force between them increases while the strong force decreases. Accelerators have shown that the forces vary in this way at distances down to 10^{-16} centimeter. Proton decay experiments may prove they are equal at 10^{-29} centimeter, where a master force emerges.

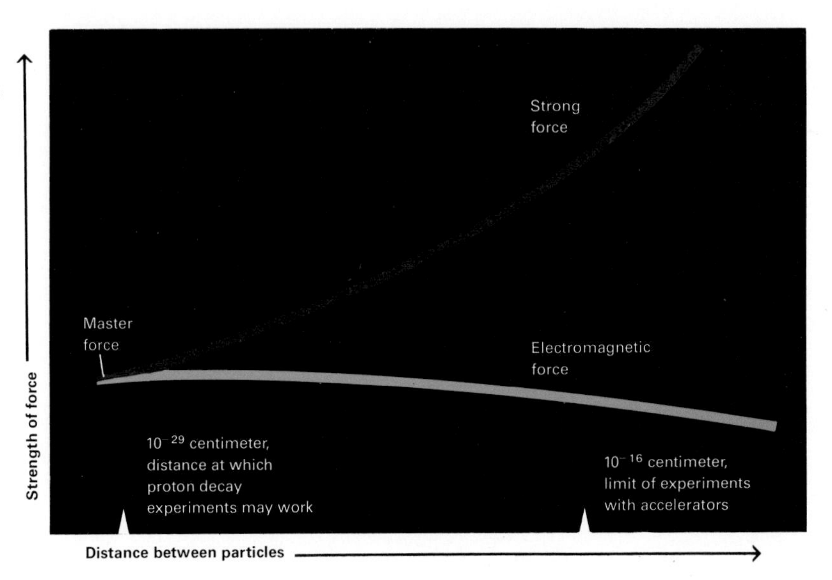

leptons, and six types, including the electron, have been discovered so far. Physicists believe that there is a close kinship between quarks and leptons—that a lepton is in some sense a quark stripped of its ability to react with gluons. For this reason, they expect to find a sixth type of quark, to match the six leptons.

The strong interaction earned its name by being about 100 times stronger than the electromagnetic force. But when a theory of this force was finally constructed in 1974, a curious feature emerged from the calculations. As two quarks approach each other, the strong force tends to get a bit weaker. See THE COLORFUL WORLD OF THE ATOM, *Science Year*, 1981.

The electromagnetic force between quarks, by contrast, tends to get stronger as the particles get closer. The difference between the strengths of the two forces continues to diminish until the quarks get within 10^{-29} centimeter of each other. Then, the two forces become equal. And when this happens, scientists speculate that another force—the "master force"—goes into action. The two quarks use this master force to transform themselves into antimatter.

Physical proof of the master force would be one of the most important events in the history of physics because of what it would tell us about the relationships among basic particles and forces. For example, the particle that transmits the master force, called the leptoquark, treats leptons and quarks in exactly the same way. This field particle even ignores the distinction between matter and antimatter. It can freely transform any pair of fundamental particles into any other particles that have the same total electrical charge. No other field particle can do this.

Thus, a number of important distinctions between particles disappear at distances less than 10^{-29} centimeter. What had seemed to be distinct kinds of particles are unified into one type. For this reason, theories that describe the master force are known as Grand Unified Theories.

For the theories to work, quarks and electrons must be small enough for their centers to get within 10^{-29} centimeter of one another. This suggests that they are unlikely to have smaller parts, and thus that they may truly be the basic particles of matter.

However, the proton decay experiments may not even be conclusive. The calculations of the Grand Unified Theories are based on imperfect measurements that were made on a much greater scale, so the predictions have a large margin of error. Protons might well decay anywhere from one-tenth to 10 times as frequently as the theories suggest. If the decay rate is much less than expected, then perhaps only the detector in the Morton Salt Company's mine will be able to bring in enough information to prove the theories.

As the experimenters begin to harvest their data, cosmologists—scientists who study the history of the universe as a whole—will be peering eagerly over their shoulders. Among the onlookers will be David Schramm of the University of Chicago, who specializes in imagining and describing the earliest moments of the big bang—the explosion that most scientists believe gave birth to our universe between 10 billion and 20 billion years ago. Schramm would like to use the instability of the proton to explain an old cosmological puzzle—why the universe contains a great deal of matter, but only tiny amounts of antimatter.

Cosmologists assume that the universe began as a burst of energy from which particles were immediately formed by the conversion of energy to matter. All known processes for converting energy into particles make equal amounts of matter and antimatter. So how, the cosmologists wonder, did the mixture of matter and antimatter become unbalanced?

According to the Grand Unified Theories, under the right conditions the master force may convert antimatter to matter more rapidly than it turns matter into antimatter. The early universe was so crowded that many particles came within 10^{-29} centimeter of one another. Thus, conversions in both directions would have been frequent. The more rapid transformations of antimatter to matter would have built up a slight excess of matter.

Later, when the particles moved farther apart, master force conversions would have become much rarer. By then, most of the matter and antimatter would have annihilated one another, leaving the small surplus of matter as a residue. An excess of 1 particle of matter for every 1 billion original particles of matter and antimatter would be enough to account for all the matter in the universe today.

Any theory that sheds light on the mystery of the origin of our universe has clearly accomplished a great deal. But is this knowledge of any practical value? The answer—as is usually the case for such abstract science—is that only time will tell.

For Further Reading

Additional information on some of the subjects covered in the Special Reports may be found in these books and magazine articles.

New Light on the Ancient Maya

Adams, R. E. W. *Prehistoric Mesoamerica.* Little, Brown and Company, 1977.

Culbert, T. Patrick. *The Lost Civilization.* Harper and Row, 1974.

Hammond, Norman. *The Ancient Civilization of the Maya.* Rutgers University Press, 1982.

Stuart, G. E., and Stuart, G. S. *The Mysterious Maya.* National Geographic Society, 1977.

Willey, Gordon R. "Maya Archaeology," *Science,* Jan. 15, 1982.

Plants that Eat Animals

Lloyd, F. E. *The Carnivorous Plants.* Chronica Botanica, 1942.

Schnell, Donald E. *Carnivorous Plants of the United States and Canada.* John F. Blair, 1976.

Schnell, Donald E. (ed.). *Carnivorous Plant Newsletter,* Rte. 4, Box 275B, Statesville, N.C.

Slack, Adrian. *Carnivorous Plants.* MIT Press, 1979.

The Hairy Stars

Brandt, John C. *Comets.* W. H. Freeman, 1981.

Calder, Nigel. *The Comet Is Coming: The Feverish Legacy of Mr. Halley.* Viking Press, 1981.

Mayer, Ben. "Bradfield's Dozen: A Guide to Comet Seeking," *Astronomy,* January 1982.

Oppenheimer, Michael, and Haimson, Leonie. "The Comet Syndrome," *Natural History,* December 1980.

Yeomans, Donald K. *The Comet Halley Handbook: An Observer's Guide.* NASA/Jet Propulsion Laboratory, California Institute of Technology, 1981.

Stalking the Medfly

Angier, Natalie. "Menace of the Medfly," *Discover,* September 1981.

Jordan, William. "A Fruitless Pursuit," *Science 82,* April 1982.

Jordan, William. "Invasion of the Medfly," *Natural History,* May 1982.

Time Bombs in the Blood

Grooms, Clarence. *Out of the Night.* Vantage, 1979.

Maugh, Thomas H., II. "New Understanding of Sickle Cell Emerges," *Science,* Jan. 16, 1981.

Maugh, Thomas H., II. "Sickle Cell (II); Many Agents Near Trials," *Science,* Jan. 30, 1981.

"Sickle Cell Disease — Chemical Warfare," *Science News,* Dec. 13, 1980.

Bringing Images to Mind

Fryrear, Jerry L., and Fleshman, Bob (eds.). *Videotherapy in Mental Health.* Charles Thomas, 1981.

Fryrear, Jerry L., and Krause, David A. (eds.). *Phototherapy in Mental Health.* Charles Thomas, 1982.

Gilman, S. L. (ed.). *Faces of Madness.* Brunner/Mazel, 1976.

Hattersley, Ralph. *Discover Your Self Through Photography.* Morgan and Morgan, 1977.

Warmer, Wetter Weather Ahead?

Bernard, Harold W., Jr. *The Greenhouse Effect.* Ballinger, 1980.

Council on Environmental Quality. *Global Energy Futures and the Carbon Dioxide Problem.* U.S. Government Printing Office, 1981.

Kellogg, William W., and Schware, Robert. *Climate Change and Society: Consequences of Increasing Atmospheric Carbon Dioxide.* Westview Press, 1981.

The Promise of Videodiscs

Edelhart, Mike. "Optical Discs: The Omnibus Medium," *Technology,* November/December 1981.

Goldstein, C. M. "Optical Disc Technology and Information," *Science,* Feb. 12, 1982.

Hawkins, William J. "Videodiscs: New Alternative to Movies at Home," *Popular Science,* December 1981.

"Videodiscs: A Three-Way Race for a Billion-Dollar Jackpot," *Business Week,* July 7, 1980.

Energy for the Eons

Clarke, Donald (ed.). *Energy.* Arco, 1980.

Furth, Harold P. "Progress Toward a Tokamak Fusion Reactor," *Scientific American,* August 1979.

Hammond, Allan L., Metz, William D., and Maugh, Thomas H., II. *Energy and the Future.* American Association for the Advancement of Science, 1973.

Kleppe, Thomas S., and Fisher, William L. *Energy Perspectives 2.* United States Department of the Interior, 1976.

Priest, Joseph. *Energy for a Technological Society.* Addison-Wesley, 1979.

Skinner, Brian J. (ed.). *Earth's Energy and Mineral Resources.* William Kaufmann, 1980.

Wilson, Mitchell. *Energy.* Time-Life Books, 1973.

The Brightest Beacons

Burbidge, E. Margaret, and Lynds, C. Roger. "The Absorption Lines of Quasi-stellar Objects," *Scientific American,* December 1970.

Chaffee, Frederick H., Jr. "The Discovery of a Gravitational Lens," *Scientific American,* November 1980.

Ferris, Timothy. *The Red Limit.* William Morrow and Company, 1977.

Osmer, Patrick S. "Quasars as Probes of the Distant and Early Universe," *Scientific American,* February 1982.

Readhead, Anthony C. S. "Radio Astronomy by Very-Long-Baseline Interferometry," *Scientific American,* June 1982.

Our Most Mysterious Sense

Cain, William S. "Educating Your Nose," *Psychology Today,* July 1981.

Hopson, Janet L. "Scents May Lead Us by Our Noses More Than We Realize," *Smithsonian,* March 1979.

Labows, John N. "What the Nose Knows," *The Sciences,* November 1980.

Winter, Ruth. *Scent Talk Among Animals.* J. P. Lippincott, 1977.

Science File

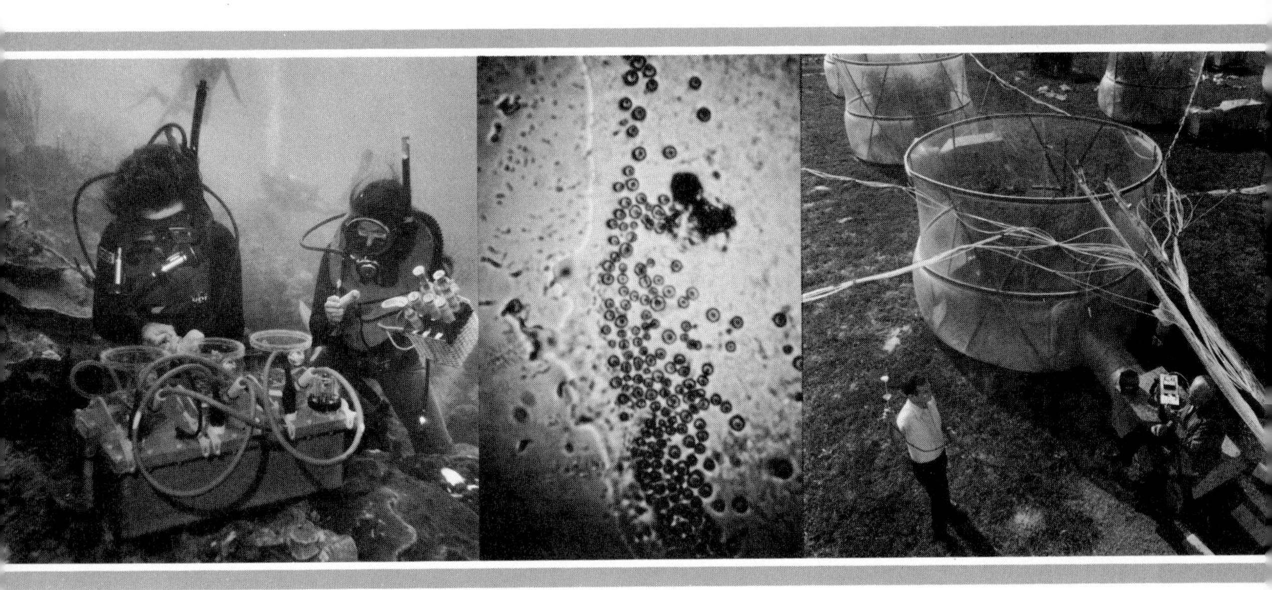

Science Year contributors report on the year's major developments in their respective fields. The articles in this section are arranged alphabetically by subject matter.

Agriculture
Anthropology
Archaeology
- Old World
- New World

Astronomy
- Solar System
- Galactic
- Extragalactic

Books of Science
Botany
Chemistry
Deaths
Drugs
Earth Sciences
- Geology
- Paleontology
- Meteorology
- Oceanography

Ecology
Electronics
Energy
Environment
Genetics
Immunology
Medicine
- Dentistry
- Internal
- Surgery

Molecular Biology
Neuroscience
Nutrition
Physics
- Atoms and Nuclei
- Particles and Forces
- Condensed Matter

Psychology
Public Health
Science Awards
Space Exploration
Zoology

Agriculture

United States Secretary of Agriculture John R. Block in June 1981 announced the production of a genetically engineered vaccine against the virus that causes the highly contagious foot-and-mouth disease. It is the first vaccine produced by genetic engineering to be proven effective against disease in animals or humans. The disease causes blisters on the mouths and feet of pigs, sheep, cattle, and other animals with cleft hoofs so that they have difficulty eating and walking.

The vaccine was developed by scientists at the U.S. Department of Agriculture's (USDA) Plum Island Animal Disease Center in New York, and Genentech Incorporated, a San Francisco-based research firm. The scientists removed small pieces of plasmids—rings of bacterial genetic material—from the bacteria *Escherichia coli* and replaced them with a gene for manufacturing the protein coat of the foot-and-mouth disease virus. They added the altered plasmid to *E. coli* cultures. The bacteria absorbed the altered plasmids and reproduced, making large numbers of the gene, and producing great quantities of the virus protein coat, which was added to serum to create the vaccine.

The vaccine is safe and effective. It cannot cause the disease in a vaccinated animal because it contains only the protein coat, not the whole virus. However, the presence of the protein coat, which acts as an identification card for the virus, alerts the animal's immune system to produce antibodies to the virus. Thus, if an epidemic of the disease should occur, the animal is prepared with a store of antibodies to ward off the viral attack. The vaccine is expected to save thousands of head of livestock and improve the quality of meat, adding billions of dollars to livestock revenues each year and increasing the world's meat supply.

Arresting other animal diseases. Scientists at the Agricultural Research Services (ARS) Regional Poultry Research Laboratory in East Lansing, Mich., announced in December 1981 that vaccinating unborn chicks through the eggshell provided im-

Scientists match an image of the items in a suitcase with the bag's contents, *below,* to test an X-ray system designed to detect smuggled food, which may carry new insects and disease agents into the United States.
A chemist collects gases emitted by an orange, *below right,* in an effort to identify volatile compounds unique to food, which can alert electronic baggage sniffers to contraband edibles.

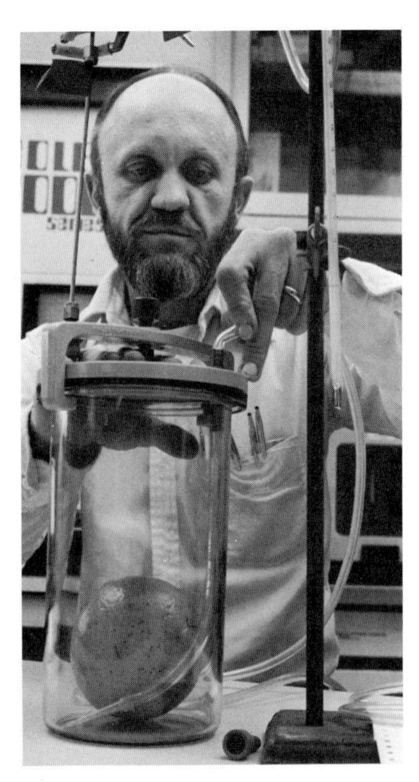

proved resistance to Marek's disease—a highly contagious infection of the lymph glands. ARS veterinary medical officer Jagdev M. Sharma reported that chicks vaccinated before they hatched are protected from the disease much better than chicks vaccinated the day they hatch—the current practice in commercial production.

The researchers inoculated a group of eggs with the vaccine three days before they hatched and vaccinated another group of chicks on the day that they hatched. Both groups were exposed to Marek's disease three days after hatching. Within a few days, 72 per cent of the chicks vaccinated after hatching—but 12 per cent of those vaccinated in the shell—had died.

Sharma also determined that chicks vaccinated in the shell 18 days after the eggs were laid had the best immunity to the disease. He advised poultry growers to inoculate eggs at this point, which is when the eggs are transferred to hatching trays.

Scientists in 1981 and 1982 learned more about the elusive scrapie agent—the infectious particle that causes a degenerative disease of the central nervous system in sheep and goats. Biochemist Stanley B. Prusiner of the School of Medicine at the University of California in San Francisco issued a report in April 1982 summarizing various research activities on the disease.

According to his report, scientists have found that the scrapie agent does not seem to contain genetic material. Unlike a virus, bacterium, or other disease agent, it is not destroyed by most substances that change genetic material. However, it is destroyed by enzymes that break apart proteins in general. Because it appears to be a proteinlike particle that causes infection, Prusiner named it a *prion*.

Scientists do not yet know how prions reproduce. Future research might lead to significant progress in the control of several degenerative diseases in livestock and humans.

Better grazing grasses. Mefluidide, a new plant-growth regulator tested in 1981 and 1982, offers great promise in improving the forage quality of field grass. Agronomist James Bond and research associate Barbara Glenn of the USDA research station at Beltsville, Md.; ruminant nutritionist Donald G. Ely of the University of Kentucky in Lexington; and chemist Timothy P. Sullivan of 3M Company in St. Paul, Minn., reported in January 1982 that mefluidide inhibited seed production, increased crude protein and total sugars, and reduced the cellulose content of the grazing grass, tall fescue.

The researchers noted that, in preventing grass from going to seed, mefluidide prolonged its vegetative stage when nutrient levels are highest. Livestock that ate mefluidide-treated grass had an easier time digesting it and gained weight more rapidly than livestock fed untreated grass. The results were the same for grazing cattle and those given cut grass treated with mefluidides. This indicates that both confined and free-range cattle can benefit from the treated grass.

The cold treatment. Horticulturists W. E. Finch-Savage and C. J. Cox of Fluid Drilling Limited in Warwickshire, England, reported in April 1982 that soaking vegetable seeds and putting them through a cold treatment greatly improved germination. A seed contains an embryonic living plant that continues to expend energy even though it may not appear to be growing. Seeds stored at room temperature may lose moisture and age beyond the point of germination. Scientists have searched for ways to extend the germination period of seeds.

The British horticulturists first soaked the seeds in 20°C (68°F.) water and then transferred the seeds from the water to a refrigerator set at 1°C (34°F.)—a temperature high enough to keep them alive but too low for visible growth. They kept the seeds at that temperature until weather conditions were suitable and then planted them in the field. Finch-Savage and Cox found that cold-treated seeds of parsnip, celery, leek, and pepper germinated earlier and more uniformly than nontreated seeds, and that cold treatments increased the percentage of all seeds that germinated.

Cotton's comeback. A team of agronomists, entomologists, and plant pathologists from Texas A&M University in College Station in April 1982 described a system for protecting cotton against insects that has signifi-

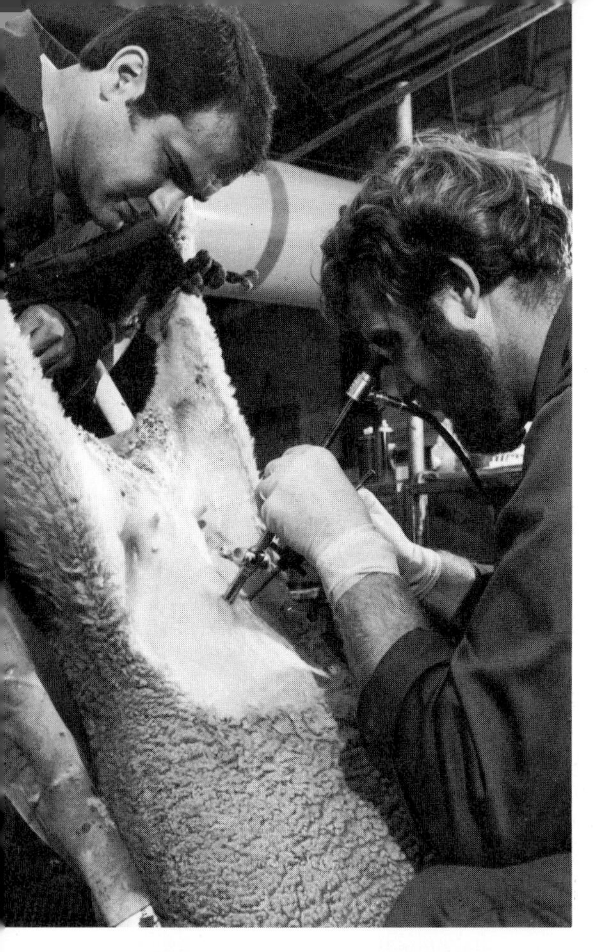

A geneticist assesses a young ewe's fertility by counting its ovaries through a lighted scope, *left*. His colleagues, *above,* use an ultrasound scanner to measure layers of fat and muscle on a sheep. Only the leanest and most fertile sheep are selected for breeding because they often produce unusually large litters of lambs, *below*.

Agriculture

Continued

cantly improved crop production in Texas. Cotton has been treated with insecticides more heavily than any other U.S. crop. As a result, all the major cotton predators have developed a resistance to a majority of the insecticides used against them. This resistance almost destroyed the Texas cotton industry in the late 1960's.

The Texas A&M team reported that their pest-control system had been in effect in parts of the state for almost 10 years. It is based on planting short-season dwarf varieties of cotton, which mature early and escape the ravages of cotton's major predators—boll weevils and budworms. Because boll weevils strike late in the season, harvested stalks are plowed under by mid-September to remove the pest's food source. An early spring spraying eliminates pests that survive the winter.

The report indicated that under this system the average net return to the cotton producer increased from $62 to $170 per acre since 1975 and that insecticide use decreased from 12.3 pounds per acre to 1.5 pounds per acre. The producers were also able to significantly reduce fertilizer, irrigation, and overall production costs.

The blue duiker, a small South African antelope, may become a prime subject for determining the nutritional value of new grazing grasses, according to a report by ruminant nutritionist Robert L. Corvan of Pennsylvania State University in State College in December 1981. Although it is a true ruminant with a four-part stomach that produces cud, it stands only about 30 centimeters (1 foot) high and weighs less than 4 kilograms (10 pounds). Corvan argued that the blue duiker could serve well as a test animal because it takes up less room than sheep, and lives happily when caged. Moreover, it requires only 10 per cent as much food as sheep, enabling laboratories to grow sufficient quantities of grazing grasses in greenhouses year-round rather than outdoors only during the summer. Thus, research projects that might take 20 years using sheep can be completed in 5 years with the blue duikers. [Sylvan H. Wittwer]

Anthropology

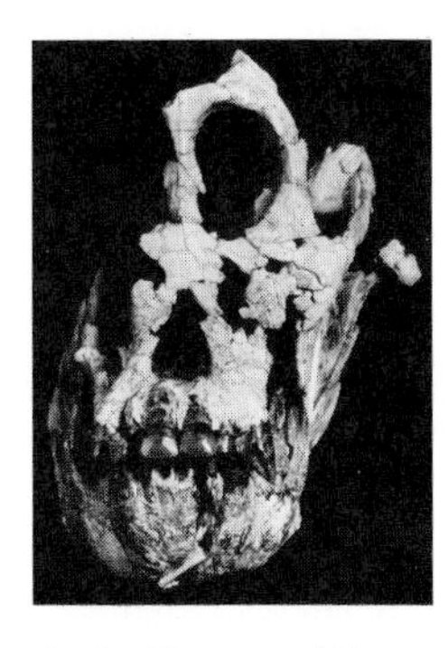

An 8-million-year-old *Sivapithecus* fossil skull found in Pakistan is changing the widely held belief that *Ramapithecus,* a nearly identical contemporary, is a direct human ancestor. The skull has many features resembling those of modern orang-utans.

Ramapithecus, thought by many anthropologists to be the earliest known hominid—an ancestor of humans, rather than apes—appears to be rapidly losing that distinction. Helping to bring about this shift is an 8-million-year-old fossil found on the Potwar Plateau of Pakistan. The fossil, a partial skull of a chimpanzee-sized creature, was discovered by members of a research project directed by anthropologists David R. Pilbeam of Harvard University's Peabody Museum and Ibrahim Shah of the Geological Survey of Pakistan.

In January 1982, Pilbeam reported that although he has classified the skull as *Sivapithecus*, he believes it is very similar to—if not identical with—*Ramapithecus* fossils found earlier in Pakistan. Pilbeam noted that many features of the skull resemble those of modern orang-utans. Since *Ramapithecus* so closely resembles *Sivapithecus*, Pilbeam suggests that *Ramapithecus* should no longer be considered a direct human ancestor. However, he theorizes *Sivapithecus* was not a direct ancestor of the orang-utan either, but rather a close relative of that ancestor. Pilbeam also suggests that the differences between his find and similar African fossils are significant enough to push back to at least 13 million years ago the point at which Asian and African apes diverged.

East African finds. Anthropologist J. A. J. Gowlett of Oxford University in England reported in November 1981 on the discovery of parts of a hominid skull, nearly 1,000 stone artifacts, and numerous animal remains at Chesowanja, near Lake Baringo in Kenya. According to Gowlett, the newly discovered hominid fossils, which are from the top and side of a skull, show a prominently developed ridge running along the top of the skull and a divided ridge on the back. Gowlett identified the new find as *Australopithecus boisei*, the extremely robust hominid best known from fossils discovered at Olduvai Gorge in Tanzania and the east Lake Turkana area in Kenya.

A cluster of burnt pieces of clay was also discovered at Chesowanja.

A 14,000-year-old sculpted stone face – half human and half animal – found at El Juyo Cave in northeast Spain presides over the oldest known religious shrine and the first intact religious sanctuary found from the early Stone Age.

Gowlett suggests they might be the remains of a campfire. If so, the clay pieces, dated to 1.4 million years ago, would be the oldest known evidence for the use of fire by hominids anywhere in the world.

Ancient butchers. Fossils found in East Africa provide strong evidence that hominids butchered and ate such animals as primitive horses and giraffes 1.5 million to 2 million years ago. Anthropologists Henry T. Bunn of the University of California, Berkeley, Richard Potts of Harvard University, and Pat Shipman of Johns Hopkins University reported in January 1982 on their analysis of hominid remains, stone tools, and fragmentary animal bones found at Olduvai Gorge and the east Lake Turkana area. The researchers analyzed fine nicks and grooves on the animal bones under both a conventional microscope and an electron scanning microscope. They concluded that the markings are different from those made by carnivores and rodents, natural weathering, and archaeologists during excavation. They further concluded that the markings were made by hominids as they removed the meat from animal carcasses with sharp pieces of stone.

However, such meat-eating was not always beneficial to the hominid, according to evidence gathered from the most complete fossil of *Homo erectus*, an adult female found in the east Lake Turkana area in 1973. The arm and leg bones of the skeleton, which is approximately 1.6 million years old, contain abnormal deposits of bone. The deposits are 7 millimeters (0.28 inch) thick near the center but thinner toward the ends. Alan Walker of Johns Hopkins University, Michael R. Zimmerman of Hahnemann Medical College in Philadelphia, and Richard E. Leakey of the National Museums of Kenya concluded in March 1982 that the changes in the bones were produced by a chronic overdose of vitamin A. They believe the disorder resulted from eating carnivore liver, an organ containing massive amounts of the vitamin.

Chinese fossils. New specimens of *Homo erectus*, consisting of a skullcap, six teeth, parts of a shoulder and hip, and a rib, were recovered from a limestone cave in Shandong Province, approximately 320 kilometers (200 miles) south of Peking, in October 1981. Thought to be from two adults, the human fossils are estimated to be between 400,000 and 500,000 years old. The thickness of the skull bones and the primitive quality of the teeth suggest that they are similar to the famous Peking man specimens that disappeared while being shipped from China during World War II.

Greek mystery solved. A team headed by G. J. Hennig of the University of Cologne in West Germany announced in August 1981 that it had finally dated a human skull found in a limestone cave near Petralona, Greece, in 1960. The age of the well-preserved primitive skull had eluded researchers because it had been found lying by itself on the floor of the cave. Using various dating methods, researchers had estimated that the skull was anywhere from 70,000 to 700,000 years old.

Hennig and his team established an age of 200,000 years for the skull by dating the brown calcite that encrusted the fossil with a method called electron spin resonance. Brown calcite is a mineral found in limestone and, like other minerals, it grows by forming crystal lattices. Electrons become trapped within these lattices and gradually take on a magnetic quality. Scientists use electron spin resonance to determine age by measuring the number of electrons with this quality.

Ancient tooth. The discovery of a tooth that may be the second oldest human fossil found in Great Britain was reported in December 1981 by Stephen Green and a team from the National Museum of Wales. The tooth, which has been dated to about 200,000 years ago, was found in Pontnewydd Cave in the lower Elwy Valley of north Wales. The oldest human fossils from Britain are the Swanscombe fossils, which are thought to be 275,000 years old.

The tooth, an upper left molar, is very similar in shape to early Neanderthal teeth found at Krapina, Yugoslavia. The right side of a lower jaw from a child or adolescent and an adult vertebra, also found in the cave, are thought to be about the same age as the tooth. [Charles F. Merbs]

Archaeology

Old World. Israel's withdrawal from the Sinai Peninsula in April 1982 put an end to a number of Israeli-sponsored archaeological excavations in the area. Archaeologist Rudolf Cohen of Israel's Department of Antiquities reported in April on excavations in the northern Sinai at Kadesh Barnea, where Israeli kings of the 700s, 600s, and 500s B.C. built three large fortresses, each on the ruins of the previous one. Cohen suggests the site also was a camp of the tribes of Israel during the Exodus, the departure of the Israelites from Egypt under the leadership of Moses in the 1200s B.C.

Along the Mediterranean coast in the northeast corner of the Sinai, archaeologist Elizer Oren of Ben-Gurion University in Beersheba, Israel, completed excavations in April on ancient Egyptian fortifications dating back to the 1200s B.C. Oren believes the existence of this powerful Egyptian military presence in the area rules out the possibility that Moses and the Israelites took a northern route across the Sinai. Despite intensive surveys, no other evidence of the ancient Israelites has been found in the Sinai.

Ancient art. In February 1982, geologist H. P. Schwarcz of McMaster University in Hamilton, Canada, reported that the world's oldest known decorative artifact may be an ivory plaque dating to about 100,000 years ago. The plaque, found at Tata, Hungary, is made of enamel separated from a mammoth's tooth. The enamel was beveled and shaped, then colored with red minerals.

Riddle of the Great Sphinx. In April 1982, Egyptologist James P. Allen and archaeologist Mark E. Lehner of the American Research Center in Cairo presented evidence that there was astronomical significance in the alignment of the Great Sphinx with its adjacent temples and with the pyramids at Giza. They noted that the hieroglyphic symbols representing the Sphinx sometimes show the sun forming a crown on the monument's head. Also, during the New Kingdom period (1570-1070 B.C.), the Sphinx was regarded as a manifestation of the sun

Four bronze horses, a chariot, and driver discovered in the tomb of Qin Shi Huang near Xian, China, are among the earliest and largest bronze statues ever found in China.

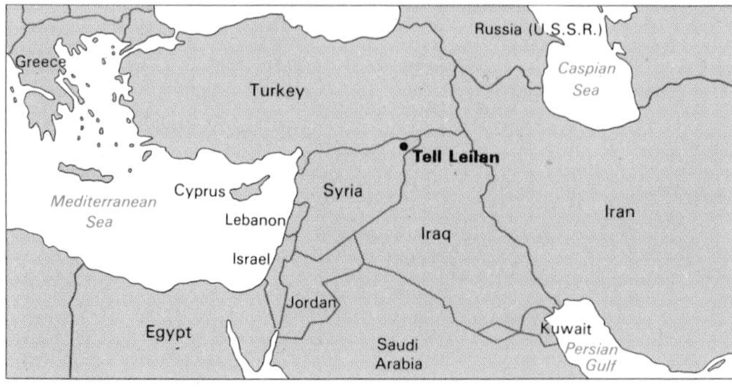

A cuneiform tablet that tells of an ancient journey through Mesopotamia is the clue that led to the discovery of Shubat Enlil, the 4,000-year-old capital of a great Assyrian empire. The ruins of the city are near Tell Leilan in northeastern Syria.

god. The scientists then showed that if one stood in the doorway of a temple near the Sphinx and looked at the setting sun on the day of the winter solstice (December 20 or 21), the sun would appear to form a crown on the Sphinx's head—just as in the hieroglyph. They also found that if one stood in front of the Sphinx and looked directly over its head on the day of the summer solstice (June 20 or 21), the sun would appear precisely between the two largest pyramids at Giza. June 21 marks the approximate beginning of the annual Nile floods.

Roman settlement. Excavations led by archaeologist Graham Webster of the University of Birmingham in England in 1980 and 1981 centered on one of the most interesting aspects of the archaeology of the Roman Empire—the study of border settlements where Roman might and custom met the "barbarians." Webster and his team studied one such town, Viroconium, whose ruins lie around the village of Wroxeter, near Shrewsbury, England. The archaeologists' findings show that by about A.D. 75 Viroconium was a Roman fortress from which attacks were directed at hostile Welsh tribes. Later, Viroconium was expanded and settled by Roman soldiers and artisans and native Britons. The town was also greatly enlarged as part of the Roman Emperor Hadrian's efforts in the A.D. 120s to wall off Roman Britain from the fierce Scots and Welsh. In later years, the town dwindled to a tiny village and fell into ruin.

Another frontier town of the classical age was Ai Khanum in northern Afghanistan. Alexander the Great may have founded the city, which was settled about 300 B.C. by Greek colonists. In January 1982, archaeologist Paul Bernard of the École Pratique des Hautes Études in Paris reported on the 15-year excavation at the site.

Although Ai Khanum was more than 5,000 kilometers (3,000 miles) from Greece, its inhabitants minted Greek-style coins, and built Greek-style temples and palaces. They also wrote in Greek. However, about 145 B.C., the inhabitants of Ai Khanum were driven from the city by central Asian nomads and probably never returned. [Robert J. Wenke]

Archaeology
Continued

New World. Archaeologists have known for decades that from 9500 to 9000 B.C. some Ice Age peoples of North and South America hunted the mammoth, an extinct animal closely related to the elephant. Now, scientists have evidence indicating that the mastodon, another relative of the elephant that became extinct about 10,000 years ago, was also the prey of early hunters.

Paleontologist Russell W. Graham of the Illinois State Museum in Springfield, Ill., reported in September 1981 that fluted stone spearpoints, called Clovis points, had been found next to mastodon bones at Kimmswick, Mo., near St. Louis. The dates established for similar spearpoints found with mammoth bones at sites in the Western United States led Graham to conclude that Kimmswick is at least 11,200 years old.

In October 1981, anthropologist Thomas D. Dillehay of the University of Kentucky in Lexington reported that he and a team of Chilean scientists had discovered mastodon bones at Monte Verde in south-central Chile. The site lies in a cold, humid forest, unchanged since the Ice Age, which ended about 10,000 years ago. The scientists found the bones next to the remnants of what may have been a dwelling, which had been preserved by a layer of peat and is from 12,000 to 15,000 years old. If scientists prove that a dwelling existed there, Monte Verde would be the oldest known dwelling site in the New World.

Looting at Maya sites. The destruction of ancient Maya sites increased during the year. In August 1981, archaeologist George E. Stuart of the National Geographic Society in Washington, D.C., reported vandalism and looting at the Maya cave of Naj Tunich in northern Guatemala. Rare examples of Maya paintings, which adorned the walls of the cave, had been defaced.

Archaeologists David M. and Elizabeth G. Pendergast of the Royal Ontario Museum in Toronto, Canada, reported in July 1981 the plundering of ancient Maya sites in Belize—even in such major tourist areas as Xunantun-

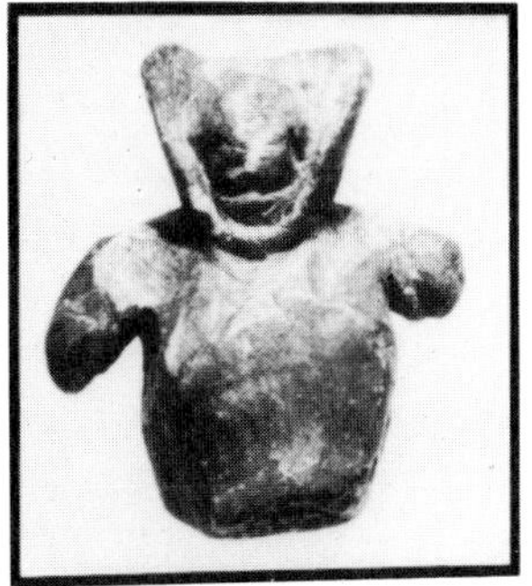

Artifacts in a 4,000-year-old settlement discovered in Labrador, Canada, provide evidence of a sophisticated Indian culture in an area thought previously to be the exclusive domain of Eskimos.

Science Year
Close-Up

Reburial Grounds for Controversy

Are ancient human bones scientific objects to be analyzed, studied, and displayed? Or are they hallowed remains that should rest undisturbed? These questions are at the heart of a conflict raging in California between anthropologists and American Indians. Ultimately, the fate of 20,000 Indian skeletons may be at stake.

The dispute erupted in September 1981 when the California Department of Parks and Recreation put into effect a decision made in 1978 allowing American Indian groups to reclaim for reburial the department's collection of 871 Indian skeletal remains and 10,000 artifacts found in Indian graves. These artifacts include shell beads and ornaments.

The Native American Heritage Commission, an Indian rights group that spearheaded the reburial effort, reclaimed a number of the remains and artifacts shortly afterward. On October 30, a group of Kumeyaay Indians reburied some remains at Cuyamaca State Park near San Diego. A month later, a group of Yurok Indians reburied remains and artifacts at Patrick's Point State Park near Eureka.

But many California anthropologists vehemently opposed the decision by the parks department allowing reburials, so they formed the American Committee for the Preservation of Archaeological Collections (ACPAC). The ACPAC members condemned the reburials as the destruction of archaeological evidence, which they contend provides vital information on the unwritten history of California's Indians.

The anthropologists argue that reburial will deprive them of valuable scientific data that can be used to study American Indian groups. For example, by examining skeletal remains, scientists can learn about the nutrition and medical history of individuals as well as the demographic characteristics of a group, including the relative ages, sex, and life spans of group members.

California scientists are particularly concerned because new methods of analyzing and dating skeletal remains and artifacts are still being developed. For example, if, before 1949, human bones had routinely been reburied, scientists would have been unable to date the remains because radiocarbon dating had not yet been discovered.

In order to test new techniques and formulate new theories, the scientists explain, they must be able to examine original remains and artifacts rather than photographs, drawings, or plaster casts. If the number of original objects available for study is limited, the data they gather may be incomplete and may prevent them from reaching a conclusion or may lead researchers to the wrong conclusions.

Finally, the scientists contend that because many of the remains are thousands of years old, no one can be sure they are directly attributed to a specific modern Indian tribe.

However, many California Indians, who consider ancestral remains sacred, view the matter differently. They believe that any disturbance of an ancestor's grave, including archaeological excavation, is a violation of their religious beliefs and brings the ancestor's spirit back to earth from its dwelling place in the other world. The Indians also feel that subjecting ancestral skeletons to scientific analysis without the consent of the concerned tribes is unjust and disrespectful.

In addition, some Indians believe the issue raises questions of racism because, they say, the skeletons of early California pioneers and explorers have not been excavated for scientific study and display.

On February 4, ACPAC obtained a court order forbidding further reburials until both the Native American Heritage Commission and the California Department of Parks and Recreation file an environmental impact report with the court. The report must evaluate the effect the reburials would have on California's scientific resources. Until the report is completed, anthropologists may study the skeletal remains and artifacts. The Indians may prevent this only if they can establish a direct connection between the bones and a specific tribe.

The stakes are high for both sides. California's museums and other scientific institutions hold an estimated 20,000 American Indian skeletons. Until the issue is settled, however, the remains will continue to be bones of contention. [Colin I. Busby] ich. Looters, digging into unexcavated mounds and tombs, have left jagged pits resembling bomb craters. See New Light on the Ancient Maya.

Ancient peoples of the Arctic. Excavation finds reported in July 1981 by archaeologist Robert McGhee of the National Museums of Canada in Ottawa have provided new information on the early inhabitants of the Canadian Arctic regions. The Brooman Point Village site on frigid Bathurst Island yielded evidence that Eskimos belonging to the Dorset and Thule cultures occupied the area from 1000 B.C. to A.D. 1100. The Dorset occupied the site until about A.D. 1000, when they were replaced by Eskimos of the Thule culture, who hunted the numerous sea mammals of the area.

The scientists found an array of Dorset artifacts, including carved ivory objects representing bears, people, seals, birds, and fish, and such bone tools as harpoon points and knife handles preserved in the frozen remains of collapsed Thule houses. Fortunately for archaeological studies, the Thule people unknowingly saved the artifacts of the Dorset people by using soil that contained Dorset refuse to build the walls of their houses.

Identifying the *Pinta*. In March 1982, the government of the Turks and Caicos Islands in the Bahamas gave the Institute of Nautical Archaeology at Texas A&M University at College Station the exclusive right to excavate a shipwreck some archaeologists believe may be the *Pinta*, one of the three ships that sailed with Christopher Columbus on his voyage to the New World in 1492. The wreck was discovered in 1977 by treasure hunters, who claimed the right to salvage the wreck and had already completed some excavations on the site.

The *Pinta* returned to the New World in 1500 as part of a small fleet and sank during the voyage. Artifacts from the shipwreck show that the vessel sank around 1500. In order to establish that the wreck is indeed the *Pinta*, archaeologists must precisely identify such items as the ship's cannon or ballast stones. [Thomas R. Hester]

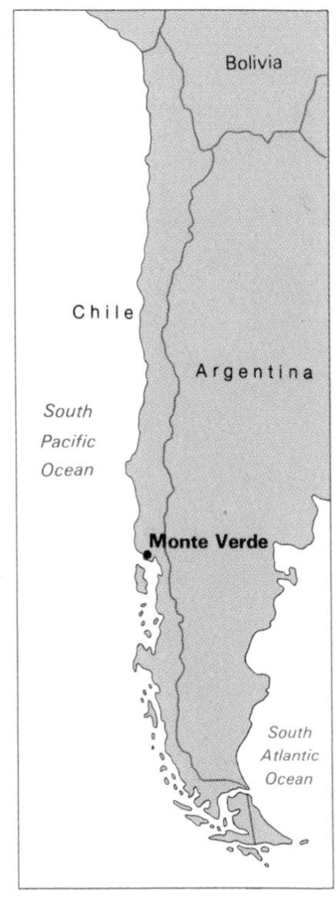

Remains of a building foundation near Monte Verde, Chile, are believed to be 12,000 to 15,000 years old. The foundation could be the oldest known architectural structure in America.

Astronomy

Solar System Astronomy. Two Russian spacecraft, *Venera 13* and *Venera 14*, touched down on the surface of Venus on March 1 and 5, 1982. For more than two hours, they radioed back to Earth excellent pictures and other scientific data about the nature of the surface. Their accomplishment is remarkable considering the incredible heat—455°C (850°F.)—and atmospheric pressure—about 95 kilograms per square centimeter (1,352 pounds per square inch)—on the surface of Venus. Barely three weeks later, Russian geophysicists Yuri A. Surkov and Valery L. Barsukov of the Vernadsky Institute of Geochemistry and Analytical Chemistry in Moscow visited the United States and reported on early scientific results of the mission.

The two landing sites were separated by about 950 kilometers (590 miles). The *Venera 13* site was 760 meters (2,500 feet) higher than that of *Venera 14*. Both craft landed near the planet's equator.

The *Venera 13* camera revealed a greatly eroded surface littered by small pieces of rock with patches of sandy material in-between. At the other site, the surface appeared to consist of more solid, but layered, rock with little sand or dust, though some erosion effects were still evident. At both sites, the rocks appeared to be of several types.

The major goal of the two lander missions was to gather data on the origin and nature of the surface rocks in order to deduce something of the history of Venus and of the processes that shaped its surface. One of the prime experiments involved a study of how the surface material fluoresces, or gives off light, when irradiated with X rays. Equipment on each lander drilled into the planet's surface to obtain a small rock sample. Surkov and Barsukov reported that compact drilling devices on the bases of both *Venera* craft drilled into solid rock. The devices then passed each sample through a set of air locks into the spacecraft for analysis. The temperature and pressure inside the spacecraft were much lower than outside, to make the measurements possible.

Bright, densely cratered regions (one 250 miles in diameter) contrast strongly with darker, smoother areas on the surface of Saturn's moon Tethys in a *Voyager 2* photo made on the spacecraft's fly-by in August 1981. The varied terrain suggests the moon's developmental history.

Unprecedented clarity of detail on the surface of Venus is revealed in photos made in March by the Russian *Venera 14*. The flat cracked rock is characteristic of cooled basalt, while a boulder pile (top) shows where gases bubbled through molten material.

Inside the *Veneras*, the samples were irradiated with X rays from plutonium-238 and iron-55. Rock samples glow when they are irradiated, giving off X rays of their own. The X rays fall at specific wavelengths on the electromagnetic spectrum. These emissions are characteristic of the elements of which the rocks are composed. By analyzing these emissions, and drawing on their experience with Earth rocks, the Russian scientists could determine the rock type and make inferences about the origin and history of that part of Venus' surface.

The scientists found that the rocks at both sites are basaltic—that is, they are igneous, or volcanic, rocks that were probably flung out from volcanoes and cooled on the planet's surface. The composition of the rocks from each site was different. The rocks from the *Venera 13* site contained much more potassium. This implies a slightly different geological history for the two samples.

***Voyager 2* at Saturn.** Four years after its launch on Aug. 20, 1977, and barely 10 months after its sister spacecraft, *Voyager 1*, encountered Saturn, *Voyager 2* flew by the planet on Aug. 25, 1981. Its mission was twofold—to look for answers to questions raised by the data from *Voyager 1*, and to make a close-up examination of some of Saturn's moons that were neglected in the earlier *Voyager* encounter. The many new findings included data showing that Saturn's rings are even more complex and dynamic than had been suspected; that the body of the moon Tethys appears to be cracked open; and that the interior of the moon Enceladus is still evolving rapidly.

Instruments on *Voyager 2* observed how light from the star Delta Scorpii flickered and changed in intensity as the star passed behind Saturn's rings. Because of the location of the star, its very small apparent diameter—which appears as a point of light—and its slow relative motion, the astronomers could use it to backlight and probe the ring structure. They learned that the F ring, which was discovered by *Voyager 1*, and appeared to consist of four or five interwoven or braided "strands," is composed of at least 10 strands. In addition, and to everyone's surprise, the new pictures showed that the braided appearance had disappeared. Under high-resolution scrutiny, the multitude of fine strands, or ringlets, that make up the larger-scale structure often appeared to form regular sequences of patterns. *Voyager 2* scientists think these are gravity waves stimulated in special regions of the ring that are strongly affected by the gravitational field of Saturn's closer moons.

The experimenters also obtained pictures demonstrating that some of the ringlets are either incomplete or spiral rather than circular. No one has yet explained these phenomena fully.

In addition, astronomers found that the surface of Tethys has one of the largest craters of any Saturnian moon. In fact, some of the other moons could easily fit within its boundaries. This crater, with a diameter of 400 kilometers (250 miles), is extremely large compared with Tethys, which is 1,050 kilometers (650 miles) in diameter. The crater floor domes up, so that at its center the floor is higher than the crater rim.

In addition to this mammoth crater, the surface has an enormous crack that runs almost three-fourths of the way around Tethys' circumference. The *Voyager* experimenters believe that this crack, or chasm, may be the result of the moon's interior freezing just after Tethys was formed. Because it was made largely of water, the interior would have expanded as it froze, cracking the surface.

Another moon, Iapetus, has one hemisphere covered with very dark material and the other with very bright material. *Voyager* returned images showing that impact craters on the bright hemisphere have very dark floors. Scientists had previously believed that the dark material came from outside Tethys, perhaps from Phoebe, the next moon, as the result of some collision in the remote past. Detecting the dark material in the floors of bright-side craters seems to indicate that the dark material has always belonged to Iapetus.

Diamonds in the sky? Our understanding of the interior composition

A scientist uses the solar diameter monitor, a supersensitive telescope, to make very accurate measurements that will help determine if the sun is shrinking. The telescope is at the High Altitude Observatory in Boulder, Colo.

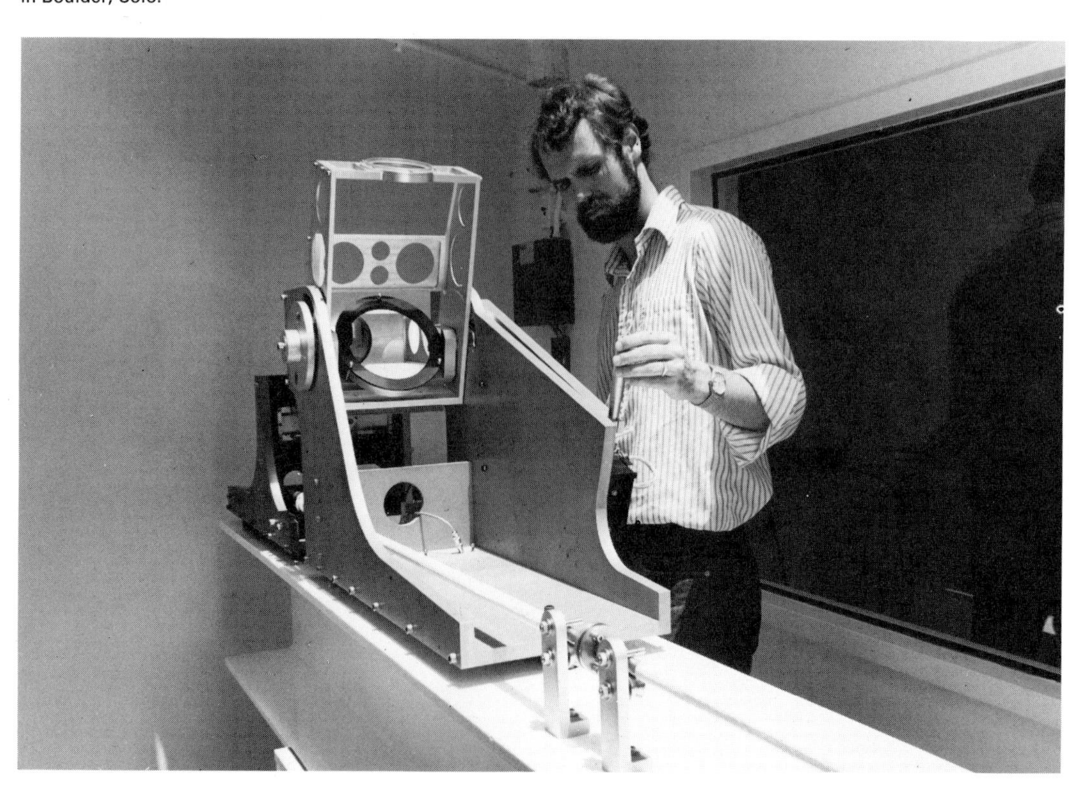

"That's not what Carl Sagan said."

and structure of the planets depends on our knowledge of how common materials behave at the high temperatures and pressures existing inside planets. Generally, this understanding rests on a rather weak foundation because the necessary laboratory data at high temperature and pressure is either incomplete, of questionable accuracy, or unobtainable.

Physical chemist Marvin Ross of the University of California's Lawrence Livermore Laboratory reported in July 1981 some new and valuable laboratory-derived data. It deals with properties of water, ammonia, and methane at the high pressures and temperatures that are believed to exist in the interiors of Uranus and Neptune. To simulate such extreme conditions in the laboratory—a temperature of about 5000°C (9000°F.) and pressure of about 1 million atmospheres (1 million times the atmospheric pressure on Earth of 1,033.2 grams per square centimeter or 14.7 pounds per square inch)—Ross passed high-energy shock waves through the materials.

Under the extreme conditions, which were similar to those on Uranus and Neptune, Ross found that the atoms that make up water and ammonia become ionized, or lose electrons. Then they form materials with the properties of metals—that is, they conduct heat and electricity very well. However, methane, which abounds in these planets, behaves somewhat differently. Instead of being ionized, the molecule actually breaks up into its elemental constituents—that is, into hydrogen and a large amount of highly compressed carbon.

Thus, in most parts of the interior of Uranus and Neptune, carbon must act like a metal, but Ross pointed out that there are large regions where conditions must be just right for the formation of diamonds. More important, knowing that the so-called compressed ice mantles of Uranus and Neptune are made of electrically conducting material will help in understanding the magnetic properties of these planets after *Voyager 2* investigates them in 1986 and 1989. [Michael J. S. Belton]

Galactic Astronomy. Investigations of past and future supernovae, or stellar explosions, were highlights of 1981 and 1982. The past supernova under investigation had been observed by astronomers in China, Japan, and the Middle East in A.D. 1054. It gave rise to the Crab Nebula—an expanding cloud of hot gas—and its associated pulsar—a rapidly spinning neutron star that emits pulsed radio waves. Astronomers suggested that the future supernova is the star Eta Carinae.

Former star. A multi-institution team led by astronomer Kris Davidson of the University of Minnesota in Minneapolis reported in February 1982 on observations they made of the Crab Nebula using the *International Ultraviolet Explorer* (*IUE*) satellite. Davidson and his colleagues gathered information on the abundance of carbon in the nebula, which enabled them to determine the type of star that exploded in 1054.

Current theory states that if the supernova's parent star had begun its life as a star nine or more times as massive as the sun, its explosion would have produced a nebula much richer in carbon than the astronomers found. On the other hand, a star that began with less than eight solar masses would have been totally shattered by the supernova explosion. Not even the condensed stellar core would have survived as a neutron star. Because a neutron star is present in the Crab Nebula, Davidson's team concluded that the parent star of the Crab Nebula supernova must have had an initial mass eight times that of the sun. However, both the Crab Nebula and its pulsar amount to no more than four solar masses. Therefore, the astronomers theorized that the star that created the nebula must have lost about four masses during its lifetime, perhaps by means of a stellar wind.

In December 1981, astronomers Paul Murdin of the Royal Greenwich Observatory in Herstmonceux Castle in Sussex, England, and David H. Clark of the Rutherford Appleton Laboratory in Didcot in Oxfordshire, England, reported that they had discovered a dimly glowing halo around the

The delicate, tenuous filamentary structure of the Orion nebula shows up more clearly than ever before on a photo taken at the European Southern Observatory in Chile. The telescope uses recently developed large interference filters that intensify the image.

Crab Nebula. The halo, which they photographed with the 1.2-meter (4-foot) Schmidt telescope at Siding Spring in New South Wales, Australia, is nearly four times larger than the nebula and may be made up of the lost mass of the parent star.

Future supernova. Davidson, with Nolan R. Walborn of the Cerro Tololo Inter-American Observatory in Chile and Theodore R. Gull of Goddard Space Flight Center in Greenbelt, Md., also observed Eta Carinae with the *IUE*. This star is believed to have at least 100 times the sun's mass, and so should eventually produce a dramatic supernova explosion. In March 1982, the astronomers reported that a nebulous cloud called the "S condensation" in the immediate vicinity of Eta Carinae has an ultraviolet spectrum dominated by emission from nitrogen atoms but lacking in carbon and oxygen, two elements commonly found in nebulae. The strong concentration of nitrogen to the exclusion of other elements in the cloud indicates that the ejecting star is not a massive young object. It must be an evolved one, because the nitrogen must have been produced by nucleosynthesis—the formation of new elements from the nuclei of other elements—within the star over a long time. Davidson, Walborn, and Gull therefore concluded that Eta Carinae is well advanced on the supernova path.

The unusual stars SS433 and R Aquarii especially interested astronomers during the year. SS433 seems to be a unique object in the Milky Way galaxy because it has two rotating and oppositely directed jets that spew out hot gas at enormous velocities. Just how the spewing occurs was reported in February 1982 by astronomers Steven A. Grandi of the University of California, Los Angeles, and Remington P. S. Stone of Lick Observatory on Mount Hamilton in California. The two scientists analyzed several series of spectrograms, taken with two telescopes at the observatory. Spectrograms are representations of the spectrum showing patterns of light emission or absorption by various elements, and can reveal such information as how fast an object is traveling toward or away from the earth. Each series was taken on consecutive nights. The scientists analyzed the amount of change in red shifts and blue shifts—the shift of light toward the longer-and shorter-wavelength ends of the spectrum—of the gas ejected from the two jets to determine its velocity. Red shifts show that the light source is moving away and blue shifts show it is moving toward the observer.

From the appearance and disappearance of spectral lines at intervals ranging from a few hours to a day, the astronomers deduced that the gas is not ejected continuously, but intermittently along one jet or the other. Material ejected in a single burst travels along as a so-called bullet. Grandi and Stone concluded that, "These bullets are born, live and die at the same velocity and have lifetimes from less than a day to several days."

R Aquarii is a well-known symbiotic star—that is, one whose spectrum is that of a cool red giant, but with some spectral lines that indicate the presence of a very hot gas. Some astronomers have thought the gas forms a small nebula. Others believe that the gas takes the form of an accretion disk—material swirling around what may be a small hot stellar companion of the red giant. In April, astronomers led by Minas Kafatos of George Mason University in Fairfax, Va., and Robert Sopka of the University of Maryland in College Park reported that they had discovered a prominent jet of radiation in the radio portion of the electromagnetic spectrum of R Aquarii. The jet points north-northeast toward an isolated radio source that may be made up of material ejected from the star. George Herbig of Lick Observatory then made photographs with the 300-centimeter (120-inch) telescope there, which showed that a jet in the visible part of the spectrum is still present; it was first seen in 1977. Jets from such objects as quasars, radio galaxies, and the peculiar star SS433 probably represent material that is forced to flow outward from the central regions of disk-shaped structures. So, the new observations of R Aquarii lend support to the accretion-disk theory.

Very low mass (VLM) stars were also of much interest in 1982. VLM stars, which are less than one-tenth as massive as the sun, are cool and dim. The sun is 10,000 times or more brighter than any such star. To determine how many such stars exist, Ronald G. Probst and Robert W. O'Connell of the University of Virginia in Charlottesville searched for VLMs among the companions of white dwarf stars. The astronomers used special instruments mounted on four telescopes at Kitt Peak National Observatory near Tucson, Ariz., and Cerro Tololo Inter-American Observatory. Although the search technique was capable of detecting VLM stars as much as 2 million times fainter than the sun, no stars that dim were among the few VLM stars found. In a January report, they concluded that an as-yet-unexplained aspect of the star-birth process must prevent stars of exceedingly small mass from forming.

Heavy molecule. Radio astronomers at the Herzberg Institute of Astrophysics in Ottawa, Canada, reported in February 1982 on their observations of a large organic molecule in space. Using radio telescopes, the astronomers detected cyano-deca-penta-yne ($C_{11}HN$) — the largest and most complex molecule yet found in space — in the atmosphere of the red giant star CW Leonis. See CHEMISTRY.

High-energy astrophysics highlights included a December 1981 report by Bradley E. Schaefer of the Massachusetts Institute of Technology in Cambridge on his discovery of what is probably the first optical counterpart of a gamma-ray burster — an object whose presence is indicated by a great burst of gamma rays at one location in the sky. Most gamma-ray bursters have been detected only once — through observation of their gamma radiation — and none had been observed optically.

Schaefer studied the burster detected by satellites on Nov. 19, 1978. In the archives of Harvard College Observatory in Cambridge, he found a 1928 photo showing a starlike object at the site of the 1978 burster. Schaefer believes it was a bursting object because its photo image showed it shining only during a fraction of the exposure time. Also, it was never photographed again. [Stephen P. Maran]

Extragalactic Astronomy included among items of interest in 1981 and 1982 the intriguing phenomena of gravitational lenses and quasars. A gravitational lens is a massive astronomical object, such as a galaxy, that can under certain circumstances "focus," or bend, light rays from an object behind it and so reflect its image. In the two previously known observations of this phenomenon, the reflection was of quasars — bright, energetic objects. In September 1981, astrophysicists Bohdan Paczynski and K. Gorski of the Copernicus Astronomical Center in Warsaw, Poland, reported that they had discovered what might be a third gravitational lens.

The Polish scientists studied a catalog of known quasars and found that three of them appear close together in the sky and about the same distance from earth. But Paczynski and Gorski suggested there might be only one quasar in that location, with two clusters of galaxies in front of it. They constructed a mathematical model to support this. Each galaxy cluster would form a gravitational lens, bending the light from the quasar to create one image. The actual quasar would be seen between the two, resulting in a total of three "observed quasars." The scientists also predicted what the size and mass of the galaxy clusters ought to be. Now astronomers will try to verify the clusters' existence optically.

Astrophysicist Claude R. Canizares of the Massachusetts Institute of Technology (MIT) in Cambridge reported another lens effect in June 1981. He said that a gravitational lens can also focus light so that quasars appear brighter than they would otherwise be. This might make detectable some quasars that could not normally be seen. The apparent quantity of bright — and presumably closer — quasars could lead to overestimates of the total number of quasars.

In addition, Canizares pointed out, the apparent association of some quasars with galaxies, which a few astronomers have used as a basis for arguing that the two objects were close to each other, might be due to the effect of gravitational lenses — the quasar might be far beyond the galaxy. See THE BRIGHTEST BEACONS.

The *Einstein* Observatory, the second High-Energy Astronomy Observatory, fell from orbit on March 25, 1982. However, astrophysicists continue to analyze data it amassed during its 2½ years of transmitting X-ray data about extragalactic objects. See X-RAY EYES ON THE SKIES, *Science Year*, 1982.

Einstein data, along with observations made by radio, optical, and infrared telescopes, have enabled astronomers to begin clarifying the relationships between galaxies of various types. Astronomer Andrew Lawrence of the Royal Greenwich Observatory in Sussex, England, and physicist Martin S. Elvis of the Harvard-Smithsonian Center for Astrophysics in Cambridge, Mass., reported on the several supposed types of Seyfert galaxies at the June 1981 meeting of the American Astronomical Society in Calgary, Canada.

Seyfert galaxies are small galaxies with especially bright spiral arms, and there is evidence that their nuclei, or cores, contain hot gas that may be heated by violent activity there. These galaxies have been divided into two types. Type 1 are strong X-ray emitters and have very broad optical emission lines. Type 2 are weak X-ray emitters and have narrow optical emission lines. Emission lines show up on spectrograms as wavelengths at which the intensity of radiation from an object is greater than at neighboring wavelengths. Broad emission lines cover more of the spectrum than narrow ones.

Lawrence and Elvis observed several galaxies that appear to resemble both types of Seyfert galaxies. They are X-ray emitters of intermediate strength and have narrow emission lines.

Their discovery made Lawrence and Elvis reconsider all types of Seyfert galaxies. They found that in every case there was a strong correlation between the strength of X-ray emission and the brightness of optical emission. This led them to conclude that all Seyfert galaxies are really similar objects with a highly energetic central source that gives rise to strong X-ray emission.

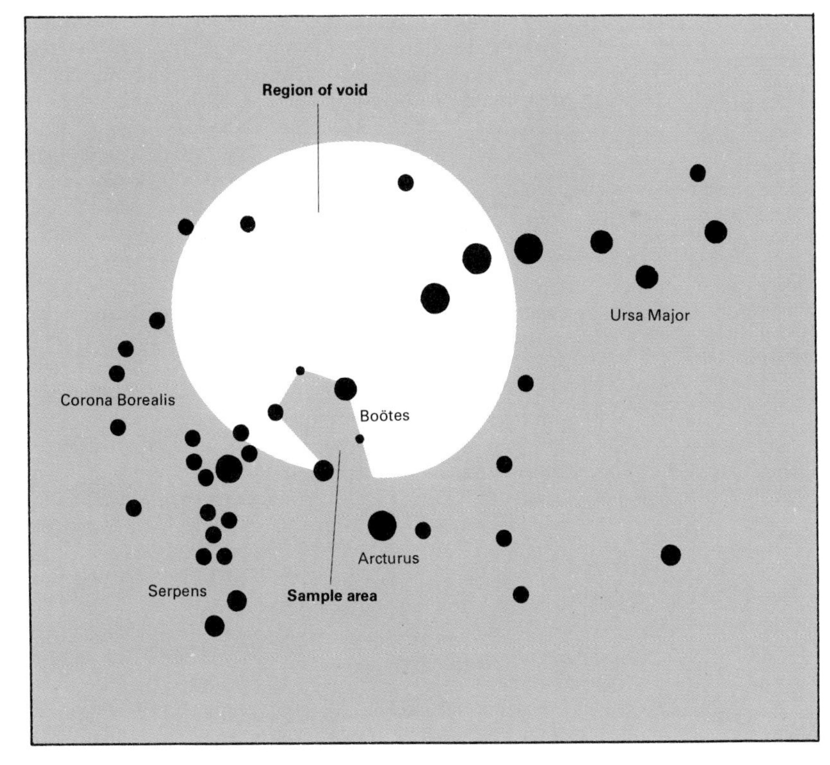

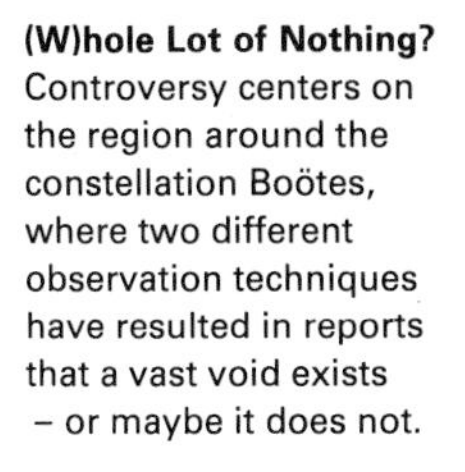

(W)hole Lot of Nothing? Controversy centers on the region around the constellation Boötes, where two different observation techniques have resulted in reports that a vast void exists – or maybe it does not.

A meticulous cleaning of its face prepares the Space Telescope's primary mirror for coating with a special reflective surface that will render it opaque. It will hide the cellular construction that gives strength to the 240-centimeter (94-inch) glass expanse.

What differentiates them is the fact that the central source is surrounded by regions of gas clouds. These clouds, depending on their number and their orientation with respect to the observer at a given time, block some of the X rays and also produce the spectral emission lines. This would make Seyfert galaxies observed under different conditions appear different, and cause astronomers to classify them as type 1, type 2, or something else.

Radio galaxies —giant elliptical galaxies that emit much more of their radiation at radio wavelengths than other galaxies do—were the subject of a report by radio astronomer Jack O. Burns and his colleagues at the University of New Mexico in Albuquerque in November. The Burns team knew that most radio galaxies are found in clusters of galaxies rather than alone. They wondered whether a radio galaxy's environment was what made it radiate so strongly.

A radio galaxy's emission originates from charged particles in orbit around magnetic fields within the galaxy, so the astronomers theorized that the particles and fields might be confined around the clusters of galaxies by a region of hot gas. Burns and his colleagues studied 11 radio galaxies in clusters with the *Einstein* Observatory's X-ray telescope. They detected X-ray emission, signifying the presence of hot gas, around 10 of the galaxies. This led them to conclude that the very presence of the hot gas not only creates the environment for radio emission, but also supplies and maintains a radio galaxy's energy.

Superclusters and great voids. Cosmologists have long wondered whether the universe will continue to expand, or whether it will stop because enough matter exists in the so-called void of space to allow the force of gravity to cause a collapse.

Astronomer Holland C. Ford of the University of California, Los Angeles (UCLA), reported in April 1981 studies of superclusters that favor the expansion theory. Superclusters are giant aggregations of 2 to 10 or more rich, or densely populated, clusters of galaxies, each of which contains hundreds to thousands of individual galaxies. The UCLA group studied the velocity and surface density of two superclusters to map their extent and mass.

The astronomers reported that the superclusters are shaped like elongated filaments and are separated from each other by huge voids in which very few galaxies are present. (Astronomers often use the term *void*, which really means an empty space, to mean a *relatively* empty space, where extremely few objects are found compared with what might have been expected.)

The UCLA team's measurements took into account both the visible material in superclusters and material that cannot be detected with optical telescopes. They found that the total mass of material is only a small fraction of the amount needed to close the universe. Therefore, they concluded, the universe will continue to expand.

A bridge of galaxies. In October, astrophysicist Guido L. Chincarini and his colleagues at the University of Oklahoma in Norman and the European Southern Observatory in La Silla, Chile, reported on a similar topic. They measured the red shift of several galaxies lying between two rich clusters near the constellation Hercules. The shift of light toward the red end of the spectrum shows how far away an object is and how fast it is moving away from us.

By comparing the red shifts, the astronomers found that these galaxies form a bridge between the two rich clusters, turning the entire aggregation of galaxies into the Hercules supercluster. The shape and mass of the newly discovered supercluster are similar to those Ford described.

Directly in front of this newly discovered supercluster, Chincarini found a vast, almost empty space with a volume of about 3 million cubic light-years. (A light-year is the distance light travels in a year—about 9.5 trillion kilometers [6 trillion miles].)

Much ado about nothing? Unimaginably immense as the volume of Chincarini's empty space is, it pales in comparison with an even more colossal void reported in September 1981 by astronomer Robert P. Kirshner and his colleagues at the University of Michigan in Ann Arbor. The scientists used telescopes at Kitt Peak National Observatory and Fred Lawrence Whipple Observatory, both near Tucson, Ariz., and on Palomar Mountain in California to study the large-scale structure of the universe. They were seeking to measure the red shifts of all the galaxies they spotted in order to determine their distance and velocity. When the Kirshner team carried out surveys in three regions of the sky in the Northern Hemisphere around the constellation Boötes, they were astonished to find no galaxies. There seemed to be a "hole in the universe" extending over an area of 30 million cubic light-years. If the hole the astronomers believe they found really exists, it is the largest "structure" of any kind ever observed. Kirshner theorized that such a vast vacant region must have originated as a big bubble, formed and sustained because of density variations in the matter of the early universe. This bubble then expanded as the universe itself expanded. Within the bubble, conditions never favored galaxy formation, so that area remained empty.

The Kirshner report became open to doubt in April 1982, when astronomer Daniel W. Weedman and graduate student Vicki A. Balzano of Pennsylvania State University in State College reported their study of the same region of the sky.

Weedman and Balzano said that the Boötes region is not empty and appeared to be so only because of the technique Kirshner and his colleagues used to probe it. It was as if they had stuck a long needle into a loaf of raisin bread three times and, never striking a raisin, concluded that there were none to be found. The Penn State astronomers studied the entire region around Boötes and found more than 100 galaxies, 12 of them within the suspected void. After Kirshner, Weedman, and Balzano conferred on their findings and compared their methods of investigation, they decided that there is a void, but it is not so large as originally estimated. Still, finding a number of empty regions makes it seem likely that not enough matter exists to cause the universe to stop expanding and collapse. [Stephen S. Murray]

Biochemistry
See Molecular Biology

Books of Science

Here are 25 outstanding new science books suitable for the general reader. They have been selected from books published in 1981 and 1982.

Anthropology. *The Making of Mankind* by Richard E. Leakey describes recent discoveries about human prehistory and the wide range of techniques used by scientists to add to those findings, including molecular biology and taphonomy, the study of fossils. Leakey also talks about his own unusual background and his interest in the study of humankind. (Elsevier-Dutton, 1981. 256 pp. illus. $24.95)

Astronomy. *Earthlike Planets: Surfaces of Mercury, Venus, Earth, Moon, Mars* by Bruce Murray, Michael C. Malin, and Ronald Greeley examines the common history that links the rocky planets of the inner solar system. The book also discusses the forces changing these planets' surfaces, from their interiors, on the surfaces themselves, and from outer space. (W. H. Freeman, 1981. 387 pp. illus. $24.95; paper, $14.95)

The Moon—Our Sister Planet by Peter H. Cadogan is a comprehensive view of our knowledge of the moon from antiquity to the present. Cadogan emphasizes current discoveries revealed by the space program. (Cambridge Univ. Press, 1981. 391 pp. $59.95; paper, $24.95)

Biology. *The Double-Edged Helix: Science in the Real World* by Liebe F. Cavalieri summarizes developments since 1940 in research on DNA (deoxyribonucleic acid), the substance in cells that carries inherited traits. Cavalieri also examines the relationship between scientific research and the political and industrial forces that make use of its discoveries. (Columbia Univ. Press, 1981. 196 pp. $14.95)

Reminiscences and Reflections by Hans Krebs, the German biochemist who shared the 1953 Nobel Prize for Physiology or Medicine, recounts his discovery of the citric acid cycle—an important part of metabolism, by which living cells change food into energy. Krebs also describes the political and social pressures that scientists experienced in Nazi Germany. (Clarendon Press, 1981. 298 pp. illus. $23.50)

The Virus That Ate Cannibals by Carol Eron tells six stories of discoveries by "virus hunters." The book includes accounts of the development of vaccines for yellow fever and poliomyelitis and of research on a disease transmitted by cannibals. (Macmillan, 1981. 193 pp. illus. $12.95)

Earth Sciences. *The Mapmakers* by John Noble Wilford is the history of mapmaking from the earliest known attempts to modern cartography aided by computers and satellites. (Knopf, 1981. 414 pp. illus. $20)

The Ring of Fire by David Ritchie describes a narrow band of intense earthquake and volcanic activity surrounding the Pacific Ocean. The book examines some of the results of that activity, including the 1980 explosion of Mount St. Helens. (Atheneum Pubs., 1981. 258 pp. illus. $14.95)

Ecology. *Freshwater Marshes: Ecology and Wildlife Management* by Milton W. Weller discusses the components of the marsh environment and the effect of human habitation. Weller also explains good marsh management. (University of Minn. Press, 1981. 146 pp. illus. $22.50; paper, $8.95)

Extinction: The Causes and Consequences of the Disappearance of Species by Paul Ehrlich and Anne Ehrlich explains how a wide variety of political, social, and technological practices have led to the extinction of thousands of species. The book also examines ways to avoid the destruction of still more species, including human beings. (Random House, 1981. 305 pp. $15.95)

Energy. *Energy: The Conservation Revolution* by John H. Gibbons and William U. Chandler systematically surveys energy use in the United States. The authors contend that the only plausible solution to the energy crisis involves reduction of demand. (Plenum, 1981. 258 pp. $17.50)

Mathematics. *The Mathematical Experience* by Philip J. Davis and Reuben Hersh outlines the astonishing breadth and variety of mathematics. The authors survey the history and philosophy of mathematics and how mathematical knowledge is gained. Birkhäuser Verlag, 1981. 440 pp. illus. $24)

Natural History. *The Camel: Its Evolution, Ecology, Behavior, and Relationship to Man* by Hilde Gauthier-Pilters and Anne Innis Dagg is a comprehensive review of the evolution and behavior of camels and their relationship to desert nomads. (University of Chicago Press, 1981. 208 pp. illus. $26)

Caribou and the Barren-Lands by George Calef combines beautiful photography with a text that takes the reader through a year in the life of a herd of caribou, now an endangered species. A short section analyzes the interaction of human beings and caribou herds on the Barren-Lands of Alaska and northern Canada. (Canadian Arctic Resources Committee, 1981. 176 pp. illus. $34.95)

Ethology: Its Nature and Relations with Other Sciences by Robert A. Hinde summarizes current research in animal behavior. Hinde explains what stimulates animal behavior, how this behavior develops, and the evolution of useful patterns of behavior within species. Hinde pays special attention to the contributions of Konrad Lorenz and Nikolaas Tinbergen, two of the founders of ethology, the study of animal behavior. (Oxford Univ. Press, 1982. 320 pp. illus. $19.95)

The New Evolutionary Timetable: Fossils, Genes, and the Origin of Species by Steven M. Stanley argues that evolution is not a gradual process as the British naturalist Charles R. Darwin theorized. Instead, Stanley suggests that evolution takes place in relatively short spurts of rapid change among isolated populations. (Basic Bks., 1981. 222 pp. illus. $15.95)

Redwoods: The World's Largest Trees by Jeremy Joan Hewes describes these majestic trees, including their anatomy and growth. Hewes chronicles the destruction of the redwoods during the logging era, as well as current efforts to protect them. (Rand McNally & Co., 1981. 192 pp. illus. $19.95)

Philosophy of Science. *Science Observed: Essays Out of My Mind* by Jeremy Bernstein is a collection of essays that exemplify the many aspects of scientific creativity. Bernstein devotes several essays to American mathematician Marvin Minsky's work on artificial intelligence. (Basic Bks., 1982. 376 pp. $16.95)

The View from Planet Earth: Man Looks at the Cosmos by Vincent Cronin shows how our view of ourselves and of the universe has been influenced by each successive wave of scientific discovery, starting with the astronomical observations of the Babylonians. (Morrow, 1981. 348 pp. $15)

Physics. *The Cosmic Code: Quantum Physics as the Language of Nature* by Heinz R. Pagels shows how quantum theory, which deals with the subatomic world, is approachable only through instruments and through its theoretical implications for reality. Pagels traces the theory's development from its earliest forms and describes the latest discoveries in particle physics, the branch of physics that investigates subatomic particles. (Simon & Schuster, 1982. 370 pp. illus. $17.50)

Psychology. *The Mismeasure of Man* by Stephen Jay Gould is the story of the various ways in which intelligence has been conceived and estimated, including such techniques as the IQ test and the measurement of heads. Gould argues that these measures are pointless and have been used to justify discrimination against minorities. (Norton, 1981. 352 pp. illus. $14.95)

Technology. *The God That Limps: Science and Technology in the Eighties* by Colin Norman shows how the political, social, and technological sectors of our society interact and why reforms are needed. The title refers to Hephaestus, the Greek god of fire and metalworking. He was responsible for keeping the world running but was the only one of the gods who was not perfect. (Norton, 1981. 224 pp. $14.95)

Gossamer Odyssey: The Triumph of Human-Powered Flight by Morton Grosser is the account of the two aircraft that won the Kremer competitions, which were sponsored by British industrialist Henry Kremer to encourage human-powered flight. The story culminates in the dramatic flight of the pedal-powered *Gossamer Albatross* across the English Channel in 1979. (Houghton Mifflin, 1981. 298 pp. illus. $14.95)

Labyrinths of Iron: A History of the World's Subways by Benson Bobrick recounts the history and development of subways in various countries. (Newsweek Bks., 1981. 352 pp. illus. $13.95)

The Soul of a New Machine by Tracy Kidder tells how a group of scientists and engineers set out to design a new computer. Kidder also explains how computers work and shows the value of speed. (Little, Brown, 1981. 293 pp. $13.95) [William Goodrich Jones]

Botany

Research reported in 1981 and 1982 reflected increasing interest in plants that employ defensive chemicals called allelochemics. In many cases, the plants' allelochemical defenses are toxins that are directed against herbivores, animals that feed on the plants. Biologist John P. Bryant of the Institute of Arctic Biology at the University of Alaska in Fairbanks reported in August 1981 on the relationship between the snowshoe hare and four species of Alaskan trees—Alaska paper birch, aspen, balsam poplar, and green alder. When hare populations are especially high—a condition that occurs at about 10-year intervals—and trees are young and close to the ground, hare browsing may severely damage trees and shrubs.

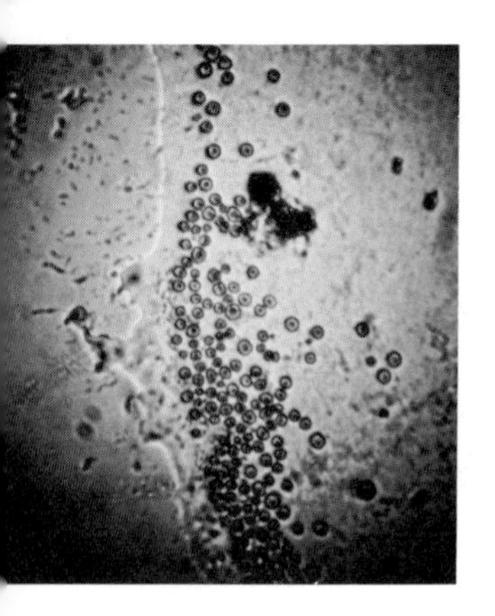

The first known magnetic plants, the green algae *Chlamydomonas* (magnified 250 times), accumulate at the south edge of a drop of water. They were photographed in Brazil where magnets point south.

As the damaged trees grow back, they produce new shoots that are highly unpalatable to the hares. Bryant analyzed the chemical composition of these shoots and found that they contained high concentrations of terpene and phenolic resins. He theorized that these resins may have accounted for the bad taste.

To test this theory, Bryant dried twigs of feltleaf willow, known to be highly palatable to hares even when dry, and covered them with various concentrations of resins extracted from the birch, aspen, poplar, and alder shoots. He then placed these twigs at various feeding stations available to the hares that lived in the woods near Fairbanks. Even when they had nothing else to eat, the hares completely avoided twigs covered with concentrations of resins higher than 8 per cent. This is about half the concentration present in new tree shoots.

Bryant's research suggests that these Alaskan trees conserve their energy reserves in their early growth by not producing high concentrates of resins—gambling that the hares will not eat them. Once they have been damaged, however, they expend their resources to produce allelochemics.

Grasses and voles. Biologist Patricia J. Berger and her colleagues at the University of Utah in Salt Lake City found that a chemical in the spring vegetation of mountain meadows triggered reproduction in the montane vole—a small herbivorous rodent. The scientists examined the vole population of a Utah meadow during the winter months, and found no evidence of reproduction.

They then set up two feeding stations—a control station and an experimental station—in widely separated areas of the meadow. They supplied the control station with ordinary rolled oats and the experimental station with oats treated with 6-methoxybenzoxazolinone (6-MBOA)—a chemical extracted from young plants. The voles fed on these diets for three weeks.

In mid-February, the scientists trapped voles in each area, tested the females for pregnancy, and weighed the testicles of the males for evidence of increased sperm production. The control group had no pregnancies or testicle-weight increases, while the experimental group had a high rate of pregnancy and significant testicle-weight increases.

The scientists concluded that the presence of 6-MBOA in its food tells the vole that the growing season is underway when there is an adequate food supply for any offspring. Because the growing season may begin as early as April or as late as June, 6-MBOA in the young shoots is a more reliable indicator of the season than other signs, such as the length of day and night.

Asters and moths. A group of eight zoologists and chemists headed by Jerrold Meinwald of Cornell University in Ithaca, N.Y., and a team of scientists in West Germany led by Dietrich Schneider of the Max Planck Institute in Seewiesen reported in March 1982 that a diet of asters and other related plants could well be crucial to the sexual functioning of two species of Asian moths. Scientists have observed that the male moths expand coremata—long, retractable hair-covered tubes—from their abdomens, which are thought to release chemicals called pheromones to attract females.

The researchers divided male moth larvae into two groups. They fed the first group a diet deficient in certain plant chemicals called pyrrolizidine alkaloids (PAs), which are found in asters and related plant species. The second group received a diet rich in PAs.

The researchers examined the moths that developed from both groups of larvae, and found that the first group

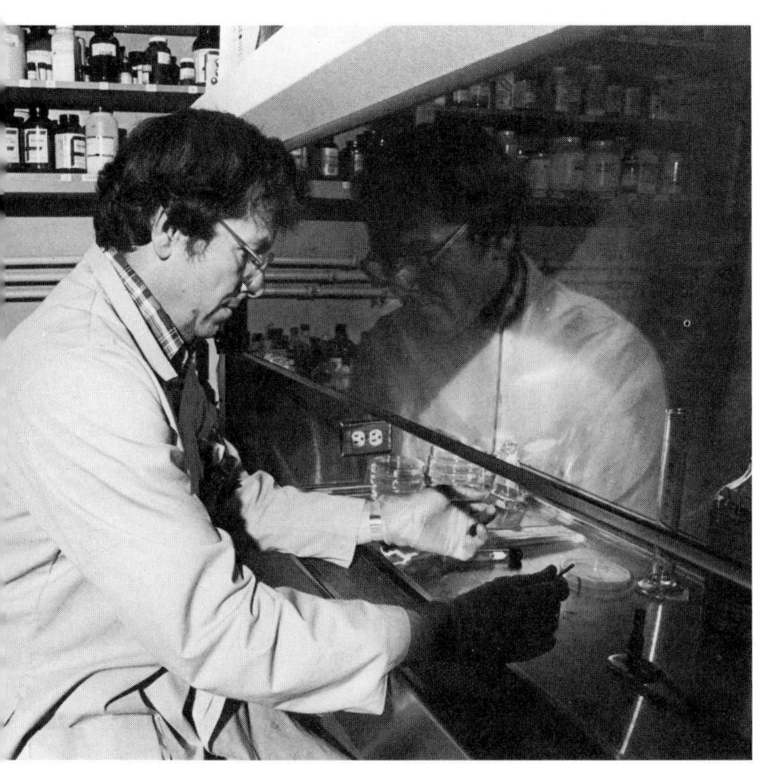

Botany

Continued

A microbiologist selects well-developed colonies of *Agrobacterium tumefaciens,* a bacterium that transfers genetic material into the plant it infects, *above left.* After protein-storage genes from a bean seed have been transplanted into the bacteria, a biochemist, *above right,* injects them into a sunflower to transfer the bean gene to the plant and thereby increase the protein content of its seeds.

of moths not only failed to produce the pheromones but also had underdeveloped coremata. The second group produced a normal supply of pheromones and sported well-developed coremata. This was the first observation of an insect that required a particular plant chemical to produce a pheromone and a pheromone-secreting organ.

Antibiotics in shrubs. Chemists Bruce B. Jarvis, Jacob D. Midiwo, David Tuthill, and botanist George A. Bean of the University of Maryland in College Park reported in October 1981 that a Brazilian shrub, *Baccharis megapotamicia*, harvested in its natural habitat, contained relatively large quantities of an antibiotic known to be highly toxic to most insects as well as to other plants. When the scientists grew the shrubs in the United States, however, the plants lacked the antibiotic.

The researchers theorized that fungi in the Brazilian soil might contribute to the formation of the antibiotic. To test this hypothesis, they supplied substances extracted from the Brazilian fungi to the roots of U.S.-grown seedlings, waited six weeks, and harvested two of the plants. When they dried the foliage and analyzed the extracted chemicals it contained, they found heavy concentrations of the antibiotic. The scientists suggested that the fungi manufacture the antibiotic, deposit it in the soil, and the shrubs absorb it through their roots. They then transform it into an even more poisonous antibiotic.

Parsnips and psoralens. Toxicologists G. Wayne Ivie, Douglas L. Holt, and Marcellus C. Ivey of the U.S. Department of Agriculture's Agricultural Research Service Laboratories in College Station, Tex., reported in August 1981 that parsnip roots contain chemicals called psoralens that are acutely toxic to mammals in moderate doses, and that have reacted with light to cause cancer in laboratory animals.

The researchers found psoralens in concentrations that may be harmful to humans in raw and cooked parsnips. They suggested that further studies to determine the risks of eating parsnips be undertaken. [Frank B. Salisbury]

Chemistry

Chemists at the Swiss Federal Polytechnic College in Lausanne announced in July 1981 that they had used solar energy to split hydrogen sulfide (H_2S) into hydrogen gas (H_2) and sulfur atoms (S). Hydrogen sulfide, a poisonous pollutant that smells like rotten eggs, forms in enormous amounts as a by-product of oil-refining and other industrial operations. For example, the process that removes sulfur from high-sulfur crude oil produces more than 2.1 million metric tons (2.3-million short tons) of H_2S in the United States each year.

Chemists Michael Grätzel, Enrico Borgarello, and Kuppuswamy Kalyanasundaram at Lausanne and Ezio Pelizzetti of Turin University in Italy developed the process. Their work is an outgrowth of Grätzel's studies of the solar splitting of water into hydrogen and oxygen.

The H_2S-splitting system uses a catalyst consisting of cadmium sulfide particles coated with small amounts of ruthenium dioxide, which acts as a sensitizer to begin the reaction. (A catalyst is a substance that speeds up a chemical reaction while itself remaining practically unchanged.) The particles are suspended in water that contains hydrogen sulfide.

When visible light strikes these particles, electrons in the cadmium sulfide absorb the light energy and leave the particle. Water molecules (H_2O) pick up the freed electrons. This causes the water to split into hydrogen gas and negatively charged hydroxide ions (OH^-). The ions then react with the hydrogen sulfide to form sulfide ions (S^{-2}) and water. Finally, the negatively charged sulfide ions turn into atomic sulfur by giving up their extra electrons to the catalyst, thus returning it to its original form.

If Grätzel's new process is economical on an industrial scale, it may provide an alternate fuel source, hydrogen. At the same time it can convert a poisonous industrial waste into the valuable chemical, sulfur.

Red-tide toxin identified. A team of researchers from three universities reported in November 1981 that they

Scientists at General Motors Research Laboratories pour used pellets from an automobile's catalytic converter into a solution that removes 83 per cent of their platinum and palladium. These extremely valuable metals can then be recycled as coatings on new pellets like those in the beaker at right.

had determined the structure of one of the poisonous chemicals excreted by the saltwater alga *Ptychodiscus brevis*. This red organism occurs in warm areas of most oceans and in many rivers. The algae sometimes reproduce rapidly, creating a dense mass that reddens the water. Masses of this alga that accumulate near a shore are called a red tide.

The algae excrete toxins that can be taken up by mussels, clams, and other shellfish. The toxins can poison humans who eat the shellfish.

An experimental detector for synthetic gas streams monitors the level of corrosive alkali metals by trapping molecular samples in its electrically charged cylindrical mesh. The detector emits electrical signals that could sound an alarm or shut down machinery.

Chemists Koji Nakanishi, Jerzy Golik, and John C. James of Columbia University in New York City; Jon Clardy and Donna Van Engen of Cornell University in Ithaca, N.Y.; and biochemists Yong-Yeng Lin and Martin Risk and marine biologist Sammy M. Ray of the University of Texas at Galveston isolated and purified three new toxins from *P. brevis* cells that had grown in a simulated seawater environment in the Galveston laboratory.

Using ether as a solvent, the researchers extracted 90 milligrams of toxins from 500 million algae cells. Next, they forced the toxins under high pressure through a column packed with adsorbent materials. As the toxins passed through the column, they separated into small amounts of three pure types. The researchers obtained 0.8 milligram of the toxin that they called *A*, 5 milligrams of *B*, and 0.4 milligram of *C*.

The chemists are still investigating the structures of brevetoxins A and C, but they worked out the structure of B mainly by an X-ray diffraction study on a single crystal. Scientists use this method to measure the positions of all atoms in a molecule except for hydrogen, the smallest element, according to how the atoms bend or diffract X rays aimed at the crystal.

The X-ray study showed that brevetoxin B's structure is entirely different from the structure known for other algae toxins. The molecule consists of 11 carbon-containing rings. Each ring has one oxygen atom. In addition, chemical groups such as methyl, which is composed of one carbon atom and three hydrogen atoms, and hydroxy, made up of one oxygen atom and one atom of hydrogen, are attached.

However, the X-ray results could not detect which of two possible optical isomers was the true structure of brevetoxin B. Optical isomers are two separate molecules that are made of the same atoms, but are mirror images of each other that differ in shape as your right hand differs from your left.

To determine which was the correct isomer, the chemists first converted brevetoxin B to a new molecule of the same handedness that they could study by circular dichroism. This method measures differences in how isomers absorb polarized light. The chemists then studied the new molecule and determined which was the correct isomer of brevetoxin B.

At least one researcher, chemist Mak Alam of the University of Houston, thinks that the new toxin is the result of alga mutations that cause it to produce ever-changing toxins. Alam plans to study *P. brevis* in a few years to see whether the chemical structure of the toxins has again changed.

NMR studies of living systems. In November 1981, biophysical chemist Robert G. Shulman, his colleagues at Yale University in New Haven, Conn., and a team of researchers from Oxford Research Systems in England used nuclear magnetic resonance (NMR) to measure for the first time body fats and the chemical conversion of glucose to starch in the molecules of living animals. NMR reveals details of the insides of living beings without damaging tissue or causing pain. Thus scientists are developing NMR technology as a tool for biological experimentation and medical diagnosis.

NMR technology is based on how magnetic fields and radio waves of various frequencies affect an atomic nucleus that has an odd number of neutrons or protons. (A radio wave's frequency is the number of times it vibrates in one second.)

A researcher places a sample of material containing such a nucleus in an instrument that sets up a strong magnetic field. He then scans the sample with radio waves of various frequencies; the nucleus absorbs energy from a wave of a particular frequency. When the radio waves are turned off, the nucleus emits a wave of the same frequency.

Science Year Close-Up

Damascus Demystified

The name *Damascus steel* conjures up images of medieval crusaders in the Holy Land battling Saracens who were armed with a mysterious blade that could cut a feather in midair and yet not lose its edge in battle. The crusaders were sure some kind of magic was involved. The blades shone with a beautiful grainy texture that Europeans could never match. Nor could European forgers produce a blade as strong and as sturdy as the blade of the Saracens.

The Europeans did not even get the name right. The crusaders first encountered the blades in Damascus, now the capital of Syria. However, the steel was actually made in India and had been made there since well before 300 B.C.

The Europeans eventually got the idea that the steel's strength was not magical, but resulted from a secret process of quenching—cooling the red-hot blade quickly. Legends abounded. Some said the blade was quenched in dragon's blood. Others suggested it was quenched in urine, either animal urine or the urine of a boy, preferably a redhead. Others suggested the red-hot blade was cooled by a man waving it madly while galloping on horseback. Apparently some Saracens quenched the steel by plunging it into the body of a muscular slave.

European forgers and scientists tried for centuries to produce Damascus steel. A Frenchman tried mixing the steel with everything from arsenic to zinc. A Russian tried diamonds. No less a luminary than Michael Faraday, the great English chemist and physicist of the 1800s, worked on the problem and failed.

Ancient metalworkers believed that the secret was the steel's carbon content of 1 to 2 per cent. They thought that the carbon added strength without making the steel brittle. But whenever the European forgers tried to mix that much carbon with their steel, the steel shattered.

Success also eluded scientists until 1981, when materials scientists Oleg D. Sherby and Jeffrey Wadsworth of Stanford University in California apparently stumbled onto the secret of Damascus steel while working on the problem of producing superplastic metals, which bend and shape easily without losing strength.

Sherby and Wadsworth prepared a steel with a carbon content of 1.3 per cent and formed and shaped it at a lower temperature than normal. The resulting metal was strong, and it looked like Damascus steel.

Stanford researchers kept the steel at a temperature of 1200°C (2190°F.) for a short period of time, then allowed it to cool to 700°C (1290°F.) while they shaped it. After it cooled further, they heated it to about 650°C (1200°F.), reshaped it, and quenched it. The grains thus produced were even finer than those of Damascus steel.

Sherby and Wadsworth believe that medieval European forgers worked their low-carbon steel at around 1600°C (2900°F.), because the metal was easiest to shape at that temperature. High-carbon steel, however, is between the solid state and the liquid state at that temperature and therefore shatters if struck.

But the ancient forgers worked blocks of steel called *wootz* at 700° to 900°C (1290° to 1650°F.). They judged the temperature by the color of the steel. First they heated the wootz to around 1100°C (2010°F.)—"the color of the sun rising in the desert." They bent and shaped the metal when its color changed to the "king's purple." Such descriptions enable modern metallurgists to determine the temperatures that the ancient forgers used.

Quenching, it turned out, was not very important. The carbon in the steel produced the steel's texture. Sherby and Wadsworth believe tiny particles of iron carbide produced in the forging process collected on the surface, producing the steel's grainy texture. If the ancient forgers had allowed these particles to become too large, the blades would have been brittle. However, they pounded on the metal to break up the particles and thus created the surface that made the steel famous.

The beauty of Damascus steel is unquestioned, but the strength may be overrated, Wadsworth says. Damascus steel was better than anything the Europeans had during the Crusades but it would not last long against modern alloy steels. [Joel N. Shurkin]

The Plastic Battery
Thin sheets of a special polymer act like metal electrodes in a high-capacity experimental battery, *below*. The sheets are assembled in a glass case with a plastic separator that prevents short-circuiting. The electrolyte solution produces no fumes as the battery operates and needs no refilling. A scientist, *bottom,* tests the ability of such a battery to hold an electrical charge during long periods of disuse.

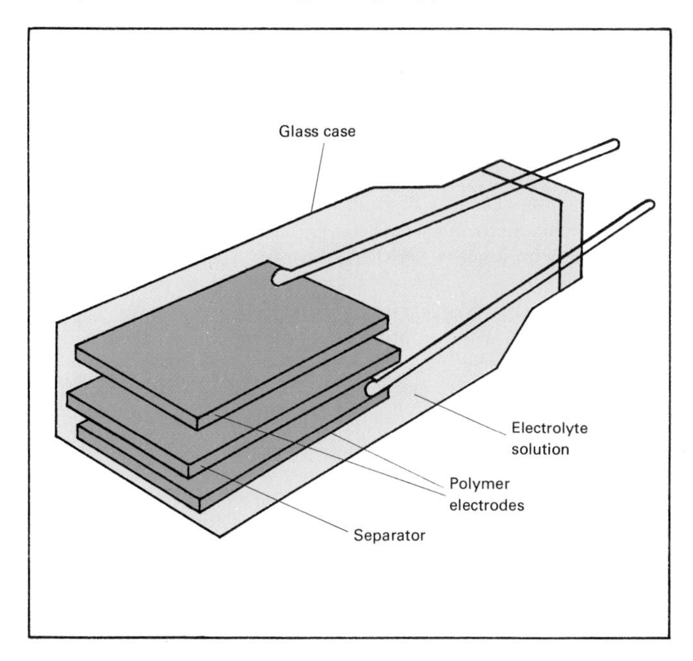

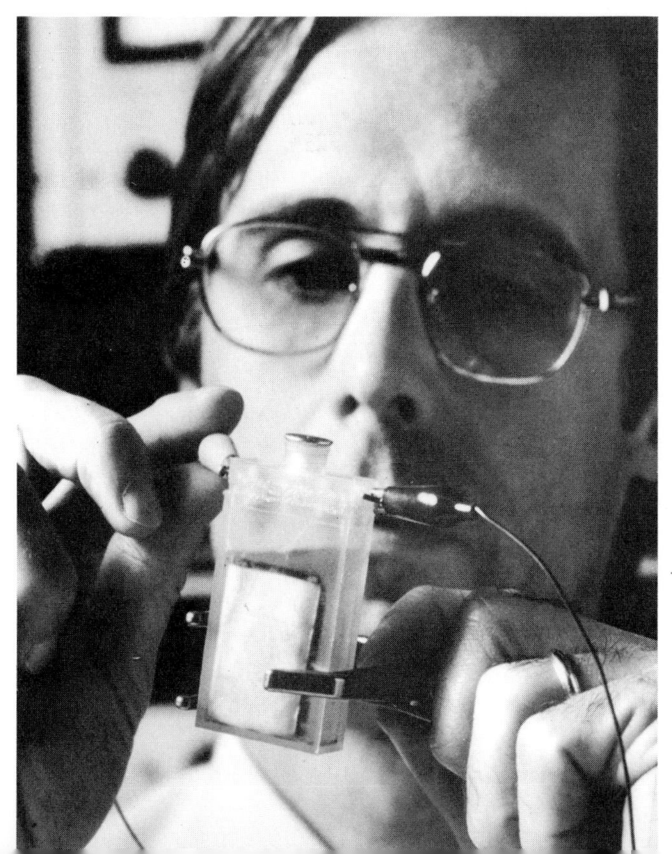

The particular frequency depends upon the kind of nucleus and upon the strength of the magnetic field at the nucleus. This field is a combination of the applied field and of the magnetic fields of atoms near the nucleus.

The NMR instrument records the frequencies and strengths of emitted radio waves on a graph. The frequencies indicate the types of nuclei in the sample and their atomic surroundings, while the strengths indicate the number of nuclei in a particular kind of surrounding.

Scientists conduct NMR scans at frequencies that will energize a particular isotope, or form of nucleus. The Yale and Oxford researchers scanned for the isotope carbon-13, which has six protons and seven neutrons. They obtained graphs showing the chemical makeup of a laboratory rat and Shulman's arm. They studied the glycerol and fatty acid parts of fat molecules, distinguished between polyunsaturated and saturated fats, and measured the parts of molecules that make up cell membranes.

In another experiment, Shulman and his co-workers fed a rat glucose that had been enriched with carbon-13. They then put the animal into the NMR instrument's sample compartment and detected the conversion of this sugar into a starch called glycogen. The highest concentration of glycogen is in the liver, so the scientists knew that they were watching most of the glucose being transported to the liver, where it is converted and stored as glycogen.

This new use of NMR in live studies may provide a powerful tool for the study of biochemical processes. For example, researchers can now investigate defects in fat metabolism or abnormalities in the conversion of fats to other body chemicals directly in living systems. See MEDICINE, INTERNAL (Close-Up).

Amino acids without lightning. Chemists Allen J. Bard, Wendell W. Dunn, and Yosihiro Aikawa of the University of Texas in Austin reported in December 1981 that they were able to form five amino acids, fundamental building blocks of proteins, by shining ordinary light on a quartz flask containing a mixture of methane, ammonia, and water and a titanium dioxide catalyst impregnated with platinum.

Many scientists believe that this mixture resembles earth's early atmosphere. Even today, many soils and sediments contain titanium dioxide along with other metals. Therefore, the experiment may provide clues to the mystery of the origin of life on earth.

Other chemists have formed amino acids in a mixture of methane, ammonia, and water, but they subjected the mixture to much more severe conditions, shooting into it high-energy electrical discharges that resembled lightning flashes. By contrast, the Texas chemists merely exposed the mixture to sunlight for a few weeks or to a special ultraviolet light for a few days.

The use of the catalyst cut the energy requirement. When light rays shine on the catalyst, a chemical reaction begins. Electrons in the catalyst absorb energy from such rays, moving farther away from the nuclei that they orbit. The electrons leave behind positively charged spaces, or holes, that will accept low-energy electrons. Electrons from water molecules are drawn to these holes, and this loss of electrons splits a water molecule (H_2O) into a positively charged hydrogen ion (H^+) and neutral hydroxy (OH). The hydrogen ions take up catalyst electrons that had absorbed light energy, becoming neutral. But the hydroxy reacts further with the methane and ammonia to form the amino acids.

The amino acids glycine, alanine, serine, aspartic acid, and glutamic acid formed in the mixture. More than 20 amino acids are found in nature.

This catalyzed formation of amino acids does not prove that acids originated in this way on the ancient earth. However, the study does show that a "flash of lightning" was not necessary.

Negative sodium ion. English scientists in December 1981 reported the first direct observation of a negatively charged sodium ion in a pure liquid. Sodium ions are common in nature—in sodium chloride (table salt), for example. But these are positive ions, formed when each sodium atom gives up one electron.

Chemists Peter P. Edwards, Sarah C. Guy, and Dolores M. Holton of Cambridge University and William McFarlane of the City of London Polytechnic dissolved metallic sodium in liquid hexamethylphosphoric triamide (HMPA) in a vacuum, then examined the solutions by NMR for the sodium-23 isotope. Next, they compared the NMR graph for this isotope with a graph for a solution of sodium chloride in HMPA. The graphs showed that the solutions absorbed waves of far different frequencies.

Finally, the chemists compared the graph for the sodium metal solution with other NMR graphs for known negative ions. They concluded that the sodium metal had accepted an electron from the powerful electron donor HMPA, forming the negative sodium ion. The research thus puts in doubt the definition of a metal—an element that forms positive ions in solution.

Organic space molecules. Radio astronomers Morley B. Bell, Paul A. Feldman, Sun Kwok, and Henry E. Matthews of the Canadian National Research Council's Herzberg Institute in Ottawa reported in February 1982 that they had detected the largest and heaviest organic molecule yet found in interstellar space. They discovered the molecule called cyano-deca-penta-yne, or cyanopentaacetylene ($C_{11}HN$) in the cool giant star CW Leo, some 600 light-years from earth. $C_{11}HN$ has a molecular weight of 147 and a length of 1.5 nanometers. (One nanometer is one billionth of a meter.) $C_{11}HN$ is also larger than any molecule found in the atmosphere of any other planet.

Scientists have now detected in space all the members of the cyanoacetylene series up to $C_{11}HN$. A cyanoacetylene is a molecule that has an odd number of carbon atoms and a carbon-nitrogen (CN) group on one end. The molecules have been found only in regions of dense concentrations of gas and dust. Astronomers suspect that high-density gas promotes the reaction of individual atoms to form molecules, while the dust grains prevent ultraviolet light emitted by nearby stars from destroying them.

How these molecules are formed in interstellar space and what eventually happens to them is still a mystery. However, scientists are optimistic that they will discover many more kinds of molecules there. [Lawrence P. Verbit]

Deaths of Scientists

Carleton S. Coon

René Jules Dubos

Benjamin F. Feingold

Notable scientists and engineers who died between June 1, 1981, and June 1, 1982, are listed below. An asterisk (*) indicates that a biography appears in *The World Book Encyclopedia*.

Arieti, Silvano (1914-Aug. 7, 1981), Italian-born psychiatrist whose work on schizophrenia dealt with the link between schizophrenic disorders and creativity. He was editor of the massive reference work *American Handbook of Psychiatry* (1959).

Bang, Frederik B. (1916-Oct. 3, 1981), physician and biologist noted for his research on infectious and parasitic diseases. He developed an important test used to detect potentially lethal infections caused by bacteria.

Bird, Junius B. (1907-April 2, 1982), archaeologist, expert on primitive cultures and a world authority on pre-Columbian textiles.

Breit, Gregory (1899-Sept. 13, 1981), Russian-born physicist who helped develop the atomic bomb. He was an originator of the nuclear resonance theory—that every element has its own vibration frequencies.

Bullard, Dexter M. (1898-Oct. 6, 1981), psychiatrist who pioneered in the use of psychoanalytic treatment for psychotic patients at Chestnut Lodge mental hospital in Rockville, Md., the setting for the 1964 novel *I Never Promised You a Rose Garden* by former patient Joanne Greenburg.

Busignies, Henri G. (1905-June 19, 1981), French-born electronics engineer whose 140 patented inventions included the first automatic direction finder for aircraft.

Charney, Jule G. (1917-June 16, 1981), meteorologist and educator who developed the use of computers in weather forecasts.

Coberly, Clarence J. (1893-Sept. 7, 1981), engineer who invented the first hydraulic pump for oil wells.

Coon, Carleton S. (1904-June 3, 1981), anthropologist noted for his contributions to the study of human transition in such books as *The Story of Man* (1954).

Corner, George W. (1889-Sept. 28, 1981), embryologist whose research explained the function of hormones in the menstrual cycle and uncovered the hormone progesterone, the key to the development of the birth control pill.

Deutsch, Helene R. (1884-March 29, 1982), Austrian-born psychoanalyst who was noted for her work on personality disorders and her classic book *The Psychology of Women* (1944).

***Dubos, René Jules** (1901-Feb. 20, 1982), bacteriologist whose research led to the first commercially produced antibiotics in 1939. His 20 books included *So Human an Animal*, which won the 1969 Pulitzer Prize.

Farber, Edward R. (1915-Jan. 22, 1982), electronic engineer and photographer credited with the invention of the portable flash for still cameras.

Federov, Yevgeniy K. (1910-Dec. 30, 1981), Russian geophysicist known for his work on climatic conditions, especially in the polar regions, and for his contributions to the space program.

Feingold, Benjamin F. (1900-March 23, 1982), pediatrician and allergist who believed that hyperactivity in some children was caused by an allergic reaction to synthetic coloring and additives in their diet. His book *Why Your Child Is Hyperactive* (1975) was a best seller.

Fisk, James B. (1910-Aug. 10, 1981), physicist who pioneered in the development of radar during World War II. He served as president of Bell Laboratories from 1959 to 1973 and was appointed first director of the U.S. Atomic Energy Commission in 1947.

Fletcher, Harvey (1884-July 23, 1981), physicist who headed physical research at Bell Laboratories from 1916 to 1949. He led a team that developed stereophonic sound in 1934.

Fraiberg, Selma (1918-Dec. 19, 1981), psychiatrist whose books on child development included *The Magic Years* and *In Defense of Mothering*.

Franklin, Edward C. (1928-Feb. 20, 1982), German-born physician and immunologist whose work on the metabolism and synthesis of proteins increased the understanding of aging. He was noted for his research on lymph system cancer and rheumatoid arthritis.

Giauque, William F. (1895-March 28, 1982), Canadian-born chemist who won the 1949 Nobel Prize for Chemistry for his study of properties of substances at extremely low temperatures.

Handler, Philip (1917-Dec. 29, 1981), biochemist noted for his research on

Deaths of Scientists

Continued

William F. Giauque

Sir Hans A. Krebs

Hideki Yukawa

nutrition and his advocacy of human rights. He served as president of the National Academy of Sciences from 1969 to 1981.

Harnwell, Gaylord P. (1903-April 18, 1982), atomic physicist who worked on sonar tracking techniques during World War II. He was president of the University of Pennsylvania from 1953 to 1970.

Harrar, George J. (1906-April 18, 1982), biologist who headed the Rockefeller Foundation from 1961 to 1971. He helped develop improved strains of wheat with increased crop yields in Mexico in the 1940s.

Hoaglund, Hudson (1899-March 4, 1982), physiologist who pioneered in the study of brain waves and the use of the electroencephalograph.

Horikoshi, Jiro (1904-Jan. 11, 1982), aeronautical engineer who designed the Zero fighter plane used in the Japanese attack on Pearl Harbor in 1941.

Ilg, Frances L. (1902-July 26, 1981), pediatrician who co-founded the Gesell Institute of Human Development in New Haven, Conn., in 1950. She co-authored 20 best-selling books on child development including *The Child from Five to Ten* (1946).

Kardiner, Abram (1891-July 20, 1981), psychoanalyst, a leading proponent of the environmental school of psychiatry and co-founder of the New York Psychiatric Institute in 1930, the first psychoanalytic training school in the United States.

Kingdon, Kenneth H. (1894-March 9, 1982), Jamaican-born physicist, a leader in the development of atomic energy. In 1939, he helped isolate U-235 from natural uranium.

***Krebs, Sir Hans A.** (1900-Nov. 22, 1981), German-born British biochemist who won the Nobel Prize for Physiology or Medicine in 1953 for discovering the ways in which food is converted to energy in the body.

***Link, Edwin A.** (1904-Sept. 7, 1981), inventor who developed the Link flight simulator in 1929—a mechanical trainer for pilots that simulates flying conditions.

Malina, Frank J. (1912-Nov. 9, 1981), aerospace engineer whose work on solid-fuel rockets helped make possible the first U.S. manned flight to the moon. He was director of Jet Propulsion Laboratory at California Institute of Technology from 1944 to 1946.

McDermott, Walsh (1909-Oct. 17, 1981), physician and educator who won the 1955 Albert Lasker Award for his work in the development of the antitubercular drug isoniazid. He co-edited *The Cecil-Loeb Textbook of Medicine* and served on the *Science Year* Editorial Advisory Board.

Ochsner, Alton (1896-Sept. 24, 1981), surgeon who, in 1931, became the first to suggest a link between cigarette smoking and cancer.

Olson, Harry F. (1902-April 1, 1982), acoustical engineer and inventor whose research over four decades with the RCA Corporation brought many advances in recording and broadcasting. His inventions included the electronic music synthesizer.

Rosen, Samuel (1897-Nov. 5, 1981), surgeon who developed the "Rosen stapes" surgical technique for treating otosclerosis—a common cause of deafness in which the stapes, a bone in the middle ear, is improperly positioned.

Schilt, Jan (1894-Jan. 9, 1982), Dutch-born astronomer who helped clarify the motion of stars in the Milky Way. He developed the Schilt photometer, which measures the brightness of stars and helps determine their distance from earth.

Soupart, Pierre (1923-June 10, 1981), Belgian-born biochemist and professor of gynecology at Vanderbilt University, the first researcher to publish scientific evidence of successful human fertilization in the laboratory.

Stern, Curt (1902-Oct. 24, 1981), German-born geneticist who helped develop the science of genetics. He discovered many rules of heredity.

Thomas, Charles A. (1900-March 29, 1982), physical chemist who worked on the Manhattan Project team that developed the first atomic bomb.

Tuve, Merle A. (1901-May 20, 1982), physicist who confirmed the existence of the neutron in 1933. In 1925, he discovered that short-pulse radio waves reflect off the ionosphere, the theoretical base for radar.

***Yukawa, Hideki** (1907-Sept. 8, 1981), Japanese theoretical physicist who won the 1949 Nobel Prize for Physics for his 1935 prediction of the meson. [Irene B. Keller]

Drugs

One of the most distressing problems suffered by a person receiving chemotherapy for cancer is the nausea and vomiting caused by some of the anticancer drugs. Research in 1981 and 1982 may lead to therapy that can substantially reduce, if not eliminate, these adverse effects.

Richard Gralla, a specialist in internal medicine, and his associates at Memorial Hospital-Sloan Kettering Cancer Center in New York City, reported in October 1981 on the results of a double-blind experiment comparing the drug metoclopramide with prochlorperazine, the standard drug used to control nausea. The researchers also compared metoclopramide with a placebo, or inert solution that looks like the real drug.

A double-blind study is one in which the two drugs being compared are administered in an identical way. Neither the patient nor the physician evaluating the effect knows which drug is given at which time. The purpose is to minimize subjective feelings about one drug or the other that might influence the results.

All patients in the Sloan Kettering program were receiving cis-platin, an anticancer drug on which prochlorperazine has had little effect. Each patient given the placebo vomited an average of 11 times for a period of six to eight hours after the cis-platin was administered. Patients given prochlorperazine vomited an average of 12 times. The patients that received the metoclopramide, however, vomited an average of only one time after receiving the anticancer drug.

Heart attack victims continue to benefit from research on adrenergic blocking drugs, which improve survival after a heart attack. In March 1982, the Beta Blocker Heart Attack Trial Group, a multicenter organization, published the results of a study of propranolol. This study, sponsored by the National Institutes of Health (NIH), compared the outcome of 1,916 people given propranolol to 1,921 people given a placebo. Each person in the study had suffered at least one myocardial infarction, or heart attack. In the placebo-treated group, 9.8 per cent died during a 25-month follow-up period, while only 7.2 per cent of the propranolol-treated group died. This difference was so striking that the study was concluded nine months early so that the patients receiving the placebo could also be treated with propranolol.

A very controversial subject in heart research is whether sulfinpyrazone (Anturan) decreases the mortality of patients who start to take it after having a heart attack. Many scientists think that heart attacks occur when platelets stick together to form a clump in a coronary artery that has been injured by atherosclerosis. This clump initiates a clotting or thrombosis in the coronary artery that stops the blood flow through the artery, causing the heart attack.

Sulfinpyrazone was known to inhibit this platelet clumping. For this reason, the Anturan Reinfarction Trial Research Group (ARTR), a multicenter organization, conducted a study from 1975 to 1980 that compared sulfinpyrazone with a placebo in patients who had recent heart attacks. ARTR thought the trial showed a decrease in sudden deaths from second attacks in the drug-treated patients.

The U.S. Food and Drug Administration (FDA) disputed this claim in 1981. It said its analysis of the data indicated that a number of the deaths were misclassified and that there really was no difference between the two groups. However, a study by the Anturan Reinfarction Italian Study Group, headed by E. Polli of the University of Milan, released in January 1981 suggests that sulfinpyrazone is beneficial for patients following a heart attack. This study showed a decrease in second attacks, however, rather than a decrease in sudden death from the attacks. The variation in results of the trials leaves important questions unanswered about how the drug affects these patients.

Quinine, the classic drug for treating malaria, is being looked at again. Carlos C. Campbell, a malariologist at the Centers for Disease Control in Atlanta, Ga., and his colleagues reported in November 1981 that quinine works better if it is given in combination with tetracycline, an antibiotic.

Malaria remains one of the major diseases of humankind. Many drugs

Science Year Close-Up

Wonder or Worrisome Drug?

"DMSO for sale" appears in the windows of health food stores, at gas stations, and in newspaper ads around the United States. DMSO is an abbreviation of *dimethyl sulfoxide*, which is widely sold in America as an industrial solvent, or "degreaser," and as a liniment for dogs and horses.

These forms of DMSO are not intended for human use. Yet many people are rubbing these industrial or veterinary preparations on their skin, or even drinking or injecting them, in the hope that DMSO will prove to be a "wonder drug" for curing ills as diverse as arthritis, sprains, bruises, burns, and cancer.

Arthritis sufferers alone represent more than 31 million Americans. The Arthritis Foundation in Atlanta, Ga., estimates that as many as half of them have tried the colorless liquid. Frederic McDuffie, senior vice-president for medical affairs, says, "One of the greatest dangers in the indiscriminate use of DMSO is that patients will neglect proven forms of treatment."

A by-product of wood-pulp manufacturing, DMSO has been on the market since the early 1940s as an industrial solvent. In 1959, scientists discovered that it was useful for preventing damage to laboratory biological tissues that are being preserved through freezing. In 1963, surgeon Stanley Jacob of the University of Oregon Medical School in Eugene reported that DMSO could penetrate skin rapidly, deaden pain, decrease swelling, and promote healing. However, it had a curious side effect—it made the user's breath smell of garlic.

The Food and Drug Administration (FDA) approved the use of DMSO for studies on humans, beginning in 1963, mainly for sprains, bruises, and minor burns. Results were extremely difficult to assess. According to a report in the September 1980 issue of the *FDA Consumer*, the early studies were not well controlled, so there was no way of knowing whether improvements some patients said they noticed in their condition were due to the drug or some other factor. Later studies showed that the drug was useful in treating interstitial cystitis, a chronic bladder disorder. The FDA approved DMSO for this use in 1978, but in a lower concentration than that approved for animal or industrial usage.

Over the years, scientists have learned more about the properties of DMSO, both those that may prove beneficial as well as those that may pose harm. Depending on the study cited, DMSO may or may not relieve pain. By removing water from tissues, it can reduce swelling, which makes it potentially valuable in treating brain and other injuries. DMSO can increase the excretion of urine, relax muscles, and dilate blood vessels.

But researchers also have identified several adverse side effects of DMSO. When applied to the skin, it may cause irritation. Even more worrisome, it is a "carrier chemical"—that is, it may introduce into the bloodstream contaminants that are present on the surface of the skin or that are in the product itself. Cataracts, or clouding of the lenses of the eyes, developed in laboratory rats given DMSO. However, no eye damage has yet been found in humans using it.

Much of the recent brisk "underground" market for DMSO stems from a favorable report on the CBS television show "60 Minutes" in 1980, followed by hearings held by the U.S. House of Representatives Select Committee on Aging. Enthusiastic users claimed that DMSO released them from pain and enabled them to resume their normal daily activities.

But scientists are still trying to find out if DMSO really works and whether it is safe for people to use. About 30 studies have been approved by the FDA to test DMSO in a large range of disorders, including some for which no satisfactory treatment is now available. The conditions under investigation include scleroderma (a crippling disorder), arthritis, tendinitis, bursitis, breast and prostate cancer, retinitis pigmentosa (an eye disorder), herpes virus infections, spinal cord injuries, stroke, head injuries, sprains, and strains.

Until all the answers are in, the FDA warns, "People are taking a risk whenever they use a substance of unknown quality and effect. It is risky business to drink, inject, or apply to the skin any substance not intended for that purpose." [Lynne Lamberg]

A diabetic patient, *top,* holds a communication head over an Implantable Programmable Infusion Pump, *above,* that has been implanted in her abdomen. The pump delivers the insulin at a programmed rate that can be changed by telemetered signals from a doctor's office, or by the patient herself. The pump can be used to deliver drugs for several other diseases.

have been developed to kill the parasite that causes it. Unfortunately, when they are used, strains of the parasite develop that prove to be resistant to the drugs.

The Campbell group conducted its study in a refugee camp in eastern Thailand. Concurrently, Nicholas J. White of Mahidal University in Bangkok, Thailand, and co-workers at the University of Oxford in England who were working in Bangkok reported in November 1981 that the anti-arrhythmic drug, quinidine, a chemical mirror image of quinine, was also effective for treating the resistant strains of malaria.

Explosions in the operating room during colon surgery may be caused by a drug that surgeons use to clean out the colon.

The development of the fiberoptic colonoscope has revolutionized diagnosis and therapy of diseases of the large intestine. Tumors, ulcers, and other lesions can be seen directly rather than only as shadows on an X-ray film. As a result, small tumors, called polyps, can be removed by colonoscopy rather than by abdominal surgery as was formerly necessary.

When surgery is done by colonoscopy, an electric current is often used to stop bleeding. Since intestinal gases contain hydrogen and methane, the potential for explosion exists. One such explosion was reported in 1979.

Susan J. LaBrooy, a gastroenterologist at Central Middlesex Hospital in London, and others have studied the various bowel-preparative techniques that can increase production of intestinal hydrogen. They reported in 1981 that giving mannitol to the patient to clean out the colon prior to surgery greatly increased the amount of hydrogen that builds up in the colon. This occurs because intestinal bacteria change the mannitol to hydrogen and other chemicals.

Preparing the bowel with castor oil did not increase the hydrogen. Manipulations of air in the bowel that accompany colonoscopic surgery nearly always dilute any hydrogen present to safe levels. Also, the researchers concluded that mannitol should not be used to prepare the bowel for electrosurgery. [Marcus M. Reidenberg]

Earth Sciences

Geology. Research into volcanic eruptions and meteorite impacts and explorations at geologic frontiers dominated geology in 1981 and 1982.

Mount St. Helens. In February 1982, the United States Geological Survey published a voluminous report describing in astounding detail the May 18, 1980, eruption of Mount St. Helens, a volcano in the Cascade Range in the state of Washington. The eruption had been expected. Yet despite continuous monitoring, volcanologists were surprised by its magnitude.

The explanation for the eruption begins with plate tectonics, the theory explaining the movement of the earth's surface. The outer shell of the earth, called the lithosphere, consists of rigid plates that ride atop a region of gently flowing soft hot rock called the asthenosphere. Motions in the asthenosphere cause the plates to collide. When this occurs, one plate may sink at a steep angle beneath the other in a process called subduction. For example, the sea floor west of the Cascade Range is moving eastward toward the North American continent at a rate of 2 to 3 centimeters (0.7 to 1.2 inch) per year. When the sea floor comes within about 100 kilometers (62 miles) of the Pacific Coast, it bends and sinks into the earth's mantle. The sinking plate reaches a depth of about 100 kilometers under the Cascade volcanoes.

At these depths, the rock from the ocean crust and the surrounding mantle melt, producing molten rock, or magma, that contains gases. Because the magma is lighter than the solid rock surrounding it, it rises through the lithosphere to a position directly under a volcano.

In early 1980, as magma continued to rise under Mount St. Helens, the upper parts of the northern slope of the volcano were gradually pushed outward, forming a bulge. Finally, probably triggered by a medium-sized earthquake, the slope broke loose from the mountain in a gigantic landslide, releasing gases trapped under pressure in the underlying magma. As a result, the magma and gases exploded from the side of the volcano like soda pop bursting from a shaken bottle.

The blast, which devastated a 500-square-kilometer (190-square-mile) region north of the volcano, was followed by the eruption of a vertical plume of ash and gas called a Plinian column. Ash in the column was ejected 24 to 27 kilometers (15 to 17 miles) into the stratosphere. As the plume drifted east, it rained 1 cubic kilometer (0.24 cubic mile) of ash on the land in a strip 1,000 kilometers (620 miles) long.

Scientists determined the timing of various stages of the eruption by synchronizing photographs taken by land-based cameras and those taken by cameras on board two U.S. Air Force satellites. Preliminary analysis of the data reveals that the principal destructive blast occurred about three minutes after the landslide and had an initial velocity of 280 kilometers (174 miles) per second.

Volcanic deposits. The mixture of gases and solids spewed from Mount St. Helens and material from the landslide flowed across the land like a fluid, leaving deposits. Scientists are studying these deposits to learn their relationship with specific phases of the eruption. For example, in January 1982, volcanologist Stephen Sparks and S. Brazier of Cambridge University in England reported on their analysis of gas bubbles in volcanic pumice from Mount St. Helens and other eruptions. Pumice is a light glass ejected during eruptions.

The scientists found three sizes of bubbles, which correspond to three phases of volcanic activity. Only the smallest bubbles are associated with the Plinian column. The coarsest bubbles formed over a period of months in the magma chamber at the base of the volcano and were probably in the magma that caused the swelling of the mountain before eruption. The information yielded by the analysis may help volcanologists understand previous eruptions by other volcanoes.

Antarctic meteorites. In August 1981, geochemist Edward J. Olsen of the Field Museum of Natural History in Chicago reported that since 1969 scientists have been more successful in finding meteorites at the edge of the ice sheet in the Antarctic than in any other area. Although an estimated 3,500 meteorites land on earth each year, the number recovered is small. The most common meteorites, called ordinary chondrites, often are overlooked because they resemble many silicate rocks found on the earth's surface. Meteorites are also easily destroyed by weathering. As a result, nearly all our information on the earliest history of the solar system has been pieced together from the analysis of little more than 1,000 meteorites. However, Olsen reported that since 1969 scientists have found 5,000 meteorites in the Antarctic, greatly adding to the number of meteorite "finds" as opposed to "falls," whose entry and impact are observed.

Although meteorites falling onto the Antarctic ice sheet are soon buried under snow and ice, they gradually work their way outward toward the edge of the sheet, where they are exposed. Olsen's calculations, based on the number of meteorites observed falling to earth each year and the number recovered in the Antarctic, indicate that about 760,000 meteorites are still trapped in the ice.

Sunspot theories. Scientists are reasonably certain that periods of glaciation, or glacier formation, are related to variations in the pattern of distribution of solar energy reaching the earth. These variations are the result of changes in the earth's orbit and angle of the earth's axis. Scientists are investigating whether glaciation is also related to sunspot activity—characterized by the appearance of dark spots on the surface of the sun.

In 1980, Minzie Stuiver and Paul Quay of the University of Washington reported that their analysis of the radioactive isotope carbon 14 in tree rings argues against a direct relationship between sunspot activity and changes in climate. Production of carbon 14 in the atmosphere increases during periods of low sunspot activity, such as the period between 1430 and 1850 known as the little ice age. If scientists could prove a relationship between varying carbon 14 levels on earth and changes in climate, they would then be able to establish a connection between sunspot activity and the variations in climate. However, the scientists observed no consistent rela-

Before Pangaea
The supercontinent Pangaea may have existed in a form, called Pangaea B, 290 million to 250 million years ago, before the continents shifted to form the traditionally accepted configuration 200 million years ago.

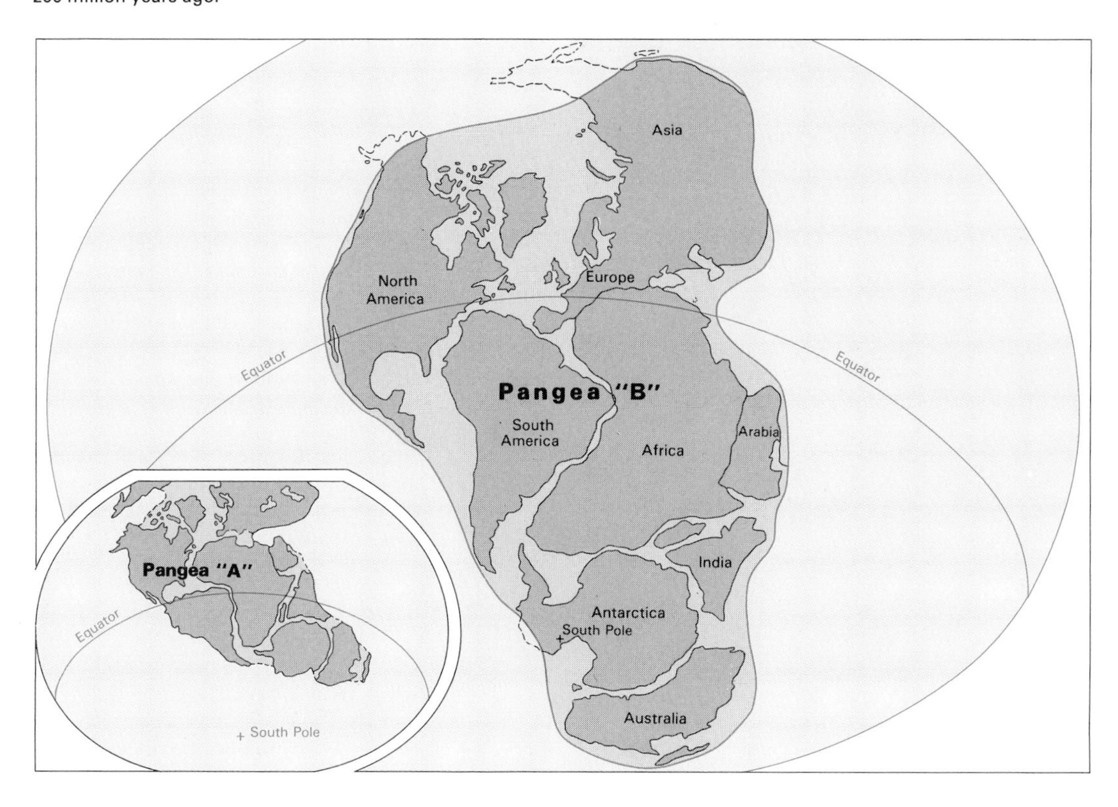

A thick column of ash and steam spews from the Chichón volcano in southern Mexico, a long-dormant volcano that erupted four times beginning on March 29, 1982.

tionship between carbon 14 levels and climatic variations during the past 1,000 years.

However, in August 1981, G. Raibeck and colleagues at the Renee Bernas Laboratory in Orsay, France, provided evidence for a connection between sunspot activity and the last major period of glaciation, which ended about 10,000 years ago. The scientists analyzed levels of beryllium 10, another radioactive isotope, in core samples of Antarctic ice. They discovered high levels of the element during periods of low sunspot activity and also during the last major ice age. They believe this data indicates some relationship between sunspot activity and glaciation.

Meteorite evidence. The theory that the collision of a giant meteorite with the earth about 65 million years ago at the end of the Cretaceous Period caused the extinction of many plant and animal species, including dinosaurs, continues to spawn related research projects. The theory was proposed in 1979 by a team of scientists headed by geologist Walter Alvarez of the University of California, Berkeley. The scientists based their theory on the presence of certain elements, chiefly iridium, in surface rocks laid down during that time. These elements are rare on earth but plentiful in celestial bodies.

In July 1981, J. Smit and G. Klaver of the Geological Institute of Amsterdam in The Netherlands reported on their discovery of sanidine spherules in the same sediment layer in which iridium was found. The spherules are somewhat similar to tectites, glass globules formed as the result of heat produced by the impact of a meteorite. The scientists theorized that the sanidine spherules may have been formed through the same process. Their presence in the same layer as the iridium may provide further support for the meteorite collision theory. See EARTH SCIENCES (Paleontology).

Hydrothermal circulations. Each year, 10 to 15 cubic kilometers (2.5 to 3.5 cubic miles) of new ocean crust forms from magma welling up from beneath the steep-sided valleys in the center of the mid-ocean ridges where the tectonic plates that form the sea floor are drifting apart. A major mechanism for cooling the newly formed rock is hydrothermal circulation—the movement of ocean water into the underlying solidified lava flows and magma chambers through the thin sediment cover on the surface of the ridges. The water, which is heated during its journey, exits through vents, or openings in the rock, around the ridge. In various deep-sea dives to explore these vents, geologists in submersible vehicles have found incredibly rich deposits of such metals as zinc, copper, lead, silver, and gold.

In July 1981, marine geophysicist Roger Anderson of the Lamont-Doherty Geological Observatory in Palisades, N.Y., reported that hydrothermal circulation is probably a major mechanism for bringing ore up to the sea floor. As it travels through the rock, the heated water absorbs minerals that then precipitate out as the hot water mixes with cool water at the bottom of the ocean.

Hydrothermal circulation also may have contributed to the material spewed out of volcanoes at areas of subduction. Geochemists Richard Armstrong of the University of British Columbia in Canada, Robert W. Kay of Cornell University in Ithaca, N.Y., and others believe some of the elements added to the ocean crust by hydrothermal circulation may be later taken into the earth's mantle by subduction, then returned to the earth's surface through volcanic eruptions, like that of Mount St. Helens.

Continental mosaics. Many modern continental masses are mosaics of microcontinents, called terrains, that may have drifted for thousands of kilometers before they were welded together by collisions, such as India's collision with mainland Asia, which resulted in the formation of the Himalayan mountains.

In 1981, geophysicist M. W. McElhinny and co-workers at the Australian National University in Canberra and scientists from the People's Republic of China used paleomagnetic measurements to document how present-day Asia consisted of smaller, separate terrains during the Permian Period, about 250 million years ago. These measurements, which indicate the angle of the earth's magnetic field at the time rocks were formed, can be used to trace the rocks' movements.

The scientists discovered that the Siberian, Sino-Korean, and Yangtze terrains—now joined—were widely separated during the Permian Period. In addition, they found that the Sino-Korean and Yangtze terrains were located near the equator at that time.

This new work does not support the theory that all continents were part of a universal land mass called Pangaea during the Permian Period. Although North and South America, Africa, and Europe were connected at that time, the discovery that the three terrains were widely separated showed that large parts of Asia had not yet been assembled and so could not have been part of Pangaea.

Suture zones. Determining the structure of the boundaries, or suture zones, between terrains is one area of research not aided by paleomagnetic data. One technique used to explore this area is seismic reflection profiling, a major exploration tool of the oil industry. A series of large trucks with synchronized vibration pads generate low-frequency sound waves that fan out below the surface. These sound waves are reflected by such geologic formations as sediments, igneous layers, and faults beneath the surface and are detected as echoes by sensitive microphones at the surface.

In May 1982, geophysicist Jack Oliver of Cornell University reported on the results of seismic reflection profiling by the Consortium for Continental Reflection Profiling at suture zones in the Appalachians. Oliver and other scientists believe that at the terrain boundaries, thin sheets of older rock from one terrain were pushed tens or even hundreds of kilometers onto younger, cool, flat-lying sedimentary rock on the other terrain.

These results are important for oil and gas exploration because the underlying flat sedimentary rock, which is within reach of deep drilling techniques, is potentially rich in oil and may be even richer in natural gas. The identification of suture zones in other regions could provide a valuable tool in the exploration for sources of energy. [Robert W. Kay]

A series of snail fossils spanning several million years found near Lake Turkana in Kenya show that new forms arose suddenly – in 5,000 to 50,000 years – after remaining unchanged for long periods. The discovery lends support to the evolutionary theory of punctuated equilibrium, which argues that evolution did not proceed at a gradual pace.

Paleontology. During 1982, paleontologists and geologists continued to debate the validity of the theory that a giant meteorite struck the earth 65 million years ago, causing the extinction of the dinosaurs as well as about 70 per cent of all other species of animals and plants.

The major evidence for such an impact comes from a concentration of iridium between sediment deposited at the end of the Cretaceous Period, when the extinctions occurred, and sediment laid down in the Tertiary Period that followed. Although iridium is rarely found on earth, it is plentiful in asteroids and meteorites.

Iridium concentrations have been found in 65-million-year-old marine sediment from Denmark, Spain, New Zealand, Italy, and the ocean bottom, as well as in continental sediment. However, despite general agreement among most scientists that the iridium resulted from the impact of a meteorite, there is still disagreement about how catastrophic the effects of such an impact would have been on life.

Geologist Kenneth J. Hsü of the Swiss Federal Institute of Technology in Zurich and a team of 18 other scientists from the United States and Europe reported in April 1982 on their study of a sediment core from the deep sea near southwestern Africa. Their findings suggest that the meteorite impact caused a sudden reduction in photosynthesis in plant plankton. This, in turn, caused environmental changes so severe that many other extinctions, most notably that of the dinosaurs, occurred.

The core showed the expected sudden increase in iridium at the boundary between the Cretaceous and Tertiary periods. However, the scientists also found three other anomalies, or irregularities, in the chemical composition of the core. First, there was a rapid decrease in the calcium carbonate content of the sediments. Most sea shells are composed of calcium carbonate. Second, the proportion of the isotope carbon-13 in relation to carbon-12 decreased. Scientists use the ratio of these isotopes to measure the level of plant growth in surface waters. Third, the ratio of the isotope oxygen-18 to oxygen-16 increased, then fell early in the Tertiary Period. Scientists use the ratio of these isotopes to determine changes in water temperature in ancient times. These anomalies in the chemistry of the core coincided with the disappearance of all but a few of the Cretaceous species of small plants and animals, possibly in as short a time as 50 years.

Hsü and his colleagues believe the anomalies indicate that the impact caused the almost instantaneous mass extinction of plankton, the tiny plants and animals that live in the surface waters of the ocean. They may have been poisoned by chemicals in the meteorite, or killed by a sudden and dramatic rise in temperature as the meteorite burned in the atmosphere. Or their death may have resulted from the inability of the plants to photosynthesize if enormous amounts of dust were thrown into the atmosphere by the impact, blocking out sunlight.

The scientists theorize that the death of the plankton would have temporarily ended photosynthesis and plant growth in the ocean, as indicated by the reduction in the level of carbon-13. The lack of plant life would have caused carbon dioxide levels in the surface water to rise, leading to an increase in carbonic acid. Because of the water's increased acidity, sea shells would have dissolved before they could settle to the ocean floor. This explains the decrease in the amount of calcium carbonate in the boundary sediments.

Eventually, the carbon dioxide in the surface waters would have been released into the atmosphere to act like a greenhouse, trapping heat from the sun and further increasing atmospheric temperatures. The decrease in the amount of oxygen-18 in the sediment core indicates that worldwide temperatures may have risen an average of 10°C (18°F.) over a 50,000-year period. The brief initial increase in oxygen-18 may have resulted from a temporary cooling of the surface waters as dust blanketed the earth.

Finally, Hsü and his colleagues speculate that the meteorite impact itself may not have caused the dinosaur extinctions. Instead, the temperature rise that followed the release of carbon dioxide into the atmosphere may have killed the dinosaurs, which were un-

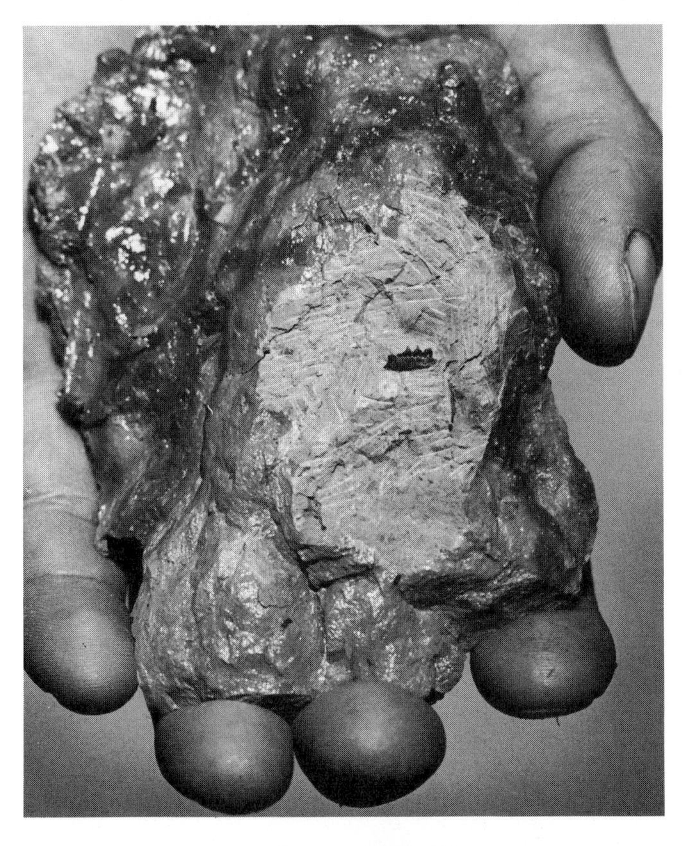

The fossil jaw of a previously unknown mammal, found embedded in rock in northeastern Arizona, is the first evidence that mammals existed in North America as early as 180 million years ago. The jaw, *above,* belonged to a primitive mammal about the size of a small mouse, which probably ate insects.

able to adjust to progressively higher temperatures. This may have happened as late as 50,000 years after the meteorite's impact.

Dinosaur speed. How fast could dinosaurs run? Contrary to popular notions of dinosaurs as slow, lumbering beasts, a study of dinosaur tracks in Lower Cretaceous sediments from Kimble County, Texas, reported by James O. Farlow of Holland, Mich., in December 1981 indicates that some dinosaurs could run faster than sprinting humans.

The tracks were made in soft mud, which later hardened into limestone, by carnivorous dinosaurs called theropods moving at various speeds. Farlow estimated that the slowest of the dinosaurs moved at 1.8 meters (6 feet) per second, and the fastest at 11.9 meters (39 feet) per second. Farlow based his estimates on the length of the stride, which he determined by measuring the distance between prints made by the same foot. He then compared these measurements to measurements of stride and speed in rapidly running hoofed African animals. The dinosaurs' top speeds were probably greater than those human athletes can attain over a short distance.

New bird fossils. The discovery and study of some early bird fossils have shed light on the evolution of birds. In December 1981, paleontologists Peter Houde of Howard University and Storrs L. Olson of the Smithsonian Institution, both in Washington, D.C., reported on well-preserved bird fossils from about 60 million years ago. The fossils clearly indicate that the birds could fly and had wing bones similar to those of present-day hawks and owls. However, bones in the palate, or roof of the mouth of the fossils, are arranged in a pattern known as paleognathous and resemble the palate of such flightless birds as present-day ostriches and emus and extinct moas.

Paleontologists believe that flightless birds evolved from flying birds. However, they had assumed that only flightless birds had a paleognathous palate and that such birds had developed from a common ancestor. The new finds make it more likely that flightless birds evolved from more than one type of flying bird. [Ida Thompson]

Science Year Close-Up

Dinoman

Sixty-five million years ago, an unknown global catastrophe wiped out the dinosaurs and more than half the other species of animals and plants on earth. No creature that weighed more than 23 kilograms (50 pounds) survived. Small mammals inherited the land that the dinosaurs had dominated for nearly 140 million years. The mammals developed new forms that replaced the dinosaurs.

Human beings, with their higher intelligence, eventually emerged from this development. But what would have happened if the dinosaurs had not been wiped out? Would they have developed high intelligence?

This question has long fascinated Canadian paleobiologist Dale Russell, curator of fossil vertebrates at the National Museum of Natural Sciences in Ottawa, Ont. To help answer the question, Russell developed a graph showing that the encephalization level of animals—brain size compared with body weight—increases with the passing of time, even though different kinds of creatures have had the distinction of being the world's most intelligent at various times. He found that just before the great extinction, the most intelligent animal on earth was a dinosaur known as the stenonychosaurus, whose fossilized remains Russell and his associates discovered near Dinosaur Provincial Park in Alberta in the 1970s.

Stenonychosaurus was a kangaroo-sized, meat-eating dinosaur that walked on its hind legs. It must have been a formidable foe for smaller creatures. Its large eyes were suitable for hunting at night and could perceive depth as today's higher mammals can. Stenonychosaurus could deftly grasp its food with its three-fingered, clawed hands, whose third finger opposed the other two, operating like the thumb of apes and humans.

By modern standards, however, stenonychosaurus was not a very bright animal. Its encephalization level was 20, ranking between today's armadillo and opossum. Worms are at the level of 1, and humans rate the top spot at 354.

An intelligent creature resembling human beings might have developed from the dinosaur stenonychosaurus by the present time if the dinosaurs had not become extinct 65 million years ago.

But stenonychosaurus had potential. Russell's graph convinced him that the rise to higher intelligence was highly probable and that a dinosaur much like stenonychosaurus would have developed high intelligence by now. He then set out to determine the physical characteristics of a highly intelligent descendant of such a creature.

He began with the fact that certain body shapes seem to be the best for certain functions. Fish and aquatic mammals such as dolphins, for example, look like ancient reptiles that lived in the water. Russell applied this fact to his task. "It is reasonable to assume that any land creature which walks on two legs and has a heavy head due to a big brain would be humanoid in form no matter what it initially evolved from," Russell concluded.

Russell explained his ideas of the creature's body structure to taxidermist Ron Seguin, who built a life-sized model of the creature and a reconstruction of stenonychosaurus for the National Museum in Ottawa. Seguin's model portrays a stunningly human-looking creature called dinosauroid that stands 137 centimeters (4.5 feet) tall, weighs about 32 kilograms (70 pounds), and has a brain the same size as that of a human of approximately the same height.

Dinosauroid's nonhuman features include a turtlelike mouth with horny biting edges. The lack of teeth "eliminates tooth decay as a hazard to health," quips Russell. Also absent are breasts, nipples, and external sex organs, in keeping with dinosauroid's ancestry. To feed its young, a dinosauroid parent would regurgitate partially digested food, as do birds today. Most paleontologists agree that birds are dinosaur descendants and, like birds, dinosauroid would be warm-blooded.

Not all scientists who have commented on dinosauroid agree with Russell. However, the idea that an intelligent humanoid probably would have developed on earth is compelling. And it supports the fascinating possibility that a single natural mold produced humanity, would have produced dinosauroid, and has produced humanoids on countless other worlds among the stars. [Terence Dickinson]

Meteorology. The Cooperative Convective Precipitation Experiment (CCOPE) was launched in May 1981 by a consortium of United States government, university, and industrial scientists. The program will study in unprecedented detail the relation of convective, or thunderstorm, clouds and precipitation, or rain and hail. The CCOPE study was co-sponsored by the Convective Storms Division of the National Center for Atmospheric Research (NCAR) in Boulder, Colo., and the Power Resources Service of the U.S. Department of the Interior's Bureau of Reclamation.

From May to August, observations focused on a 150-kilometer (90-mile) radius area around Miles City, Mont. The researchers were seeking to understand what produces the summer storms that bring the rain needed for High Plains grain crops and pasture grasses. Within the study area, a fleet of 17 instrument-carrying planes and an array of 7 Doppler radars were only a small part of the data-gathering force. In addition, there were five upper-air rawinsondes — radio-transmitter-equipped instruments that are lofted on balloons and then floated down to earth on parachutes while gathering and transmitting data.

There was also a network of 125 solar-powered weather stations, many of them transmitting data every five minutes via satellite. All of these monitors provided detailed information on the structure and variation of temperature, pressure, humidity, precipitation, and wind during a typical summer storm. With these data, CCOPE researchers hoped to learn more about the complex series of physical and chemical interactions that take place before, during, and after a large thunderstorm.

They are particularly interested in the relationship between airflow and the growth of cloud ice and water droplets into precipitation, because these processes have a direct bearing on the possibility of rainmaking — and profit-making. In North Dakota and South Dakota, a 1 per cent increase in rainfall during the growing season could increase the worth of annual crop yields by $100 million.

Where lightning strikes. Atmospheric scientists Richard E. Orville and Bernard Vonnegut of the State University of New York at Albany reported during the year that for the first time they had produced maps showing the frequency of lightning over the entire area between 60° north and 60° south latitude. The scientists used data collected by an earth-orbiting satellite operated by the U.S. Air Force.

Their observations of lightning occurring around midnight between September 1977 and August 1978 confirmed that lightning predominates in the tropics, as the scientists expected. However, they also found the unexpected result that there is relatively little midnight lightning over the oceans compared with that over land. This may be the result of convection—the upward flow of sun-warmed air—during the preceding day. This keeps electrically charged clouds far above the earth's surface. Nighttime convective storms at low latitude were not thought to depend on daytime events.

Monitoring the ozone layer in the earth's upper atmosphere was the subject of reports by several scientists at the annual meeting of the American Geophysical Union in San Francisco in December 1981. Ozone (O_3) is formed when a free oxygen atom (O) joins an oxygen molecule (O_2).

The thin layer of ozone in the earth's upper atmosphere was formed millions of years ago, as the earth evolved. It acts as a shield that absorbs most of the shorter wavelength rays in the sun's radiation, which would be harmful to living things if they reached the earth's surface. The amount of ozone in the atmosphere is affected by changes in solar radiation and by human activities, such as the use of fluorocarbons in aerosol sprays and emissions from supersonic planes.

Monitoring changes in the ozone layer is one of the tasks of the Solar Mesosphere Explorer (SME) satellite, which was launched on Oct. 16, 1981. It is expected to reveal processes occurring in the mesosphere—the region of the atmosphere from 32 to 80 kilometers (20 to 50 miles) above the earth's surface, between the stratosphere and the ionosphere.

A balloon as big as a football field carries instruments to measure water vapor in the stratosphere. It is one of a group launched by the National Center for Atmospheric Research to cross-check seven measurement techniques.

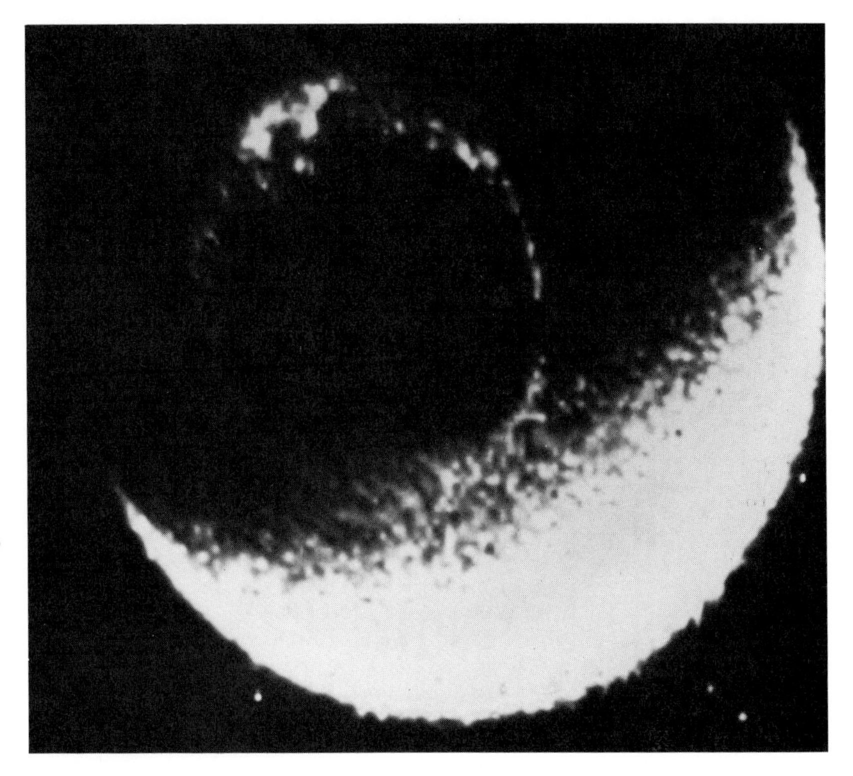

The aurora around the earth's North Pole is seen completely for the first time in photos transmitted by special cameras on NASA's new *Dynamics Explorer A* satellite. The spacecraft was designed to investigate interaction of the earth's upper atmosphere with its extensive magnetic field.

A record-breaking heat wave occurred in the Western United States in the summer of 1981, in association with an unusually strong ridge of high pressure that became established over North America. During the second week of August, highest-ever temperatures were observed at many meteorological stations in the Pacific Northwest. The highest reading was 49°C (121°F.) on August 7 at Red Bluff in northern California, an all-time record. In the Southwest, the August heat wave resulted in the hottest month ever recorded in Phoenix, with an average daily temperature of 35.5°C (95.8°F.). It was also the hottest August on record in normally temperate San Diego, with an average daily temperature of 24.5°C (75.8°F.). Records for the second-hottest August were set in Salt Lake City, Utah, and in Portland, Ore., while much of the Central and Southeastern parts of the United States were cooler than normal.

In most regions west of the Rocky Mountains, the heat was accompanied by unusually dry conditions, while in the Central and Eastern regions, rainfall occurred in a scattered fashion that seemed to bear little relation to average air circulation and temperature patterns. For example, in Arkansas, Illinois, and Texas, several stations recorded the wettest August ever, while stations in southern New England had the driest August on record and areas in the southern Appalachian Mountains experienced a near-record dry month. The drought in these regions was broken by rains in September.

Forecasting seasonal anomalies, or departures from the general rule of behavior of temperature and precipitation, such as occurred during the summer of 1981, has long been a goal of meteorologists. In December, atmospheric scientists Thomas W. Bettge, David P. Baumhefner, and Robert M. Chervin of NCAR reported the results of a study in which they evaluated the accuracy of several long-range forecasts issued prior to winter each year from 1976-1977 through 1980-1981. These winter forecasts covered December, January, and February.

The scientists studied predictions made by the National Weather Service (NWS) and by meteorologist Jerome Namias of Scripps Institution of Oceanography in San Diego. They compared the NWS and Namias predictions of how much each winter season's mean temperature would differ from the long-term climatological average with what actually happened. The temperature anomaly forecasts for the winters of 1979-1980 and 1980-1981, in particular, had received wide general publicity because those were the first years that the NWS and Namias both issued predictions.

Bettge, Baumhefner, and Chervin checked what the actual temperature had been during the five winters at 100 points spaced equally over the United States. They found that the winter-temperature forecasts made by the NWS were correct an average of 43 per cent of the time, while those made by Namias were correct an average of 41 per cent of the time. When the seasonal anomaly is forecast in terms of three categories—above-normal, near-normal, or below-normal—there is a 33 per cent probability of any category being correctly forecast at a particular station, purely by chance.

Perhaps the most intriguing finding was that the NWS and Namias forecasts tended to resemble each other more closely than either resembled the actually observed conditions. Both the NWS and Namias based their forecasts on analysis of meteorological conditions in the past, on considerable experience in studying varying climates, and on statistical interpretations and projections. Both methods were most successful in predicting the above-normal temperatures observed in the Western United States in the winter of 1976-1977, when drought conditions were widespread west of the Rocky Mountains. However, both the Namias and the NWS forecasts failed to predict the excessively low temperatures that occurred over most of the United States in the winter of 1978-1979. Despite intensive research, neither government nor university groups have been able to determine the reasons for these and similar failures. Skillful long-range forecasting remains an elusive goal. [W. Lawrence Gates]

Oceanography. Today's oceanographic treasure hunters often go to sea in search of natural riches. Alexander Malahoff, chief scientist of the National Ocean Survey, part of the United States National Oceanic and Atmospheric Administration (NOAA) in Rockville, Md., reported a new mineral find in August 1981.

Malahoff discovered and mapped an extensive ore deposit 2,480 meters (8,150 feet) beneath the eastern Pacific Ocean about 560 kilometers (350 miles) west of Ecuador. Ore samples gathered at the site by the submersible *Alvin* contained copper, silver, cadmium, iron, lead, tin, molybdenum, vanadium, and zinc. Malahoff estimated that the deposit was 40 meters (130 feet) thick, 200 meters (656 feet) wide, and about 1 kilometer (0.5 mile) long, and contained about 22.5 million metric tons (25 million short tons) of minerals.

Scientists aboard the United States Geological Survey ship *S. P. Lee* reported in September that they had found metal-rich deposits near a submarine volcano at a depth of 2,200 meters (7,200 feet) located about 400 kilometers (250 miles) west of Newport, Ore. Chief Scientist William Normark said preliminary analysis showed the dredged samples contained heavy concentrations of zinc, plus lesser amounts of silver, copper, iron, and cadmium. Water spewing from an active sea-floor vent contained 100 times as much manganese as surrounding water.

These metal-bearing deposits, or polymetallic sulfides, appear to be formed when extremely hot water, at a temperature of 350°C (662°F.), containing high concentrations of minerals, shoots from cracks in the sea floor into the near-freezing bottom water, which is at a temperature of 2°C (35.6°F.). The abrupt change in temperature causes the minerals to settle out on the ocean floor, where they form chimneylike "smokers" as high as 18 meters (60 feet).

Probing the Bering Sea. John J. Goering and C. Peter McRoy of the University of Alaska's Institute of Marine Science in Fairbanks reported in November 1981 on findings from the project known as Processes and Resources of the Bering Sea Shelf (PROBES). Begun in 1976, PROBES was a six-year effort by scientists from six university and government agencies to understand the processes that contribute to the abundance of marine life in the Bering Sea, part of the North Pacific Ocean. About 5 per cent of the total annual world catch of seafood comes from the Bering Sea.

The scientists concentrated on three fronts, or sharp breaks in the features of ocean water, which divide the 500-kilometer (310-mile)-wide southeastern Bering Sea shelf into three distinct domains. The domains are: *coastal* (80 to 150 kilometers [50 to 95 miles] from shore); *middle* (150 to 400 kilometers [95 to 250 miles] from shore); and *outer* (400 to 500 kilometers [250 to 310 miles] from shore). These areas are defined by different temperatures, salinity, layering, circulation, and marine life. A frontal zone marks the seaward boundary of each domain.

The PROBES researchers found that more animal and plant life exists in the frontal zones than in the waters on either side. The waters separating the coastal domain from the outer domain are especially productive, because nutrients from both areas mix in the surface layers and are able to support an abundance of marine life. At the same time, the outer frontal zone of this middle domain acts as a barrier that blocks the movement of plankton and other nutrients to the deeper waters off the shelf. The reduced amount of phytoplankton in the outer domain results in a pelagic, or open-water, food web. There, such fish as Alaskan pollack and yellowfin sole eat most of the phytoplankton.

Much of the abundant plankton in the middle domain waters goes unused by pelagic fish. It falls to the sea floor where it becomes part of a food web for benthic, or bottom-dwelling, creatures such as king crabs.

Warmer climates, rising seas? Scientists generally agree that the sea level is rising, but they do not fully agree on the reasons, or the way these changes reflect simultaneous changes occurring in the global climate.

University of Georgia researchers using a specially developed instrument called a respirometer measure the respiration rates of corals disturbed by sediment on the floor of the Caribbean Sea near the island of Jamaica.

Earth Sciences
Continued

Geologist Vivian Gornitz and atmospheric scientists Sergej Lebedeff and James E. Hansen of the Goddard Space Flight Center's Institute for Space Studies in New York City reported in March 1982 that they made a comprehensive study of sea-level change during the past 100 years based on measurements from 193 tide-gauge stations around the world. Using a variety of statistical techniques, the scientists estimated that average global sea level rose about 10 centimeters (4 inches) during that period. That is a very small change compared with the long-term trends of 100 centimeters (3.3 feet) per century or more that occurred during periods of rapid continental ice-sheet melting.

The scientists concluded that a large part of the sea-level rise over the past century was due to warmer air temperatures, which caused the upper layers of the ocean to expand. Only a small portion of the rise was the result of some melting of the polar ice sheets.

The researchers suggested that if predictions about the continued warming of the earth's climate are correct and the ice sheets continue to melt at their current rates, the sea level could rise between 40 and 60 centimeters (16 and 24 inches) by the year 2050.

Robert Etkins and Edward S. Epstein of NOAA agreed that thermal expansion of the oceans is one condition responsible for the rise in sea level over the past 40 years, but not the only one. They reported in January 1982 that the average global sea level rose nearly 13 centimeters (5 inches) since 1940, or three times the rate of rise measured between 1890 and 1940.

They observed that a global warming trend prior to 1940 might have caused the oceans to expand, but that the trend since 1940 has been toward cooler average global temperatures. The only plausible explanation for the accelerated sea-level rise after 1940 is the increased melting of the polar ice sheets. This melting ice would also absorb the heat from the air and reduce the surface warming that might otherwise occur. [Feenan D. Jennings and Lauriston R. King]

Ecology

Ecological research found a practical application as part of United States efforts toward energy independence in 1981. In a report released in September, the U.S. Department of Energy (DOE) detailed the preliminary results of an ambitious program to increase wood production. The program, begun in 1977, was carried out at universities and at the Department of Agriculture-Forest Service laboratories throughout the United States.

DOE surveys indicated that wood has great potential as a major energy source but, without improved growing systems, the United States could experience a wood shortage by the year 2000. The program focused on growing species of hardwood trees that can produce sprouts from stumps and can be reharvested every 3 to 10 years.

Density and drainage. Forest scientist Donald L. Rockwood of the University of Florida in Gainesville assessed the water requirements of high-density wood stands, areas in which trees are planted close together. He set tension tube lysimeters—devices for measuring drainage—near each tree in two sand pine stands. In one stand, the trees were planted at a density of 1 tree per 1.5 square meters (16 square feet). In the second, less dense stand, the trees were spaced at 1 tree per 4 square meters (43.5 square feet).

Rockwood found that the volume of runoff water from the widely spaced trees was greater than that from the more densely planted trees. These results suggest that each sand pine may consume more water when the trees are planted closer together and that potential growers should take water requirements into account when deciding how densely to plant sand pines.

In similar studies with eucalyptus trees on plots at La Belle, Fla., Rockwood found that densely planted trees consumed no more water than did sparsely planted trees. His results indicate that, in terms of water requirements, eucalyptus trees are good candidates for high-density planting.

Nutrient demands. Several researchers investigated the nutrient requirements of trees and their demands upon

Ecology
Continued

Researchers from Oak Ridge National Laboratory in Tennessee, studying the effects of harvesting whole trees, weigh a cut tree, *above,* to provide data with which to calculate the weight of a standing forest plot. Ungainly Coshocton Wheels, placed throughout a harvested forest, measure water runoff from the denuded plot, *above right.*

the soil. Forest scientist Gary L. Rolfe of the University of Illinois in Urbana monitored nutrient levels in trees and soil at sites on the top and bottom of a hill in southeastern Illinois for two growing seasons. At the end of the period, he found that the nitrogen and phosphorus content in the top 61 centimeters (24 inches) of the soil in both sites had decreased. But these losses varied with the tree species grown.

At both sites, losses were greatest in areas planted with eastern cottonwood, followed by those planted with royal paulownia, black locust, autumn olive, European black alder, and sycamore. However, overall nutrient losses at the bottom of the hill were lower than at the hilltop site, which had been fertilized with nitrogen and phosphorus to increase productivity. The researchers did not fertilize the initially richer soil at the bottom of the hill.

Silviculturist Douglas J. Frederick of North Carolina State University in Raleigh researched the effect of growing conditions on the nutrient levels in trees. A high nutrient level indicates a high growth rate. Frederick collected leaf samples from trees on both unfertilized and fertilized plots at two sites—a poorly drained, clay-loam site and a well-drained, sandy-loam site. He analyzed the leaves for nitrogen and phosphorus and found that leaf samples from fertilized trees on the well-drained site had a higher nitrogen and phosphorus content than those from unfertilized trees on the same site. However, leaf samples from unfertilized trees on the poorly drained site had more nitrogen than those from fertilized trees on the same site.

Frederick concluded that, because constant water runoff had carried nitrogen and phosphorus away from the sandy-loam site, the soil in this site was naturally low in nutrients. When he added fertilizers, they became immediately available to the trees because low moisture levels had prevented weeds, which would have used up the added nutrients.

In contrast, the wet soil on the poorly drained site gave rise to a heavy growth of weeds, providing intense

Instruments to collect precipitation are placed above, *top,* and below, *above,* the canopy of a forest in research to determine how leaves and branches change the chemical composition of rain and snow. The project is part of a study conducted by Oak Ridge National Laboratory to determine the long-term effects of acid precipitation.

competition for nutrients. Moreover, because the weeds are naturally faster growing than the trees, they consumed a large amount of the fertilizer. Thus the leaves of the nutrient-deprived trees contained relatively low levels of nitrogen and phosphorus. However, when the poorly drained plot was not fertilized, the weeds did not flourish, leaving more of the nutrients for the trees. Frederick's studies underscored the importance of weed control when growing trees on fertilized sites.

Soil scientist Linda S. Dolan of the Seattle City Light Company in Washington examined the requirements for growing the black cottonwood and red alder. Dolan planted cottonwood seedlings on one stand and red alder on another. She divided each stand into three growing plots. One plot on each stand was fertilized, one plot was fertilized and irrigated, and the remaining plot, a control group, was neither fertilized nor irrigated.

At the end of the trees' second growing season, she measured the biomass—the weight of the plant matter—and analyzed the nutrient content of tissues from plants grown in the three plots on both stands. She found that trees grown on the fertilized plots had the greatest biomass, followed by trees grown on irrigated and fertilized plots. The control plots had the least biomass. Nitrogen and phosphorus content was highest in tissue taken from trees grown on the fertilized plots and lower in trees grown on irrigated and fertilized plots, as well as in trees grown on the control plots. These results indicate that fertilization produces trees rapidly, but that excessive irrigation removes nutrients.

Dolan also analyzed soil samples collected at depths of up to 20 centimeters (8 inches) and from 20 to 60 centimeters (8 to 24 inches). She found that the samples from fertilized plots had a markedly higher phosphorus and nitrogen content than those from the other plots. However, when she compared the nutrient concentrations with those of samples taken from the same plots at the beginning of the project, she found that nitrogen and potassium levels of all of the samples had decreased over the two growing seasons. These early results suggest that fertilization alone is not sufficient to replace depleted soil nutrients.

Mixing nitrogen-fixers. Other researchers studied the effect of planting nitrogen-fixing tree species with non-nitrogen-fixing species. Nitrogen-fixing plants have root nodules harboring bacteria that transform atmospheric nitrogen into ammonia—a form that can be used by plants. When these bacteria die, they add ammonia to the soil around the plant roots.

Crop management specialist Thomas B. Crabb of the Bio-Energy Development Corporation of Hilo, Hawaii, evaluated the advantages of planting tropical nitrogen-fixing trees with eucalyptus as part of a broader study of the potential for growing eucalyptus for firewood in Hawaii.

Crabb planted two stands—one with two species of nitrogen-fixers, *Acacia* and *Albizia*, in addition to eucalyptus, and the other, as a control, with eucalyptus alone. He found that after two growing seasons, eucalyptus trees planted with nitrogen-fixers were taller and larger in diameter than those in the control stand. In addition, tissue taken from eucalyptus trees in the mixed stand had a significantly higher nitrogen concentration than tissue from eucalyptus trees grown in the control stand. Crabb's results suggest that the eucalyptus benefited from the nitrogen returned to the soil by the nitrogen-fixing tree species.

Forest geneticist Reinhard F. Stettler of the University of Washington in Seattle and silviculturist Paul E. Heilman of Washington State University in Pullman established two stands to evaluate cottonwood production. One was planted with hybrid cottonwood clones—genetically identical plants—and the other with a mixture of the hybrid cottonwood clones and red alder—a nitrogen-fixer. They analyzed the nitrogen concentrations of the tissues and measured the biomass of the cottonwoods from both stands at the end of each growing season following the initial plantings.

Stettler and Heilman noted that after the first and second growing seasons, the nitrogen content of the tissues from cottonwoods grown with the nitrogen-fixer was higher than that of tissues from cottonwoods grown alone. However, they found that there was no difference in nitrogen content after the third year. The researchers speculated that the nitrogen-fixing red alders grew more slowly than normal because of competition for soil nutrients from the faster growing cottonwoods, and thus, the rate at which they fixed nitrogen decreased.

When Stettler and Heilman analyzed the biomass after three growing seasons, they determined that the mean annual yield for cottonwoods growing alone was 9.8 dry metric tons per hectare (4.4 short tons per acre), while yield of cottonwoods grown with the nitrogen-fixer was 9.5 dry metric tons per hectare (4.1 short tons per acre). Although the yield of cottonwoods growing with the red alders increased slightly from the first to second growing season, it decreased significantly after three years.

In other trials using different cottonwood clones, clones with average or better growth rates had lower biomass yields when planted with alders than when grown alone. However, the yield of slower growing cottonwood clones substantially increased when the cottonwoods were grown with alders.

Forest scientist Klaus Steinbeck of the University of Georgia in Athens established separate stands of sycamore and sweet gum trees, and of two nitrogen-fixing tree species—black locust and black alder. He also planted each of the nitrogen-fixers with sycamore and sweet gum. He found that sycamore and sweet gum yielded a lower biomass when planted with black alder than when planted alone. Pure black locust growing alone and sycamore growing with black locust produced the greatest yields.

Goals for the future. The DOE report concluded that firewood, as a high-yield annual crop, is still in the future. It recommended that research teams develop and propagate superior strains of trees, determine which trees are best suited for certain sites, and design and develop more efficient equipment for harvesting and transporting wood. The report also proposed studies of the availability of land for intensive tree cultivation and the environmental effects of such cultivation. [Stanley I. Auerbach]

Electronics

A TV set, *below,* 2.5 centimeters (1 inch) thick, another TV set, *bottom,* whose screen measures 4 centimeters (1.5 inches) diagonally, and a computer, *below right,* whose depth is only 4 centimeters represent the latest in miniaturized consumer products.

Sinclair Research Limited in Cambridge, England, and Sony Corporation in Tokyo developed ways of flattening television picture tubes in 1981 and 1982, bringing us closer to the day when pocket-sized television receivers will be available to the consumer.

Sinclair's tube, announced in May 1981, measures just 5 centimeters (2 inches) diagonally and is only 1.9 centimeters (0.7 inch) deep.

An ordinary TV set produces an image by firing a beam of electrons toward the front of the picture tube. The electrons strike the inside of the front of the tube—the screen—which is coated with phosphors, substances that give off light when struck.

However, the screen in the Sinclair TV set is not at the front of the tube. Instead, it is placed behind a transparent electrode that covers the same area as the screen. The electron beam is fired from one side and passes between and parallel to the screen and the electrode. As the beam travels across this area, it is deflected toward the screen by the electrode and by electrostatic plates at the side of the screen. These plates require 30 milliwatts—only 10 per cent of the power that a regular TV set consumes in guiding its electron beam magnetically.

The viewer sees the image on the same surface that the electrons strike, rather than on the opposite surface as in an ordinary picture tube. Therefore, an electron beam of a given strength will produce an image on the Sinclair set that is twice as bright as the image formed on an ordinary tube by a beam of the same strength. In February 1982, Sony unveiled a handheld TV that has a flat picture tube similar to the Sinclair device.

Filmless camera. Sony announced in August 1981 that it had developed an experimental camera that records 50 color images on 4.4-centimeter (1.7-inch) magnetic disks. Light rays enter the camera through a lens, as in an ordinary camera. However, instead of striking photographic film, the rays hit a light-sensitive chip that converts them into electrical signals for the magnetic disk.

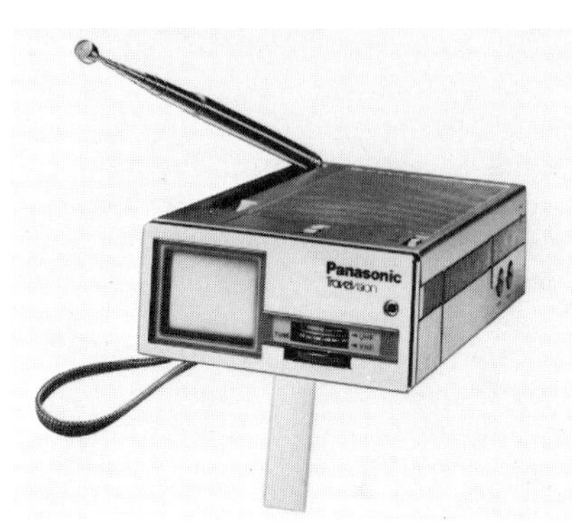

"It says it's sick of doing things like inventories and payrolls, and it wants to make some breakthroughs in astrophysics."

Electronics

Continued

The photographer would shoot the pictures, remove the disk from the camera, and place it in a playback device that would produce the pictures on any TV set. Called Mavica (Magnetic Video Camera), the camera is expected to be available in mid-1983.

The Mavica is the same size and weight as a 35-millimeter single-lens reflex camera and takes pictures at the same lighting as ASA 200 film. However, the prototype model has a fixed shutter speed of 1/60 second. Sony is also developing a printer and a device that would transmit the pictures over telephone lines.

More memories. Researchers at two Japanese firms—Nippon Electric Company Limited in Kawasaki and the Electrotechnical Laboratories in Ibaraki—announced in March 1982 that they had built an experimental dynamic random access memory (RAM) that stores 1 million bits of information on a tiny silicon chip. This is enough capacity to hold four pages of a daily newspaper. The previous record for bit capacity on a dynamic RAM chip was 524,288 bits. The largest in general use today are 65,536-bit (64K) RAMs.

The new RAM's design differs from that of an ordinary RAM. Both the Japanese device and a conventional RAM are an array of microscopic cells, one for each bit. Each cell is made up of a storage unit and a switch. However, the components of an ordinary RAM are set side by side, while in the Japanese device they are stacked on top of one another.

The area of the 1-million-bit memory chip is 140,000 square mils—90 square millimeters or 0.14 square inch. (One mil equals one-thousandth of an inch.) By comparison, the area of an ordinary 64K RAM is 35,000 to 55,000 square mils (23 to 35 square millimeters or 0.035 to 0.055 square inch).

The Japanese researchers want to make the 1-million-bit chip even smaller. The minimum size of an individual electronic component on a chip depends upon the minimum width of lines that can be etched out of the chip or out of material deposited

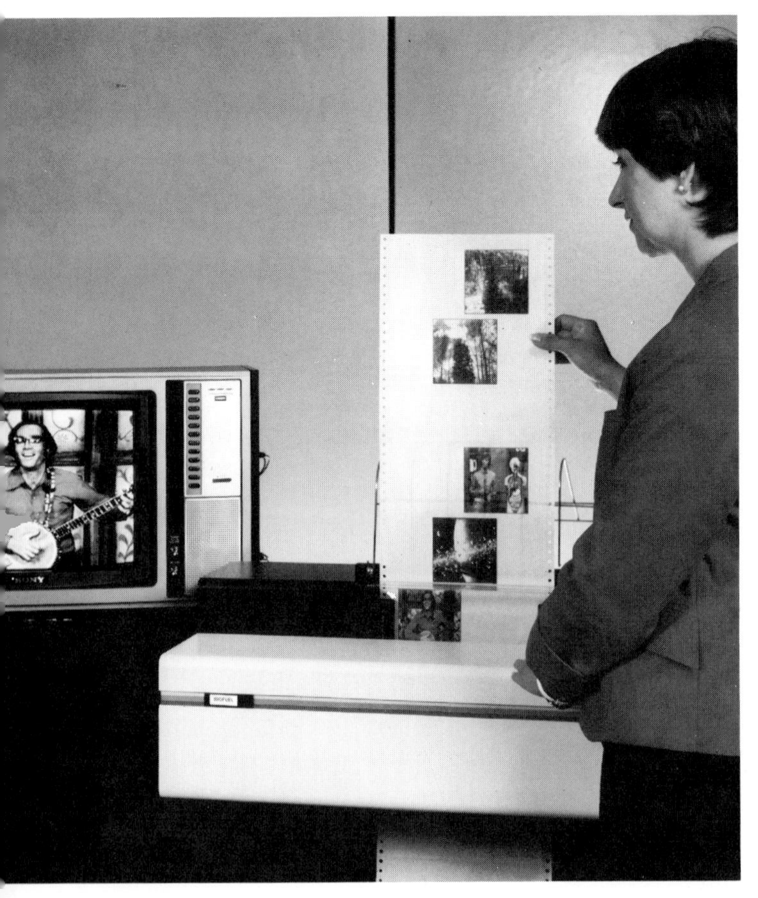

The Mavica, *top,* looks like a standard 35-millimeter camera, but it records up to 50 full-color images in electronic code on a magnetic disk that fits inside it. A playback unit, *above,* displays the images on an ordinary television set, while a printer makes permanent copies.

on the chip. Today's 64K RAMs have line widths of 2 micrometers. (One micrometer equals one-millionth of a meter.) However, a number of companies have built experimental chips that have 1-micrometer lines. If the Japanese device had this line width, it would be smaller than the 64K RAM with a 2-micrometer line width.

The Japanese scientists are also developing a more compact cell design, even though the cells are already about one-quarter the size of those in a 64K RAM. A 1-million-bit RAM with the compact cell and the 1-micrometer width could be as small as 16,000 square mils (10 square millimeters or 0.016 square inch).

One of the designers' most difficult challenges was coping with the small amount of electrical charge-holding capacity available in the cells. Each storage unit holds its information in the form of an electrical charge. The charge of even a 64K RAM's storage unit is so small that the impact of an alpha particle—a helium nucleus—from a shower of cosmic rays can discharge the unit.

The Japanese engineers minimized this problem by using tantalum oxide (Ta_2O_5) for the part of the storage unit that prevents discharge. Ta_2O_5 has 5.6 times the charge-holding power of silicon dioxide, the usual material for this application.

Light circuits. In 1981 and 1982, researchers continued to experiment with optical circuits, which manipulate beams of light and receive and transmit data over clear glass fibers, rather than electrical current through wires. Most of these optical circuits have electronic parts, however, that generate, receive, and control the light rays.

An optical circuit has a number of advantages over electronic circuits. In addition to consuming less power and operating more rapidly, it is free of distortion caused by electronic signals in adjacent circuits.

Researchers at the Crawford Hill facility of Bell Laboratories in Holmdel, N.J., announced in September 1981 that they had developed an AND gate for optical circuits in computers. An AND gate is one of the parts that control the flow of signals within a computer. It has two or more input terminals, which receive incoming signals, and one output terminal that transmits a signal. When all the input terminals receive signals, the gate emits an output signal, thus relaying the data carried by the signals to the next input terminal in the circuit.

Electrical AND gates use transistors that respond to electrical currents. Bell Labs' optical AND gate consists of two photodiodes—devices that emit an electrical current when two light beams of different wavelengths strike the gate. (Wavelength is the distance a light ray travels as it vibrates through one cycle.) This current could operate an electronic device called a light-emitting diode or a tiny laser to convert the output signal back into optical form for the next gate.

The photodiodes are built on top of one another on a substrate of indium phosphide. One is made of indium phosphide and indium gallium arsenide phosphide while the other is indium gallium arsenide. One photodiode is sensitive to light at a wavelength of 1.07 micrometers, while the other reacts to rays that have a 1.3-micrometer wavelength.

Bell Labs' gate responds to light signals in about five-billionths of a second. Bell now plans to build a chip that contains an optical AND gate and a laser.

Bending rays of light. In February 1982, TRW Incorporated's Electronics Technology Research Center in El Segundo, Calif., announced an all-optical logical-OR gate that accepts, delivers, and bases its operation on light signals. An OR gate functions similarly to an AND gate in a circuit. The OR gate has two inputs and one output terminal. When one or the other input terminal receives a signal, the output terminal relays it.

The optical OR gate consists of three parallel strips of titanium on a lithium niobate chip and a pair of electrical connections that generates a voltage across one of the outside strips. This voltage alters the outside strip's ability to bend light rays.

The two outside strips function as input devices, while the center strip is the output. Many of the light rays that strike the strip without the electrodes jump over to the center strip and flow out of this strip as an output signal. However, large numbers of light rays that strike the input strip with the electrodes will jump to the center strip only if the voltage is on. Thus, turning the voltage on and off changes the gate's manner of operation. The all-optical OR gate has a potential response time of 100 picoseconds (trillionths of a second).

Faster electrons. Researchers are finding that gallium arsenide (GaAs) is also useful for all-electronic circuits because its electrons are eight to nine times easier to move than those of silicon, the material most commonly used in all such circuits. Easier movement means greater electron speed—faster current—for a given amount of electrical power.

In the autumn of 1981, Japan's Fujitsu Laboratories Limited in Kawasaki and Thompson-CSF's Central Research Laboratories in Orsay, France, reported that they had independently developed a GaAs structure that dramatically increases the material's already high electron mobility.

Fujitsu calls its device the high electron mobility transistor (HEMT). The HEMT structure consists of alternating layers of pure GaAs and layers of gallium aluminum arsenide impregnated, or doped, with a small amount of silicon. Free electrons from atoms that are in the doped layers flow readily into the GaAs films and become extremely mobile.

Fujitsu workers have already measured mobilities of 37,800 square centimeters per volt-second and report that values of 100,000 are theoretically possible. By contrast, theory states that the mobility of electrons in silicon transistors can only go up to 2,000, and that electron mobility in components made of ordinary GaAs cannot be much more than 8,000.

The higher mobility translates directly into greater speed. At room temperature, a HEMT switches in less than 50 picoseconds and Fujitsu researchers think that cooling the HEMT to −196°C (−321°F.) will reduce that delay to 10 picoseconds. This would make the HEMT as fast as today's Josephson junctions—microscopic circuits that switch faster than any other device. [John G. Posa]

Energy

The Ford Motor Company, in keeping with efforts to free the United States from dependence on foreign oil, unveiled the Alternative Fuel Vehicle (AFV) in January 1982. The AFV operates on compressed natural gas, but can be easily modified to operate on methanol, ethanol, or propane.

The AFV is a two-passenger front-wheel-drive car suitable for shopping, commuting, and other short trips. The vehicle has a modified 1.6-liter (97.6-cubic-inch) engine.

The fuel is stored at a pressure of 2,500 pounds per square inch (176 kilograms per square centimeter) in a 4.3-cubic-foot (0.1-cubic-meter) tank, which holds enough methane to provide the energy equivalent of 25 liters (6.6 gallons) of gasoline. The AFV gets the equivalent of about 14 kilometers per liter (32 miles per gallon) of gasoline, giving it a cruising range of 338 kilometers (210 miles) in the city. A small air compressor can refuel the vehicle at home in four hours—about half the time required to charge the batteries of an electric vehicle. A commercial compressor can refuel the AFV in 15 minutes.

Electric cars. Under a cost-sharing agreement with the United States Department of Energy (DOE), Detroit Edison Company initiated a program in 1981 that will help U.S. industry and government evaluate electric cars.

Detroit Edison is collecting operational and maintenance data on 24 Volkswagen Rabbits converted to electric power. Detroit Edison's motor pool uses eight of the cars and the remaining 16 cars are leased to employees for commuting and family transportation. The company installed electrical outlets in the employees' garages so that the cars' batteries can be charged overnight.

In addition, the company has placed charging stations at strategic locations in Detroit. The cars have a range of 48 to 64 kilometers (30 to 40 miles) between charges.

Detroit Edison also built an Electric Car Service Center that provides road service 24 hours a day, 7 days a week. During the period from June to De-

Thermodecor wall covering, *below,* looks like ordinary wallpaper but conserves energy by reflecting infrared radiation such as that emitted by the human body, *below right.* Ordinary wallpaper, *below center,* reflects little such radiation.

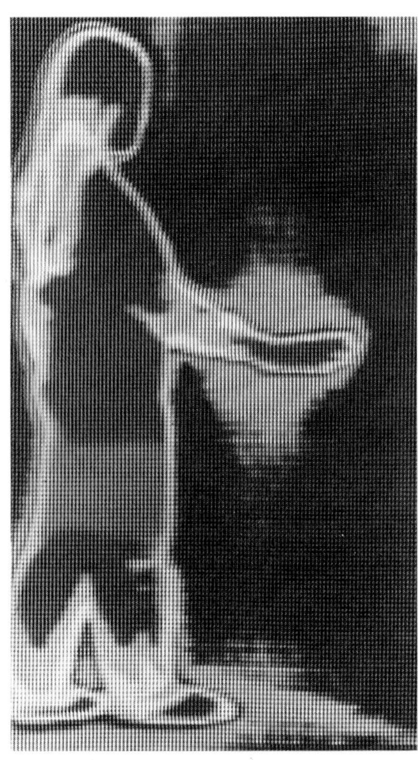

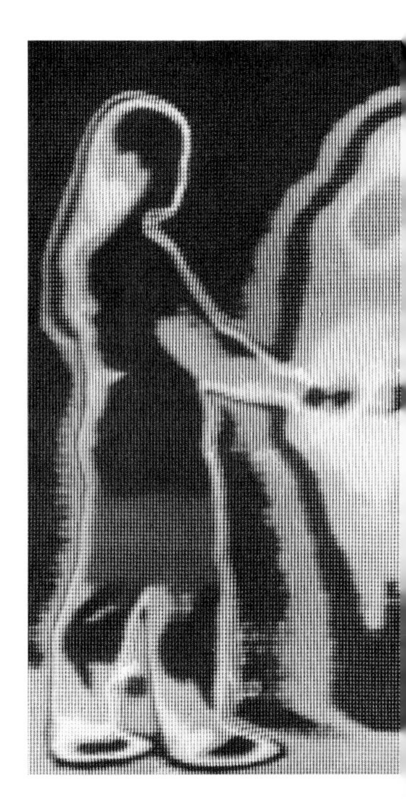

cember 1981, the 24 cars traveled more than 81,000 kilometers (50,000 miles) and required only 12 road-service calls.

The Electric Power Research Institute estimated that 13 million electric cars would save 100 million barrels of oil annually if the electricity that charged the cars' batteries were generated at coal-burning power plants.

Sun plane. After six unsuccessful attempts—and a month's wait for the right combination of wind and sunshine—the sun-powered *Solar Challenger* flew from France to England on July 7, 1981. Some 16,128 photovoltaic cells mounted on the craft's wing and horizontal stabilizer transformed solar energy into electricity for two motors that produced up to 2.7 horsepower. Paul B. MacCready, the aeronautical engineer who built the first successful human-powered airplane, the *Gossamer Condor*, in 1977, designed the 98.4-kilogram (217-pound) vehicle. See THE FLIGHT OF THE GOSSAMER CONDOR, *Science Year*, 1979.

The photovoltaic cells were provided by the National Aeronautics and Space Administration. The *Solar Challenger*'s pilot was Stephen Ptacek, who weighed 55.3 kilograms (122 pounds).

The 265-kilometer (165-mile) trip took 4 hours and 42 minutes. The plane circled its landing site for an additional 41 minutes. The craft cruised at an altitude of 3.3 kilometers (11,000 feet) at an average speed of 60 kilometers per hour (kph) or 37 miles per hour (mph).

Solar home. In the summer of 1981, Solar Design Associates of Lincoln, Mass., built a house that gets 80 per cent of its annual supply of electricity from a 7.3-kilowatt array of photovoltaic cells mounted on a roof that slopes southward at a 45-degree angle. The 98.4-square-meter (1,059-square-foot) array contains 9,082 photocells that convert 10 per cent of the solar energy that strikes them to electrical energy when the sun is shining. The house is part of DOE's Solar Photovoltaic Residential Project.

The Carlisle, Mass., house has 288 square meters (3,100 square feet) of living space. On sunny days, the cells generate more electricity than the house needs. Boston Edison Company, the local power company, buys the extra power. Solar Design expects the house to generate more electricity than it uses each year. A 9.3-square-meter (100-square-foot) solar heat collector mounted over the garage provides all the water heating, while direct sunlight satisfies 60 per cent of the space-heating requirements. In addition, a wood stove and an electrical heat pump are available for water and space heating. The house is cooled during the summer by the natural venting of warm air at the top of the house and the entry of cool air below.

Big windmill. In the summer of 1981, a 29-meter (95-foot) vertical axis wind turbine (VAWT) began providing Tisbury, Mass., on the island of Martha's Vineyard, with electricity to pump water. The VAWT, built by the Aluminum Company of America, consists of two D-shaped blades connected to the top and bottom of a rotating vertical shaft. The VAWT provides up to 100 kilowatts of power when the wind blows at 53 kph (33 mph).

The turbine runs on wind that blows in any direction, which gives it an advantage over an ordinary horizontal axis wind turbine, which must face the wind. A horizontal machine requires a device to turn it when the wind shifts. Furthermore, the horizontal unit requires a complex tower structure because the generating equipment is at the top of the tower. By contrast, the VAWT's generator is at ground level.

Steam well. In July 1981, a 3-megawatt geothermal power plant opened on the upper east rift zone of the active volcano, Kilauea, on the island of Hawaii. Hawaii thus became the second U.S. state to use steam produced by the earth's heat to generate commercial electrical power. Geysers north of San Francisco have run a power plant for about 20 years.

Steam for the Hawaiian power plant is supplied from a 1,920-meter (6,300-foot) well. This is one of the hottest geothermal wells in the world, with temperatures of about 370°C (700°F.). The well has a capacity of about 100 megawatts for 100 years. Because Kilauea is active, and therefore could erupt, all major components of the power plant have been designed so that they would be easy to move quickly to safety.

The island uses more than 90 megawatts of power, of which 40 per cent is supplied by the burning of bagasse, the pulp of sugar cane, to produce steam. Hawaii has granted permits to private developers to drill more wells. The state's goal is to provide 50 per cent of the island's power requirements from geothermal energy over the next few years.

Melt and pump. Scientists from Sandia National Laboratories in Albuquerque, N. Mex., and Geokinetics, Incorporated, in Salt Lake City, Utah, conducted research during the autumn of 1981 that may enable the United States to reduce its oil imports. Their three-month experiment proved the feasibility of recovering a waxy substance called kerogen from underground shale—a fine-grained rock formed from hardened clay or mud—without mining the shale. Chemists had already discovered how to convert kerogen to oil but the cost of mining shale made the material prohibitively expensive.

The new process may help scientists determine how to tap the vast U.S. deposits of oil shale. The Green River oil-shale formation in Colorado, Utah, and Wyoming may contain enough kerogen to provide about 2 trillion barrels of oil. By contrast, the world's supply of petroleum that present-day techniques can bring to the surface amounts to 640 billion barrels.

The scientists experimented on an underground deposit of 7,260 metric tons (8,000 short tons) of shale in Vernal, Utah. First, they drilled blast holes through the shale bed. Next, they put explosives into the blast holes and set them off. The explosion fractured the shale bed and lifted the 12.2 meters (40 feet) of rock and dirt that covered it about 100 centimeters (3 feet). The resulting network of holes in the shale, called the void, increased the space that the deposit occupied by about 12 per cent.

The researchers then drilled oil wells at one end of the fractured zone and wells for the injection of air at the other end. Finally, they ignited the shale at the injection wells and pumped air into the fractured bed.

The fire moved horizontally through the fractured shale, heating kerogen ahead of it. The waxy kerogen melted, flowed out of the shale, and drained to the bottom of the bed, from which the oil wells pumped it to the surface.

The scientists brought 58 per cent of the kerogen to the surface. This was the first significant recovery of oil from a bed with such a small void. About 27 per cent of the kerogen was burned and 15 per cent broke down chemically, forming a solid that did not melt and therefore could not be pumped.

Coal to gas. Scientists at the University of California's Lawrence Berkeley Laboratory (LBL) announced in January 1982 that they had developed a simple, experimental process that turns graphite—a form of pure carbon—and water vapor into methane at temperatures as low as 250°C (482°F.). Natural gas is made up mostly of methane, so this process could supply fuel for burners that use natural gas. However, a full-scale methane factory would use more economical sources of carbon, such as coal and plant material.

In the experiment, the scientists deposited a catalyst of potassium hydroxide and potassium carbonate on the surface of the graphite. (A catalyst is a substance that speeds up a chemical reaction while itself remaining practically unchanged.) Then they heated the graphite in the presence of water vapor at atmospheric pressure, producing methane.

Burn down. In the summer of 1981, scientists at the Los Alamos National Laboratory in New Mexico successfully burned radioactive material typical of nuclear-reactor waste in an incinerator. Much of the waste generated at nuclear power plants is not highly radioactive but it is bulky. The Los Alamos scientists burned typical waste products, such as clothing and plastic components, contaminated with radioactive fission products.

The experiment showed that burning can reduce the bulk of such waste by 99 per cent without releasing dangerous amounts of radioactive material into the air. The resulting radioactive ash could then be embedded in concrete or glass, which would be placed in canisters and stored underground.

Energy

Four rows of double-paned glass panels collect solar energy on the roof of a test dwelling made of mobile-home modules. Water-filled plastic bags between the roof and the ceiling absorb heat from the collectors and then radiate it into the living space.

Making rocks. During the winter of 1981 and 1982, scientists at DOE's Pacific Northwest Laboratory developed a new way to solidify burned radioactive and other hazardous wastes. The process, called in situ vitrification, melts and resolidifies the waste and the surrounding soil and rock, forming a durable solid made of glass and other crystals.

To form the solid, technicians bury the waste in shallow ground and place electrodes into the soil around the waste. Electricity flowing to the electrodes generates heat that melts the rock, soil, and waste. The melted materials mix together and then cool, forming a solid mixture. Such mixtures could be left in place with little chance of escape of radioactive materials.

The Los Alamos researchers melted more than 9 metric tons (10 short tons) of soil. The electricity needed to solidify 1 cubic foot (0.03 cubic meter) of material cost $2.

Energy pool. In October 1981, Argonne National Laboratory near Chicago dedicated a unique solar pond that can provide useful heat day and night, all year. Even when covered with ice, Argonne scientists expect the water at the bottom of the pond to reach temperatures as high as 82°C (180°F.). They will use the pond to develop ways of providing a steady source of heat for such jobs as drying grains, heating nurseries and greenhouses, and treating sewage.

Salt water is the key to the pond's ability to collect and store solar energy. Salt concentration increases with depth, making the lower layers of the pond heavier than those above them.

The sunlight penetrates the surface, warming the deep water. If this were a freshwater pond, the warm water would rise to the surface and transfer energy to the atmosphere. But the lower layers of the Argonne pond are so heavy that they cannot rise, and therefore their heat is trapped.

The pond is about 3.7 meters (12 feet) deep. It holds 2.65 million liters (700,000 gallons) of water and about 635 metric tons (700 short tons) of salt. [Marian Visich, Jr.]

Environment

Acid rain, rainfall with a high concentration of sulfuric and nitric acid due to air pollution, was a major focus of environmental concern during 1981 and 1982. Such rain pollutes lakes and streams, endangers wildlife, and damages plants and soil.

In the United States, the problem of acid rain has been especially severe in the Northeast. In April 1982, the Office of Technology Assessment, an advisory agency of Congress, reported that one of every four lakes and streams in the Northeastern States has been damaged by acid rain.

Scientists measure acidity by the pH scale, a 14-point scale that runs from 14 (highly alkaline) to 0 (highly acidic). A neutral solution, such as pure water, is neither acid nor alkaline and has a pH of 7. A drop of one pH equals a tenfold increase in acidity.

Normal rainfall is slightly acidic, with a pH of about 5.6, because it absorbs carbon dioxide from the air to form a weak acid, carbonic acid. In the last five years, however, precipitation has become markedly more acidic because it absorbs sulfur dioxide and nitrogen oxides released by automobiles, power plants, and factories that burn fossil fuels, such as coal and oil. These gases combine with moisture in the air to form the strong acids sulfuric and nitric acid, which fall to earth with rain or snow. In the late 1970s, ecologist Gene E. Likens and his colleagues at Cornell University in Ithaca, N.Y., measured rain and snow in New Hampshire that had a pH of 3.9, 80 times more acid than normal. This level of acidity is sufficient to kill fish and slow the growth of trees.

Acid rain spreads. Scientists once believed that the Western States, where low-sulfur coal and oil is burned, had escaped the problem of acid rain. In January 1982, however, Michael R. Hoffmann, an environmental engineer at the California Institute of Technology in Pasadena, reported acid fog in Los Angeles with a pH as low as 2.2. The fog was more than 2,500 times as acidic as normal fog.

Most of the acid precipitation falling on New England does not arise from local sources. Scientists once thought it was only produced by sulfur dioxide released from coal-fired power plants in the Midwest. Prevailing winds transported the pollutants northeast to New England and Canada. However, in a study released in February 1982, atmospheric chemist Kenneth A. Rahn of the University of Rhode Island in Kingston found that the Midwest is not the only source of such pollution. Rahn analyzed traces of metals in the air to track the pathways of the acid-forming gases and discovered that they may also come from the Southern and Middle Atlantic states.

Controlling acid rain. In March 1982, engineers Dwain F. Spencer, Michael J. Gluckman, and Seymour B. Alpert of the Electric Power Research Institute in Palo Alto, Calif., reported a new system for converting coal to gas and then to electricity, while efficiently removing sulfur and nitrogen. This promising technology, which would help control acid rain, is being tested in a pilot power plant in California, scheduled to be completed in 1984.

In the spring of 1982, Congress began to debate amendments to the Clean Air Act of 1970. In February 1982, Representative Henry A. Waxman (D., Calif.) proposed an amendment requiring the major sulfur-dioxide producing states in the Midwest and Atlantic regions to reduce sulfur-dioxide emission by about 9 million metric tons (10 million short tons) in the next 10 years. Sulfur-dioxide discharges are a major cause of acid rain. To promote interstate cooperation, the Waxman amendment would allow states that reduced sulfur-dioxide emission by more than their quotas to sell the right to excess pollution to neighboring states that failed to meet their cleanup goals.

Nuclear power plants continued to arouse public anxiety about safety in 1981 and 1982. A series of events aggravated this concern. In the fall of 1981, Pacific Gas & Electric Company weathered weeks of public protest against the building of the Diablo Canyon nuclear plant near San Luis Obispo, Calif., within 4 kilometers (2.5 miles) of a major earthquake fault. Then, in October, the utility company announced that it had discovered a series of construction errors at the plant. On November 19, the Nuclear Regulatory Commission (NRC), the federal

Scientists at the Agricultural Research Service of the U.S. Department of Agriculture, *top,* test how air pollution affects crops by pumping pollutants into open-top chambers surrounding the plants. A soybean leaf grown in filtered air, *above* (left), looks healthier than one exposed to ozone and sulfur dioxide, two common air pollutants, *above* (right).

agency that oversees nuclear power, suspended the plant's test license.

On Jan. 25, 1982, an accident resulted in the release of radioactive gases from the Ginna nuclear plant near Rochester, N.Y. In February, the NRC confirmed that there had been a cover-up of safety violations at the Perry nuclear plant near Cleveland.

Although representatives of the nuclear power industry and of the federal government expressed confidence that the technical problems in each of these three cases were minor and could be resolved, the public's trust in nuclear power continued to wane. In California alone, seven of nine proposed nuclear power plants were temporarily or permanently halted by April 1982.

Watt's proposals. In July 1981, United States Secretary of the Interior James G. Watt proposed the leasing of federal offshore lands for oil drilling near a number of sensitive marine ecosystems and popular beaches. In February 1982, he also proposed that federal wilderness areas, which were to be permanently closed to mining by 1983, be reopened in the year 2000. In addition, Watt suggested that such areas be opened to mining earlier if the President decided there was an "urgent national need" for minerals. Furthermore, in February 1982, Watt proposed that no more land be added to the federal wilderness system after 1987. Many environmentalists believed that these proposals would diminish the nation's stock of wilderness resources to unacceptably low levels.

In March 1982, economist Henry M. Peskin and his co-workers at Resources for the Future, Incorporated, an independent research organization concerned with the conservation of natural resources, completed a directory of data measuring U.S. environmental assets county by county. The directory represented a first step toward keeping an inventory of the country's environmental treasures. Such information may ultimately help Americans decide how much of their environmental heritage is left and how much they can afford to expend.

Hazardous-waste disposal was another area in which considerable environmental activity took place in 1981 and 1982. Many state and local gov-

The Ginna nuclear power plant near Rochester, N.Y., *top,* cools down after a ruptured pipe caused the release of radioactive gases on Jan. 25, 1982. An employee of Rochester Gas & Electric Corporation, which owns the plant, checks for radiation on cars leaving the site, *above.*

ernments in the United States formulated and implemented new regulations to ensure safe disposal of hazardous wastes in landfill sites. Officials in many communities examined local toxic-waste disposal practices. They found that many dump sites failed to comply with federal safety regulations, which went into effect in 1980 under the Resource Conservation and Recovery Act of 1976.

In December 1980, Congress had authorized a $1.6-billion fund called the Superfund to clean up spilled toxic wastes and repair leaks from abandoned hazardous-waste disposal sites. In addition, the Environmental Protection Agency (EPA), the chief federal agency working to control pollution, began to take major violators to court in mid-1979, filing 7 suits that year and 43 in 1980. After Ronald Reagan became President in 1981, however, the federal government's policy changed from one of prosecution to one of negotiation. The number of court cases dropped to seven in 1981 and to zero by April 1982. At the same time, under the Administration's policy of reduced spending, appropriations for the Superfund decreased.

On March 1, 1982, the EPA temporarily lifted a ban on the dumping of hazardous liquid wastes in landfills. But on March 17, following public hearings, the agency reimposed the ban. The EPA further required that all dangerous liquid wastes be sealed in barrels, and that landfill operators monitor the contents of waste containers being dumped on their sites. Many operators, however, objected to the new regulations as unworkable.

A major reason for the controversy over hazardous-waste disposal is that the number of adequate disposal sites in the United States is extremely limited. In addition, chemical manufacturers complain that the new requirements for safe disposal are costly. Reportedly, some companies save money by purposely allowing their toxic wastes to spill onto highways as trucks carry the wastes to dump sites. So government, industry, and public interest groups are still trying to find a workable, affordable system for the safe and efficient disposal of hazardous wastes. [Walt Westman]

Genetics

A team of molecular biologists at Massachusetts Institute of Technology (MIT) and at Tufts University School of Medicine in Boston in December 1981 showed that an unusual form of deoxyribonucleic acid (DNA) exists in nature. DNA comprises genes, which determine all characteristics.

DNA molecules are organized into a ladderlike structure. In most forms of DNA, this ladder twists evenly toward the right, like a spiral staircase. However, in 1979, an MIT group headed by Alexander Rich discovered that under certain laboratory conditions some DNA ladders could be made to zigzag to the left. The scientists called this left-handed form *Z-DNA*. However, they did not know whether Z-DNA had any biological function or whether it even occurred naturally.

Rich and his colleagues—Alfred Nordheim, Mary Lou Pardue, and Achim Moller of MIT, and Eileen M. Lafer and B. David Stollar of Tufts—cleared up these uncertainties when they found Z-DNA in the chromosomes of fruit flies. Chromosomes are rodlike structures in the cell nuclei that carry genes. In order to detect Z-DNA, the Boston scientists first injected rabbits with a small amount of purified Z-DNA that had been synthesized in a laboratory. Rabbits normally do not have DNA circulating in their bloodstream, so their immune systems produced antibodies to the injected DNA. Antibodies are small proteins that are produced in response to a foreign substance. They fit molecules on the surface of that substance like a lock fits a key. The resultant antibodies could lock onto Z-DNA molecules but not onto right-handed DNA.

The team studied giant chromosomes from cells in certain glands of immature fruit flies. Each of these chromosomes is very thick, consisting of about 1,000 identical copies of a single chromosome pressed together, and is therefore easy to see. Each chromosome has a particular pattern of dark horizontal bands where the DNA is tightly coiled. Geneticists do not know what roles the bands and the regions between the bands play.

Natural Z-DNA
A naturally occurring form of Z-DNA with a zigzag, left-handed backbone, *below* (left), was discovered in 1981. Most DNA has a smooth spiral right-handed backbone, *below* (right). Fluorescent antibodies to synthetic Z-DNA glow at the sites where the natural form of the molecule occurs in fruit fly chromosomes, *below, far right.*

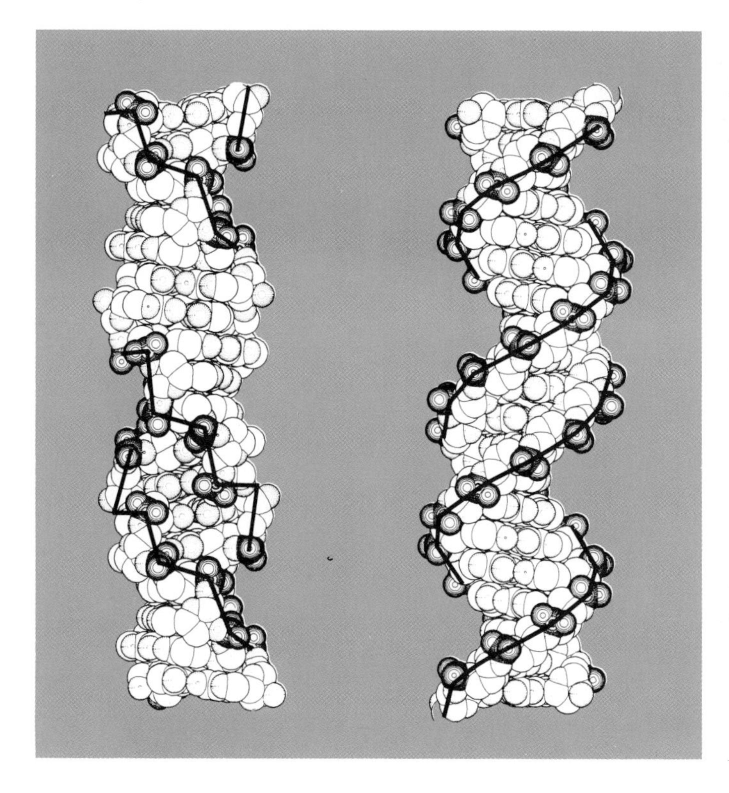

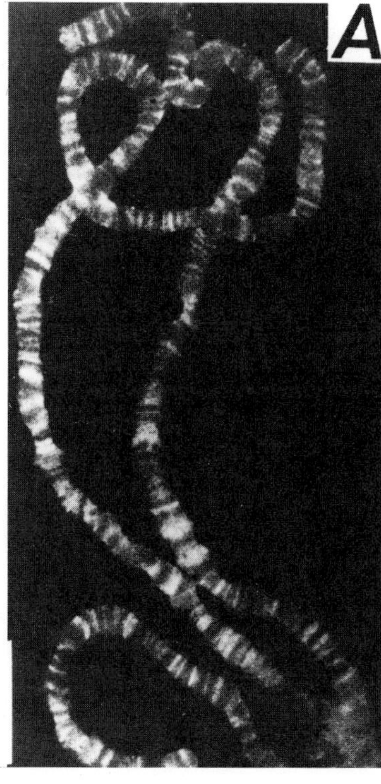

Science Year Close-Up

The Mystifying Marker

As many as 7 million people in the United States are unable to reason and perform tasks as well as most of the rest of us. We know that almost 3 million of these retarded people inherited this condition, and that accidents and environmental conditions account for retardation in another 2 million. It is the remaining 2 million — the men and women who appear to be retarded for no apparent reason — who have baffled scientists and are the focus of continued research.

In 1969, geneticist Herbert Lubs of the University of Miami Medical School was studying a family that had an unusually high number of retarded males among its members. Running standard chromosome surveys on these men, he found that four of the retarded males had a peculiar X chromosome. The X chromosome is one of the chromosomes that determines an individual's sex. A female has two X chromosomes and a male has an X chromosome and a Y chromosome, so the X chromosome is always transmitted to the male by the mother.

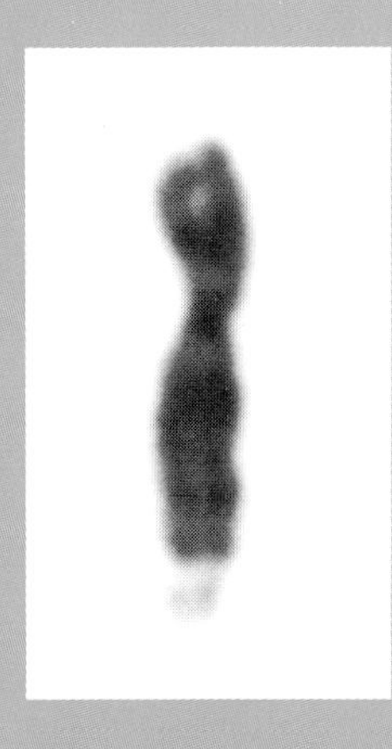

A small pale segment (bottom) that appears to have been pinched off the X chromosome is linked to mental retardation in the males who carry it.

The X chromosomes of some of these men captured Lubs's attention because one end of the long arm of the chromosome appeared to be pinched off — a small portion was slightly removed from the rest of the chromosome. This abnormality was termed the fragile-X chromosome because the fracture seemed to indicate a certain weakness. Lubs traced the fragile-X chromosome back to these men's mothers, who carried the chromosome, but had normal intelligence.

Unlike other chromosomes, which are present in every cell, the fragile X had initially appeared in only a minority of the cells Lubs sampled. Even more mystifying, he was unable to locate it at all in the cells of the mother of one of the men who had the chromosome, although he knew that this woman must have transmitted it. Moreover, neither Lubs nor any other researcher was able to find a similar family with that genetic marker during the next six years.

In 1976, Australian geneticist Grant R. Sutherland, working at the Adelaide Children's Hospital, discovered the reason. Sutherland and his colleagues demonstrated that the fragile-X chromosome appears only when the culture medium in which the cells are maintained is particularly low in folic acid and other nutrients. Although such cultures were common in the late 1960s, when Lubs made his studies, they were replaced by a richer medium shortly thereafter. Switching back to the earlier culture medium, geneticists renewed their search for the fragile X, and with immediate rewards. By 1977, researchers in France and Australia had located 10 families with the fragile X. Now, known fragile-X families number in the hundreds and, by some projections, 1 male in 1,000 may carry the marker.

Lubs could make no easy connection between physical traits and the fragile-X patient from the single family he studied in 1969. But, as more cases were reported, a clearer picture of the fragile-X syndrome has emerged. Many victims have large ears, jaws, and testes; abnormal speech; and poor coordination; although most do not have all of these characteristics. While their intelligence quotients (IQs) range from below 20 to 80 — considerably below the average IQ of 100 — these patients are usually socially well adapted. Their ability to mingle with the general population and their relatively normal appearance accounts for the fact that the abnormality was not discovered sooner.

Although scientists are becoming better able to track the fragile X through families and to associate it with some physical characteristics, we are still searching for an explanation of its effects. Some feel that the impairments of fragile-X men might be due to the loss of genetic material from the chromosome at the fragile site. Others theorize that the pinched chromosomes might indicate a mutant gene — one incapable of programming for full intellectual function.

Scientists have been successful, however, in predicting mental retardation in an unborn child by detecting signs of the fragile-X chromosome in fetal cells. And some researchers have proposed that this condition may even be treated with folic acid, the substance responsible for the disappearance of the fragile X in the laboratory. [Herbert A. Lubs and Enrique Lujan]

Rich and his colleagues removed the glands containing the giant chromosomes from immature fruit flies, separated the cells, and released the chromosomes. They then added the rabbit antibodies to Z-DNA to the chromosome preparation. They assumed that the antibodies would stick wherever Z-DNA was present.

To find out where the antibodies had stuck, the researchers added a fluorescent antibody from goats that glows when viewed under a special light. They used this goat antibody because several molecules of goat antibody attach to a single molecule of the rabbit antibody, thus amplifying the effect. The fluorescent goat antibody would show where the rabbit antibody was, and thus where the Z-DNA was.

When the scientists examined the giant chromosomes under a fluorescent microscope, they saw glowing stripes throughout the chromosomes, indicating that the chromosomes must contain Z-DNA. Moreover, the fluorescent stripes occurred between the dark bands, indicating that the Z-DNA must be present primarily in the regions between the chromosome bands.

The scientists knew that in the laboratory a particular stretch of DNA is able to switch back and forth between the left-handed Z form and the right-handed form. However, because the scientists saw the same pattern in hundreds of chromosomes—Z-DNA almost exclusively in the areas between the bands—they assumed that in the fruit fly this DNA must be permanently locked into the Z form.

The reason for this is still unclear, and the functions of Z-DNA are still unknown. However, the Boston group opened research that may explain the regions between the dark bands.

Viral designer genes? Molecular geneticists Kira Lueders, Aya Leder, and Edward Kuff of the National Institutes of Health in Bethesda, Md., and Philip Leder of Harvard Medical School in Boston, in February 1982 reported on their studies of a pseudogene—a stretch of DNA that chemically resembles a gene but does not code for any substance—in the mouse. The pseudogene they studied resembles the gene for hemoglobin, the red oxygen-carrying protein of the blood, but it is located on a different chromosome than the hemoglobin gene.

Moreover, the hemoglobin pseudogene has no intervening sequences—DNA with no known function. Many normal genes, including the hemoglobin gene, have intervening sequences.

When a cell begins to make a protein from the instructions in the gene, enzymes in the nucleus first make a molecule of ribonucleic acid (RNA) using the DNA of the corresponding gene as a blueprint. RNA is a mirror image of one side of a DNA molecule. Enzymes cut out the intervening sequences and join those that remain.

The mouse hemoglobin pseudogene had the same structure as the hemoglobin gene after its intervening sequences were removed. They also suggested that a type of virus called a retrovirus might have been involved.

Retroviruses have genes composed of RNA instead of DNA. They reproduce by using the machinery of cells they have invaded to copy their RNA. They also manufacture an enzyme called reverse transcriptase that can produce DNA corresponding to a given segment of RNA and another enzyme that can insert this DNA into a chromosome in the host cell.

Lueders and her co-workers suggested that, as a retrovirus was reproducing, its RNA mistakenly became attached to the RNA for normal hemoglobin from which the intervening sequences had already been removed. When reverse transcriptase copied the retrovirus RNA to make DNA, it copied the hemoglobin RNA as well. Finally, the retrovirus-hemoglobin DNA was inserted into the chromosome by the other viral enzyme.

To test this theory, the researchers inserted a large piece of DNA containing the hemoglobin pseudogene into bacteria. The bacteria then reproduced, making millions of copies of the pseudogene. The researchers found retroviruslike DNA segments on both sides of the pseudogene, indicating that the reverse transcriptase had probably copied the hemoglobin RNA while copying the viral RNA. They concluded that retroviruses may play a role in creating new genes and in changing the position of genes in chromosomes. [Daniel L. Hartl]

Geology
See Earth Sciences

Immunology

New Antibody Theory
Several determinants connected by the chemical spine of an antigen attach to receptors on the surface of a B lymphocyte and form an immunon, which initiates antibody production, *below.* Unconnected or too few determinants cannot form the immunon needed to make antibodies, *bottom.* Researchers at Johns Hopkins University in Baltimore proposed the theory in 1982.

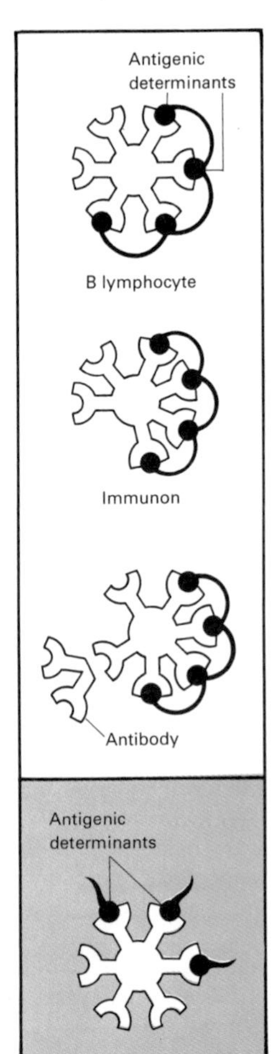

Major developments in immunology in 1981 and 1982 centered around a new understanding of the antibody's role in regulating the immune system. Antibodies are proteins that recognize and attach to antigens, foreign molecules such as certain chemicals or molecules on the surfaces of viruses or bacteria that have entered the body. Antibodies are among the molecules and cells of the immune system that protect the body against infections and cancer. When the immune system is not regulated properly, the body may develop an immune deficiency, in which too few cells and molecules are enlisted against disease, or an autoimmune disease, in which the immune system turns against the body's tissues.

In reports published in May 1981 and July 1981, immunologists J. Hiernaux of the National Institute of Allergy and Infectious Diseases in Bethesda, Md., and Raif S. Geha of Harvard Medical School in Boston discussed the development of a second generation of antibodies that is provoked by the initial production of antibodies. The process begins when an antigen enters the body. The antigen molecule has smaller structures on its surface that lock onto receptor molecules on the surface of two kinds of white blood cells called B lymphocytes and helper or T_H lymphocytes. These receptor molecules on the B and T_H lymphocytes, which specifically attach to the antigen, are chemically identical to each other as locks to the same antibody key. However, there is only one type of each B and T_H lymphocyte among millions that fit those particular antigenic molecules.

Once this lock has been established, the T_H lymphocyte sends a chemical message to the B lymphocyte to start producing antibodies. Antibody molecules are Y-shaped, and the ends of each "arm" of the Y have the same chemical structure as the receptors on the B lymphocytes. This structure, or antibody idiotype, enables the antibody to lock to the original antigen.

A newly produced antibody is a newcomer to the body and is treated like a foreign substance. Like the molecules on the antigen, the antibody's idiotype may lock to receptors on other B and T_H lymphocytes, triggering the production of a second antibody with an idiotype that will lock onto the idiotype of the first antibody. This second-generation antibody is called an anti-idiotype antibody.

Research has shown that anti-idiotype antibodies usually lock onto receptors on another lymphocyte—a suppressor or T_S lymphocyte. The function of this cell is to suppress the T_H lymphocyte so that it does not inform the B lymphocyte to make antibodies to slow antibody production.

The immunologists injected mice with an antigen—the chemical trinitrophenol (TNP). After a few days, they removed the mice spleens and extracted B lymphocytes producing anti-TNP antibodies. They injected these antibodies into another group of mice, waited a few days, and removed their spleens. These spleens yielded B lymphocytes that were producing antibodies to the anti-TNP antibodies. These antibodies—anti-idiotype antibodies—were injected into a third group of mice that had just been injected with TNP. This group did not produce anti-TNP antibodies. The scientists concluded that the anti-idiotype antibodies had suppressed production of the anti-TNP antibodies.

Anti-anti-idiotype antibodies. In August 1981, immunologists Rose R. Bernabe and A. Carlos Martinez at the Basel Institute for Immunology in Switzerland, Antonio Coutinho at Umeå University in Sweden, and Pierre A. Cuzenave at the Laboratory of Analytic Immunochemistry of the Pasteur Institute in Paris reported further studies that revealed more generations of antibodies and anti-idiotype antibodies in mice. They injected one group of mice with TNP and found that the spleens of these mice contained some lymphocytes producing antibodies to TNP and others producing anti-idiotype antibodies. They injected a second group of mice with anti-TNP antibodies to produce anti-idiotype antibodies. When they removed the spleens from this group they found few B lymphocytes that were producing anti-TNP antibody.

They then injected the anti-idiotype antibody into a third group of mice, and, after a few days, removed spleens containing B lymphocytes producing

Putting the Brakes on Antibody Production
Antigens attach to receptors on B and T_H lymphocytes (B_1 and T_{H1}). T_{H1} sends a chemical message to B_1, instructing it to make antibodies to the antigen. The resultant antibodies attach to receptors on a second set of B and T_H lymphocytes (B_2 and T_{H2}), and T_{H2} instructs B_2 to make antibodies, called anti-idiotype antibodies, to the antibody. The anti-idiotype antibodies attach to a third set of B and T_H lymphocytes (B_3 and T_{H3}) and to a T_S lymphocyte. T_S prevents T_{H3} from instructing either B_3 or B_1, which have chemically similar receptors, to make antibodies, thus slowing down production of the original antibodies.

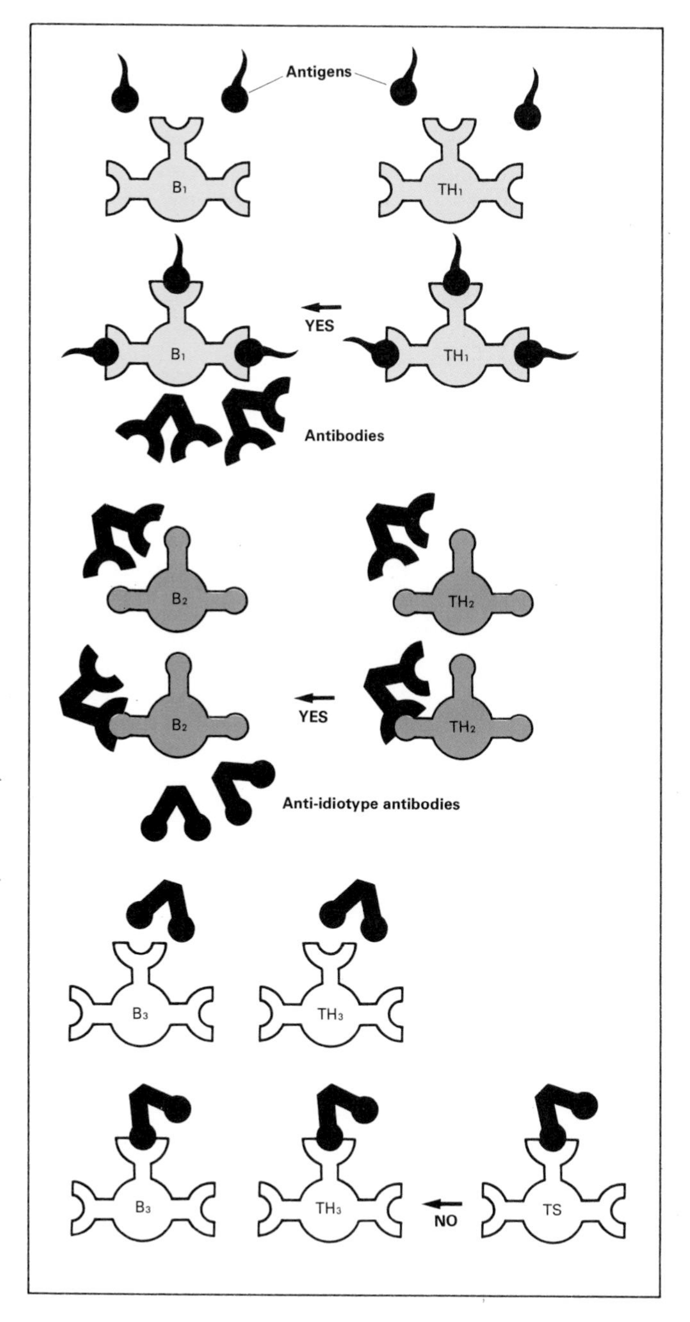

anti-anti-idiotype antibody. However, when they injected the anti-anti-idiotype antibody into a fourth group of mice, the mice produced a large number of antibodies to TNP, indicating that the third generation of antibodies stimulated the production of the original antibodies. These results show that the normal immune system produces anti-idiotype antibodies to suppress the production of original antibodies and anti-anti-idiotype antibodies to stimulate that production.

Recent studies show that these multigeneration antibody networks may be responsible for the decline in the immune response associated with aging. Norman R. Klinman of Scripps Clinic and Research Foundation in La Jolla, Calif., reported on the effects of aging on antibody production in August 1981. He injected mice of different ages with the antigen dinitrophenol (DNP), waited a few days, and then removed their spleens. He found that lymphocytes from the spleens of the older mice suppressed production of antibodies to DNP more than did those of younger mice. These results suggest that older individuals over a lifetime develop several generations of antibodies and anti-idiotype antibodies to suppress their own responses to many antigens.

Link to disease. Immunologists Yoram Shechter, Dana Elias, Ruth Maron, and Irun R. Cohen at Weizmann Institute of Science in Israel reported in May 1982 that human diseases may result from abnormalities in the anti-idiotype-antibody network. The immunologists injected mice with insulin and found that they not only developed the expected anti-insulin antibodies but also produced antibodies that attached to insulin receptors on fat cells. These second antibodies were apparently anti-idiotype antibodies directed at the antibodies to insulin. Because their structures were identical to surface molecules on insulin, they locked to the receptors on fat cells in place of insulin, depriving the fat cells of insulin. The Israeli scientists see this as evidence that antibodies against a hormone such as insulin ultimately result in the production of antibodies that cause certain diseases, such as diabetes. [Ralph Snyderman]

Medicine

Dentistry. Tooth decay, or caries, in children in the United States has fallen dramatically since 1973, according to a report issued in December 1981 by the National Institute of Dental Research, a part of the National Institutes of Health. The institute surveyed 40,000 American children between 5 and 17 years old.

Researchers found that children had an average of 4.8 decayed or filled tooth surfaces. Each tooth has five surfaces, and a cavity may affect more than one tooth surface. These results were a great improvement over those found in a survey conducted from 1971 to 1973 by the National Center for Health Statistics, which reported that American children had an average of 7.1 decayed or filled tooth surfaces. The 1981 report noted that children in all age groups averaged 2.9 decayed, filled, or missing teeth. Although almost 8 per cent of the children had nine or more affected teeth, more than 33 per cent had no caries at all. The study also found children in the Northeast and Far West were more likely to have tooth decay than those in the Southwest.

Eliminating caries. Clinical studies of schoolchildren in Sweden have demonstrated that professional removal of dental plaque every two weeks during the school months, plus instructions on oral hygiene and encouragement to brush and floss, resulted in the nearly total elimination of caries and gingivitis, or inflammation of the gums.

In June 1981, periodontal disease researchers Per Axelsson and Jan Lindhe of the University of Göteborg, Sweden, reported similar results in a six-year clinical trial with two groups of adults. One group received instructions in oral hygiene, and dental plaque was removed from their teeth every two to three weeks. The researchers reported that in these adults, periodontal disease—disease of the bone and tissue surrounding the tooth—was halted and tooth decay was prevented. However, periodontal disease and caries were not prevented in a control group, who were treated once a year. [Paul Goldhaber]

Tooth bonding rebuilds broken, chipped, or irregularly shaped teeth, or closes gaps between teeth, *below*. Thin layers of paste made of plastic and finely ground quartz, glass, or silica are applied to teeth, *below right,* then hardened and bonded to teeth by exposure to light beams, *bottom left,* filling gaps between teeth, *bottom right.*

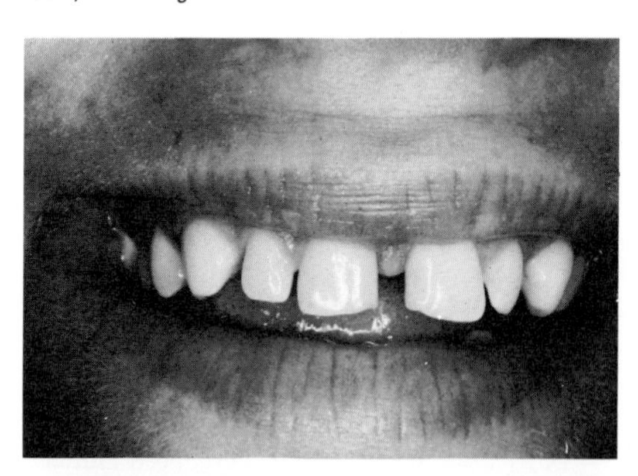

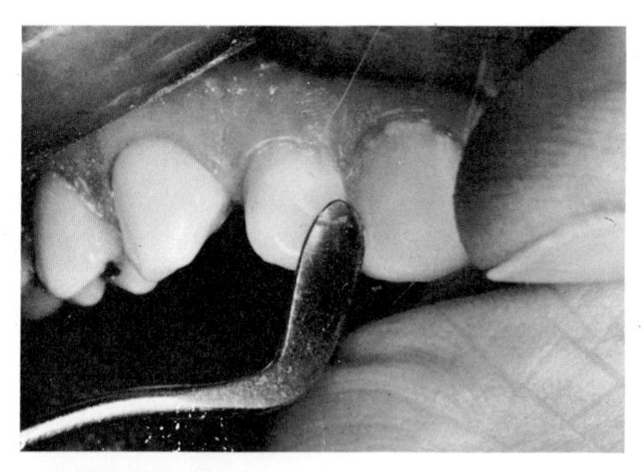

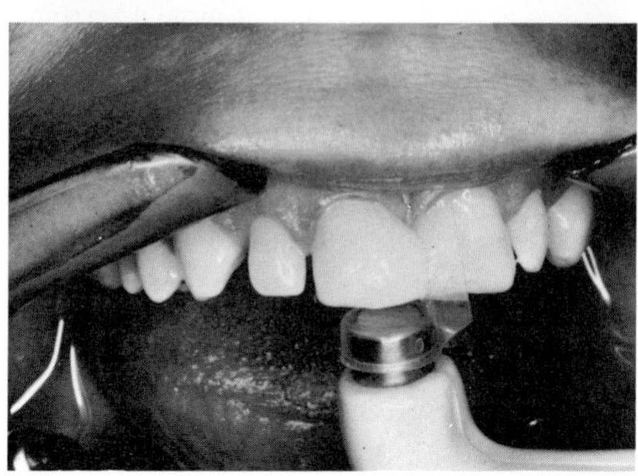

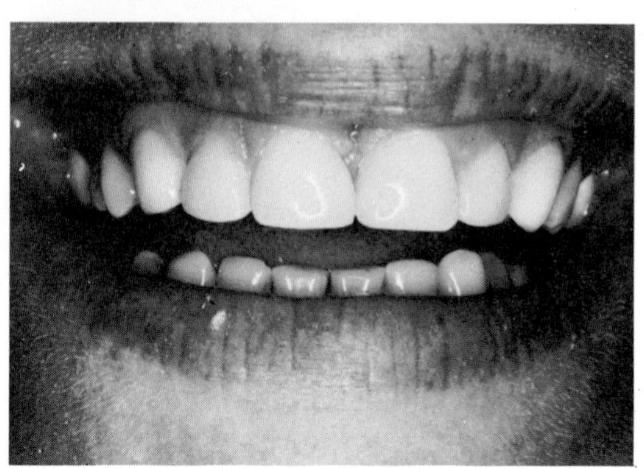

Medicine

Continued

Internal drug pump
The first drug pump, *below left,* that can be implanted entirely within the body, can deliver a continuous supply of an anticancer drug through a blood vessel to a cancerous liver. A doctor can refill the pump, *below right,* by inserting a hypodermic needle through the patient's skin and into a rubber membrane in the pump.

Internal Medicine. In October 1981, clinical studies of a drug for preventing second heart attacks were concluded nine months ahead of schedule because the drug proved so effective that researchers felt it should be made available to heart patients. Heart attacks, or myocardial infarctions (MI), account for nearly half of all deaths in the United States each year.

The drug is propranolol, one of a group of beta-blocking agents that block the transmission of nerve impulses to the heart and blood vessels. This tends to reduce heart rate and relax blood vessels, lowering blood pressure and lessening the workload on the heart. Propranolol has been widely used to treat high blood pressure and angina pectoris, or heart pain.

The results of the study—conducted by Beta-Blocker Heart Attack Trial Group (BHAT), a part of the National Heart, Lung, and Blood Institute—were reported in March 1982. Over a 27-month period, researchers studied 3,837 men and women between the ages of 30 and 69 who had already suffered one heart attack and were believed to be at high risk of suffering a second attack. The patients were randomly divided into two groups: 1,916 persons received propranolol and 1,921 received a placebo, or inert substance. Patients received the propranolol or placebo 5 to 12 days after hospitalization for an acute MI. They were excluded from the study if they had severe congestive heart failure, asthma, a life-threatening illness other than coronary heart disease, or if they were taking another beta-blocker.

The researchers found that deaths occurred more frequently in the group taking the placebo than in the propranolol-treated group. The mortality rate was 7.2 per cent in the propranolol group compared with 9.8 per cent in the placebo group. Serious side effects from the drug were minimal.

Although the study with propranolol was not designed to answer the question of how long drug treatment should continue after an MI, BHAT investigators recommended the use of the drug for at least three years.

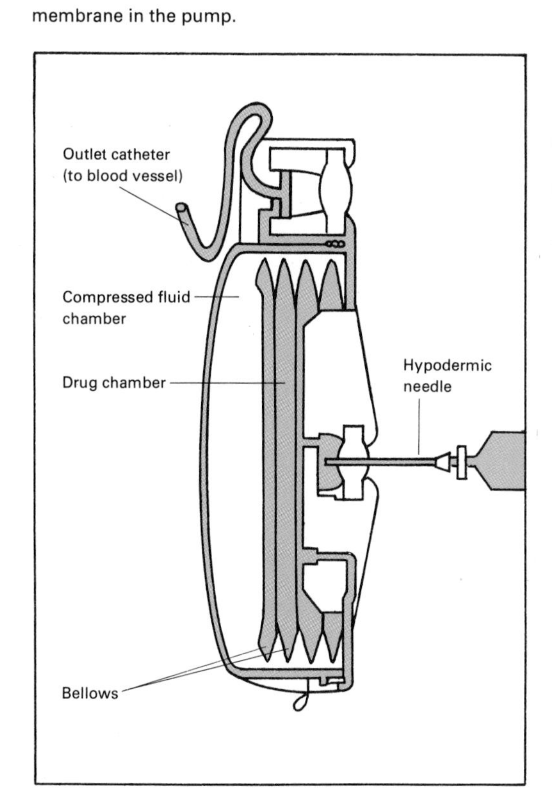

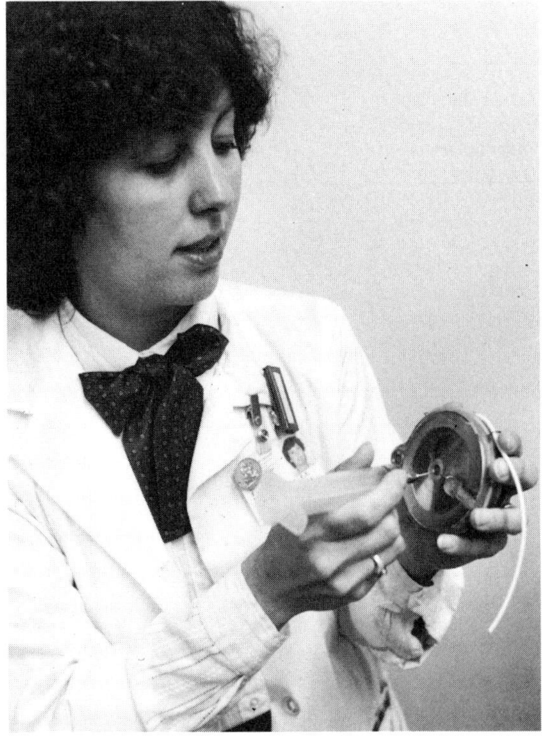

Calcium-blockers. In 1982, the Food and Drug Administration approved the use of two new drugs that may significantly change the ways doctors treat patients with angina pectoris. The drugs, nifedipine and verapamil, appear to relieve angina by blocking the entry of calcium into cells.

The chest pain characteristic of angina occurs when the heart muscle receives less oxygen than it needs. This oxygen deficiency may be caused by a spasm of the coronary arteries that supply the heart muscle or, more commonly, by the narrowing of the coronary arteries caused by atherosclerosis, the build-up of deposits of cholesterol and other fatty acids on the blood-vessel walls. Calcium-blockers interfere with the capacity of the smooth muscle cells in the arterial wall to contract. The resulting relaxation of the vessel permits a greater blood flow and thus the delivery of more oxygen to the heart muscle.

A team of physicians headed by Gary Gestenblith of Johns Hopkins Hospital in Baltimore reported in April 1982 on the results of a clinical trial of nifedipine in the treatment of unstable angina, a type of angina believed to be caused by spasm of the coronary artery.

The physicians compared the experience of 138 patients over a four-month period. All the subjects had been hospitalized at Johns Hopkins, and their medical histories and electrocardiogram tests indicated they suffered from unstable angina. The patients were divided into two groups: 68 were given nifedipine; 70, a placebo.

The researchers considered the treatment a failure if the patient still needed coronary-artery bypass surgery, if the angina persisted, or if the patient suffered a heart attack or died suddenly. After four months, 43 of the 70 patients given the placebo but only 30 of the 68 given nifedipine were classified as treatment failures.

Reducing atherosclerosis. Various studies have shown that exercise, drugs, surgery, and, possibly, quitting smoking may reduce coronary atherosclerosis — the hardening and narrow-

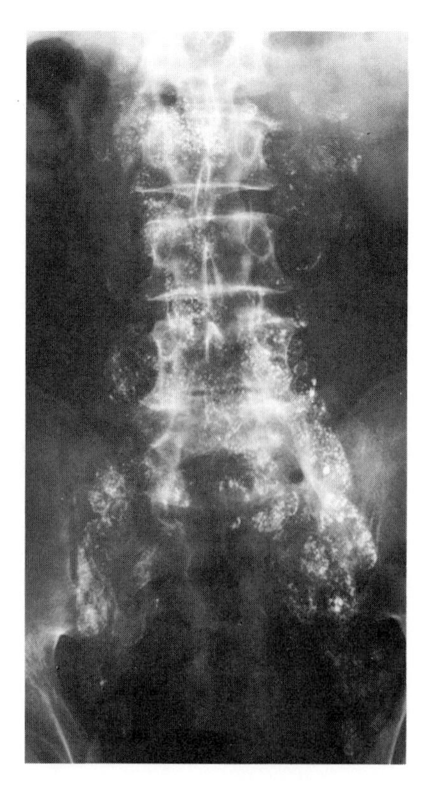

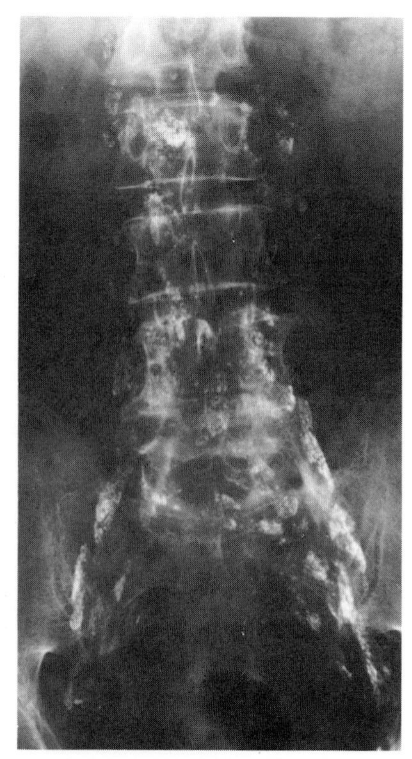

Diffuse white areas surrounding the spinal column of a cancer patient indicate widespread lymphatic tumors, *right*. After two months of treatment with monoclonal antibodies to the tumor cells, the white regions have shrunk markedly, *far right*, indicating a remission of the disease.

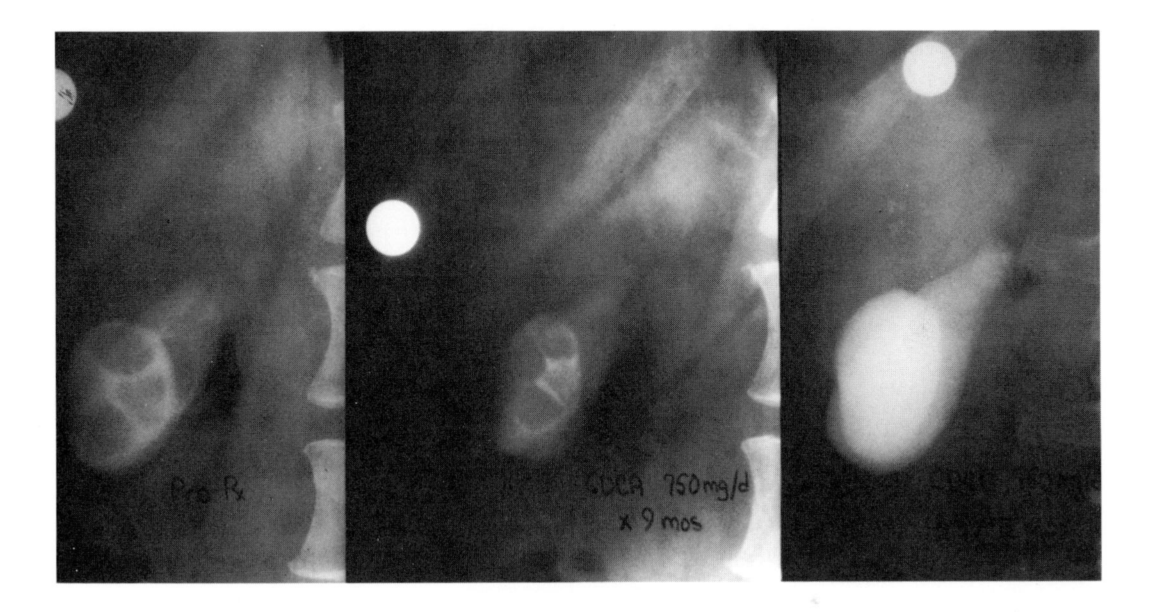

Medicine

Continued

Gallstones, *above left,* in a patient taking chenodeoxycholic acid, a recently approved drug, are much smaller after nine months, *above center,* and dissolved after 16 months, *above right.*

ing of the large and medium-sized arteries. Coronary atherosclerosis, which has been associated with a life style characterized by lack of exercise and a high-fat diet, plays a major role in the development of cardiovascular disease.

In December 1981, hypertension specialist Dieter M. Kramsch and coworkers at Boston University Medical Center reported the effect of moderate exercise on coronary atherosclerosis in monkeys eating a diet high in fats. One group was placed on a diet containing a normal amount of fat for 12 months, then a high-fat diet for 24 months, while maintaining a sedentary life style. The second group was given a normal-fat diet for 18 months, then a high-fat diet for 24 months. This group also exercised on a treadmill for the entire 42 months. A third group, studied for 36 months, only followed the normal-fat diet and maintained a sedentary life style.

Post-mortem studies revealed striking coronary atherosclerosis in the sedentary monkeys on the high-fat diet, but not in the monkeys that exercised, indicating that long-term regular exercise, even at moderate levels, may be capable of slowing the process of atherosclerotic coronary heart disease.

In another study, reported in November 1981, pathologist Robert W. Wissler and veterinarian Dragostlava Vesselinovich of the University of Chicago's Pritzker School of Medicine studied the size of atherosclerotic lesions, or damaged tissue on blood-vessel walls, in monkeys who were fed a diet high in coconut oil and butterfat for two years. During the second year, two groups of monkeys received one of two cholesterol-lowering drugs; one group received both drugs; and one group was untreated. Atherosclerotic lesions were found to be four times larger in the untreated animals than in the animals that received both drugs. In addition, fatty deposits covered 46 per cent of the surface area of the aorta, a major artery, in animals given the two-drug combination, compared with 71 to 75 per cent in animals given only one drug, and 81 per cent in the untreated group.

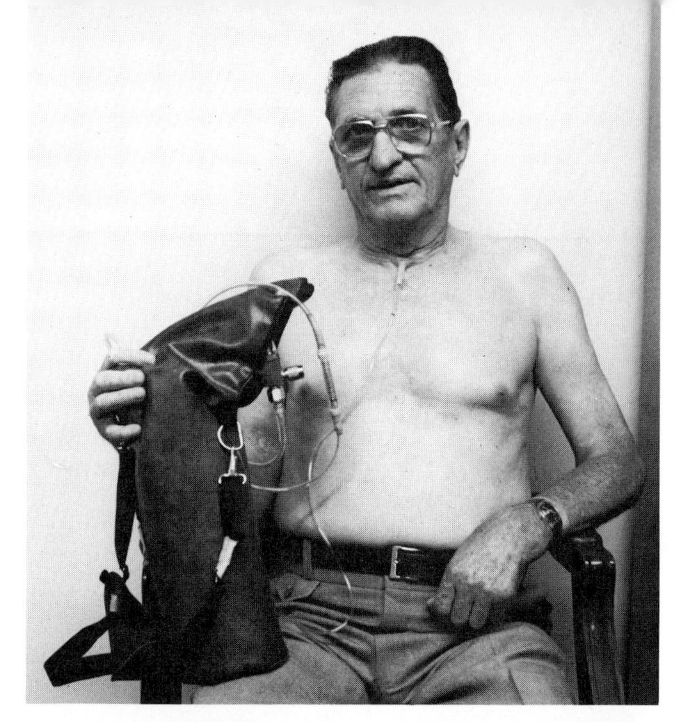

A portable oxygen system pipes oxygen into the body through a hole in the trachea, *top,* which can be concealed by clothing. The system, which provides a 12-hour supply of oxygen and can be carried in a shoulder bag, *above,* gives patients with lung disease greater mobility.

New diabetes marker. A team of researchers headed by endocrinologist Ahmed H. Kissebah at the Medical College of Wisconsin in Milwaukee has found that the pattern of body fat in women may be a tool for predicting the risk of developing maturity-onset, or adult-type, diabetes. In a six-year study reported in February 1982, the researchers observed 52 women with three body types. Twenty-five women were upper-body obese—that is, their excess weight was concentrated in the waist, chest, neck, and arms. Eighteen were lower-body obese, with weight concentrated in the hips, buttocks, and thighs. Nine women were of normal weight and served as a control group.

The team found that all the upper-body-obese women were glucose-intolerant—that is, they were unable to efficiently use or store glucose. Sixty per cent of these women showed a prediabetic condition; 16 per cent had diabetes. These women also had significantly higher levels of fatty acids in their blood serum and insulin in their blood plasma. The test results were normal for the other two groups. The findings indicate that upper-body-obese women appear to be seven times more likely to develop diabetes than are lower-body-obese women or women of normal weight.

Biopsies of fat cells show that in women with lower-body obesity, fat cells are normal in size but are much more numerous than in normal-weight women. The upper-body-obese women had normal numbers of fat cells, but each cell was greatly enlarged.

The enlarged fat cells, which have a reduced number of molecules called insulin receptors on their surface, appear to be less efficient at processing glucose than are normal cells. This, in turn, appears to provoke the body into producing more insulin. Researchers theorize that excessive levels of insulin in women who are genetically susceptible to diabetes lead to maturity-onset diabetes. Dieting can shrink the size of fat cells and appears to alleviate the symptoms of diabetes.

The researchers suggested that a simple way to identify women who are likely to have or develop glucose intolerance is to calculate the ratio of waist to hip size. Normally, this ratio is

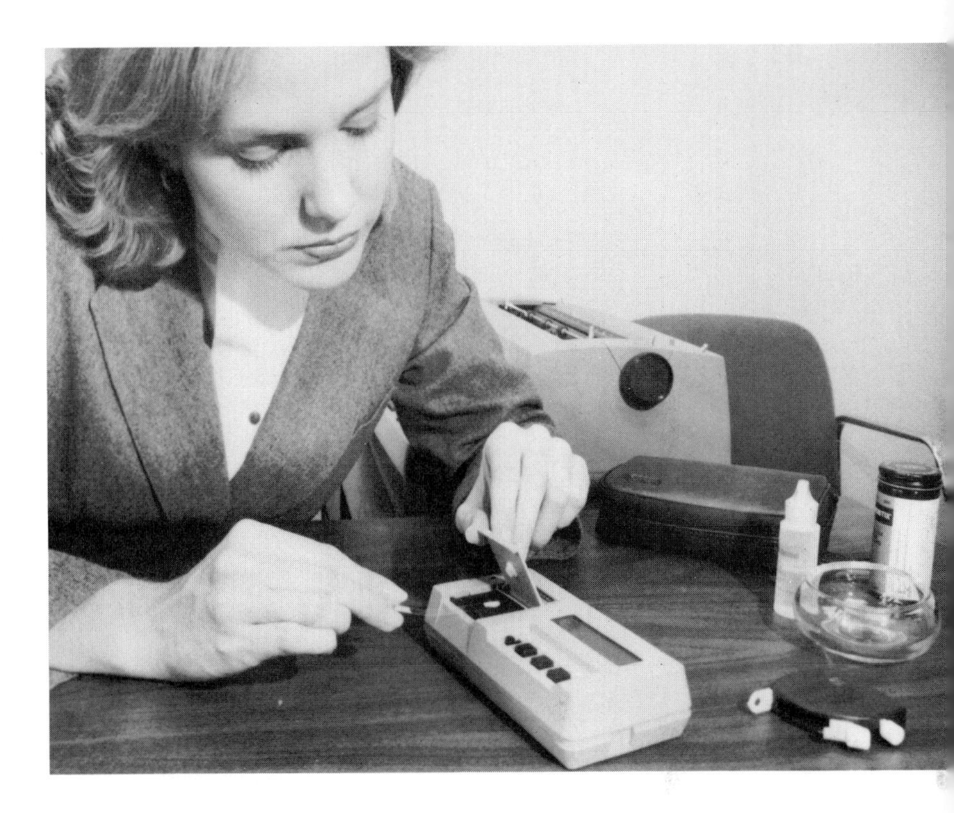

A portable machine called a Glucometer enables a diabetic to test the glucose level of her blood anywhere.

about 0.7. A ratio higher than 0.7 indicates upper-body obesity. The researchers suggested that women with a ratio above 0.85 should be singled out for further testing.

Kaposi's sarcoma, a rare form of cancer that affects the immune system, has suddenly appeared with unexpected frequency, primarily among homosexual men. Kaposi's sarcoma is one of several disorders associated with a breakdown in the immune system that is being called gay-related immunodeficiency disease or gay compromise syndrome. Other cancers associated with the syndrome, which is often characterized by swellings of the lymph glands, include Hodgkin's disease, Burkitt's lymphoma, and cancer of the tongue and anus.

In January 1982, the Centers for Disease Control (CDC) in Atlanta, Ga., reported that at least 335 people had contracted the syndrome by March 1982, and that 136 died. The cause of the disorder is unknown.

Kaposi's sarcoma, a malignant tumor that is rare in the United States, was formerly found chiefly in older men or in persons undergoing therapy to suppress the immune system, such as kidney-transplant recipients. In Africa, the disease is more common. Anticancer drugs can cause complete remission in 90 per cent of the African victims. However, the newer cases seen in the United States are generally fatal, with remission occurring in only 15 per cent of the cases. Most of these new cases occur among homosexual men, particularly those who have had numerous sexual partners. The CDC found that men affected by the syndrome had twice as many sexual partners during their lifetime and used illicit drugs to a greater extent than did male homosexuals who were not suffering from the disease.

Some researchers are concerned that tens of thousands of homosexual men may already have an immune dysfunction. They may, in fact, be at risk of developing Kaposi's sarcoma or one of many other infections that may occur in people in a weakened immunological state. [Michael H. Alderman]

Science Year Close-Up

Opening Windows into Our Cells

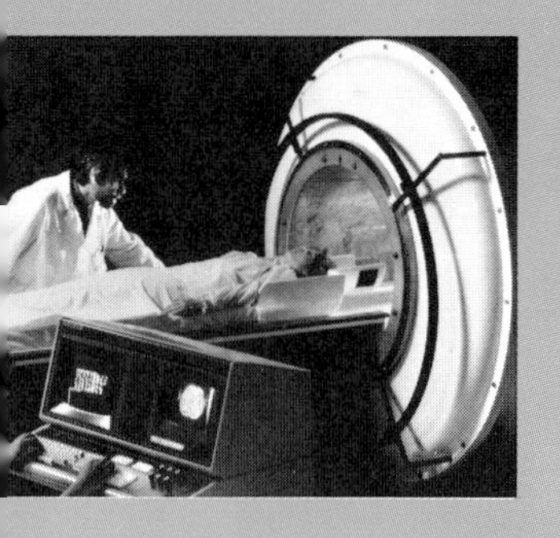

A patient is being made ready for examination by a nuclear magnetic resonance (NMR) machine, which enables doctors to diagnose disease by studying the activities of living cells without destroying or altering them.

A technique that revolutionized the way chemists determine the structure of molecules is changing the way scientists investigate the activities of living cells and doctors diagnose and study disease. What distinguishes this technique, called nuclear magnetic resonance (NMR), from other methods of analysis is its ability to provide information on biochemical processes without destroying cells or disrupting their activities. NMR has shed new light on the processes by which food becomes energy and has been used to diagnose such diseases as cancer and muscle disorders.

NMR detects the magnetic properties of atomic nuclei in a magnetic field. Each nucleus contains positively charged particles called protons and uncharged particles called neutrons. Atoms with the same number of protons belong to the same element. However, some atoms of the same element have different numbers of neutrons. Such atoms are called isotopes. The nuclei of some isotopes have spin—that is, they rotate on their axes like tops. They behave like little magnets that interact with external magnetic fields. Only isotopes with spin can be detected by NMR.

In the absence of an external magnetic field, the nuclei of most isotopes may point in any direction. However, in the presence of a magnetic field, nuclei with spin point only in certain directions. The axes around which such nuclei spin also precess, or rotate around the external magnetic field at a fixed rate called the Larmor frequency.

Differences in the Larmor frequency of individual isotopes can be detected by causing the nuclei to change the direction in which they point. This is done by bombarding the sample with radio waves. When the frequency of the radio waves matches, or is tuned to, the Larmor frequency of the nuclei, resonance occurs and the nuclei absorb energy. Some of the nuclei pointing in one direction in relation to the magnetic field flip, and point in another direction.

When the radio waves are turned off, the nuclei return to their original state. These nuclear spin flips produce detectable changes in the magnetic properties of the sample. By noting the resonance frequency of a specific isotope in a sample, scientists can obtain information about the abundance and structure of molecules in the sample.

Scientists are using NMR techniques to study biochemical processes and to distinguish between healthy and diseased tissue by obtaining images of tissue and organs and by establishing chemical profiles of living tissue. NMR images resemble those made by X-ray imaging scans, but often provide greater detail. To obtain NMR images, scientists monitor the signals emitted by hydrogen nuclei in water molecules, the most abundant molecule in living tissue. Since the water content of such different types of tissue as bone and fat varies, a contrasting image can be obtained.

One technique used to obtain a chemical profile of living tissue is topical magnetic resonance (TMR), which allows researchers to obtain NMR signals from a specific region in the body. Using TMR, researchers can study specific tissues and organs such as muscles, kidneys, and brains. Scientists are also using TMR to study the metabolic activities of cells.

In using NMR to diagnose disease, researchers have concentrated on the analysis of signals emitted by phosphorus nuclei in cells. Chemicals containing phosphorus help the cells extract energy from food and oxygen. Since some diseases cause changes in the metabolism of the affected cells, scientists monitoring signals from phosphorus nuclei can detect these changes and so determine the disease causing them.

For example, NMR can detect the effect of decreased oxygen levels on phosphorus nuclei in cells. Such changes occur as a result of blood clots and cardiovascular diseases in which the blood does not circulate normally. Phosphorus NMR also may someday be used to detect cancer and to monitor its treatment.

Among diagnostic techniques, NMR is almost unique in its ability to provide information on biochemical processes without surgery or the danger of altering or damaging the sample. As a result, NMR promises to become one of the most effective weapons in the war on disease. [Jerry D. Glickson]

Medicine

Continued

Surgery. The first successful operation in which surgeons removed a fetus from the womb, performed corrective surgery, and then replaced the fetus in the womb, where it was carried to term, was reported in November 1981 by a medical team from the University of California, San Francisco. The team consisted of Mitchell Golbus, Michael Harrison, and Roy Filly. Performed in the 21st week of pregnancy, the operation corrected a blockage in the fetus's urinary tract.

An ultrasound examination — an analysis of reflected sound waves — showed that backed-up urine was swelling the fetus's kidneys, a condition that eventually would have led to kidney failure and death. After administering drugs that prevent premature labor by calming uterine contractions, the surgeons cut through the mother's abdominal wall and into the uterus.

The fetus, with its umbilical cord still attached, was removed from the womb, and the ureters — tubes that carry urine from the kidneys to the bladder — were extended outside the fetus's body, by-passing the obstruction in the urinary tract. The fetus was then replaced in the mother's uterus, after spending about 30 minutes outside the womb. The entire procedure lasted 1½ hours.

Although physicians were concerned that cutting into the uterus would cause contractions and that the fetus would be expelled prematurely, this did not occur. The birth took place four months later, but the infant died of kidney failure because the damage had progressed too far by the time the corrective surgery was performed. However, the San Francisco group has shown for the first time that a fetus can be carried to term after being removed from the womb and returned.

Preserving spleens. In the past several years, a revolution has taken place regarding surgery of the spleen, formerly regarded as a completely expendable organ. The spleen's chief functions — storing red blood cells and removing damaged, defective, or old red blood cells from the blood — can be easily taken over by the liver and bone

A synthetic mesh wrap that is surgically implanted around the stomach to keep the stomach from expanding can help obese people lose weight.

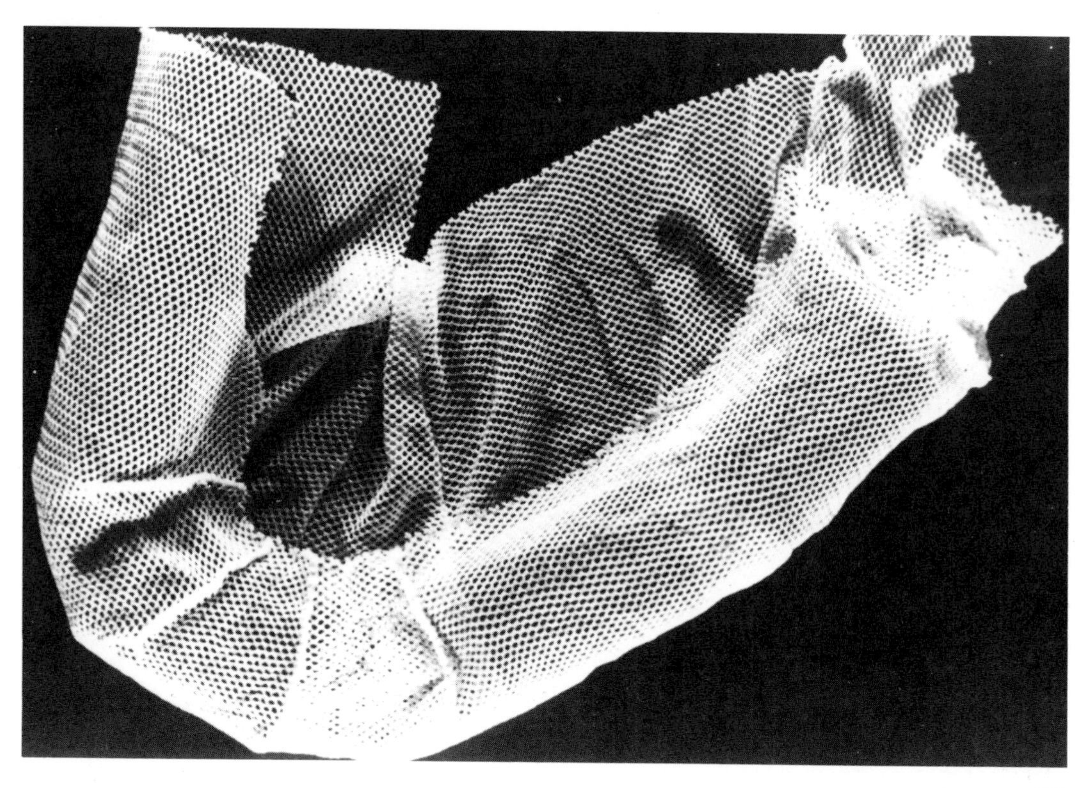

Medicine

Continued

marrow. Since the spleen's pulpy consistency makes suturing difficult, surgeons usually removed a damaged spleen, even if the injury was trivial.

Recently, however, doctors have discovered that the spleen plays an important role in the body's immune defenses, especially in children. A splenectomy—or removal of the spleen—plays havoc with an infant's immune system, leaving the child at increased risk of infection, particularly from *Hemophilus influenzae*—bacteria associated with respiratory infections and meningitis—and pneumococci. Half of all such infections in infants are fatal. While the situation is less dramatic in adults who have undergone a splenectomy, they may also suffer sudden severe infections.

A new method of treating infants with severely damaged spleens was reported in August 1981 by Karl Aigner of the University Clinic in Giessen, West Germany. Aigner conducted animal experiments using tiny particles of splenic tissue up to 1 millimeter (0.3 inch) in diameter. He implanted the particles of spleen into the animals' peritoneal, or abdominal, cavity and into the muscles of the abdominal wall. Capillaries from surrounding tissue grew into the particles, which formed red and white pulp characteristic of normal splenic tissue.

Aigner then applied the technique to six infants born with spleen injuries. In each operation, Aigner removed the injured, bleeding spleen and tied the splenic blood vessels in order to stop hemorrhaging. The damaged spleen was ground up into small particles. Then, 12 to 15 milliliters (about 0.5 ounce) of the splenic material was spooned into pockets or folds in the peritoneum, the membrane that lines the abdominal cavity. Sophisticated laboratory tests showed that the implanted splenic tissue continued to perform its immune function. Despite these encouraging early results, it will take many years of careful follow-up of large numbers of such patients to determine whether long-term immunity is really provided by this ingenious new approach.

Surgery in the womb
A procedure to relieve a build-up of fluid in a fetus's urinary tract consists of inserting a catheter through the mother's abdominal and uterine walls into the fetus's bladder. Part of the catheter is left in the bladder to allow urine to drain into the amniotic fluid in the uterus. The operation was performed on the male of a set of twins.

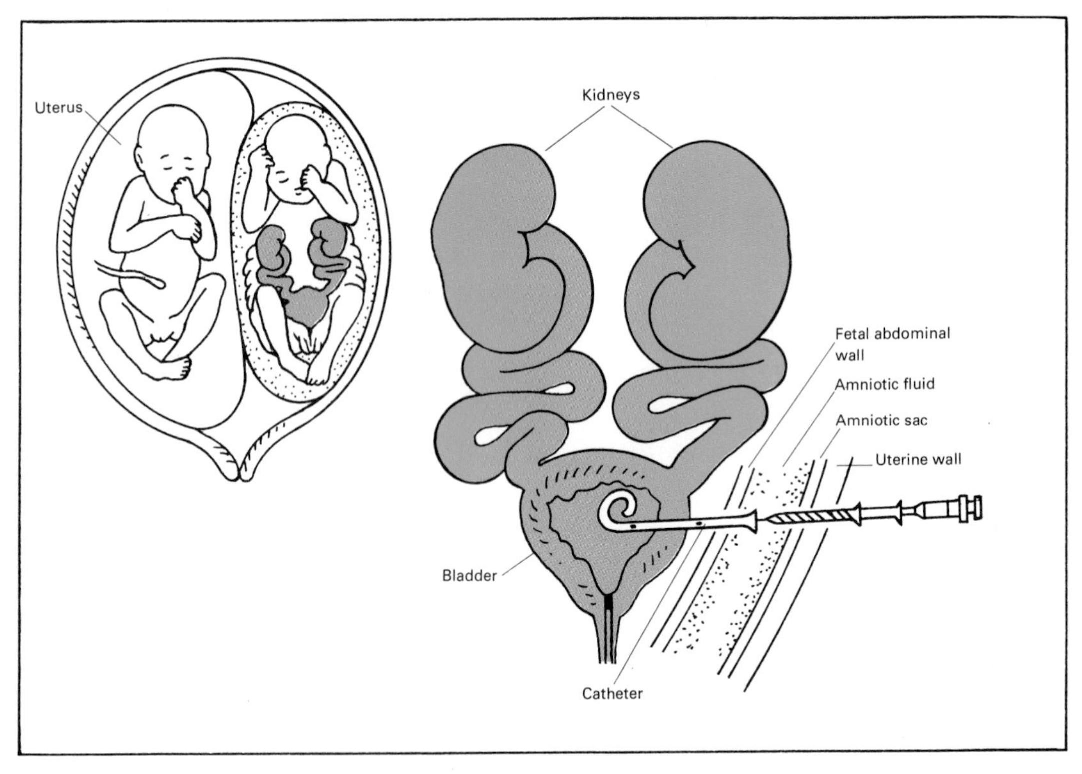

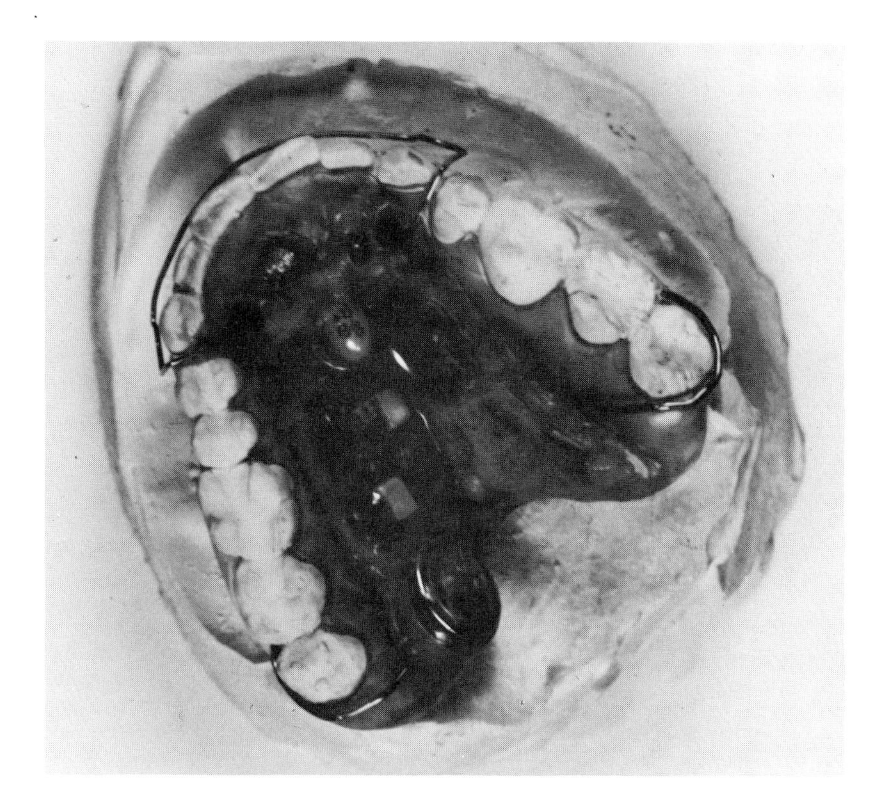

An electronic larynx that is held against the roof of the mouth by wires around the teeth allows people whose larynx has been removed to speak by activating the device with their tongue. The larynx differs from most other artificial larynxes, which are hand-held or surgically implanted.

Correcting offbeat hearts. In May 1981, cardiologist Mark Josephson of the University of Pennsylvania reported on the surgical treatment of 60 patients with arrhythmia, or irregularities in heart rhythm. Arrhythmias vary from premature ventricular contractions—skipped beats—which do not seem dangerous, to such life-threatening arrhythmias as ventricular tachycardia—a rapid heart rate—or fibrillation—a rapid, irregular twitching of the heart muscle. Severe arrhythmias often are fatal; although the heart muscle still has adequate pumping strength, it is unable to generate or conduct the electrical impulses that cause coordinated contractions of the heart muscle.

The principal method of treating arrhythmia has always been drugs. Josephson's new surgical approach is based on the assumption that fatal ventricular arrhythmia occurs because an area of the heart lining has been damaged by an inadequate blood supply. This deficiency usually occurs because of a build-up of fats in the walls of the coronary arteries. Even though the area of dead tissue may be far too small to affect the heart's pumping action, the damaged cells may alter the heart's ability to conduct and generate electrical impulses.

Josephson selected 60 patients whose ventricular tachycardia could not be controlled by anti-arrhythmic drugs. During the operation, the patient's heart was exposed, and surgeons attempted to identify the damaged area by mapping the heart's electrical system with a special sterilized electrode applied to the surface of the heart. Unfortunately, this type of mapping works in only about 25 per cent of the patients. Therefore, in the remaining cases, the heart must be cut open for endocardial mapping, or mapping within the heart. The patient was hooked up to a heart-lung machine and the heart was stopped. The surgeon then mapped the electrical pathways inside the heart with a thimble-sized device that fits on the end of a finger. Once the damaged area of the lining was located, it was peeled away.

Medicine

Continued

Josephson reported that the surgery cured 42 of the 60 patients; arrhythmia was controlled in five other patients with lowered dosages of anti-arrhythmic drugs. Five patients died after surgery, and the treatment failed to correct the arrhythmia in eight others. Although surgeons had removed such damaged areas of the heart with occasional success, the use of endocardial mapping has produced a dramatic improvement in the treatment of some types of arrhythmia.

Closing the chest wall. Openings in the chest wall caused by shotgun blasts, infection, and surgery to remove tumors have long posed special surgical problems. Normally, surgeons close any opening in the body with a skin graft. However, such soft tissue lacks the rigidity the chest needs to maintain a low internal air pressure so the lungs can expand during breathing. In November 1981, surgeons Henri Echapposse of the University of Toulouse Medical Center in France and Arthur Boyd of New York University reported on a procedure for reconstructing large chest wall openings using a plastic "sandwich" along with a graft of skin, muscle, and fat.

The plastic sandwich consists of two layers of mesh filled with a gluelike plastic paste that hardens quickly. The surgeons performed 28 operations, using the sandwich in 13 operations. In the remaining 15, the surgeons used only one layer of mesh. The sandwich or mesh was molded to fit the opening in the chest then sutured into place.

Surgeons then covered the implant with a myocutaneous flap—a graft consisting of skin, subcutaneous fat, and underlying muscle. A normal skin graft could not be used to cover the plastic implant because the implant prevents blood vessels at the edges of the chest wall opening from growing into the new tissue. Therefore, the surgeons used a graft with muscle in which there was an artery and a vein, and thus, its own blood-supply system. The surgeons connected these blood vessels to vessels in the chest. In this way, the entire graft could be nourished. [Frank E. Gump]

Meteorology
See Earth Sciences

Microbiology
See Molecular Biology

Molecular Biology

In December 1981, scientists at Tufts University Medical School in Boston and the Massachusetts Institute of Technology in Cambridge reported evidence that a very different form of deoxyribonucleic acid (DNA), known as Z-DNA, may occur in nature. Z-DNA has the same chemical composition as B-DNA—the most common form of DNA—but has a very different three-dimensional shape. The most striking difference is that Z-DNA is a left-handed helix, while B-DNA is right-handed. Z-DNA was discovered in 1979, in synthetic DNA. The Boston researchers' findings provided the first evidence that it also occurs in nature. See GENETICS.

Unconstant genes. In 1981, several teams of molecular biologists reported the first evidence that completely novel gene sequences can arise during cell differentiation—the process by which cells of an embryo take on their final identities as blood cells, bone cells, or cells of other organs. Molecular biologists have long known that, to a good approximation, every cell in an organism contains the same set of genes—segments of DNA that determine inherited characteristics—and that these genes are identical to the parental genes in the germ cells—the sperm and egg—from which the new multicelled organism arose. More recently, however, much research has been directed at understanding a number of interesting exceptions to this rule.

In mammals, white blood cells called B lymphocytes provide one of the best understood examples of how genes determine specialized cells. B lymphocytes synthesize vast numbers of different antibody molecules, each of which can lock onto a specific antigen. Antigens may be molecules on the surface of invading objects, such as viruses or bacteria, or they may be simpler chemicals. The question of how B lymphocytes can make so many different antibodies has occupied many molecular biologists for some time (see DIVERSIFYING OUR DEFENSES).

Many researchers have determined that this diversity can arise at several points during the differentiation of a

Molecular Biology

Continued

particular B lymphocyte. Part of the diversity is due to the fact that during lymphocyte differentiation millions of different genes can be formed to code for antibodies, by piecing together the several parts of an antibody gene that can be assembled in many different ways. Thus a vast number of fully assembled genes can arise from a much more limited number of gene segments that are passed from one generation to the next in the germ cells.

In 1981 and 1982, several teams of molecular biologists provided evidence that there is still another mechanism of diversification — the final antibody genes can have fundamentally new DNA sequences that did not exist in the germ cells at all. Each team was seeking to confirm the hypothesis that somatic mutations — alterations in the DNA sequence of a body cell rather than a germ cell — are responsible for much of antibody diversity. To prove this hypothesis, the scientists needed to compare the chemical structure of a gene for a specific antibody as it appeared in the germ cell and as it appeared in the B lymphocyte to determine what parts of the gene had changed. To do this, they used a combination of several experimental methods that have been developed since the mid-1970s.

First, they needed an adequate supply of a particular antibody. To provide this supply, the scientists used techniques for creating hybridomas, hybrids of B lymphocytes and cancer cells that reproduce rapidly in laboratory cultures.

They injected laboratory mice with a particular antigen and waited a few days until the mice produced antibodies to that antigen. They then removed the spleens of the mice, which contained large numbers of B lymphocytes, and separated out these cells in laboratory dishes. To each of these dishes they added myeloma cells — cancerous B lymphocytes — and the chemical polyethylene glycol. In this preparation, the antibody-producing B lymphocytes and the myeloma cells fused, producing hybridomas — hybrids that can multiply profusely in laboratory cultures and to provide a vast supply of a particular antibody.

The scientists then added the antigen to each of the hybridoma cultures to determine which of the cultures produced the desired antibodies. In some of the cultures, antibodies combined with the antigens. The scientists placed these cultures in a growing medium to form clones — large numbers of copies of the hybridoma cells that produced the desired antibody.

The resultant antibodies were chemically analyzed to determine the sequence of amino acids, the chemical building blocks of protein, in the molecule. Once the scientists had charted this sequence, they applied the genetic code — a formula that indicates the correct DNA sequence for a given amino acid — to the antibody molecule. The genetic code enabled them to predict the composition of the gene sequences that code for the antibody.

To determine whether or not the predicted gene sequences are present in the germ cells of the mouse strains that were employed in these experiments, the scientists then had to make large numbers of these genes for use in chemical sequencing. To do this, they took a plasmid — a circular ring of genetic material — from a bacterium, and removed a small section of the plasmid. They replaced this section with the antibody gene and added the altered plasmid to a bacterial culture. The bacteria absorbed the plasmid and reproduced, with each new bacterium containing copies of the plasmid, and as a result, of the antibody gene.

The researchers were then able to show that the gene sequences that code for many antibody molecules are not in the germ line, but have newly arisen in mature B lymphocytes.

Embryologist Patricia J. Gearhart of the Carnegie Institution in Washington, D.C., and molecular biologists Nelson D. Johnson, Richard Douglas, and Leroy E. Hood of California Institute of Technology in Pasadena reported in May 1981 on studies of antibodies to the chemical phosphorylcholine. Gearhart's team compared the amino acid sequences of two classes of the antibody in mice.

There are five antibody classes — M, G, A, E, and D — each with a different specialized function. Class M molecules are bound to the membrane of the B lymphocyte and even when circulating are confined to the blood vessels. Class G antibodies are general-purpose antibodies that circulate in the spaces between the cells as well as in the bloodstream; class A antibodies are found in mucous membranes; and class E antibodies are implicated in allergic reactions. Scientists do not yet know the role of class D antibodies.

The scientists have found that there was much greater variation among class G molecules than among class M molecules, indicating that a mutation in the antibody gene occurred during the class change, by which an M-producing cell differentiates into a G-producing cell. When they analyzed the composition of the germ-cell gene taken — they found that the gene did not contain the right DNA sequence to code for any of the observed class-G antibody molecules. They concluded that the gene undergoes a mutation, acquiring new DNA during or after the switch to class G production.

Michael Pech, Josef Hochtl, Hannelore Schnell, and Hans G. Zachau of the University of Munich in West Germany in June 1981 reported that they had located a difference in the variable region of an antibody from a mouse tumor, myeloma T, that could not be coded by the germ-cell gene.

Other teams reported additional mutations in the variable regions of antibodies. Variable regions determine which molecules antibodies will attach to. In each case, the antibody carried an amino acid sequence that could not have been coded for by the germ-cell gene. Their results indicated that although the germ-cell genes are extremely stable, antibody gene sequences change at a very high rate as B lymphocytes diversify. Because gene-analyzing techniques have enabled scientists to identify all the genes that code for a particular antibody family in the germ cell, they could rule out the possibility that the antibody variations were encoded by some germ-cell genes that they had missed. They therefore concluded that subsequent gene mutations as the organism diversifies account for the much greater variety of gene sequences pres-

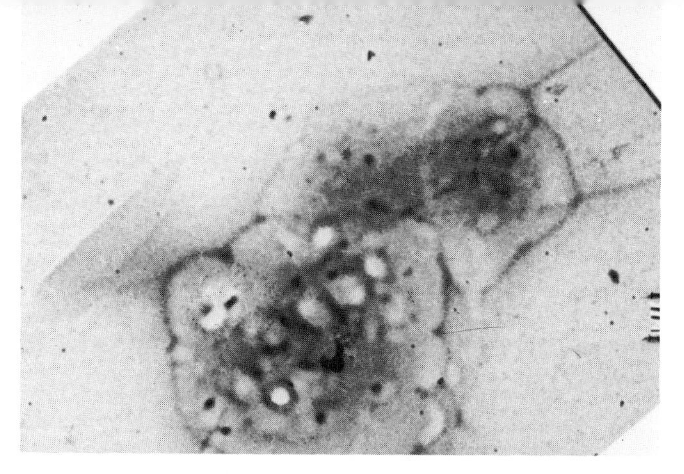

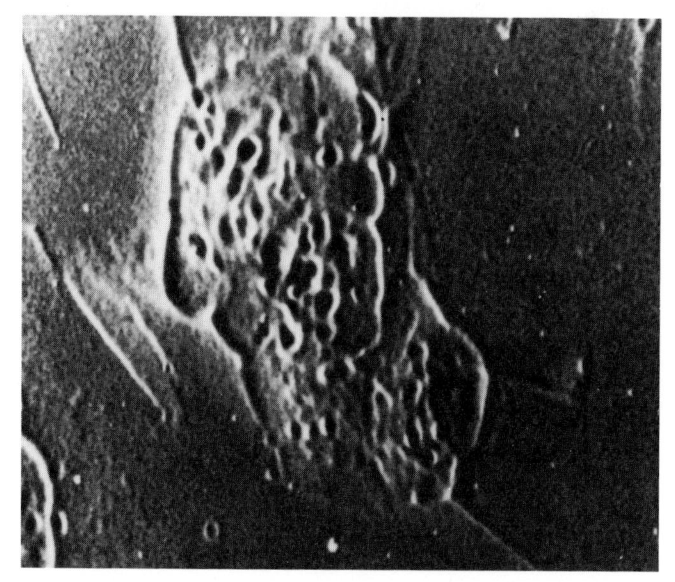

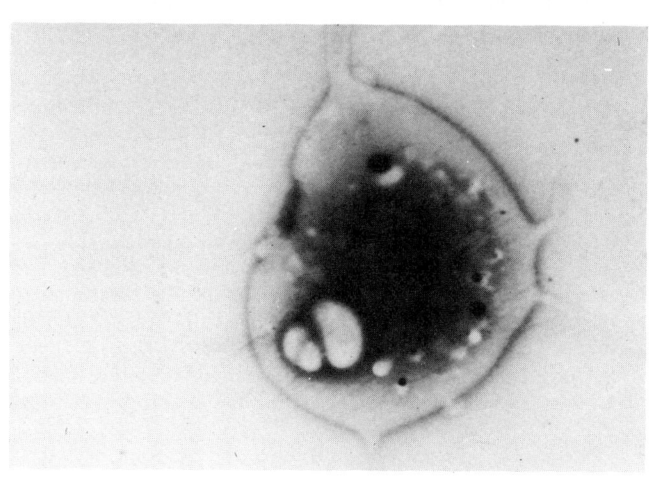

An X-ray replica of a blood platelet viewed by a transmission electron microscope (TEM), magnified 6,000 times, reveals previously unseen cores within the tentaclelike pseudopods extending from the platelet, *top*. These structures were not visible in the same replica seen by a scanning electron microscope, magnified 6,000 times, *above center,* or in the actual platelet seen by TEM, magnified 12,000 times, *above*.

ent in B lymphocytes, and that these mutations play an important role in providing a specific antibody for each of the millions of molecules that can invade the body. Perhaps, however, these findings are the first discovered example of a broader developmental principle. As developmental biologists amend the older idea that all cells contain the same genes, new discoveries in this field will be eagerly awaited.

Spliced mice. In 1981, molecular biologists made an important advance in transplanting genes into higher organisms. Although foreign DNA had been previously introduced into lower organisms, such as bacteria and yeast, and even into human cells in laboratory cultures, it had not been introduced into animals so that its effects on a whole animal and its many different tissues could be studied.

A team of molecular biologists led by Richard Palmiter of the University of Washington in Seattle reported in November 1981 that they had spliced together a hybrid gene from different organisms and inserted it into laboratory mice. It was the first time that such a hybrid had been introduced into all cells of an adult mouse.

Palmiter and his colleagues — Ralph L. Brinster, Howard V. Chen, Myra Trumbauer, Allen W. Senear, and Raphael Warren — constructed a gene that coded for two functions. The gene coupled regulatory sequences — those that turn genes on and off — from a mouse gene that programs the body's reaction to certain heavy metals, with coding sequences for a common viral gene, the herpes simplex virus thymidine kinase gene. The researchers chose these particular mouse gene regulatory sequences because they turn on the gene when heavy metals such as cadmium or mercury, which can be easily administered, enter the body. They chose the viral thymidine kinase coding region because it produces the enzyme thymidine kinase, which is easy to detect in mouse cells.

Palmiter's team separated the DNA from the nucleus of a mouse embryo and added restriction enzymes — enzymes that cut DNA molecules at a particular place — to cut out the regulatory sequences. They also used restriction enzymes to remove the thy-

Molecular Biology

Continued

midine kinase gene from herpes virus DNA. They then used another enzyme to splice the two segments together. Next, the researchers injected the spliced gene into fertilized mouse eggs, which they then implanted into the uterus of a surrogate mother. After the mice were born, the scientists took cell samples from them and separated out the DNA. They used a radio-tagged gene probe to search for the spliced gene and found that it was present in about 10 per cent of the mice.

To find out whether this gene functioned, the scientists injected heavy metals into the affected mice. They found that, soon after the injections, the mouse tissues contained high levels of thymidine kinase, indicating that the hybrid gene's regulatory sequences responded normally to the injection—turning on the gene for thymidine kinase production. This observation suggested that the Palmiter group had correctly identified the parts of the mouse gene that turn the gene on and off and had successfully used them to turn on a foreign gene.

However, scientists still must overcome a much more difficult problem—controlling the site on the mouse chromosomes at which the foreign gene becomes incorporated. With present methods, multiple copies of the inserted gene may become incorporated at unpredictable sites on a variety of chromosomes. Therefore, although the gene was definitely functioning in a living mouse, it was unlikely to be subject to all the biological controls that keep genes dividing and functioning normally. Many studies have indicated that some of these controls operate properly only when a single copy of the gene is present at a specific site in an organism's chromosomes.

The work of the last year, however, represents a large step in bridging the gap between inserting genes in laboratory cultures and transplanting genes that function perfectly in living animals. Such studies may also lead to treatments for genetic diseases. Normal genes could be introduced into a patient's cells to compensate for a mutant gene. [Maynard V. Olson]

Neuroscience

Canadian neuroscientists in March 1982 announced a nerve-implanting technique that increases the length of damaged nerve fibers in the brain. Albert J. Aguayo and Martin Benfey of Montreal General Hospital and McGill University, both in Montreal, Canada, used 20 anesthetized rats in their experiments.

The scientists inserted short sections of sciatic nerve from each rat's leg into or near various parts of the rat's brain. From 5 to 23 weeks following the operation, they removed the rats' brains and studied the nerve cells and the axons—the fibers that grow out from the cells—under a microscope.

Aguayo and Benfey traced over 400 separate nerve cells from the area of the implant in all the rats. In most cases, the axons of these cells were found to have grown at least 13 millimeters (0.5 inch) beyond the area at which the sciatic nerve was grafted on. Never before had injured axons been known to grow that well.

The same team had also recorded axon growth in earlier work in which they had grafted nerves to the brain stem and spinal cords of rats. These results indicate that certain nerve grafts can create a condition in the brain that produces greater-than-normal fiber growth. Further studies of the biological or chemical factors that trigger such growth may provide a new understanding of how nerve cells develop normally, as well as produce new treatments for patients who suffer from brain or nerve damage.

Rabid transit. Cell biologists Thomas L. Lentz and Thomas G. Burrage and epidemiologists Abigail L. Smith, Joan Crick, and Gregory H. Tignor of Yale University Medical School in New Haven, Conn., reported an advance in understanding the action of the rabies virus. The disease that results from rabies infection, usually from the bite of a rabid animal, is almost always fatal if untreated. Scientists know that nerve fibers carry the rabies virus to the brain, but they do not know exactly how it is transported.

The Yale researchers removed the diaphragm muscles and their attached nerves from mice and divided the tissue into two groups. They dipped one tissue group in a solution containing rabies virus, waited a few hours, and added fluorescent rabies antibodies to the group. Antibodies are molecules that attach to "foreign" molecules, such as rabies virus. Fluorescent antibodies are treated so that they will glow when viewed under a special microscope. This allowed the scientists to see where the rabies virus went.

The scientists added only one solution to the other group—a preparation containing fluorescent antibodies to acetylcholine receptors. Acetylcholine is a chemical that acts as a link between nerves and muscles and attaches to acetylcholine receptors, specific receptor molecules on the muscle cells.

When the researchers viewed both tissue groups under a fluorescent microscope one hour later, they found that both the rabies antibodies and the acetylcholine-receptor antibodies had attached to the diaphragm muscle cells at the same sites. The researchers determined that the acetylcholine-receptor antibodies had attached to the receptor sites, indicating the position of these receptors on the muscles that were not exposed to virus. The rabies antibodies had attached to the rabies virus at sites of acetylcholine receptors on the treated muscles. The Yale researchers concluded that acetylcholine receptors may serve as passageways for the virus to the nerves. They reported similar results using muscle cells from chick embryos. Their findings may well provide the basis for additional research into the role of acetylcholine receptors in this disease.

Brain tangles. Neuroscientists Doris Dahl, Amico Bignami, and their associates at West Roxbury Veterans Administration Medical Center in Massachusetts and Harvard Medical School in Boston in January 1982 implicated neurofilaments—a component of all neurons—in Alzheimer's disease—a premature form of senility. The disease is characterized by the appearance of "neurofibrillary tangles," masses of twisted fibers in some of the neurons, in various parts of the brain. A small number of these tangles are also seen in the brains of most normal people over 70 years of age.

The Massachusetts researchers examined tissue from the brains of two patients who had died of Alzheimer's disease. They treated the diseased brain tissue with fluorescent antibodies to the proteins in normal neurofilaments. When they viewed the brain tissue under a fluorescing microscope, they discovered glowing antibodies attached to the neurofibrillary tangles, indicating they contained normal protein. The scientists concluded that because normal neurofilaments and neurofibrillary tangles have fundamentally the same protein composition, the process that tangles normal fibers may play a role in Alzheimer's disease, as well as in the natural aging process.

Reducing spinal damage. Neuroscientist Alan J. Faden and researcher Thomas P. Jacobs of the Uniformed Services University of the Health Sciences in Bethesda, Md., and John W. Holaday of Walter Reed Army Institute of Research in Washington, D.C., in October 1981 reported on a treatment that may lessen the severity of spinal cord damage. The treatment is based on injections of thyrotropin releasing hormone (TRH)—one of the hormones produced in the hypothalamus area of the brain. TRH is known to block the action of other hormones that reduce blood flow. It is the reduction of blood flow to the injury site that is thought to inhibit recovery.

The scientists anesthetized 26 cats, damaged their spinal cords, and one hour later began treatment. Six cats were injected with TRH; 10 cats were treated with dexamethasone—a drug that is currently used to reduce spinal cord inflammation in human accident victims. The remaining 10, the control group, were given a saline solution of no therapeutic value. Each cat was monitored for six weeks and tested for coordination and motor function.

The tests showed that cats given TRH regained normal motor control while those in the other two groups suffered from spastic limb movements. Moreover, the dexamethasone treatment seemed no more effective than the saline solution. If further animal experiments are equally promising, the scientists plan to test TRH on human accident victims who have sustained spinal injuries. [George Adelman]

Nutrition

A major study reported in December 1981 by Norwegian researchers provided what may be the best evidence yet that eating less animal fat and cholesterol can reduce the risk of heart attack. A team of researchers in Oslo conducted the study, which began in 1972.

The Norwegian researchers selected 1,232 healthy men in their 40s who had normal blood pressure but high levels of cholesterol in their blood. The experimenters randomly assigned the men either to a control group or to an experimental one. No diet change was made for the control group. However, the researchers urged the experimental group to stop smoking and to follow a cholesterol-reducing diet low in animal fats. For example, they advised the subjects to have only one egg a week and to eat fish instead of meat.

Five years later, the men in the experimental group had cholesterol levels 13 per cent lower than those of the control group. Even more important, the experimental group had a 47 per cent lower rate of heart attacks.

The Norwegian study was the first to show the benefits of diet changes for a large group of healthy men living normal lives. Most previous studies had been done with small groups, men in prisons or other institutions, or patients with heart disease.

Large doses of vitamin C may create a need for extra vitamin E, according to research reported in June 1981 by biochemist and nutritionist Linda H. Chen of the University of Kentucky. Chen carried out her study on rats. She gave half of the rats huge doses of vitamin C and the other half only normal amounts. Both groups were divided into smaller groups that received various levels of vitamin E.

Chen found that the animals receiving high doses of vitamin C, but only average amounts of vitamin E, had fragile red blood cells and liver cells, easily damaged in the test tube.

Chen concluded that the combination of high vitamin C and low vitamin E levels reduced the rats' ability to withstand tissue damage from oxidation, the process of combining with ox-

A worker at the potato research laboratory of the U.S. Department of Agriculture, *below left,* slices potatoes as part of research to develop a less fattening potato chip. Researchers test the oil content of chips, *below right.* Potatoes low in moisture absorb less oil in frying and make lower calorie chips.

ygen. Oxidation is responsible for such decay processes as the rusting of metal and the decomposition of organic matter. However, Chen discovered that even a small increase in the vitamin E in a rat's diet counteracted the bad effects of the extra vitamin C.

The same results may or may not occur in human beings. Healthy adults have enough vitamin E stored in the body to handle large doses of vitamin C, but infants and people with nutritional deficiencies may not.

Slight zinc deficiency causes low sperm counts and weight loss in human males, according to a study reported in March 1982 by researchers at Wayne State University in Detroit. Scientists have long known that severe zinc deficiency can cause infertility and other problems. But the leader of the Detroit team, physician Ananda S. Prasad, said, "We have shown that even mild zinc deficiency can cause such effects." Mild zinc deficiency is widespread, especially in developing countries where people eat little meat, the main source of zinc.

The researchers put nine male volunteers on a low-zinc diet for about six months. The men experienced a drop in their sperm count and in their level of the male hormone testosterone. They also lost about 10 per cent of their body weight. Their sperm count, testosterone level, and weight returned to normal on a high-zinc diet.

Caffeine controversy. Studies in the late 1970s and early 1980s linked caffeine—a stimulant found in coffee, tea, cola drinks, and chocolate—with several health problems, including birth defects and breast lumps. In 1982, two studies indicated that caffeine may not be as harmful as once feared.

One study, reported in January 1982, showed evidence that coffee drinking during pregnancy does not, as previously believed, contribute to premature birth or birth defects in human beings. A research team at Brigham and Women's Hospital, Harvard Medical School, and Harvard School of Public Health—all in Boston—interviewed and analyzed the medical records of 12,205 women who gave birth at the hospital.

The researchers, headed by physician Shai Linn, found that premature deliveries and small babies appeared to be much more common among women who drank four or more cups of coffee a day than among those who drank none. However, by further analyzing the data, the scientists found that the problems were caused by cigarettes, not coffee. Frequent coffee drinkers in the study were three times as likely to smoke as were nondrinkers. The researchers found no link between coffee use alone and premature birth, low birth weight, or birth defects.

Another group of researchers uncovered reassuring evidence about the relationship between caffeine and fibrocystic breast disease, a disorder characterized by noncancerous breast lumps. Epidemiologist Virginia Ernster and her colleagues at the University of California in San Francisco reported in March 1982 that they found no link between caffeine and fibrocystic breast disease. The researchers studied 140 women with the disease over a four-month period. Seventy-two of the subjects reduced their intake of caffeine by an average of 99.7 per cent. Sixty-eight of the women, serving as a control group, made no diet changes. The researchers examined all the women at the beginning and end of the study. Their findings, they said, gave "little support for the claim that caffeine-free diets are associated with a major, clinically significant improvement in benign breast disease."

New sweeteners. On July 15, 1982, the U.S. Food and Drug Administration (FDA) approved a new low-calorie artificial sweetener called aspartame. G. D. Searle & Company of Skokie, Ill., developed the sweetener, which it sells under the brand name Equal. The FDA cleared aspartame only for dry foods and table use.

At the March 1982 meeting of the American Chemical Society, scientists at the University of Dayton in Ohio announced the development of another low-calorie sweetener. The substance, called polysugar, is still years away from use. Arthur M. Usmani and Ival O. Salyer created polysugar by linking a sugar molecule to a longer molecule called polyvinyl alcohol. The polysugar molecule is so large that it passes through the body without being digested. [Sara Dreyfuss]

Oceanography
See Earth Sciences

Paleontology
See Earth Sciences

Physics

Atoms and Nuclei. In 1981 and 1982, the major news in atomic physics involved the coming of age of the free electron laser (FEL), which has great potential for research and as a practical tool for industry. For more than 20 years, progress in atomic physics, the study of the internal motions of atoms and molecules, has gone hand in hand with laser development.

Physicists use laser light to deliver energy to atoms and molecules. Whether a certain atom or molecule absorbs energy from a ray of light depends upon that ray's wavelength—the distance between wave crests.

Unlike ordinary light, which is composed of rays at many different wavelengths, a laser's light is very pure. The individual light rays are almost perfectly uniform. As a result, they can deliver sharply focused, precisely timed energy, often in short bursts.

Ordinary lasers produce uniform light by controlling the manner in which electrons in a so-called active medium absorb and release energy. In a typical laser, energy is pumped into the active medium. The medium can be a gas, liquid, or solid, and the energy source can be anything from a flash of light to a chemical reaction. This energy alters the motion of electrons in the medium. These electrons then release energy by emitting light of a certain wavelength. These emissions, in turn, cause other electrons to give up energy by emitting still more light in the same wavelength. Two mirrors—one partially transparent—at the ends of the laser reflect some of these rays back and forth through the active medium, stimulating even more emissions. A powerful pulse of light finally bursts from the partially transparent end.

The wavelength of the laser light depends upon the active medium. Lasers emit light that ranges from the infrared, whose wavelengths are longer than those of visible-light rays, to the ultraviolet, which have shorter wavelengths than the light we can see. However, no ordinary single laser covers the entire range. Rather, each emits light of just one wavelength or a limited band of wavelengths. Furthermore, no conventional laser can emit light in certain parts of the range.

The FEL, however, can in principle be tuned to any desired wavelength in this range. This is because the source of the FEL's light is not electrons in an active medium. Rather, the energy source of an FEL is the motion of an electron beam in a magnetic field, which the experimenter can control.

In an FEL, a beam of electrons from a machine called a particle accelerator is sent through a magnet, appropriately named a wiggler, in which the direction of the magnetic field reverses every few centimeters. This reversal causes the electrons to wiggle, or oscillate, about their path. As the electrons oscillate, they emit light waves that match the frequency of the oscillation. This frequency can be changed simply by altering the energy, and thus the speed, of the beam.

Physicist John J. M. Madey of Stanford University in California and his co-workers built the first FEL in 1976. The feat has since been duplicated at about a dozen laboratories in Europe, Russia, and the United States. By 1981, the development of FELs as research facilities rather than demonstration projects was underway at a number of centers, including Bell Laboratories in Murray Hill, N.J.; Brookhaven National Laboratory on Long Island, N.Y.; and the University of California at Santa Barbara.

Lasers are now common in industry. However, one obstacle to their wider use has been their inefficiency. More than 90 per cent of the energy put into a laser goes into heat rather than light. FELs, however, may prove to be as high as 30 per cent efficient.

New jobs for old accelerators appeared during the year. The United States alone boasts more than 100 such outmoded machines, most of them built for the expansion of nuclear physics in the 1950s and 1960s.

By the 1980s, these machines had completed their task of providing detailed, accurate data on the structure of nuclei. Many nuclear physicists had then moved on to other areas of research. The development of the earliest FELs coincided with the wide availability of outmoded accelerators in the right energy range—millions to tens of millions of electron volts of energy. (One electron volt is the energy

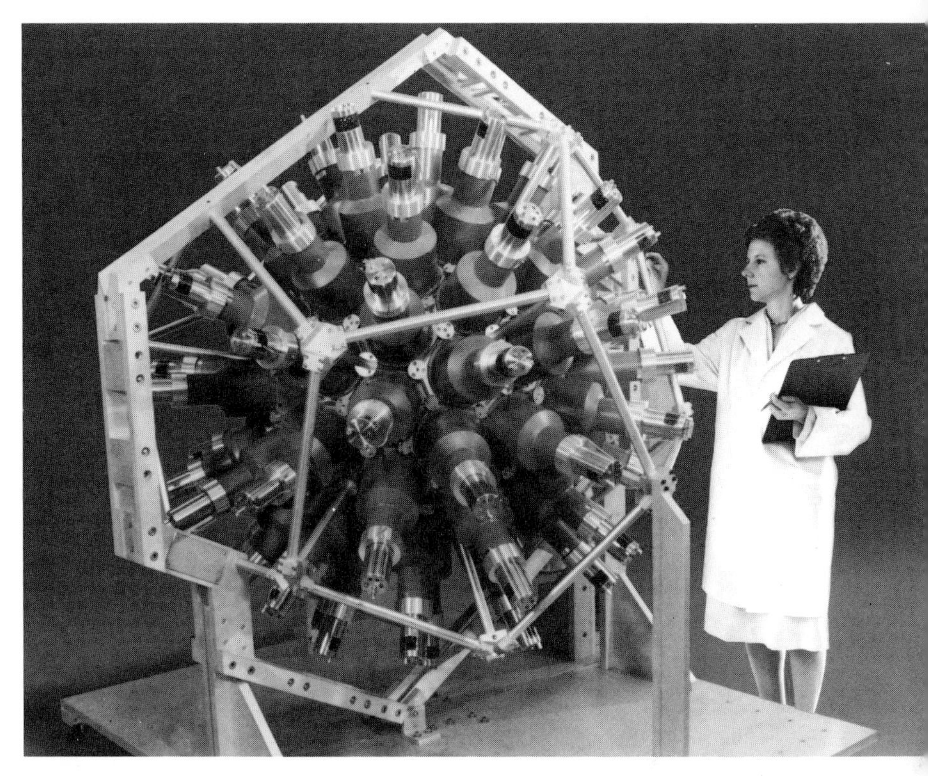

An array of 72 photomultiplier tubes installed around a spherical chamber is designed to detect gamma rays, neutrons, and charged particles traveling outward from the chamber in all directions during experiments on subatomic structures at Oak Ridge National Laboratory.

an electron gains as it moves across an electrical field of 1 volt.)

Most of the old accelerators are of the Van de Graaff type, in which a metal sphere is charged to a high voltage by friction. These machines can accelerate any kind of particle or nucleus, as long as it carries electrical charge. Physicists can use this capability in new areas of study, so some of these machines have a new lease on life. One of the more interesting applications has been a major improvement in techniques for radioisotope dating.

The age of an object can sometimes be determined by looking for a radioactive isotope that was present in the object when it was formed, and has now partially decayed away. A radioisotope disappears at a known rate, so the age of an object can be estimated by measuring how much of the radioisotope remains.

The conventional dating technique detects the radioisotopes by their radiation. Radioisotopes take a long time to decay, so only a small fraction of their atoms emit radiation while the measurement is in progress. Therefore, researchers need fairly large samples.

But in accelerator dating, the machine speeds up small numbers of nuclei from the sample and directs them along a straight path. Magnets along the path then deflect the nuclei. Different isotopes are deflected by different amounts, depending on their weight. Detection devices then count individual nuclei of the radioisotope, without having to wait for it to decay. Accelerator dating of plant and animal remains according to the number of nuclei of the carbon-14 isotope requires only milligrams of the sample, compared with the grams needed for radioactive counting. Accelerator dating is also faster and more accurate.

One of the more intriguing proposed uses of this technique would be to date the Shroud of Turin, which many people believe is the burial shroud of Jesus Christ. The nuclear physics laboratory at Rochester University in New York has offered to perform the test and claims it needs only a few centimeters of thread. [Robert H. March]

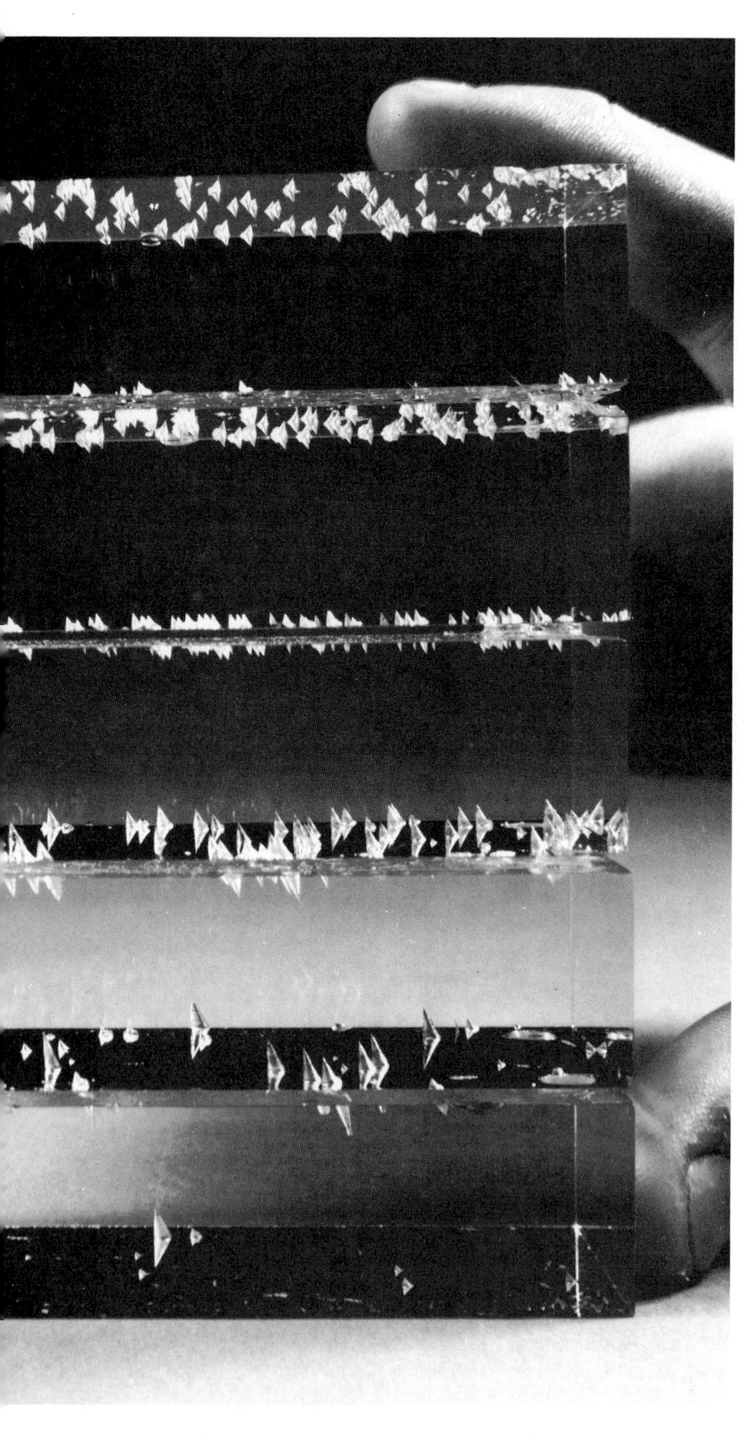

Tracks made by iron nuclei in plastic slabs are revealed by an etching process. Such tracks contain information about the electrical charges, speeds, and directions of motion of the particles that left them.

Particles and Forces. July 7, 1981, was a red-letter day for particle physics. On that day, the Proton-Antiproton Collider began operation at the multinational European Center for Nuclear Research (CERN) near Geneva, Switzerland. This machine produces head-on collisions of a beam of protons with one of antiprotons, their antimatter counterparts. Physicists search the debris from these collisions for clues to the behavior of fundamental particles and forces.

The two beams circulate in opposite directions inside the Super Proton Synchrotron (SPS)—an oval-shaped vacuum pipe 7 kilometers (4.4 miles) long. Powerful electromagnets steer the beams around this track.

The particles in each beam carry 270 billion electron volts (GeV) of energy, making their collisions the most violent ever produced in a particle accelerator. (One electron volt is the energy that an electron gains as it moves across an electric field whose potential is 1 volt.) The previous record, held by the smaller Intersecting Storage Rings (ISR) at CERN, had been 33 GeV.

The Collider is also by far the world's most complicated particle accelerator, because producing an intense beam of antiprotons is extremely difficult. Protons can be produced simply by discharging electrical energy in a chamber containing hydrogen gas. The discharge strips electrons from the hydrogen atoms, leaving the nuclei, which are single protons.

However, antiprotons are not part of ordinary matter, so researchers cannot obtain them by manipulating atoms. Instead, scientists create them by colliding protons with nuclei in a smaller accelerator. These collisions produce a proton and an antiproton. Then the scientists collect the antiprotons by deflecting them magnetically into a ring-shaped vacuum chamber, where they are stored. It takes nearly a full day to accumulate the hundreds of billions of antiprotons the Collider needs for optimum performance.

Inside the SPS, each beam consists of short bunches of particles, about 1.5 meters (5 feet) long and a few millimeters in diameter. They whirl around the 7-kilometer track at nearly the speed of light. When the beams meet,

A 525-ton superconducting electromagnet at Lawrence Berkeley Laboratory in California can set up an extremely large and powerful magnetic field that separates the paths of all fragments emerging from a nuclear collision. The changes in the paths provide complete information about the fragments' weights, electrical charges, and speeds.

most of the particles pass each other unscathed, for even an intense particle beam is mostly empty space. Nevertheless, when the Collider is running perfectly, there are a few thousand collisions each second.

When the particles collide head-on, much of their energy is quickly converted to mass in the form of more particles, which fly out in all directions. Large, complex detectors track the charged particles. The largest such detector, the UA-1, tracks the positions of particles at many points along their paths and sends the data to a computer, which generates a three-dimensional picture.

Staying competitive. The Collider widened the already substantial lead of Europe over the United States in particle research facilities. To remain competitive, U.S. physicists are gambling on high technology to make machines that are not only more powerful, but also cheaper to build and operate. The key is to use superconductors, materials that offer no resistance to electrical current, in the electromagnets that steer and focus particle beams.

The Fermi National Accelerator Laboratory (Fermilab) in Batavia, Ill., in 1982 was building its own version of the CERN Collider. But superconducting magnets should enable the Fermilab machine to reach 1,000 GeV in each beam, even though the two machines have nearly the same circumference.

An even bolder gamble was considered by physicists at Stanford Linear Accelerator Center (SLAC) in Palo Alto, Calif. They want to collide beams not in the usual subatomic race track, but in a small loop at the end of a straight track, the Stanford Linear Collider (SLC).

The particles would make a single pass along the track then divide into two beams of opposite charge, entering the loop going in opposite directions. They collide halfway around the loop.

At first glance, this seems foolish. In a race-track design, one batch of particles can pass through another billions of times, while SLC would use each batch only once. To make up for this limitation, SLC designers would pump more particles into each batch. They could not do this in a circulating machine, because the dense concentration of charged particles would generate electrical forces that would quickly disrupt the beams. To increase the likelihood of collisions, the SLAC physicists also propose packing these particles into the thinnest beams ever produced.

Finally, SLC would use electrons and positrons, their antimatter counterparts, in two 50-GeV beams. An electron-positron machine has some advantages over a proton-antiproton collider. For one thing, positrons are nearly 2,000 times lighter than antiprotons, and so they require less energy to produce. Researchers produce them by directing high-energy electrons against a solid target. When the electrons strike, they emit gamma rays, which then hit another target, producing electrons and positrons.

Another advantage stems from the fact that positrons and electrons have no smaller parts, so their collisions are relatively easy to interpret. Protons and antiprotons are not simple objects, but have parts called quarks, antiquarks, and gluons. This construction adds complexity to proton-antiproton collisions, making them extremely difficult to interpret.

In addition, each part of a proton or antiproton carries only a fraction of the particle's total energy. But all of an electron's or positron's energy is concentrated in a single object. Thus, an electron-positron collider can provide the same sort of data as a proton-antiproton collider whose particles have several times more energy.

The main disadvantage of circular electron-positron machines has been that the particles lose large amounts of energy as they circulate, compared with the energy losses of proton-antiproton colliders. The SLC design minimizes the disadvantage, because the particles will lose little energy by turning once in a small loop. The SLAC physicists may have SLC running by 1985. [Robert H. March]

Argonne National Laboratory's new particle accelerator operates at temperatures near absolute zero (−273.15°C or −459.67°F.), where resistance to electrical current disappears. It uses little more electrical power to accelerate particles than it needs to keep cool. The accelerator is thus about 50 per cent cheaper to run than it would be if it operated at room temperature.

"It started with just the particles being accelerated, but now everything around here has speeded up."

Condensed Matter Physics. Physicist Charles V. Shank and his colleagues at Bell Laboratories in Holmdel, N.J., reported in April 1982 that they had produced the shortest pulse of laser light ever achieved in the laboratory. The pulse lasted for only 30 femtoseconds (quadrillionths of a second). Light travels only 10 micrometers (millionths of a meter)—less than one-tenth the thickness of a human hair—in 30 femtoseconds. Flashing pulses of light of such short duration will enable scientists to "freeze" chemical reactions, much as flashing a strobe light on a dance floor makes the dancers appear to be stationary for short periods of time. Chemists will use this technique to observe the individual steps of molecular motion and chemical reactions. For example, scientists may be able to trace the motion of individual electrons as they participate in photosynthesis, the method by which plants convert sunlight and carbon dioxide into energy and oxygen.

Researchers will be able to study molecules directly by observing how they absorb and reflect light, as we do when we see an ordinary object. Brief laser pulses will also be used to study molecules indirectly. Shortly after a molecule absorbs a light ray, it emits another ray. The wavelength of the emitted light—the distance the ray travels as it vibrates through one cycle—depends upon the energy level and shape of the molecule. Researchers will flash light on molecules and then study the wavelengths of molecular emissions to determine the state of the molecules shortly after the flash. And by studying the successive emissions that follow a series of flashes, scientists can trail step-by-step changes in molecules all the way through a chemical reaction. Once they know all these steps, scientists can synthesize molecules that perform the same functions as the original molecules or can alter original molecules to improve their efficiency.

Fiber optic gyroscopes. In October 1981, two groups of scientists—one at Stanford University in California and the other at Massachusetts Institute of

Technology (MIT) in Cambridge—announced a major step toward the development of fiber optic gyroscopes for civil and military aircraft. A mechanical gyroscope is a spinning top inside a frame that allows the axis of the top always to point in the same direction. Gyroscopes permit navigation without referring to magnetic compasses or radio beams.

Airplanes traveling long distances now use extremely sensitive mechanical gyroscopes to determine their direction and position. However, such devices are very delicate, require a long start-up time, and the axis tends to rotate from its original direction as their spin rate slows, during sudden accelerations, and in sharp turns.

Optical gyroscopes are free of these defects. In an optical gyroscope, two rays of light travel in opposite directions along a thin glass fiber bent into a circle. The beams are timed so that they interfere destructively with each other where the two beams meet at a light detector. That is, when the two beams strike the detector, the wave of one beam is at its crest, while the other beam is at its trough. They cancel, so the instrument detects no light.

Such a gyroscope might be mounted in an airplane, for example, parallel to the cockpit floor. If the plane turned to the left, the gyroscope would naturally turn with it. However, the light traveling in the direction in which the plane turned would travel a longer distance to the detector than the beam moving in the opposite direction. The velocity of light is constant, so when the beam that traveled farther crested at the detector, the beam that traveled the shorter distance already would have vibrated past its trough. Thus, the two beams of light no longer would cancel each other exactly and the detector would receive light. The detector would convert the light into an electrical signal that indicated the rotation rate. A small computer would then use this rate and the length of time during which the gyroscope rotated to determine the net rotation of the aircraft.

The experimental optical gyroscopes are extremely compact. Hair-thin fibers of glass or quartz carry the light. The more times the light goes around in a circle in an optical gyroscope, the more accurate is the instrument. So the fibers are wound like thread on spools. Physicist John Shaw and his Stanford group wound 580 meters (1,902 feet) of optical fiber on a 7-centimeter (2.8-inch) spool, while physicist Shaoul Ezekiel and his MIT group wound 200 meters (656 feet) on a 9.5-centimeter (3.7-inch) spool. The Stanford group believes that ultimately a fiber-optic navigational device could be fitted into a container the size and shape of a box of chocolates.

To be useful in airplanes, a gyroscope must be able to detect rotation rates of 0.1 per cent of the earth's rotation rate. However, problems associated with the scattering of light within the optical fiber and elsewhere have limited sensitivity to only 1 per cent of the rotation rate of the earth. Researchers hope to increase sensitivity to make the device useful by using longer fibers and more intense light.

Cooperative electrons. The usual picture of a metal that carries an electrical current is one of individual electrons moving more or less freely, scattered by defects or other imperfections in the metal and by the thermal vibrations of the metal's atoms. This picture, however, neglects the influence of electron charge on electron motion. All electrons have a negative charge and therefore repel one another. So, in a phenomenon known as the coulomb interaction, the motion of one electron affects the motion of nearby electrons.

Scientists have left the coulomb interaction out of the usual description of electronic motion in metals because electrons move through pure metals so rapidly that the scientists thought the interaction had little effect.

However, theoretical physicists Patrick Lee of Bell Laboratories in Murray Hill, N.J., and Boris Altschuler and A. G. Aronov of Leningrad Nuclear Physics Institute in Russia had shown in 1981 that when impurities and imperfections slow the electrons, the coulomb interaction is greatly enhanced. This is because an electron in impure, imperfect materials spends more time in a particular region of space, so it is more likely to be affected by the charge of nearby electrons.

The coulomb interaction locks electrons together in a collective motion when they are slowed down by impurities or imperfections at low temperatures. This in turn greatly enhances the ability of impurities and imperfections to scatter electrons and thereby disrupt electrical current. Scattering can become so pronounced that the electrons cannot carry electrical current at low voltages. This results in a so-called coulomb gap, or absence of conductivity, in the range of energy states of electrons that carry current in a metal at low voltages.

The existence of a gap means that the electrons cannot carry current at low voltages and that, at low temperatures, an unusually large amount of energy (equal to the coulomb gap) is necessary to excite the electrons into an energy state in which they can carry current. At low temperatures, the electrons cannot obtain the necessary energy from the heat of the metal and so the coulomb effect strongly suppresses the metal's electrical conductivity.

In the spring of 1981, physicists William L. McMillan and Jack M. Mochel at the University of Illinois in Urbana-Champaign reported experiments that seem to support the theory. They found that as they made gold more impure by increasing the amount of germanium in a gold-germanium alloy, the ability of the metal to conduct electricity dropped sharply for very small voltages. This suggests that the experimenters had detected the charge-scattering enhancement predicted and that the number of low-energy conducting states was reduced significantly because of it. Whether all the energy states in the coulomb gap are nonconducting, as required by the theory, remains to be seen.

New angle. In 1981 and 1982, chemists David R. Herrick of the University of Oregon in Eugene and Michael E. Kellman, now at Northeastern University in Boston, continued to develop a theory that may simplify the task of determining the relative positions of electrons in atoms. An atom's electrons orbit its nucleus at distances that

IBM scientists adjust a device that demonstrated for the first time that an electron can travel as a wave through a vacuum from one atom to another. Scientists can use the phenomenon to measure distances of a few ten-billionths of a meter between surfaces.

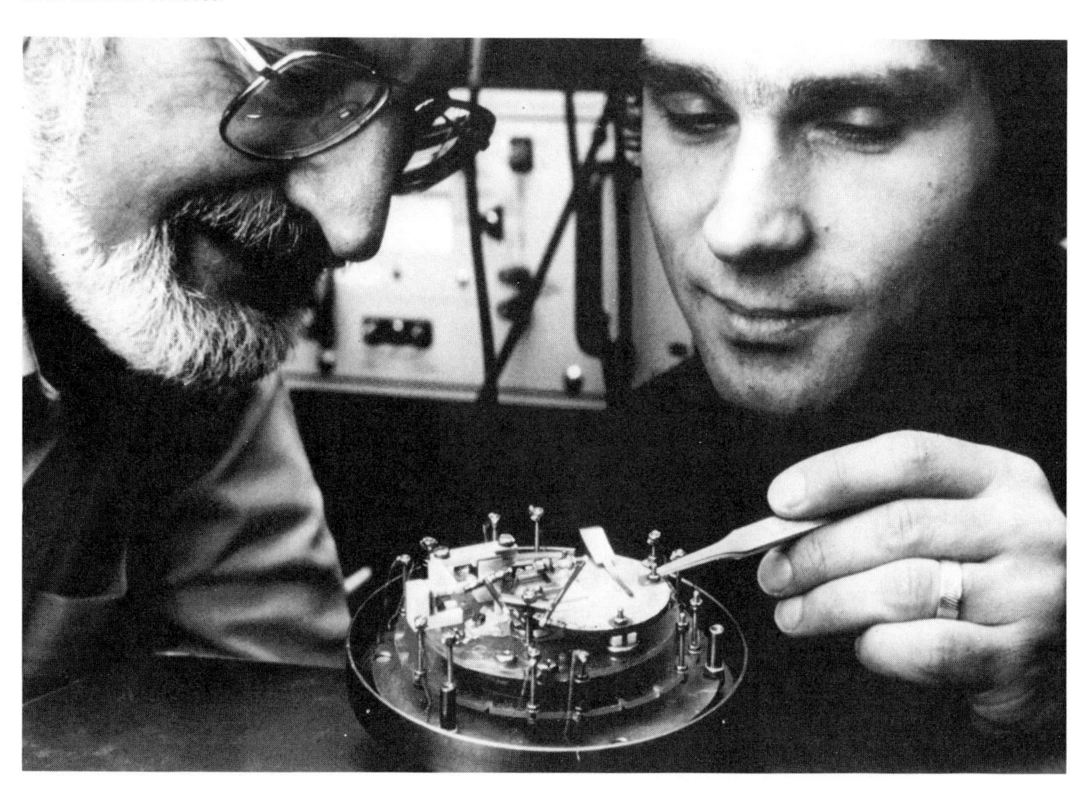

Science Year Close-Up

Life in 2-D

An Ardean raises a toast to the planiverse.

Let us imagine a vast, expanding bubble whose surface is speckled with galaxies of billions of flat stars—some with disklike planets in tow. As we approach one of these disks, we begin to make out a variety of flat figures perched on its rim. Some of these forms are dwellings, some are machines, and some are plants and animals—all lined up edge-to-edge on the circumference of their circular world.

We have just made contact with the planiverse, a kind of two-dimensional playground for the imagination. We can wander through the planiverse and its model planet, Arde, only in our imaginations. Our three-dimensional bodies will not fit into the planiverse.

The planiverse, though young, is not exactly new. Its antecedents can be traced to 1884 when an English clergyman, Edwin A. Abbott, published *Flatland*, a book about a tabletop world inhabited by geometric beings who slid about their two-dimensional realm being born, living, and dying without suspecting that a universe of a higher dimension existed. Abbott's tale, an allegory intended to illustrate such human frailties as complacency and prejudice, was riddled with logical inconsistencies. Flatland had no gravity, for example, nor was there any explanation of how its inhabitants got around.

However, these defects were corrected in 1907 by American logician Charles A. Hinton, who improved Abbott's world in a book entitled *An Episode in Flatland*, which laid out the kind of world that I have eagerly been exploring. An early account of my diversions, published in the July 1980 issue of *Scientific American*, generated from readers a fund of two-dimensional theories and system designs, many of which I have incorporated into a forthcoming book, *The Planiverse*.

The planiverse, like our universe, began with a big bang and is still expanding, but the gravity that holds it together is somewhat different. Planiverse gravity follows an inverse linear law rather than the inverse square law of our universe. Using this law, physicists have calculated that the planiverse must cease to expand and eventually collapse back on itself.

Until this day of reckoning, however, life goes on under Arde's semicircular sky. The surface or edge of the planet, which bears an interesting topography of mountains, valleys, and rivers, is considerably altered after each rainfall. Water cannot go around objects, since that could only happen in a three-dimensional world, and therefore accumulates behind rocks on slopes, eventually pushing the rocks to the bottom of the hills. Windstorms have a similarly disruptive effect.

However, the Ardeans have evolved to survive in these rather inhospitable environs. They are roughly triangular creatures with binocular vision provided by an eye on either side of their apex. Nonetheless, life is no visual feast—their view is limited to the closest edge of the nearest linear object.

These visual limitations account for the fact that Ardeans have two pairs of arms—one pair on either side of the body. This allows them to see what they are doing whenever they are carrying something in two hands. If they raised two opposing arms like ours, their visual field would be cut off.

Ardean locomotion is a simpler proposition. They propel themselves along the horizon with a series of sideways hops and are never required to pursue complicated directions. They can only go east or west; up or down. North and south do not exist on Arde.

The absence of a third dimension in which to expand has forced difficult social decisions upon the Ardeans as their numbers have grown. Rather than wreak havoc on the environment by erecting cities of skyscrapers, they have gone underground, constructing habitats and transportation systems.

It is these systems and the machines that operate within them which show the greatest hope of becoming useful to us. I have received designs for Ardean steam engines, rockets, and internal combustion engines from scientists and laypeople. These plans can be used to construct three-dimensional machines from thin materials. Such machines may prove valuable in situations where there is limited room, such as on space flights.

We need not feel guilty for exploiting Ardean technology; some fourth-dimensional beings may be similarly adapting our humble third-dimensional technology. [A. K. Dewdney]

Physics

Continued

A 30-meter (100-foot) electron accelerator is the heart of Lawrence Livermore National Laboratory's Flash X-ray (FXR) machine, the most powerful X-ray device in the United States. Intense bursts of rays from the FXR will photograph nonnuclear explosions inside nuclear warhead models.

depend upon their energy levels. More energetic electrons are farther from the nucleus than less energetic ones.

An electron's position also depends upon the coulomb interaction that other electrons exert on it. The presence of these forces complicates the job of calculating electron positions tremendously. In fact, the only easy such calculation is that of determining the distance from the nucleus of a hydrogen atom's single electron.

Herrick and Kellman devised a picture that simplifies calculations for a helium atom, which has two electrons. The picture describes what happens when both electrons are excited simultaneously from their lowest energy state into a higher energy state. Physicists have understood that each electron then occupies one of many energy substates—energy levels that differ slightly from one another—but they had found it extremely difficult to simply describe the likely relative positions of the electrons.

Herrick and Kellman depict the doubly excited atom as rod-shaped, with the nucleus at the center and the electrons at the ends. This rod can make two kinds of small movements. It can rotate about the nucleus or it can bend at the nucleus.

Exciting one electron changes the rate of rotation of the rod, while the other electron's additional energy causes the bend. The two chemists assume that the motions are relatively independent of one another and therefore associate an individual energy level of the doubly excited atom with a particular rotational energy and a particular bending energy.

Herrick and Kellman were able to group nearly all the combinations of energy substates of the doubly excited helium atom into this classification scheme, indicating that their picture might closely resemble the actual arrangement of excited atoms. This scheme also provides an idea of the appearance of atoms that have many excited electrons, so it may help to simplify the calculations necessary to determine the relative motions of such electrons. [Raymond Orbach]

Psychology

In April 1982 researchers at Rockefeller University in New York City reported evidence relating to the concept of a set point, or natural weight level, for each individual. For years, psychologists have struggled with the problem of why some obese individuals cannot lose weight. Their efforts have centered on motivating these people to diet and modify their eating habits. But many scientists now believe certain individuals cannot lose weight permanently despite sincere dieting efforts because their bodies are made to be an above-normal weight.

Michael J. Lyons and five other researchers at Rockefeller University discovered that, at least in mice, the set point might be altered by the effects of viral illness in the brain. While testing the effects of canine distemper virus on mice, they noticed that some animals became unusually fat after recovering from the virus. Autopsies on the mice revealed no abnormalities in brain areas known to regulate appetite. However, levels of one category of brain chemicals, catecholamines, were abnormally low. Lyons and his colleagues suggest the virus disrupted a catecholamine pathway in the brain, which they believe regulates weight gain. The researchers believe similar viruses might account for some cases of obesity in children and adults.

Eye movements. University of Michigan psychologists John Jonides, David E. Irwin, and Steven Yantis reported in January 1982 on how we combine information from different visual fixations into one image.

Psychologists know the eyeball moves in rapid jumps from one point in the visual field to another. For example, the eyes of a person who is reading make several jerky movements, called saccades, each second. Every time the eyes hold still, the brain receives a "snapshot."

To explore how the brain puts all these snapshotlike fixations together, the University of Michigan researchers asked volunteers to pinpoint the location of a missing dot in a matrix made up of five rows that should contain five dots each. The psychologists did not present the volunteers with a complete image of the matrix. Instead they flashed on a screen two separate exposures, $\frac{4}{100}$ second apart. Each contained 12 of the 24 dots. To find the missing dot, the volunteers had to combine the information from the two flashes into a single mental image.

The volunteers began by focusing their eyes on a mark on a screen directly in front of them. The first flash occurred off to one side of this mark. The psychologists had instructed the volunteers to shift their focus instantly to the point where this first image appeared. The second image then flashed $\frac{4}{100}$ second later at the same place as the first. Because the volunteers had been staring straight ahead when the first image flashed, the psychologists knew that each pattern of 12 dots had fallen onto slightly different locations within the eye.

The volunteers reported that they saw a single display of 24 dots rather than two separate images, and they easily located the missing dot. Jonides, Irwin, and Yantis believe this shows that the brain matches up information from different visual fixations within a split second. They theorize that the resulting integrated image is stored in a very short-term memory system. Information instantly played back from this memory system, not "snapshots" from our eyes, tells us what we see when we look at the world.

Psychologists Eileen Kowler of Rutgers University in New Brunswick, N.J., and Albert J. Martins of the University of Maryland in Baltimore reported in February 1982 on another study of eye movements. They were interested in finding out if the eye movements of preschoolers differed from those of adults.

They found there was a major difference. Their primary subjects—two children, ages 4 and 5—were not nearly as accurate as adults at directing their saccades.

Kowler and Martins asked the children to focus upon a dot of light in a dark room as though they were looking at a star and then monitored their eye movements with special equipment. The children's gaze wandered 100 times as much as did that of adults.

Adults are able to pick out details of a visual scene because they can direct their eye movements accurately to any area of the visual field. Kowler and

Martins point out that children who have problems guiding their saccades will not be able to "acquire information from a visual display." This may be one reason why some preschoolers have a hard time learning how to read.

Does weather affect your mood? If so, it might be due to changes in concentrations of positive ions, according to research reported in September 1981 by psychologists Jonathan M. Charry of Rockefeller University and Frank B. W. Hawkinshire V of New York University. High concentrations of positive ions, atoms that have been stripped of electrons, appear during severe weather conditions, such as strong hot winds.

For years, scientists have suspected a relationship between human behavior and powerful seasonal winds, such as the Santa Ana winds of California, chinook winds of the Pacific Northwest, and sirocco winds in Italy. Various studies have shown that these winds are accompanied by an upsurge in crimes, suicides, and accidents. These same weather conditions appear also to cause sleeplessness, nausea, or vomiting in some individuals.

To explore the possible effects of differing ion concentrations, Charry and Hawkinshire placed human volunteers inside a large chamber into which the psychologists could pump ions and carefully control their levels. The volunteers believed they were participating in a test of pilot and driver errors, because the psychologists did not want them to anticipate changes in mood.

Each volunteer spent 1½ hours in the ion chamber for each of two days, pressing a button whenever a red light came on. During this time, the psychologists raised or lowered ion concentrations. Charry and Hawkinshire found that high elevations of ions produced irritability, feelings of nausea, and diminished ability to concentrate on driving or piloting tasks in some volunteers whose nervous systems were particularly sensitive.

Most people would not be surprised to hear that weather affects mood. The more important finding is that ions can affect some people's ability to con-

"Stress!"

Psychology

Continued

centrate on activities of life-and-death importance, such as driving cars.

Mind over matter. Two University of Rochester researchers, psychiatrist Robert Ader and microbiologist Nicholas Cohen, reported in March 1982 that the body's immune system responds to learning and that this may have implications for the treatment of defective immune responses.

The immune system is a complex search-and-destroy system devoted to fighting disease. Beginning in 1975, Ader and Cohen conducted experiments that showed rats could learn to shut off their immune responses. The 1982 study showed this learned immunosuppression could affect a disease called systemic lupus erythematosus (SLE), which is caused when the immune system turns against the body.

For the experiment, the scientists used rats specially bred to be afflicted with SLE. These rats die young unless treated with some immunosuppressive drug. Ader and Cohen divided the rats into three groups and gave one group water sweetened with saccharin, followed quickly by an injection of an immunosuppressive drug. They did this at the same time every day. After several months, they reduced the drug dose to levels that were not adequate for preventing SLE. The rats continued to receive saccharin water at the same time each day. As long as the researchers continued to give them saccharin, along with the greatly reduced drug dose, these rats proved just as resistant to SLE as a second group, which received large doses of the drug and no saccharin water.

The scientists gave a third group of rats saccharin and the immunosuppressive drug at different times, so the rats never learned to associate the sweet-tasting substance with immunosuppression. When the scientists cut back the drug dose, these rats died.

Although a great deal more research remains to be done in this area, the Ader and Cohen findings suggest a tie between learning and health, adding one more reason to believe that mental processes can affect physical well-being. [Russell A. Dewey]

Public Health

A 19-year study reported in November 1981 provided evidence that a diet rich in a substance called beta-carotene may reduce the risk of lung cancer. Beta-carotene is found in carrots, in dark-green leafy vegetables such as broccoli and spinach, and in yellow and red fruits and vegetables such as peaches and tomatoes. It is converted to vitamin A in the body.

The study, which began in 1957, was done by epidemiologist Richard B. Shekelle and others at Rush-Presbyterian-St. Luke's Medical Center and Northwestern University School of Medicine in Chicago, Harvard Medical School in Boston, and the University of Michigan in Ann Arbor.

Shekelle's team analyzed the dietary intake of 1,954 middle-aged male employees of the Western Electric Company. Nutritionists obtained information about each man's diet, using both a personal interview and a questionnaire given to the family homemaker. Analysis of the data indicated that the risk of lung cancer was lower among men who ate large amounts of beta-carotene, even among those who had smoked cigarettes for many years.

Among the 488 men who had the lowest levels of beta-carotene in their diet, there were 14 cases of lung cancer. Among the 488 men who had the highest levels of beta-carotene intake, only two men had lung cancer. Other nutritional intake, including consumption of vitamin A itself, was similar among the men who developed lung cancer and among those who did not.

The record on abortion. Since 1973, abortion has been legal and generally available throughout the United States. Physician Willard Cates, Jr., of the U.S. Centers for Disease Control (CDC) in Atlanta, Ga., reviewed the public health effects of the first decade of legalized abortion in a report published in March 1982.

Perhaps the most heartening finding was an overall decline in illness and death among women of childbearing age between 1972 and 1979. The number of abortion-related deaths in the United States dropped from 90 to 29 during this period. The number of

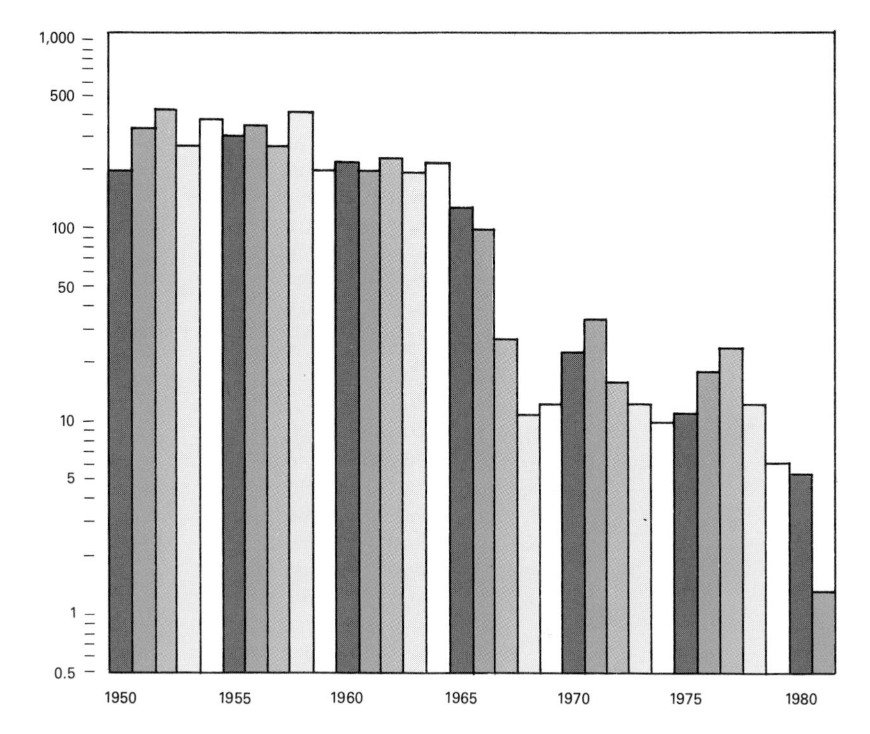

Measles Fading
The incidence of measles in the United States hit a record low in 1981, falling to 1.3 cases per 100,000 population. That was a 99.4 per cent drop from the average yearly rate of 315 cases per 100,000 before 1963, when a measles vaccine was first introduced.

women hospitalized because of abortion complications also declined.

The factors responsible for making abortion safer include the increased skill of physicians, who gained more experience in performing abortions after they became legal, and the more favorable conditions under which medically supervised abortions are performed. Also important in reducing the risks are better anesthetic techniques and surgical methods.

Although the overall evidence regarding the health impact of abortion is favorable, Cates reported some less encouraging findings. Preliminary data indicated that women who have repeated abortions may have an increased risk of miscarriage in subsequent pregnancies. An additional concern is that interrupted pregnancies may fail to provide the health benefits of full-term pregnancies, such as a reduced risk of breast cancer.

The fight against leprosy. The long-held belief that leprosy, also called Hansen's disease, has been controlled began to fade in 1981 and 1982. The disease is only mildly contagious, but there are still about 12 million cases of leprosy worldwide. In the United States alone, the incidence has more than tripled since 1965.

The organism that causes the disease is *Mycobacterium leprae*, a rod-shaped bacterium of the type called a bacillus. *M. leprae* has begun to develop resistance to dapsone, the chief drug used to treat leprosy. In January 1982, the CDC reported that as many as 40 per cent of the bacillus samples obtained from patients in southern India were resistant to the drug.

Although the organism *M. leprae* was identified more than a century ago, it was difficult to study because scientists were unable to grow the bacillus in a laboratory or to infect animals with it. In November 1981, however, workers at the Institute for Experimental Biology and Medicine in Borstel, West Germany, reported that they had succeeded in growing *M. leprae* in a culture medium derived from peat moss.

In 1979, a research team headed by microbiologists Peter J. Gerone of the

Public Health
Continued

Delta Regional Primate Research Center in Covington, La., and Wayne M. Meyers of the Armed Forces Institute of Pathology in Washington, D.C., successfully transmitted the disease to a central African monkey called a mangabey. Because of the similarities between monkeys and human beings, the mangabey will provide an ideal subject for studying leprosy.

This new ability to infect mammals with *M. leprae* will also provide the large amounts of leprosy bacilli needed to develop a vaccine, which will be made from bacilli killed by extreme heat. In two separate studies in 1960, epidemiologist Charles C. Shepard of the CDC and researcher Maurice J. Lefford of the Trudeau Institute in Saranac Lake, N.Y., found that guinea pigs injected with heat-killed *M. leprae* exhibited the delayed hypersensitivity reaction, an immune response characteristic of successful vaccination.

The World Health Organization (WHO), a specialized agency of the United Nations, will begin safety trials of an experimental leprosy vaccine in the fall or winter of 1982. WHO investigators will first give the vaccine to healthy volunteers in Europe and the United States. After they have determined the appropriate dose, public health workers will administer the vaccine in developing countries in much more extensive trials.

A leprosy vaccine may be useful not only in preventing the disease, but also in treating it, according to research performed at the Dermatological Institute in Caracas, Venezuela, and reported in February 1982. The Venezuelan experimenters, led by physician Jacinto Convit, gave repeated injections of leprosy vaccine to patients who already had lepromatous leprosy, the most severe form of the disease. The vaccine cleared bacilli from the patients' bloodstream within 18 months and halted the development of skin lesions. Although there is no precedent in public health for using a vaccine against a disease as rare as leprosy, the disease's increasing resistance to drugs may soon make vaccination a necessity. [Michael H. Alderman]

Science Awards

Eight scientists—five Americans, two Swedes, and a Japanese—were awarded Nobel Prizes for chemistry, physics, and physiology or medicine in 1981. The awards were presented in formal ceremonies in Stockholm, Sweden, on Oct. 19, 1981. The cash value of each award was about $180,000.

Chemistry. The Nobel Prize for Chemistry was shared by two scientists—a Japanese whose work in explaining chemical reactions had gone virtually unrecognized for decades and an American who independently developed similar theories. The winners were Kenichi Fukui, professor of physical chemistry at Kyoto University in Japan, and Roald Hoffmann, chairman of the Department of Chemistry at Cornell University in Ithaca, N.Y.

Each scientist applied the principle of quantum mechanics, a sophisticated mathematical theory of the behavior of particles in the subatomic world, in a way that made it possible to predict the outcomes of a wide range of chemical reactions. Fukui's major contribution, his "frontier orbitals" theory involving electrons, showed that the chemical reactivity of molecules is greatly affected by certain properties of the electron orbits of atoms in the molecule. Fukui reported his theory more than 25 years ago but it was largely ignored by the scientific community.

Scientists attribute this neglect to the fact that Fukui's papers were published in Japanese journals that few international chemists read. Also, the mathematics were beyond the comprehension of most practicing chemists.

Hoffmann also developed a theory about electron orbits that gave practicing chemists a basis on which to predict the outcomes of many organic chemical reactions by using certain rules. The theory was developed in collaboration with Robert B. Woodward, winner of the 1965 Nobel Prize for his work in synthetic organic chemistry. Their Woodward-Hoffmann rule governs reactions in organic chemistry. It was based upon their discovery that the major factor in determining chemical reactions was the motion of the electrons surrounding the atomic nu-

Major Awards and Prizes

Winners of the Nobel Prizes and their work are treated more fully in the first portion of this section.

AAAS-Newcomb Cleveland Prize (oceanography): Robert Axelrod, William D. Hamilton

AAAS Scientific Freedom and Responsibility Award: Morris Baslow, Paul Berg, Maxine Singer, Norton Zinder

AAAS Socio-Psychological Prize: Gary W. Strong

ACS Award in Petroleum Chemistry: Irving Wender

Amateur Achievement Award (astronomy): Ben Mayer

American Institute of Physics-United States Steel Foundation (science writing): Marcia F. Bartusiak

Apker Award: Mark Ritter

APS High Polymer Prize: Sir Samuel Edwards, Pierre Gilles-de Gennes

Arthur Cope Award (chemistry): Frank H. Westheimer

Association of American Medical Colleges Award (biomedical sciences): J. Michael Bishop

Ayerst Award (molecular biology): W. Ford Doolittle

Boehringer Manheim Prize (molecular biology): Michael Smith

Bonner Prize (nuclear physics): Gerald E. Brown

Bowie Medal (geophysics): Henry M. Stommel

Bruce Medal (astronomy): E. Margaret Burbidge

Buckley Solid State Physics Prize: Bertrand I. Halperin

Charles Doolittle Walcott Medal (geology): Martin F. Glaessner

Collier Trophy (astronautics): Space Shuttle team — National Aeronautics and Space Administration, Rockwell International Corporation, Marietta Corporation, Thiokol Corporation, and entire government and industry team.

Delmer S. Fahrney Medal (telecommunications): Arthur M. Bueche

Elliott Cresson Medal (chemistry): M. King Hubbert

Ewing Medal (geophysics): John I. Ewing

Fermi Award: W. Bennett Lewis

Franklin Medal (physics): Stephen W. Hawking

Gairdner Awards (medicine): Michael S. Brown, Georges J. Köhler, Wai Yiu Cheung, Elizabeth Neufeld, Saul Roseman, Bengt Samuelsson, Louis Siminovitch, Jerry H.-C. Wang, César Milstein, Joseph L. Goldstein

Garvan Medal (chemistry): Sara Jane Rhoads

George H. Henderson Medal (engineering): Louis T. Klauder

Gilbert Morgan Smith Medal (biology): Luigi Provasoli

G. K. Warren Prize (geology): John T. Hack

Goddard Award (astronautics): John F. Yardley

Hazen Award (medicine): Aaron B. Lerner

Heineman Prize for Mathematical Physics: John C. Ward

Horton Medal (geophysics): John R. Philip

Horwitz Prize (biology): Aaron Klug

Howard N. Potts Medal (chemistry): A. Uno Lamm

James Craig Watson Medal (astronomy): Stanton J. Peale

Klumpke-Roberts Award (contributions to public understanding of astronomy): Bart J. Bok

Lasker Awards: basic research, Barbara McClintock; clinical research, Louis Sokoloff

Lilly Award (microbiology): Thomas E. Shenk

Louis E. Levy Medal (economics): George Leitmann, Henry Y. Wan, Jr.

Luck Award (scientific reviewing): Victor A. McKusick

Macelwane Award (geophysics): Rafael Luis Bras, Donald W. Forsyth, Steven C. Wofsy

Marvin J. Johnson Award (chemistry): Stanley N. Cohen

Mary Clark Thomson Medal (geology or paleontology): William A. Berggren

Michelson Medal (optics): Hermann P. J. Haken

NAE Founders Award (engineering): Jacob P. Den Hartog

NAS Award for Initiatives in Research: Kerry E. Sieh

NAS Award in Chemical Sciences: Gilbert Stork

NAS Public Welfare Medal: Paul G. Rogers

Nobel Prize: chemistry, Kenichi Fukui, Roald Hoffmann; physics, Nicolaas Bloembergen, Arthur L. Schawlow, Kai Siegbahn; psychology or medicine, David H. Hubel, Torsten N. Wiesel, Roger W. Sperry

Oersted Medal (physics teaching): I. I. Rabi

Oppenheimer Memorial Prize (physics): Robert E. Marshak, Maurice Goldhaber Perkin Medal (chemistry): Howard C. Brown

Pierce Prize (astronomy): Marc Davis

Pisart Vision Award: Louise L. Sloan, Eleanor E. Faye

Priestley Medal (chemistry): Bryce L. Crawford, Jr.

Ross G. Harrison Prize (biology): Donald D. Brown

Selman A. Waksman Award (microbiology): I. C. Gunsalus

Speedy Award (medicine): Inder Perkash

Stuart Ballantine Medal: Amos E. Joel, Jr.

3M Life Sciences Award (biology): G. Bernard Amos

Trumpler Prize (astronomy): Bruce Twarog

USDA Award (nutrition): Hamish N. Munro

U. S. Steel Foundation Award (molecular biology): Joan A. Steitz

Vetlesen Prize (geophysics): M. King Hubbert

Waterford Biomedical Science Award: A. Dale Kaiser

Wetherill Medal: Frank F. Fang, Alan B. Fowler, Webster E. Howard, Frank Stern, Phillip J. Stiles

Wolf Prize in Medicine: Barbara McClintock, Stanley N. Cohen

Science Year Close-Up

A Chemical Centenary

Joel H. Hildebrand

Professor of Chemistry Joel H. Hildebrand of the University of California, Berkeley, in 1981 celebrated a milestone in a career as remarkable as it is long. During the year, he published the latest in a lengthy series of scientific papers—and on November 16, he celebrated his 100th birthday.

Hildebrand has said he considers having taught chemistry to 40,000 freshman students his proudest academic achievement, but many other accomplishments mark his career. He received the Ph.D. degree from the University of Pennsylvania in Philadelphia in 1906, then after doing research in Germany, served on his alma mater's faculty until 1913. In that year, he joined the faculty at Berkeley and became one of a small group of scientists who established its renowned Chemistry Department.

Hildebrand served as president of the American Chemical Society in 1955, and received its highest award, the Priestley Medal, in 1961. Reflecting his abiding interest in the advancement of scientific thought, Hildebrand served as associate editor of the *Journal of the American Chemical Society*, the *Journal of Physical Chemistry*, and the *Journal of Chemical Education.*

His accomplishments outside his profession are equally impressive. After teaching himself to ski, he became manager of the United States Olympic Ski Team in 1936. As president of the Sierra Club from 1937 to 1940, he was a prime mover in establishing Kings Canyon National Park in California.

As a research chemist, Hildebrand made the first investigations of a variety of phenomena in his favorite field of interest, the chemistry and physics of liquids. The American Chemical Society's new Hildebrand Award, created in his honor and presented to him in 1981, will be given annually to the scientist doing the best work in that field. [Richard M. Lemmon]

clei, rather than some property of the nuclei themselves.

Physics. The Nobel Prize for Physics was awarded to three scientists. Nicolaas Bloembergen of Harvard University in Cambridge, Mass., and Arthur L. Schawlow of Stanford University in Palo Alto, Calif., shared half the prize and the other half went to physicist Kai Siegbahn of Uppsala University in Sweden.

Bloembergen and Schawlow were cited for their contribution to the development of laser spectroscopy. (Laser spectroscopy involves aiming a beam of laser light at a substance and determining what atoms are present by analyzing the wavelength of radiation emitted from the substance that has absorbed energy from the beam.) Schawlow, one of the inventors of the laser, had refined its use to allow "extremely high precision" in the study of substances. Bloembergen was cited for "having drastically extended the range" of wavelengths accessible to laser spectroscopy studies by generating laser light outside the visible range at both the infrared and ultraviolet ends of the spectrum.

Siegbahn, the second member of his family to win a Nobel Prize, was cited for "his contribution to the development of high-resolution electron spectroscopy." His father, Karl M. G. Siegbahn, won the 1924 Nobel Prize for Physics for the use of X rays in similar work.

Physiology or Medicine. The Nobel Prize for Physiology or Medicine was awarded to three scientists who were honored for research that greatly enhanced knowledge about the functioning of the human brain.

Half the prize was divided between Harvard University's David H. Hubel and Torsten N. Wiesel—still a Swedish citizen although he has worked in the United States since the 1950s. Together they discovered that the ability of the human visual system to interpret images is developed immediately after birth and that distorted visual experience during the early stages of life can permanently impair the brain's ability to process visual information.

Science Awards
Continued

The work of these two scientists demonstrated that the brain's processing of images is far more complex and less directly pictorial than had previously been thought.

The other half of the Nobel Prize for Physiology or Medicine was given to Roger W. Sperry of the California Institute of Technology for research that identified the separate and independent functions of the left and right hemispheres of the human brain. In most individuals, the left half of the brain controls logical, analytical thought; speaking and writing; and mathematical calculations. It also controls the right side of the body and, because it controls the nervous system, is considered the dominant hemisphere. The right half, which controls the left side of the body, is in charge of creative and artistic thinking, spatial relationships, and the interpretation and comprehension of music.

Sperry was the first to show that when the two halves of the brain are separated, one side is often unaware of the other's functions. The patients he studied had already undergone operations to sever the corpus callosum, the thick bundle of nerve fibers that normally connect the right and left hemispheres of the brain. The surgery had been done to halt serious epileptic seizures for which all other treatment had proved ineffective.

In his experiments, Sperry let a patient see a dollar sign with the left eye while the right eye saw a question mark. When Sperry asked the patient to draw what he saw with his left hand, the patient drew a dollar sign. When Sperry asked the patient what he saw, however, the patient replied, "A question mark." Speech is usually controlled by the brain's left hemisphere, and the question mark observed by the right eye was the only information available to it.

The work done by the three scientists has led to major revisions in the understanding of the human brain. In each case, the work has also spurred many others to pursue the same basic lines of research and to branch out into related areas. [Irene B. Keller]

Space Exploration

The National Aeronautics and Space Administration's (NASA) space shuttle *Columbia* completed its series of test flights with a flawless fourth mission. U.S. Navy Captain Thomas K. Mattingly 2nd, 46, and Henry W. Hartsfield, Jr., 48, piloted the craft from June 27 to July 4, 1982, on its best flight yet. Now the shuttle can begin deploying and servicing satellites and carrying out scientific and industrial experiments.

Columbia's second flight in 1981 was planned to extend mission length from 54 hours to 124 hours. Prior to the launch, a high-volume water spray was installed on the launch pad. It sprayed the pad with 265,000 liters (70,000 gallons) of water per minute to reduce the violent backwash of rocket exhaust that had shaken *Columbia* severely on its first launch.

With U.S. Air Force Colonel Joseph H. Engle, 49, a pioneer X-15 rocket plane pilot, and U.S. Navy Captain Richard H. Truly, 44, on the flight deck, the mission began on Nov. 12, 1981. *Columbia* had just reached cruising altitude at 254 kilometers (157.5 miles) when one of three fuel cell batteries that supply its electricity failed. Although *Columbia* could fly safely on the remaining two batteries, flight controllers at Mission Control in Houston reduced the mission to 54 hours. Working furiously, Engle and Truly managed to complete most of the flight test program.

One task was to test the 15-meter (50-foot) Canadian-built Remote Manipulator System (RMS), which was carried in the cargo bay. The RMS is an electronically controlled mechanical arm with shoulder, elbow, and wrist joints, like the human arm, and a grasping end-effector, or hand. It was designed to lift satellites from the cargo bay, deploy them in space, and retrieve them for repair in orbit or return to Earth. Despite the shortened time in orbit, the astronauts tested the RMS successfully.

The most spectacular mission results were continuous photographic strips of the Mediterranean Sea and Australia made by an experimental radar camera. The device produced detailed images of Earth's surface through clouds and at night.

The second flight ended when *Columbia* landed smoothly on Rogers Dry Lake at Edwards Air Force Base in California's Mojave Desert early on Nov. 14, 1981.

A technician applies a waterproofing spray to the heat shield of the *Columbia* space shuttle during the orbiter's preflight preparation.

***Columbia*'s third test flight,** scheduled for seven days in orbit, began on March 22, 1982, with U.S. Marine Corps Colonel Jack R. Lousma, 46, a veteran of *Skylab 3*, and U.S. Air Force Colonel C. Gordon Fullerton, 45, as the orbiter's crew.

Columbia's prime landing site in California could not be used because of rain-soaked runways. Then a sandstorm at the alternative landing site at White Sands Missile Range in New Mexico forced the ship to remain in orbit an extra day. On March 30, the weather cleared at White Sands and *Columbia* landed smoothly, partly under automatic control, after 8 days and 4 minutes aloft.

The ship was flown back to Florida on April 6 aboard its Boeing 747 carrier aircraft. Despite loss of 38 heat-shield tiles at launch and failure of part of the main radio transmission channel, two critical television cameras, and the toilet—plus a leaking nitrogen tank—NASA declared the mission a success. It had achieved its two main objectives. One was the first use of the manipulator arm, which lifted a plasma, or electrified particle, monitor out of its niche in the cargo bay and held it aloft 14 meters (45 feet). Also, the orbiter proved its ability to withstand temperature extremes as its nose, tail, and topside were turned toward and away from the Sun.

On its third flight, *Columbia* also was tested as a flying laboratory for scientific experiments. One end of the 18-meter (60-foot) cargo bay held a pallet bearing a cluster of scientific instruments. These were designed to study the ionosphere, the electrified region of space at the upper boundary of the Earth's atmosphere. The 241-kilometer (150-mile) altitude at which *Columbia* cruised was in the middle of this region, which extends from about 80 to 480 kilometers (50 to 300 miles) above the Earth. *Columbia*'s instruments recorded changes in the ship's electrical charge as it passed through the ionosphere, observed ultraviolet and X-ray emissions on the Sun, collected dust, and identified contaminant particles and gases emitted by the spacecraft.

In the cabin were experiments dealing with plant growth and with the behavior of bees and moths in low gravity. The bees perished but the moths survived in an experiment designed by 18-year-old Todd E. Nelson, a senior at Southland High School in Adams, Minn.

NASA announced two crew assignments for flights of the second space shuttle orbiter, *Challenger*, scheduled for 1983. Astronaut Sally Ride, 30, a physicist, will be the first American woman to fly in space. She was named to the crew of the seventh shuttle flight as mission specialist. The first black astronaut to win a flight assignment is U.S. Air Force Lieutenant Colonel Guion S. Bluford, who was posted to the eighth shuttle mission.

Russian activities continued while NASA was putting the shuttle through its paces. The Soviet Union completed 44 months of manned use of the *Salyut 6* space station in 1981. *Salyut 6* was closed out on May 26, when its last crew, cosmonauts Viktor Savinykh and Vladimir Kovalyonok, returned from a 75-day stay in space. Eleven months later, on April 19, 1982, they launched *Salyut 7* for a new round of long-term research. The first crew to use it was launched on May 13 in a new *Soyuz T-5* spacecraft. The commander was Lieutenant Colonel Anatoli Berezovoy, and the pilot was Valentin Lebedev.

Russia landed the first automated soil samplers on Venus on March 1 and 5, 1982. The *Venera 13* and *Venera 14* landers came down in the Phoebe region of Venus, south of the planet's equator. A preliminary sample analysis showed the surface was ordinary basalt, an igneous rock covering the ocean floor on Earth and the maria, or seas, on the Moon. Close-up photographs sent back by the landers showed a barren, Moonlike surface. See ASTRONOMY, Solar System.

U.S. planetary exploration continued with the *Voyager 2* grand tour of the outer planets. The probe encountered Saturn on June 5, 1981, and made its

Space Exploration

Continued

Lacking a coat of white paint – and the 245 kilograms (540 pounds) it added to *Columbia*'s weight – the orbiter's external fuel tank is moved to Kennedy Space Center's Vehicle Assembly Building prior to the third test flight.

closest approach on August 25 at an altitude of 101,000 kilometers (63,000 miles) above the clouds. The spacecraft's cameras confirmed the multiple-strand structure of several rings.

Studies of the *Voyager* photos raised the number of confirmed Saturnian moons to 21; 3 more were tentatively identified. Scientists confirmed that Titan, Saturn's planet-sized moon, has a nitrogen atmosphere denser than Earth's and temperatures low enough to liquefy methane, so that methane seas, rain, or snow may exist. *Voyager 2* sailed on to Uranus, which will be its next port of call in January 1986.

Meanwhile, *Pioneer 10*, which made the first close-up survey of Jupiter in 1973, made another significant discovery as it flew between Uranus and Neptune in March 1982. Its tiny radio continued to transmit important new findings about the extent and behavior of the heliosphere — the Sun's atmosphere. Scientists hope that *Pioneer 10* will help them determine the boundary between the heliosphere and true interstellar space.

Scientific satellites. Two drum-shaped *Dynamics Explorer* satellites were launched into polar orbit on Aug. 3, 1981, from Vandenberg Air Force Base in California. Both are designed to study the ionosphere. On June 22, *NOAA-7*, which was designed to measure sea-surface temperatures for the National Oceanic and Atmospheric Administration, was launched from Vandenburg. And on October 16, the *Solar Mesosphere Explorer* satellite was launched to study ozone production at altitudes of 32 to 88.7 kilometers (20 to 55 miles). See EARTH SCIENCES, Meteorology.

Ariane, the European Space Agency's heavy launch vehicle, completed its test series and became operational on Dec. 19, 1981, with the successful fourth test launch from French Guiana. It carried *MARECS*, a European maritime communications satellite. On June 19, its third flight, *Ariane* orbited *Meteosat 2*, Europe's second meteorological satellite, and *Apple*, India's experimental communications satellite. [Richard S. Lewis]

Surgery
See Medicine

Zoology

A birdwatcher's dream came true in November 1981 for Philip Humphrey, director of the University of Kansas Museum of Natural History in Lawrence, and biology professor Max C. Thompson of Southwestern College in Winfield, Kans., when they reported the discovery of *Tachyeres leucocephalus*, the white-headed flightless steamer duck. It is the first new species of duck, goose, or swan to be identified since 1917.

The new species, a stocky duck with a heavy head and thick neck, lives among the rocks, kelp, and seals of the Chubut coast on the Atlantic Ocean in Argentina. Humphrey and Thompson named this species *leucocephalus* (Greek for *white head*) because the male's head has a distinctive white color during most of the year. The female's head is dark brown. Males, which weigh slightly more than females, average 4 kilograms (8.5 pounds). The battleship-gray body and yellow-orange bill and legs make this duck barely distinguishable from the three other known species of steamer ducks.

Like two of the other species, this duck cannot fly, but escapes predators by surface swimming, or "steaming." Its fancied resemblance to a sidewheeler steamboat is responsible for the duck's name. When they are frightened, these ducks escape from enemies by using long, alternating swimming strokes made with their powerful webbed feet and a synchronous oaring motion in which their wing tips strike the water. "When you get a flock of 40 or 50 ducks steaming together, all you can see is spray," said Humphrey.

Until Humphrey and Thompson's report, the white-headed flightless steamer duck had been confused with both the Magellanic flightless steamer duck, which lives farther south, and another species found on the Falkland Islands. By comparing the skeletal structure, weight, bill length, wing length, plumage, and genetic makeup, Humphrey and Thompson determined that the Chubut coast duck is unique.

Whose gaur was this ox? In August 1981, a domestic Holstein cow made

Cancún, the first panda born in captivity in a zoo outside of China to survive, plays with its mother, Ling-Ling, in a cage at Chapultepec Zoo in Mexico City.

Zoology

Continued

At New York City's Bronx Zoo, a Holstein cow that served as surrogate mother tends a gaur, or wild ox, calf that had been transplanted as an embryo to her uterus. The birth is the first of its kind resulting from an embryo transplant between wild and domestic cattle.

history by giving birth to a gaur, a rare wild ox that is native to Southeast Asia. This birth was not a freak accident, but the result of a technique called embryo transfer. Born in New York City's Bronx Zoo, the 33-kilogram (73-pound) male gaur calf was the first endangered wild mammal to have a domestic surrogate mother—an animal that carries a different animal's baby through pregnancy.

Since 1967, cattle breeders have used embryo transfer to boost production of prized cows by surgically implanting embryos from a superior cow into others of lesser quality. Why not use the technique with a wild cow?

With the help of James Evans, head of the Embryo Transfer Service at the University of Pennsylvania School of Veterinary Medicine in Philadelphia, the veterinary staff of the New York Zoological Society in New York City applied this technique to the rarest of wild cattle, *Bos gaurus*. This species, whose adult males weigh up to 900 kilograms (2,000 pounds), is endangered in its native habitats.

Sorry, wrong number. Many animals use songs or calls to attract mates. Unfortunately for them, predators can sometimes home in on the calling sounds and capture the callers. Behaviorists Merlin D. Tuttle of Milwaukee Public Museum and Michael J. Ryan of Langmuir Laboratory at Cornell University in Ithaca, N.Y., reported in November 1981 that the fringe-lipped bat uses acoustic cues to capture calling frogs.

The investigators studied the hunting behavior of the bat in several frog-breeding sites on Barro Colorado Island in the Panama Canal. On a typical evening, the bats captured about six frogs per hour of the genus *Physalaemus*. They were most successful in capturing the prey when many frogs were calling and least successful when no frogs were calling.

In laboratory tests of the ability of frog-eating bats to detect their prey, the researchers played the calls of several frog species on a tape recorder whose two speakers were located in opposite corners of a cage of bats.

They observed the flight of bats to see which frog calls they preferred.

Tuttle and Ryan learned that fringe-lipped bats do not respond to every call, but can discriminate among frog calls. The bats preferred calls of edible frogs over a poisonous toad and preferred calls of a small frog species that they could easily capture to calls of a large frog species. Because large frogs make louder calls, the researchers played the recorded smaller frog calls as loudly as that of larger frogs. But the bats still preferred the smaller frog calls, indicating that they are attracted to the kind of song, not just its volume.

Skewed sex ratios, often in favor of the female, occur among many groups of animals. This imbalance is influenced by both prenatal and postnatal factors. In 1981, several researchers reported on situations in which environmental conditions after fertilization can affect the real — or apparent — proportions of males to females in groups of fish, rats, and birds.

David O. Conover and Boyd E. Kynard of the University of Massachusetts in Amherst reported in July 1981 that the sex of the minnowlike Atlantic silverside was controlled by both the genotype, or genetic makeup, of the fish and the temperature of the water surrounding it during a specific period of its larval stage. The Atlantic silverside, *Menidia menidia*, is commonly found along the eastern North American coast. It breeds in the spring and completes its life cycle in one year.

Over several years, Conover and Kynard were puzzled to find that, though their catches in July in Essex Bay and Salem Harbor in Massachusetts contained many more females than males, they found equal numbers of male and female fish by September. A second confusing observation was that females tended to be larger than males, although previous research showed that under similar conditions both sexes grow at the same rate.

The scientists began in 1980 to raise clutches of eggs under two different sets of experimental conditions. They kept one clutch at cool temperatures similar to the Massachusetts climate in

Having a Grant's zebra for a mother and a donkey for a father gave the 1-week-old "zebroid" born in February in Japan's Tohoku Safari Park the latest fashion look – striped socks.

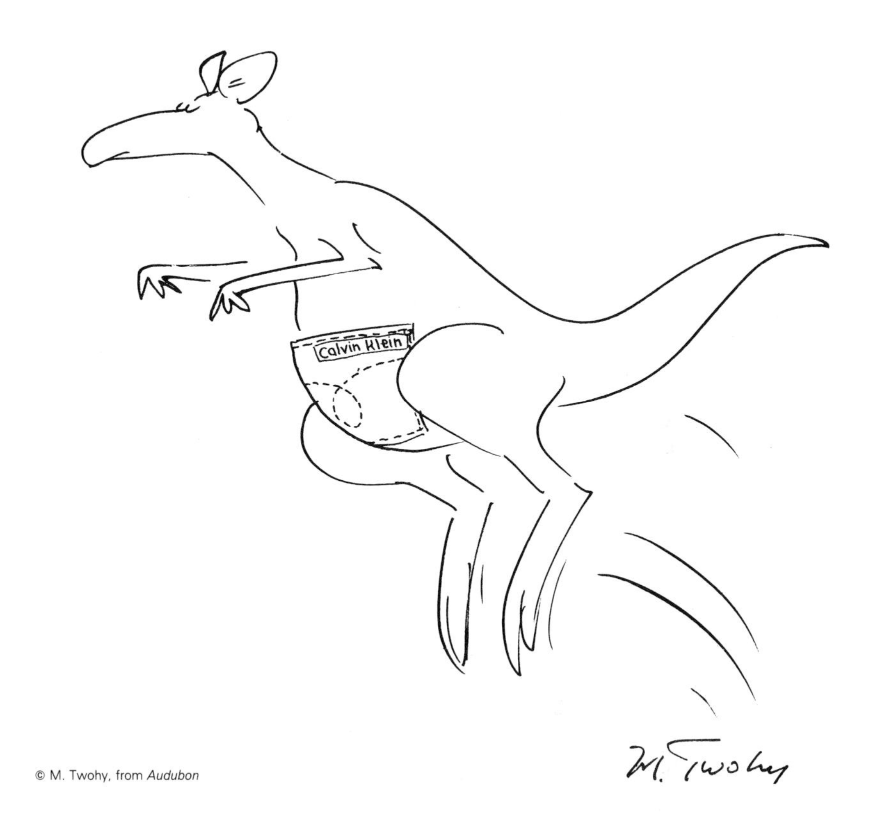

Zoology
Continued

early May. Another clutch was raised in warm conditions at July temperatures. From the eggs raised in May temperatures, many more females than males hatched, while the July temperatures had the opposite effect.

To determine whether temperature affects the sex of a fish after it hatches, the researchers divided newly hatched larvae into two groups. One group was raised in warm water and the other in cool water. Again, higher temperatures resulted in more males, while cooler temperatures resulted in more females. They concluded that water temperature at the larval stage determined a fish's sex.

According to Conover and Kynard, this effect has ecological significance for the Atlantic silverside. Because more females are born earlier, they have a chance to grow larger by the next breeding season than most males, which are born later in the year. And because more males are born later in the year due to the effect of higher water temperatures on larvae, an approximate 1 to 1 ratio between the sexes can be maintained within each year's hatch. Furthermore, when the fish do mate, the larger females have more body mass to devote toward the rigors of reproduction.

Overcrowding or lack of adequate food supplies may explain increased survival of females over males in a litter of nestling wood, or pack, rats. Biologist Polley Ann McClure of Indiana University in Bloomington found that mother wood rats rejected their male young when food was limited. When McClure reduced the diets of mother rats by 50 to 70 per cent, she observed that rather than making sure all the young were gathered for feeding, the mother either ignored the male young or pushed them away from her nipples. Within a few days, these males, now the runts of the litter, were usually found outside the nursing group at mealtime. By the time the young were weaned 20 days later, the males that managed to survive weighed less than their female siblings.

McClure suggested that this sex-biased feeding helps the wood rats to

Zoology

Continued

A white-headed flightless steamer duck, a newly identified fowl species, sends up a spray as it moves rapidly along the waves with its unique surface-swimming motion in the Atlantic Ocean east of Argentina.

survive fluctuations in food levels. When parents lack sufficient food, the health and size of the young are affected. A small, underweight male is not likely to secure and hold territory, and therefore is less likely to attract mates and father young. But a mediocre female can still reproduce successfully enough for the group's survival.

Another skewed sex ratio seems to occur in groups of Western gulls on the Channel Islands off the California coast. In this case, the imbalance may be due to toxic chemicals.

Channel Islands gulls were subjected to massive DDT contamination in 1970. Although gull egg shells are not susceptible to the thinning effects of the insecticide, as are pelican and cormorant eggs, ornithologists D. Michael Fry and C. Kuehler Toone of the University of California at Davis performed an experiment to see if DDT affected reproduction in another way.

The researchers selected birds from other areas with no known DDT contamination. After collecting uncontaminated, unincubated eggs from breeding colonies at Mono Lake in California, Fry and Toone injected 264 eggs with a mixture of corn oil and DDT. Previous tests had shown that this method approximated the effect of contaminants on eggs in the wild.

When the eggs hatched, the researchers found that male gull chicks had been feminized by the pollutants. Ovarylike tissue was found in their testis, or male sex organ. When the scientists injected the eggs with higher doses of pollutant, female shell-producing glands and oviducts developed in males and the size of the testis was reduced. This feminization of male embryos naturally affects their reproductive behavior as adults. Other researchers had demonstrated that feminized adult male birds do not show typical courting behavior. According to Fry and Toone, feminized male gulls may not even migrate to breeding sites. The Western gulls' breeding problems could be a result of two factors—an almost 4 to 1 female to male ratio and female-female adult pairing.

[William J. Bell and Elizabeth Pennisi]

Science You Can Use

In areas selected for their current interest, *Science Year* presents information that the reader as a consumer can use in making decisions — from buying products to caring for personal health and well-being.

Fundamental Facts About Fitness

Fitness is fashionable and the pressure is on. It comes from newspapers, television, and even our neighbors. But underlying much of the hoopla surrounding the fitness craze is the deceptive message that getting fit is so easy that it can be done practically overnight. Even worse, an overwhelming amount of misleading and erroneous information about fitness is published every day. The result is injury, disappointment, and a high dropout rate.

So before you begin a fitness program, you should understand what fitness is and why it is important. Then you can set your goals and decide on an appropriate and sensible program.

First, here are some warnings. Getting fit is not easy. You must set aside time for regular exercise and plan to work hard. And once you have achieved your goal, you should not quit. Getting your body in shape is like buying a car—you have to maintain it to keep it looking good.

There are four generally recognized categories of physical fitness: cardiorespiratory endurance, body composition, flexibility, and strength.

Cardiorespiratory endurance indicates the heart's efficiency in pumping blood to exercising muscles and delivering the oxygen necessary for the muscles to generate energy. This type of fitness also has a bearing on cardiovascular disease, or disease of the heart and blood vessels. Studies have shown that exercise benefiting the cardiovascular system can reduce obesity and lower blood cholesterol levels and blood pressure, factors that increase the risk of cardiovascular disease.

Furthermore, if your heart is working more efficiently, you can do the same or a greater amount of work while expending less energy, rather like driving a more fuel-efficient car.

Body composition—the relative amounts of bone, fat, and muscle in the body—is actually a more accurate measure of a person's body fat than weight alone. But most people do not know how to determine their body composition and so rely on height-weight tables for that information. However, these tables give only average weights for the general population, not ideal weights. So it is possible for a person with a large frame to be overweight according to the table, but not be "overfat." And someone whose weight falls within the range stated in the table could, nevertheless, be carrying too much fat.

The best ways to determine body fat are by weighing a person under water and by measuring the thickness of skin folds at various places on the body. These tests should be done by an exercise physiologist or other expert.

Body composition is closely related to cardiorespiratory endurance, because obesity can increase the risk of high blood pressure and diabetes, which, in turn, increase the risk of cardiovascular disease.

Flexibility is the ability to move the joints in a full range of motion. Most people probably think flexibility is more closely related to athletic performance than to overall health. But lack of flexibility plays an important role in such conditions as lower back pain, injuries to muscles and bones, poor posture, and fatigue.

Strength is the force muscles can exert. The larger and stronger your muscle fibers are, the easier it is to do everyday tasks. And because you use a smaller percentage of your total strength, you become fatigued less easily and so can work harder and longer.

In addition, strength could be a lifesaver in an emergency—if you had to lift someone, for example, or run for help, or even run away. Strength also may be a factor in recovery time after an injury. Although fit people certainly are not immune to injury, they seem to bounce back faster because their bone structure is denser and their connective tissue is tougher.

Achieving fitness in all four categories requires different types of exercise,

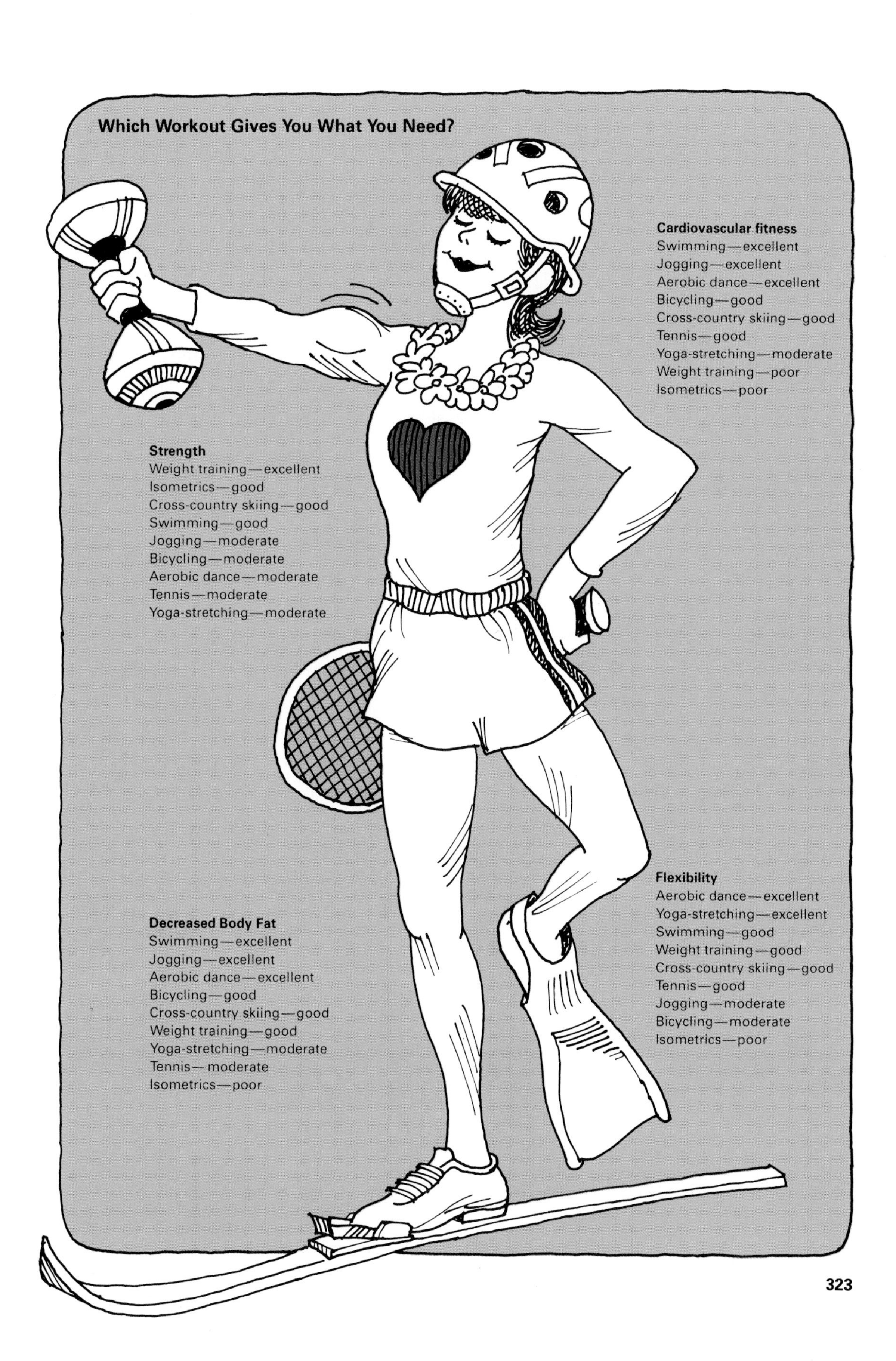
Which Workout Gives You What You Need?
Cardiovascular fitness
Swimming—excellent
Jogging—excellent
Aerobic dance—excellent
Bicycling—good
Cross-country skiing—good
Tennis—good
Yoga-stretching—moderate
Weight training—poor
Isometrics—poor
Strength
Weight training—excellent
Isometrics—good
Cross-country skiing—good
Swimming—good
Jogging—moderate
Bicycling—moderate
Aerobic dance—moderate
Tennis—moderate
Yoga-stretching—moderate
Decreased Body Fat
Swimming—excellent
Jogging—excellent
Aerobic dance—excellent
Bicycling—good
Cross-country skiing—good
Weight training—good
Yoga-stretching—moderate
Tennis—moderate
Isometrics—poor
Flexibility
Aerobic dance—excellent
Yoga-stretching—excellent
Swimming—good
Weight training—good
Cross-country skiing—good
Tennis—good
Jogging—moderate
Bicycling—moderate
Isometrics—poor

although some exercises provide benefits in several categories. To improve your cardiorespiratory endurance, choose an exercise that works the large muscle groups rhythmically and continuously. Such exercise, called aerobic exercise, includes running, swimming, cross-country skiing, and cycling. Walking is also good exercise, but because it is less intense, it takes longer to achieve the same results. Circuit weight training—weight training done with little rest between exercises—and aerobic dancing can also strengthen the cardiorespiratory system. Intermittent activities such as golf or bowling do not increase endurance.

You should exercise three times a week for 15 to 60 minutes at a time. The intensity of the exercise should raise your heart rate to between 60 and 90 per cent of its maximum rate. To compute your maximum rate, subtract your age from 220.

Swimming, jogging, and aerobic dancing are excellent ways to reduce body fat. But for best results, reduce your caloric intake too. In one study of weight reduction that evaluated the benefits of calorie reduction, exercise, and a combination of both, subjects in all three groups showed a similar weight loss. The group that cut calories alone lost weight, body fat, and muscle. But the other two groups lost significantly more body fat and increased their muscle tissue.

At first glance, it seems unfair. A person who both exercises and cuts calories should, theoretically, lose more weight. And, in fact, people who exercise often feel discouraged when they step on the scale. However, a cubic centimeter of muscle weighs more than the same amount of fat. Fat just takes up more space. So substituting a tape measure for the scale would probably be more encouraging.

Flexibility exercises should be a part of any fitness program, especially since some forms of exercise, such as running, can reduce flexibility.

Stretching movements should be used to warm up before strenuous exercise and to cool down afterward. Stretching before exercise increases blood flow to the muscles, gradually preparing them for the demands that will be made on them. Stretching after exercise helps return the body to a resting state, relaxes the muscles, and helps prevent muscle soreness. Remember to stretch the individual muscles gently; do not move your whole body. Pushups and squats are strenuous exercises in themselves; do not use them to warm up.

Weight training is the best way to increase strength. Because studies have shown that strength improves more rapidly when muscles are allowed to rest between workouts, such exercise should be done every other day. The key to increasing strength is overload. You must stress the muscle until it cannot work any longer. If you want to build muscle endurance, or the ability to repeat a task, lift lighter amounts many times. If you want muscular strength, or the ability to lift heavy weights, lift heavier amounts fewer times. Exercising with expensive barbells in a fancy health club is not necessary. You can get the same results with tin cans filled with sand.

The current profusion of fitness books and fitness experts can make choosing an exercise program a bewildering task. Here are some guidelines to help you choose a reliable book on fitness. Does the author have a college degree and experience in the fitness field? Is he or she a teacher at a college or university or a staff member of a fitness organization? Does the book carefully describe the fitness program? Does it provide ideas to motivate you? If it guarantees anything or makes exaggerated claims, beware.

For expert advice, you can call the physical education department of a local college or university and talk to an exercise physiologist. You also can call YMCAs or YWCAs, which have specific requirements, for their fitness consultants. However, some fitness and sports medicine centers have no such requirements, so evaluate the instructors' credentials carefully.

No one has yet proved that fitness leads to a longer life, but feeling and looking good can help you enjoy life more. In other words, if you increase your cardiorespiratory endurance, reduce your body fat, and increase your flexibility and strength, you will be able to do a day's work and still have energy left for play. [Frances Caldwell]

Making Spot Spotless

You might call Mario Altissimo's assertion—not to mention his invention—dogmatic. The creator of an "automatic apparatus for cleaning dogs and similar animals" says his device "allows the operations which are usually carried out manually to be mechanized . . . completely."

Obviously the product of a tidy mind, the machine offers new hope to owners of dusty dachshunds, tarred terriers, and other muddy mutts. As the patent application clearly states, "it comprises a substantially cylindrical casing having a flat bottom wall, a portion which can be opened to allow an animal to enter and to leave the casing, and a vertical end wall formed with an aperture for the head of the animal positioned inside the casing."

Once you have your pup positioned (no advice is offered on how to do this), the rest is easy. Replacing not-so-fond memories of old times when the bathee (an otherwise acquiescent Airedale) managed to land soapy and smirking on the bathroom floor, while the bather (you) found himself unaccountably in the tub, is the new scientific method: "The casing is provided internally with a plurality of spray nozzles to which water or a mixture of water and detergent under pressure is supplied." Now that's more like it!

Any pet owner who has wrestled with a sopping St. Bernard will also be glad to learn that once the dog is clean, a "means for supplying hot air under pressure" can be activated "to effect a drying cycle at the end. . . ."

The unique apparatus is nicely designed to fill a long-felt need for dog owners. But what about those "similar animals"? Will this arrangement of pumps, valves, ducts, and hoses really make a dirty coyote come clean, or whiten the fleece of a wolf in sheep's clothing? [Marsha F. Goldsmith]

The Canine Cleaner

Curbing those Electricity Gluttons

"Will the last one out please turn off the lights?" became a catch phrase in the early 1970s when the cost of electricity started its steep climb. Since then, it has become evident that you will have to do more than switch off a few light bulbs to lower your electric bill substantially. However, if you learn to analyze how you use this expensive form of energy, you may be surprised at how much you can cut your electricity consumption.

To understand electricity, you must know three terms—current, voltage, and power consumption. Current is the flow of electrons through wires. It is measured in amperes (amps), which indicate the number of electrons passing through the wire each second. Voltage, measured in units called volts, can be thought of as the pressure pushing the current. Power consumption, measured in units called watts, is calculated by multiplying voltage (in volts) by current (in amps).

Every appliance is labeled with figures that give the voltage at which it operates and either its power consumption in watts or the current in amps required to run it. For example, an electric saw that requires 115 volts and 9.5 amps consumes 115 × 9.5 or 1,092 watts, or 1.09 kilowatts. A kilowatt is 1,000 watts.

Utilities usually charge by the kilowatt-hour—the amount of energy that a 1,000-watt appliance uses if it runs for one hour. The average cost of electricity in the United States in 1982 was about 6 cents per kilowatt-hour, but ranged from less than 3 cents in the Northwest to almost 10 cents in some areas of the Northeast. To calculate the cost of running an appliance, multiply the number of kilowatt-hours used by the cost of a kilowatt- hour.

In general, appliances with heating elements use much more power than others. For this reason, the electric water heater is usually the biggest electricity glutton in homes with this type of appliance. The easiest way to cut the heater's electricity consumption is to lower its thermostat, which has probably been set at 140° to 160°F. in the factory. A setting of 120°F. will provide water warm enough for most needs and can lower the cost of heating water by as much as 40 per cent.

About 20 per cent of the energy used by a water heater goes to keeping the heated water warm. You can reduce this by wrapping the water heater in an extra layer of insulation and turning it off when you go on vacation. However, never work on your water heater without shutting off the power.

The air conditioner is another voracious energy-eater, but new energy-efficient models, which can cool the room just as well as an ordinary model while drawing fewer amps, are now available. They are more expensive than other models but usually are worth the extra cost.

You can use the watts-determining formula to calculate the cost of running both units for one hour. The difference, multiplied by the number of hours you expect to run the air conditioner each year, will give you the annual electric-bill savings. You can then multiply this savings by the five- to seven-year lifetime expected of the machine to determine if the overall savings in electricity costs are greater than the price difference.

Some small appliances, such as toasters and irons, also have deceptively large appetites. You can limit their power consumption by turning them off when they are not in use.

Unlike appliances, light bulbs usually do not wear out, but succumb to thermal shock when they are turned on or off. A typical 80-cent, 40-watt bulb lasts for 1,000 on-and-off cycles, costing about 0.08 cent to turn off. Using the formula, you can find that the bulb uses about 0.08 cent worth of electricity if it burns for 20 minutes. So if the last ones out are returning within 20 minutes, they should not turn off the lights. [James S. Trefil]

The Appetites of Electricity-Eaters

Hair dryer
14

Toaster
39

Vacuum cleaner
46

Iron
60

Refrigerator
with automatic
defrost
1,795

Quick-recovery
water heater
4,811

Washing machine
103

Coffeemaker
106

Radio-
phonograph
109

Color
television
320

Dishwasher
363

Air conditioner
860

Clothes dryer
993

Electric range
with oven
1,175

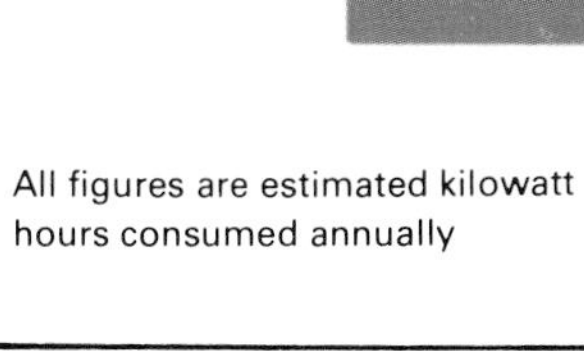

All figures are estimated kilowatt
hours consumed annually

Should You Buy a Home Video Game?

The mushrooming popularity of video games for the home is revolutionizing the toy industry. The first video game that could be played at home on the television screen came on the market in the early 1970s. It was called "Pong," essentially electronic ping-pong. In 1982, you can play more than 400 different games.

Video games come in a bewildering variety of sizes, shapes, colors, sounds, and prices. Some connect to your TV set, while others have their own screens. Some have built-in controls, others have separate but permanently connected controls, and still others have removable, replaceable controls.

If you have enjoyed playing a video game at the local arcade or at a friend's house, you may be considering buying a game for your home. Consider your purchase carefully. Buying a video game is not like buying a board game, such as Monopoly or parcheesi. If the family loses interest in the board game after a few tries, the game can sit on the shelf or be disposed of at a garage sale at no great loss. But even the least expensive video game can cost considerably more than a board game.

The simplest video games are handheld instruments, similar to a pocket calculator, with a small display screen. Suppose a $10 video game of this type that simulates an automobile race catches your interest. The instructions are simple, and the objective is clear—to get your car across the finish line by avoiding other cars that swerve in front of you. You try the game once at the store, like it, and buy it. At first, success seems to depend on the accuracy of your hand-eye coordination. However, after about 10 tries, you conclude that the outcome depends more on luck than on skill, so you put the game down, perhaps forever. Or

maybe after playing 10 games you discover that you are not really interested in simple driving games after all. At $1 per play, this is an expensive game.

If you want a wider variety of games—and games that offer more challenges—consider purchasing more sophisticated, and more expensive, video-game equipment. This will allow you to shoot down spaceships, guide a hungry creature through a maze, control rockets, or play football or basketball. Or you might want to play a quiz game, try a game of electronic chess, or sharpen your card-playing skills.

Some of these games have their own screens, others plug into your TV set. There are two questions you should consider when you begin your selection: How much money do you want to spend? Will you always have a color TV available when you want to play?

If you are interested only in sports games, you can buy a $50 tabletop machine that is about 30 by 30 by 10 centimeters (12 by 12 by 4 inches) and has its own screen. Up to four people can play some of the games on this machine. Other games in the $50 price range with their own screens include PAC-MAN, a popular maze game, or the shooting game, Space Invaders. Some machines in this price range handle up to four video games.

There is a wider variety of choices for game equipment that plugs into your TV set. But you will have to spend from $150 to $300 for a game console and control boxes. The boxes, which include keyboards, levers, push buttons, and steering wheels, are connected to the console by electrical wires, and the console is wired to your TV set.

The players handle the controls, which send electrical signals to the console. The console then translates these signals into electrical instructions for the TV set. The individual games for these systems are computer programs contained in interchangeable cartridges that you insert into the console. A cartridge provides from one to six games and costs from $10 to $30.

Even if you settle on this video-game system, there are still more options to consider. Some sets have control boxes that are permanently attached to their consoles, while other sets have removable, replaceable controls. Which type you choose depends on how often the equipment will be used and how the user treats it. If you and your friends and relatives are extremely enthusiastic players, you should consider buying a set that has controls that can be replaced if they break or wear out.

The most sophisticated video-game sets are actually home computers equipped to play games. Some of the games played on these computers present good-quality, detailed images, especially of athletes and playing fields. If you or other members of your family would benefit from the various uses of a home computer, such as helping with the family budget or providing programmed instruction, you should consider buying one of these machines. If you are truly devoted to video games, you eventually might want to devise and program your own games. Then a home computer probably would be your best choice. And if you are willing to pay the additional cost, you can get a home computer that has its own screen, thus avoiding conflicts with other members of the household who might not want to forego their favorite TV programs so you can play games on the TV set.

But before you purchase any type of game, you should spend a few quarters at the local arcade or try it out at a store that sells video games. Also, compare the benefits of purchasing equipment for your home with playing video games at an arcade. A cartridge that costs $30 is the equivalent of 120 plays at the arcade. Therefore, if you do not get at least 120 plays out of the cartridge before you tire of it, you would be better off at the arcade.

And even if you find that the home games are more economical, you may decide that the arcade games are worth the extra money you spend on them. Arcade games are more complex and challenging, their pictures are sharper, and their sound effects are more realistic (if that is important to you). Also, arcades introduce new games with astonishing frequency. Thinking carefully about how you want to spend your money and your time will enable you to win at least one game—that of choosing the right system. [E. Joseph Piel]

Range of Games

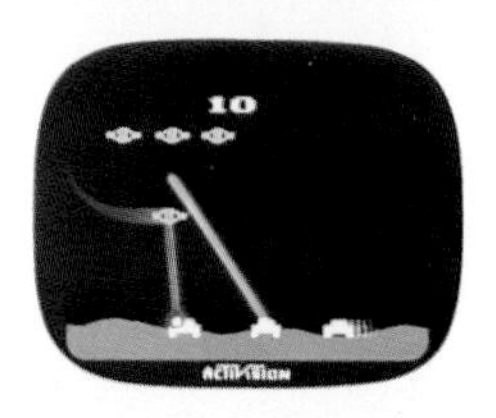

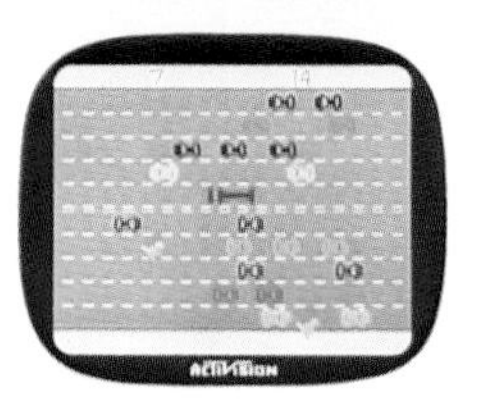

Making the Grass Greener on Your Side of the Fence

A beautiful, well-cared-for lawn is a source of pride to any homeowner. It provides a pleasant area for family recreation and increases the value of the property.

Caring for the lawn might not be as difficult as you think. It is, however, similar to any consumer product in that you get what you pay for. And in addition to money, you must spend time—working on the lawn and watching for potential problems.

No lawn can become a showpiece if it has not been properly established. This includes preparing the lawn area correctly and choosing the right grass or grass mixture. Turfgrass scientists have developed many different turfgrasses for different environments and different purposes.

The two most important considerations in selecting a turfgrass are its ability to tolerate stress and the amount of time and money you are willing to spend on caring for the lawn. Wear from play, temperature extremes, drought, and shade all put stress on a lawn.

Turfgrasses have been developed to grow best in one or more zones or regions of the United States. For example, bent grass grows well in the soils and cool wet weather of the Northwest; St. Augustine grass thrives in the moist warmth of the Southeast. You should consult a turfgrass specialist at

Where Grass Grows Best

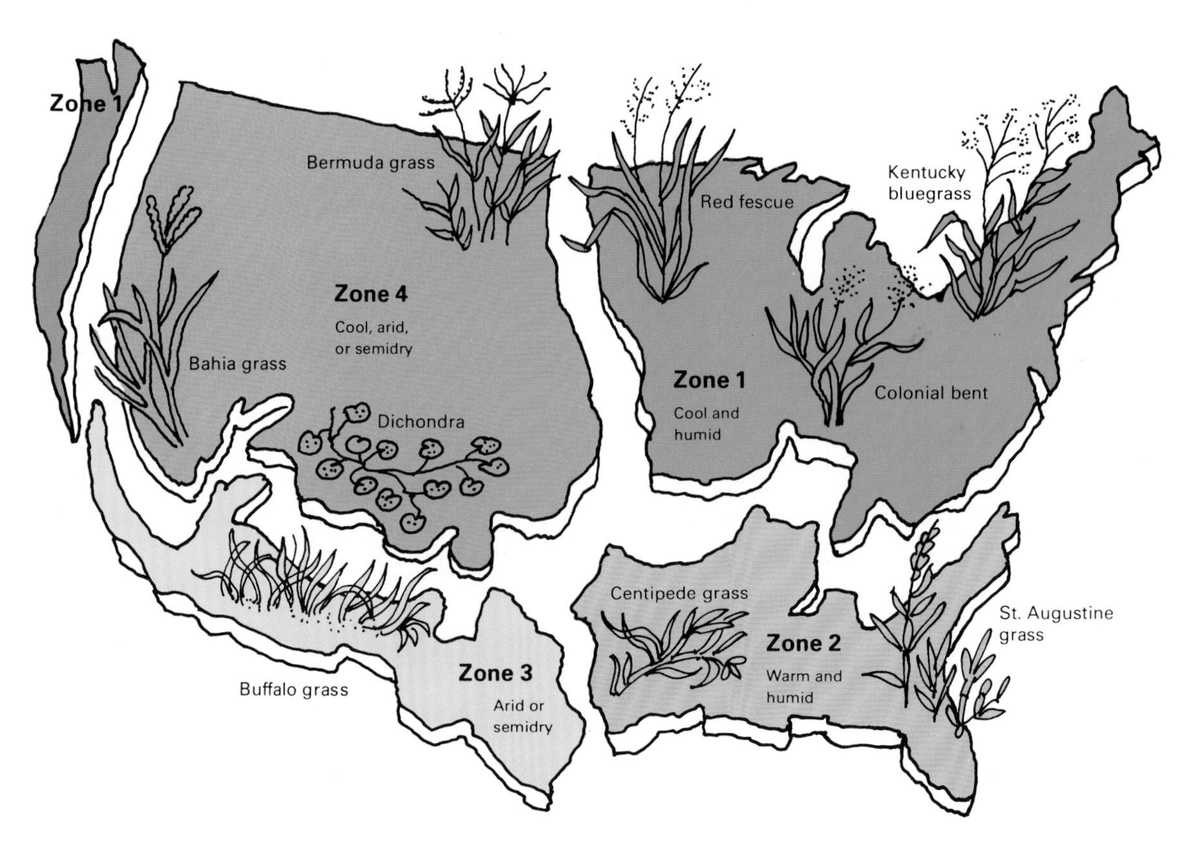

your state university for recommendations on a turfgrass that is best for your local conditions.

A new lawn should be planted early in the growing season. The work begins with measuring the area. You need to know how many square feet you have whenever you purchase seed or other materials for the lawn. Dig up samples of the upper three inches of topsoil and take or send them to a soil-testing service. The analysis will tell you the quantity and type of fertilizer or other additives, such as lime, you will need to put down.

Apply the nonselective herbicide, or weedkiller, glyphosate (Roundup and Kleenup are the commercial names). Do not disturb the lawn site for at least seven days after applying the weedkiller. Then remove all debris, such as rocks, wood, and construction materials from the site.

Remove and stockpile all topsoil. Grade the area on a slope of at least 1 per cent away from the building. This is equivalent to a drop of 1 foot in elevation over 100 feet of lawn.

Rototill or spade the soil as deeply as possible. Then replace the stockpiled topsoil and thoroughly rake or rototill in the suggested fertilizer and soil additives. Smooth the surface. You should also apply a starting fertilizer.

Turf can be planted by one of three methods: seeding, sodding, or vegetative establishment—plugs, sprigs, or stolons. Use a fertilizer spreader to spread one-half of the seed over the lawn. Work at right angles to the first spreading with the second half of the seed. This technique should also be used when applying a fertilizer or pesticide. It helps to eliminate any "skipped" spots.

Sod should be laid in staggered patterns similar to the way bricks are laid for a wall. On steep slopes, use stakes to hold the sod in place.

Stolons or plugs are planted at the intersection of an imaginary grid of 6-inch or 1-foot squares. Each plug will grow out in all directions to cover the area. Depending on the type of grass, this can take from weeks to years.

After the planting is completed, the area should be rolled to provide a firm, even surface. Rolling will also ensure good contact between the turf materials and the soil. The soil surface should then be covered with a light layer of mulch. Use weed-free straw,

TLC (Turfgrass Loving Care)

Grass	Wear	Shade	Fertilizer (lbs per 1000 sq. ft. per year)	Mowing Height In (inches)	Watering Frequency
Bahia grass	good	medium	1-2	1.5-2.5	low
Bermuda grass	good	poor	2-4	0.5-1.0	low
Buffalo grass	medium	poor	1-2	0.5-1/5	low
Centipede grass	poor	good	1	1.0-2.0	medium
Colonial bent	poor	medium	4-6	0.5-1.0	medium
Dichondra	poor	good	4-6	0.5-1.0	medium
Kentucky bluegrass	medium	poor	2-6	1.5-2.5	medium
Red fescue	medium	excellent	2-3	1.5-2.5	low
St. Augustine grass	medium	excellent	4-6	1.5-3.0	high

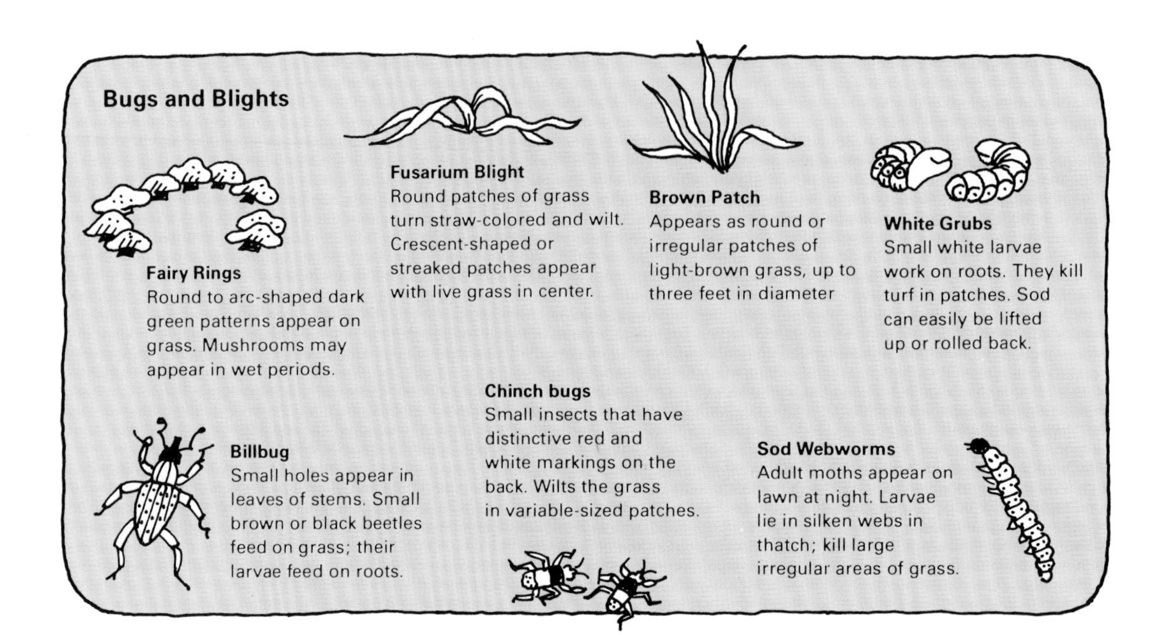

or a synthetic material, such as shredded paper. A mulch helps to minimize the frequency of watering—the final step in establishing a lawn.

The site should be watered daily over the next several weeks to ensure good germination of the seed, or rapid growth for the young seedlings or plants. Once the lawn is established you should water in the mornings, thoroughly saturating the upper six inches of soil. You can tell this by placing an empty can in the sprinkler pattern. Periodically remove a plug of turf and soil to check moisture depth. When it has reached six inches, mark the water level in the can. Thereafter, water until the can fills to that point.

Once growth is well underway, only rewater when the turf shows signs of drought stress, indicated when the grass does not quickly spring back from a footprint.

On lawns that have been established for several years, areas of the turf may thin out and bare spots may appear. These areas can be renovated following more or less the procedures for establishing an entire lawn. Remove debris and apply chemical weedkillers—very carefully. Loosen the soil by raking it vigorously. Then plant, fertilize, and water the areas.

If you have worked hard and effectively, before long the new lawn will need to be mowed. Whenever the grass grows more than 35 per cent higher than the maintenance height—which varies from ½ inch to 3 inches, depending on the type of grass—it is time to mow. Mowing frequency will change throughout the growing season, depending on how fast the turf grows. If you mow too close, the roots will shorten and there will be too little leaf surface to adequately convert sunlight to carbohydrates for food storage. If you mow too high, you will reduce the turf's tendency to spread and it will thin out.

The best time of year for fertilizing varies for each planting zone. Again, consult the turfgrass specialist at your state university cooperation extension for recommendations for your area.

Among the problems that can develop over time are the build-up of a layer of thatch and the compacting of the soil due to heavy traffic. Thatch consists of partially decomposed plant materials. It forms a layer between the green growing tissue and the soil. This layer can prevent water, pesticides, and fertilizer from reaching the soil.

Machines are available from tool-rental agencies that remove small cylinders of grass and soil. This helps to promote the rapid decomposition of thatch and can also be used to break up compacted soil.

The major cause of lawn problems is pests. These can generally be classified as diseases, insects, and weeds.

Turfgrass diseases are caused by inadequate aeration, or drainage of the soil, overwatering, the wrong fertilization practice, or improper mowing practices. One result is the appearance of various fungi.

Fungicides can control these problems, but the underlying reasons for the fungi being there in the first place must be rectified. You should also consider planting a variety of turfgrass that resists disease.

Insects can be another barrier to a healthy lawn. The grubs of May beetles, Japanese beetles, or Asiatic garden beetles feed on the roots of the grass. Army worms and cutworms feed on the leaves and stems. Chinch bugs and leaf hoppers suck juices from the grass. Ants can wreck a lawn by building anthills. Chemicals to control these pests can be toxic. Consult your turfgrass specialist about what to use.

Larger pests — moles, pocket gophers, and field mice — may follow the smaller ones. They feed on grubs and other insects. So, insect control will remove their food supply, and they too will go away.

The best way to avoid weeds is to remove them from the soil before you establish the lawn. Be sure that your materials — seed, sod, topsoil, mulch — and your tools — mowers, rollers — are free of weed seeds. It also helps if you can convince your neighbors to control weeds in their yards.

You can use a long-stemmed digging tool to remove the occasional weed that appears in a lawn, being sure to get the entire root. Or you can treat it with a spot-spray herbicide. General weeds are best controlled by application of a granular material or wet spray of an appropriate herbicide over the entire lawn.

Once more, your best source of information on turf pests, or any turf-related problem, is your friendly turfgrass specialist.

A dense, vigorously growing turfgrass is its own best defense against pests. It will compete for light, moisture, and nutrients successfully to crowd out weed seedlings. And it will overcome the effects of insects and diseases. [Thomas W. Fermanian]

Pesticides: Handle with Care

Pesticides used improperly can be injurious to man, animals, and plants. Follow the directions and heed all precautions on the labels.

Store pesticides in original containers–out of reach of children and pets–and away from foodstuff.

Apply pesticides selectively and carefully. Do not apply a pesticide when there is danger of drift to other areas. Avoid prolonged inhalation of a pesticide spray or dust. When applying a pesticide it is advisable that you be fully clothed.

After handling a pesticide, do not eat, drink, or smoke until you have washed. In case a pesticide is swallowed or gets in the eyes, follow the first aid treatment given on the label, and get prompt medical attention. If a pesticide is spilled on your skin or clothing, remove clothing immediately and wash skin thoroughly.

Dispose of empty pesticide containers by wrapping them in several layers of newspaper and placing them in your trash can.

It is difficult to remove all traces of a herbicide (weed killer) from equipment. Therefore, to prevent injury to desirable plants do not use the same equipment for insecticides and fungicides that you use for a herbicide.

Reprinted from USDA Bulletin No. 51

Where There's a Smoke Detector, There's Safety

The solemn-looking celebrity on the television screen warns that you could be one of the 6,000 people who die in the United States every year in home fires — unless you buy the smoke detector he is selling. Before you rush out to purchase one, however, there are some things you should know.

You have a choice of two basic types — photoelectric detectors and ionization detectors. The photoelectric type contains a small light bulb and a photoelectric sensor, which converts light to electricity. Light from the bulb does not shine directly on the sensor; instead, air molecules reflect enough light onto it to generate a minute electrical current. Smoke particles entering the detector reflect more light than normal onto the sensor, increasing the current. An alarm — a loud buzzer, horn, or bell — sounds when the current reaches a certain level.

An ionization detector uses a tiny bit of radioactive material to generate a stream of ions, atoms that have been stripped of their electrons. Smoke coming between the radioactive material and an electrical sensor interrupts the ion flow, and the alarm goes off.

Some people are concerned about having a radiation source in their homes. However, the Nuclear Regulatory Commission claims that there is no danger from such a small amount of radiation.

According to the National Bureau of Standards, both photoelectric and ionization detectors are equally effective for alerting people to home fires. But each one has its own advantages.

The ionization type is more sensitive to invisibly small smoke particles produced by hot, open flames. Photoelectric detectors more readily sense larger particles from smoldering fires. If you want to cover all possibilities, install one of each type. Put the photoelectric detector in or near bedrooms, and the ionization detector near stairs, where it will react quickly to a blaze that might block your escape route.

Smoke detectors of either type are powered by batteries or house current. Battery-powered detectors are easier and cheaper to install. They involve no unsightly wires along the walls or the expense of putting the wires behind the walls. However, batteries wear out. If you choose a battery model, be sure it includes an alarm to tell you when to replace the single 9-volt cell, which lasts about a year.

With a detector operating off household current, you do not have to worry about batteries wearing out. But this type will not operate if the fire damages the circuit to which it is connected. If you select this type, plug it into, or wire it to, a circuit that does not power kitchen appliances or television equipment. The ideal solution would be to install one battery-powered and one wired-in detector so that neither dead batteries nor power failures leave you unprotected.

Battery models attach directly to ceilings and walls with screws, adhesives, or expansion fasteners. Plug-in alarms require outlets near the points of installation. If you decide to connect one or more detectors to your household wiring, plan the locations before you call an electrician.

Where should smoke detectors be located? The simplest rule for placing only one detector is between the bedrooms and the rest of the house. This usually means in the hallway into which the bedrooms open. If a long distance separates two or more bedrooms, or the occupants sleep behind closed doors, two detectors would have a much better chance of awakening the sleepers.

In multilevel homes, one detector installed on each level gives the most protection. If the house has a basement, the best setup consists of one alarm on the basement ceiling near the steps leading to the rest of the house, one on the main escape route on the first floor, and a third where it will awaken sleepers in upstairs bedrooms.

If only one alarm is installed in a multi-level dwelling, it should be placed near the top of the stairway leading to the bedrooms.

Do not install detectors where walls and ceiling meet; there is not enough air circulation there. Mount detectors 15 to 30 centimeters (6 to 12 inches) below the ceiling or, if on the ceiling, at least 15 centimeters away from walls. Keep them clear of heat ducts and cool-air returns to the furnace in houses with forced-air heating. Airflow, hot or cool, can "wash" smoke out of a detector. Also, avoid installing them near kitchen exhausts, air conditioners, fans, and ceilings that are substantially warmer or cooler than the rest of the house.

To make sure alarms work, test them at least once a month. All detectors are equipped with a test button. Push it to determine if the warning sound can be heard in a closed or distant room. A better way to test a detector is to expose it to flame or smoke from a candle held about 15 centimeters below the opening. Test ionization detectors with the flame of a candle. To test a photoelectric detector, blow the flame out and let the smoke drift into the detector.

When you test each detector, clean dust from the grill that covers the smoke chamber. Bulbs in photoelectric detectors must be replaced periodically. Keep spares on hand.

Finally, plan main and alternate escape routes and walk through them in the dark. You should be able to get out of a burning house in three minutes or less, according to the National Bureau of Standards. Properly working smoke detectors should give you more time than this to escape, and could save your life. [William J. Cromie]

People in Science

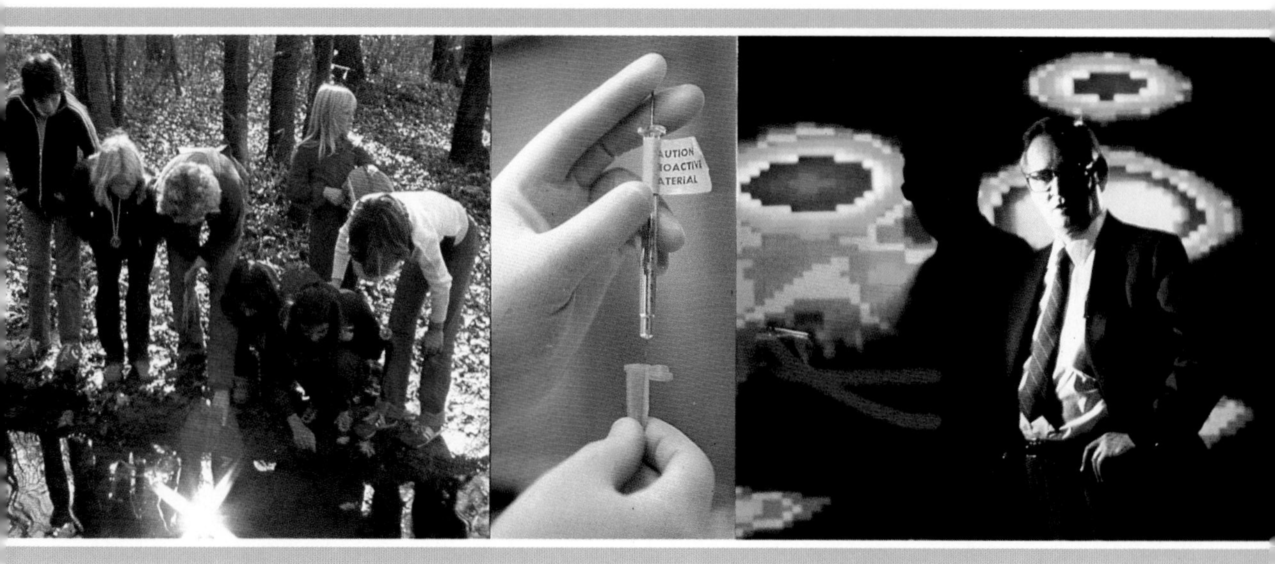

Because nature is such a maze of interconnected atoms and bodies and systems, it takes the reasoning of many people to analyze its parts and put them together in a comprehensible whole. This section, which relates science to people engaged in understanding it, examines the learning spectrum. At one end is a father-and-son team of scientists working to fill in the blanks on a human reference chart. At the other end are young people learning about science and nature in a program that someday could set some of them off on the same kind of pursuit.

Norman and Leigh Anderson

By William J. Cromie

Mapmakers of the human body's molecular landscape, this father-and-son team searches for the proteins that make us what we are

Norman Anderson thinks of the proteins in the human body as "biological nuts, bolts, gears, and levers. Their interaction makes life possible." They repair damaged cells, build new tissues, operate the muscles and the senses, carry vital oxygen to all parts of the body, and protect against disease. They comprise the major part of all organs and tissues, including skin, bone, muscle, and blood.

In 1959, when he was 40 years old, Norman decided to compile a catalog of all human proteins—what they look like, where they are located, and what they do. Such a catalog, he reasoned, would be invaluable for understanding how and why people become sick. Virtually every illness involves a lack of the right protein in the right amount. Proteins also are at the bottom of most of the important problems in biology, including aging and immunity. They are responsible for the development of a human being from a barely visible fertilized egg to a moving, reproducing, thinking complex of a trillion specialized cells.

The search for proteins has been an enormous undertaking. A few had been characterized by 1959, but Norman estimates that our bodies contain about 50,000 different ones. (Some scientists put the number at 10,000; others at more than 50,000.)

Norman's son, Leigh, joined his father in 1975 to help with the work. Today they search for proteins at the Argonne National Laboratory, a research center located 43 kilometers (27 miles) west of Chicago. Norman G. Anderson, a molecular biologist, is director of the molecular anatomy program. N. Leigh Anderson, a physicist, is assistant director of that program. Their titles describe their goal—studying human anatomy, protein molecule by protein molecule, and producing an index of these vital substances.

A human protein index would be to biologists and physicians what star charts are to astronomers—a basic reference against which normal and abnormal changes could be measured and evaluated. The word *protein* usually brings to mind nutrition, and the food we eat causes many of these changes. Digestion breaks food proteins into amino acids—the building blocks from which these complex molecules are assembled. Blood carries the amino acids to our cells where they are reassembled into other proteins according to instructions coded in genes in the cell nuclei.

Each human cell contains as many as 5,000 proteins, the Andersons estimate. These are constantly in need of repair or replacement, which newly assembled molecules provide. Enzymes, which speed up biochemical reactions, are proteins. So are antibodies, which defend the body against invading bacteria and viruses, and most hormones, which regulate growth and body functions.

Norman has searched for proteins for 23 years, and Leigh has worked at it for 11 years. Other researchers have spent lifetimes studying these molecules. All this effort, however, has yielded data on the composition and function of only about 1,000 of the body's proteins. "If one makes the plausible assumption that the 49,000 or so unknown proteins are as important as the known ones, then 98 per cent of the protein content of human cells remains a mystery," comments Leigh.

Potential gains from solving this mystery could be enormous. For example, birth defects result from genes that make the wrong kinds or amounts of proteins. Cancer involves uncontrolled production of some proteins, and a failure to make others. Injured and diseased cells leak proteins into the body, and these show up in urine and blood samples. Being able to detect these proteins will improve the diagnosis, treatment, and even prediction of many diseases.

Proteins that consume other proteins may cause various degenerative conditions, from arthritis and muscular dystrophy to aging. Learning how all proteins function might lead to discovery of those that block such destructive action. "It also should be possible," Norman declares, "to detect harmful pollutants by noting the difference in protein makeup between people who have and have not been exposed to them."

Norman's interest in proteins is an extension of his lifelong curiosity about how things work. Born on April 21, 1919, he grew up in Minneapolis, Minn., where his father was a Lutheran minister. Norman's brother also became a minister and both his sisters married clergymen. "I get along with them, but my scientific interests made me the black sheep," Norman admits. "As a boy, I constructed crys-

The author:
William J. Cromie is a free-lance science writer and executive director of the Council for the Advancement of Science Writing.

Norman and his wife, Mary Lloyd, share happy memories as they look over family photographs, *above left*. A snapshot from 1960, *above,* shows Leigh and his sister, Elizabeth Ann, with their pet rabbit, Spinco.

tal sets and built a telescope in the basement. My father and mother may not have been overjoyed by this, but they encouraged me all they could."

After attending a religious high school, Norman spent a year at Augsburg College, a small Lutheran college in Minneapolis. "I transferred to the University of Minnesota because Augsburg did not have the science courses I wanted," Norman says. "I became interested in biology when my father contracted pernicious anemia, and I spent much time taking care of him. I also wanted to solve a deep-seated problem that I had with evolution. I finally convinced myself that God established a system whereby humans evolved gradually from other life forms."

While he attended the University of Minnesota, World War II broke out in Europe. Norman left school and enlisted in the United States Navy in November 1941. He was assigned to fly antisubmarine patrols in blimps based at Weeksville, N.C. During this duty, Norman's inventive talents first earned recognition. He designed a photographic system to measure how close depth charges dropped from the blimps came to bombing targets. The Navy developed a bombsight based on this system and rewarded Norman with a commission as an ensign. Antisubmarine duty aroused his curiosity about submarines themselves, and he asked to try life on the other end of the bombsight. The submariners used his talents to develop better systems for combat photography through periscopes.

In North Carolina, Norman met Mary Lloyd Glidewell of Elizabeth City. They were married in 1943. The Navy discharged him two years later. He and his wife then headed for Minneapolis by automobile. On the way, a football-game traffic jam delayed them in Durham, N.C., home of Duke University. Norman took the time to look over the Duke campus, and it impressed him so much that he enrolled in the university later that year. He spent the years 1946 to 1951 at Duke, earning his B.A., M.A., and Ph.D. degrees.

Norman fondly remembers his favorite teacher, physiologist Karl M. Wilbur. "Professor Wilbur gave us new experiments to do for which there were no previously published answers. This immediately split the class into two distinct groups. One insisted that this was unfair because they had no set results to work for and their work could not be graded in a normal way. But my group saw it as a chance to discover new information."

Wilbur, who retired from Duke in 1982 at age 69, remembers Norman as "the best student I had in 35 years. As an undergraduate, he concerned himself with the methods of getting answers, not with just the answers alone. As a graduate student, he did outstanding experiments to advance both knowledge and methodology. His master's and doctorate theses involved work with high-speed centrifuges. He used these to isolate parts of cells, particularly nuclei. His research on proteins grew out of these experiments."

Leigh was born on Aug. 3, 1949, while his father was a graduate student at Duke. Norman spent many hours working in the laboratory, and Mary Lloyd often helped him. She would bring Leigh with her, and he slept in a basket amid the test tubes and centrifuges while his parents worked together. Norman says that "for Leigh, the lab was as normal a place to be as a playground was for other kids."

Norman completed his Ph.D. program in biology in 1951 and went to Oak Ridge National Laboratory (ORNL) in Tennessee on a postdoctoral fellowship. ORNL turned out to be a good place for Leigh to develop an interest in science and invention. On Saturday mornings, the laboratory held sales of its excess equipment, which it sold by the pound. "You could buy 20 pounds of electronics in good condition for less than $2," Norman recalls. "This gave Leigh the thing that Thomas Edison referred to as the first requirement for invention — a pile of workable junk."

Norman did not push Leigh into science. He encouraged Leigh to follow his own interests, just as Norman's father had encouraged him to do. Norman gave the same support to his daughter, Elizabeth Ann, who was born in 1956. She chose dancing rather than science. After graduating from Stuttgart Ballet School in West Germany, she worked as a dancer before marrying and settling in Los Angeles as a musician and composer.

Norman's quest for proteins originated at ORNL. Until 1959, ORNL had been involved chiefly in research on atomic weapons and nuclear energy. The head of the laboratory, physicist Alvin M. Weinberg, asked the staff to suggest projects that could be undertaken as ORNL diversified into nonatomic work. Norman proposed that he and his colleagues break down all the different types of human cells and determine the function of each of their proteins. "It was, quite obviously, an impossible project at the time I proposed it," Norman admits. "The technology did not exist. But I was at the right place to try to develop the technology, and I hoped to gain valuable new insights along the way."

Researchers at ORNL had solved the problem of separating minute amounts of useful isotopes, such as the uranium-235 needed for

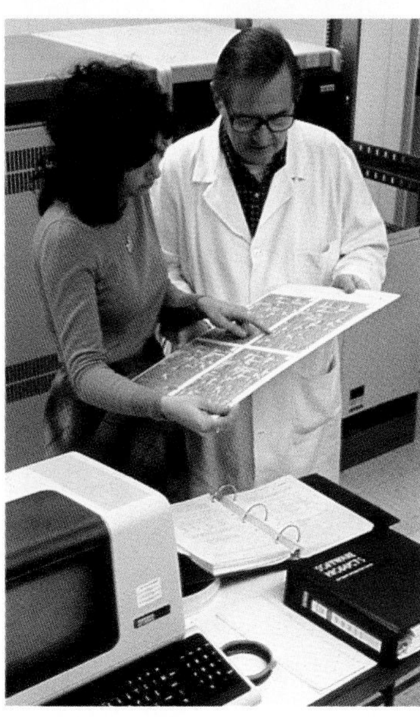

Lunch at the Argonne Lab, *top left,* doubles as an informal meeting for the Andersons and the research team. Later, Norman and Leigh confer with a colleague in a hallway, *above far left,* and Norman discusses a problem with a University of Chicago student, *above left.* No clock watcher, Norman works into the evening, *above.*

nuclear weapons and reactors, from huge amounts of less useful material. Norman faced the comparable problem of separating microscopic parts of the cells, such as nuclei, from large volumes of tissue and whole cells. He began by enlisting the knowledge and help of the ORNL uranium-separation team and using a centrifuge that he had invented in 1955.

"Essentially, this centrifuge is a special kind of high-speed cream separator," Norman explains. "You put in a batch of broken-up cells and, just as milk collects in one part of a spinning separator and cream in another, the cell fractions separate into zones of different weight, size, or density. These zones then can be unloaded one at a time." This device, known as the zonal centrifuge, has now been adapted by laboratories all over the world to purify vaccines for influenza and polio. It is still used for such purposes today. A vaccine for hepatitis B, which became available in 1982, would not have been possible without the zonal centrifuge.

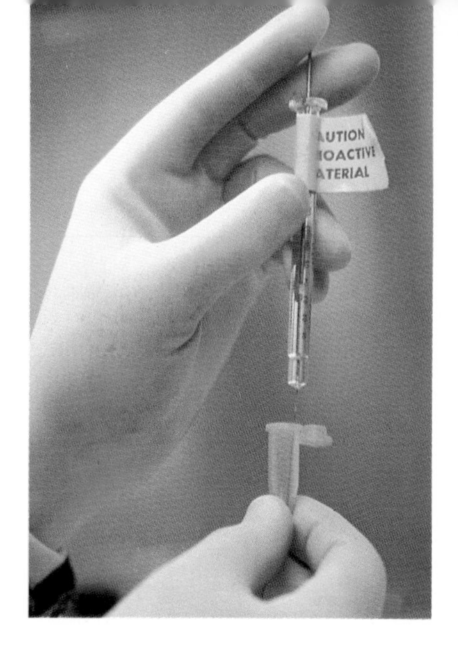

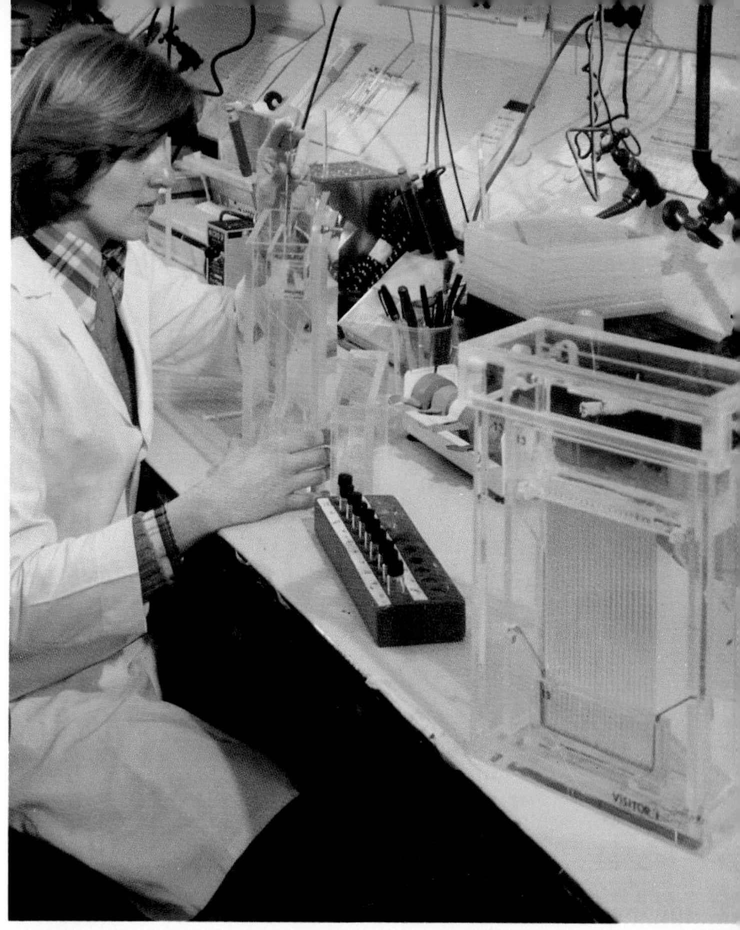

The first stage of the two-dimensional electrophoresis process, which separates proteins according to their chemical composition, begins with the injection of a tissue sample into a tube of gel, *above*. Several tubes are then placed in an apparatus where they are exposed to an electrical field, *right*.

In the second stage, the gels are placed on glass plates, which are then immersed in a chemical solution and exposed to an electrical field, *left,* separating the proteins by size. The gel is then viewed over a light table, *above*.

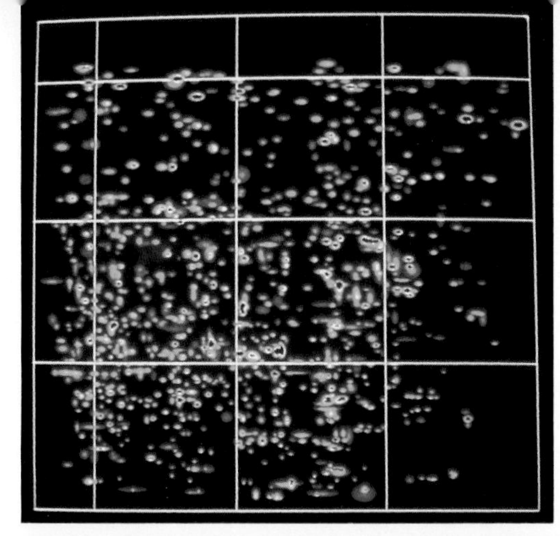

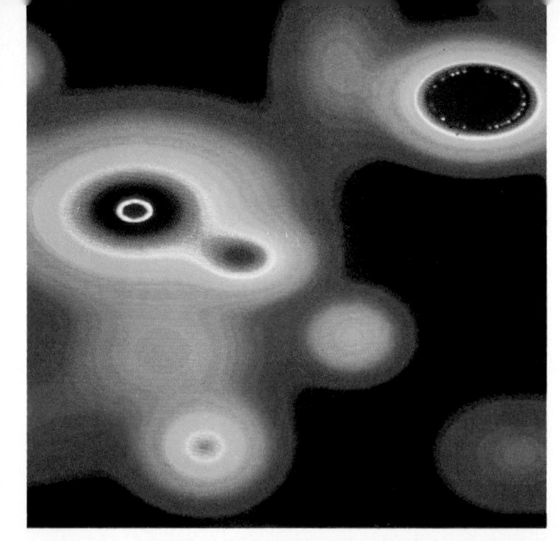

After a photograph of the gel has been analyzed by computer, a finished protein map is displayed on a television screen, *top left*. The display zeros in on just a few of the protein spots, *top right,* in response to a command from Leigh, *above*.

After he separated the cell's parts, Norman needed to subject each part to a series of tests to determine which proteins it contains. Doing these tests one at a time would require dęcades of tedious work. Clearly, another invention was necessary. Norman met the challenge by developing the centrifugal fast analyzer, a machine that does 20 to 30 chemical tests simultaneously. The chemicals mix in small chambers attached to a centrifuge rotor. As the rotor spins, changes in the intensity of a light beam shining into each chamber record the progress of the reaction. The rotor revolves hundreds of times per minute, and, says Norman, "Data is acquired at such blinding speed a small computer is needed to handle it." He completed development of the fast analyzer in 1969 and, by 1982, more

At home in his book-filled condominium, Leigh relaxes by reading. He is especially fond of science fiction.

than 5,000 such machines were being used in hospital laboratories all over the world.

The fast analyzer did not solve all of Norman's problems. "I could run a series of specific tests to find a protein if I suspected its existence," he notes, "but I had no way to systematically discover all the proteins in a given source of cells. This was a discouraging point to reach. If cancer, for example, could not be explained in terms of known proteins, I would need to discover the unknown ones. Unfortunately, the most important protein might be the last one I would find after an effort that took years. If I had a method to test each cell type rapidly and find all the proteins in it—known and unknown—I could compare cancerous and noncancerous cells and immediately spot the proteins that are different."

It took six years to solve this problem, and the solution came in the form of a suggestion by Leigh.

While his father pursued his work at ORNL, Leigh majored in physics at Yale University in New Haven, Conn. He graduated in 1971 and won a scholarship that enabled him to continue his education at Churchill College at Cambridge University, England. There, he studied X-ray crystallography in a laboratory headed by British biochemist Max F. Perutz, one of the world's foremost experts on this technique. X-ray crystallographers determine the structure of a protein by crystallizing it, shooting an X-ray beam at the crystal, then studying the pattern produced on film by the radiation. "I enjoyed the work immensely," Leigh remarks, "but I spent all my time studying one protein—hemoglobin. Eventually, I decided that looking at one protein in minute detail won't solve the major problems of biology." As he finished up at Cambridge, in 1975, Leigh happened to read a scientific paper by microbiologist Patrick

O'Farrell. This paper dramatically changed Leigh's life, and his father's as well.

O'Farrell, then a graduate student at the University of Colorado, made important advances in the field of gel electrophoresis, one method of separating the proteins in a complex mixture. Electrophoresis, which means carried by electricity, involves separation by electrical charge. In standard, or one-dimensional, gel electrophoresis, a sample of blood, for instance, moves through a column of gel in an electrical field. Each type of protein moves to a different position in the gel because each type carries a unique electrical charge, which depends on its chemical composition. Different proteins thus collect in clearly defined bands. O'Farrell developed a technique that separates proteins in two dimensions. After the first separation, the gel is turned on its side and a chemical that interacts electrically with the proteins is added. This causes the proteins to move in a second direction, perpendicular to the first. The first stage separates the proteins by their chemical composition, the second separates them according to size. The result is a complex pattern or map in which the proteins appear as spots in the gel. It struck Leigh that two-dimensional (2-D) electrophoresis could be used to look into a cell and see all its proteins — known and unknown — simultaneously.

Norman had moved to Argonne shortly after O'Farrell published his paper. "I did not know about the paper," Norman says, "but I had bought electrophoretic equipment and was dabbling with it when Leigh returned from Cambridge." Leigh suggested that 2-D electrophoresis might be used to make a series of maps on which proteins could be located and cataloged by their charge and size. Each protein then would be characterized by specific map coordinates, just as places are located on maps by their latitude and longitude. Norman responded to Leigh's suggestion by saying, "Well, why don't you do that?"

Since that time, the Andersons have made more than 40,000 maps, searching for new proteins or for changes in proteins associated with disease. They photograph the gel pattern for each sample. A sample of white blood cells, for instance, might produce a photograph containing 1,000 spots. The Andersons then employ electronic scanners to "read" the spot pattern. The scanner divides the photograph into a million or more squares. Data from each square go into a computer programmed to locate the position and measure the size of every protein. The computer uses this data to generate a map that can be displayed in color on a television screen.

"You can't tell much by looking at one gel or map," Leigh points out. "You have to compare maps to find meaningful changes produced by disease, injury, or pollutants. For example, we have compared maps of urine samples from healthy men with those from men who have prostate cancer. Jesse Edwards of our group discovered a new protein that always appears in the urine of patients with ad-

Sunday, generally his only day away from the lab, finds Norman hard at work on a different sort of project, *top*. Later, Leigh joins his parents for dinner, *above,* and father and son share a domestic moment at the kitchen sink, *above right*.

vanced prostate cancer. The next step is to test men in early stages of the disease, to determine if we can diagnose the onset of prostate cancer simply by mapping a urine sample."

Norman and Leigh spend most of their waking hours working with proteins or reading and writing about them. A usual day at the lab starts about 8 A.M. and ends about 6 P.M. The Andersons also work on the gels on Saturdays. Father and son get along well in the laboratory. Their physical resemblance is minimal — Leigh is much taller and more slightly built than Norman — but they share many personality traits. Both are quiet, deliberate, and calm; however, each has strong opinions on scientific matters. When they disagree, their discussions are frank and, stresses Norman, rational. "We usually settle scientific differences by experiments that prove one of us correct," he says.

Norman and Leigh treat each other as colleagues. Their output of new inventions is about the same. There is no sense that the son is overshadowed by his father, and with good reason. Each one concentrates on different aspects of the project — Norman on supervising preparation of specimens and gels; Leigh on automation and data processing. "Many parts of the system, particularly those involved with handling the data, were invented or set up by Leigh," Norman notes. Leigh, for his part, paid his father the highest compliment by seeking to work with and learn from him. "People are surprised that a father and son can work well together," Mary Lloyd comments, "but I'm not sure why. My father and brother were lawyers, and they worked together."

A frequent traveler, Norman packs his bags for one of the many scientific meetings he attends each year.

Much of the Andersons' work involves mapping lymphocytes, a type of white blood cell that plays a major role in the immune system. The maps reveal proteins that identify different types of leukemia. Such information enables physicians to prescribe specific and effective treatment. Other researchers in their group have discovered lymphocyte proteins associated with mononucleosis.

"It is not necessary to give a name or function for all the proteins on a map," Norman explains. "You can worry about naming them later. It's the changes in patterns from map to map that provide the vital information. When you have good, identifiable patterns, you can exploit them. For example, suppose certain proteins show up on a map when someone gets cancer. You could treat that person with various drugs, until you find the ones that clear the map of the proteins associated with cancer. Such treatment might reverse the progress of this disease."

Leigh experiments with tumor promoters — compounds that appear to make cells more susceptible to cancer-causing agents. He compares protein maps from normal cells with maps of cells that have been exposed to tumor promoters. "Air pollutants can act as tumor promoters," Norman notes. "Protein maps allow us to follow the changes produced by such pollutants.

"The maps also permit us to test the effectiveness of drugs by noting changes in proteins. Instead of experimenting with mice, rats, and other animals — then trying to guess from the results how humans would be affected — we look directly at changes in human cells grown in culture. A tremendous amount of uncertainty can be eliminated by these means."

Each human protein is the product of one or more genes. Therefore, protein maps provide information on our genetic health. Thousands of diseases and defects result from genes that produce excesses, deficiencies, or alterations of proteins. Protein maps that reveal these abnormal molecules might lead to the diagnosis and treatment of genetic defects before obvious symptoms appear.

Geneticists now use recombinant DNA, or gene-splicing, techniques to transfer human genes to bacteria. This transforms the bac-

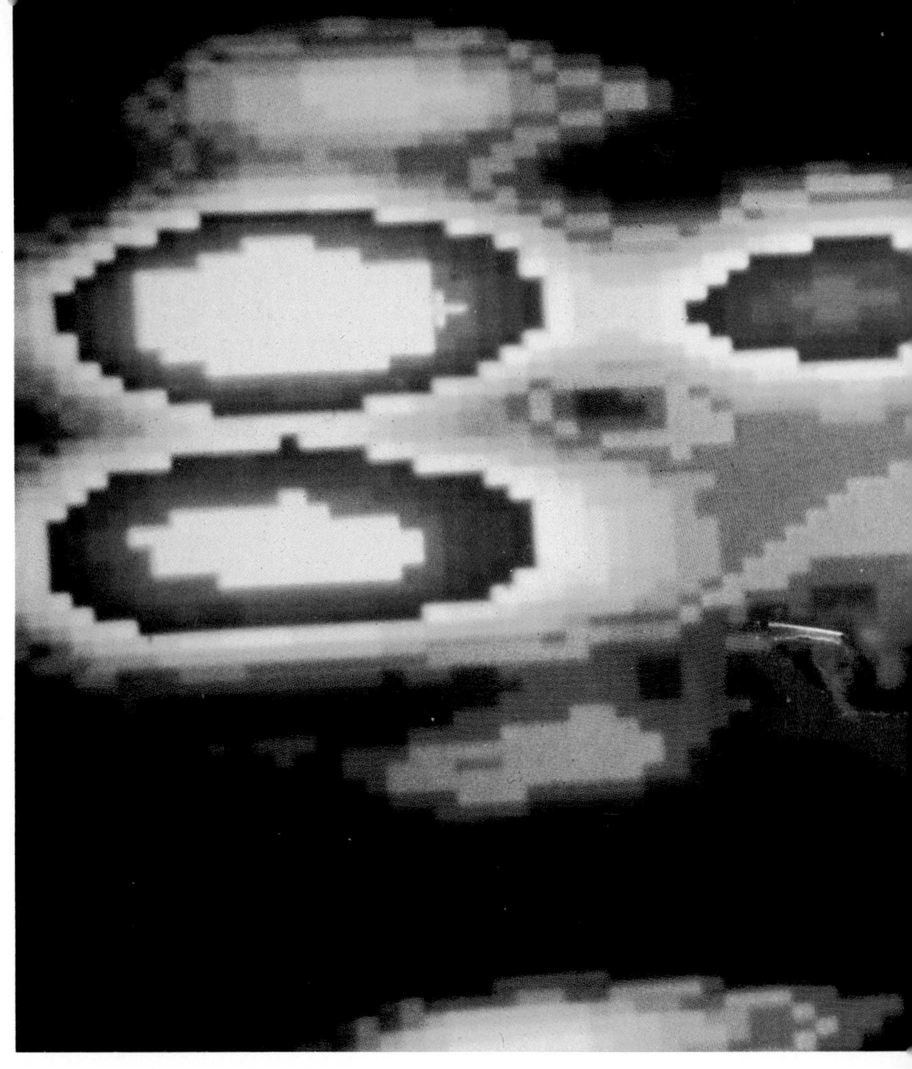

With a slide projection of a protein map as his backdrop, Norman lectures on two-dimensional electrophoresis and the potential of the human protein index. He often gives such talks at scientific meetings and to scientists visiting the Argonne Laboratory.

teria into tiny factories for production of medically valuable proteins, such as insulin to treat diabetes, and human growth hormone to treat certain kinds of dwarfism. The biological identity of all of these proteins can be evaluated by comparing a map of the bacterial product with a map of the normal human protein. The Andersons currently perform such tests for pharmaceutical companies that produce insulin by gene-splicing. In the future, physicians hope to develop the means to insert normal genes directly into the cells of victims of genetic disorders. Protein maps, in these cases, could be employed to determine whether the implanted gene actually produces the desired protein.

The ultimate goal of Norman and Leigh is to understand how genes control the development of human beings. "After a human egg becomes fertilized," Norman explains, "certain sets of genes switch on, and these in turn switch other genes on and off. Such switching, for example, causes one group of cells in the gut of an early embryo to develop into a liver. Presently, we don't know the makeup of even one of these gene sets, or anything about their switching schedules.

If we can isolate the proteins produced by each switching and then determine when these first appear, we could follow the development of tissues and organs. In other words, we could actually see what turns a cell into a liver cell, a heart cell, or a brain cell."

This goal and that of a complete human protein index lie many years away. So far, the Andersons have used 2-D electrophoresis to construct protein maps of human plasma, or the liquid portion of blood, as well as red blood cells, lymphocytes, urine, muscles, hair follicles, and saliva. This work was done in a search for proteins associated with specific diseases, such as prostate cancer and leukemia. The Andersons have not yet begun to systematically map each type of human cell to catalog each of its proteins. The main roadblock is money. Norman and Leigh now receive about $1.2 million a year from the Department of Energy. They would need $5 million annually to pay for the additional facilities, equipment, and people necessary to work on the human protein index while still doing specific medical projects. With this funding, "one could have a usable portion of the index within 15 years," Norman estimates.

He and Leigh believe that the immense potential for successfully treating diseases justifies the price tag of $75 million or more. Senator Alan Cranston (D., Calif.) agrees and has organized a task force composed of scientists and business people to find ways to raise the necessary money.

Many biologists, however, oppose spending so much on a single project. Physicist Rosalyn S. Yalow, co-winner of the 1977 Nobel Prize for Physiology or Medicine, states flatly, "This is not the optimal way to spend research money at this time." She and other critics point out that large projects seldom have been successful in biology. They argue that such projects take funds away from bright individual researchers, who traditionally have made the important discoveries in this science.

One faculty member at a well-known medical school wrote to Norman: "I'm uncomfortable with the concept that the spending of so many millions of dollars . . . to utilize a new technology and develop a protein index must provide useful information. Isn't it a bit like fingerprinting everyone in America in the expectation [that] useful patterns must emerge?" This scientist typifies critics who believe that finding particular protein abnormalities responsible for various diseases is more important than doing a whole protein catalog. Norman responds, "This is the way that aboriginals would attempt to understand a Boeing 747 airplane—taking it apart one piece now and one piece later. Our proposal is to make a complete parts list, such as all aircraft have. What we must do is to convince critics that the short-term costs will be more than offset by the value of the long-term understanding and usefulness."

Other scientists oppose the project on technical grounds. In 1982, there was no standard way to prepare and read 2-D electrophoresis gels. Therefore, there is no assurance that different researchers will find the same protein at the same place on their maps. The Ander-

Father and son, silhouetted against a protein map, contemplate their work—which they are certain will yield immense benefits in understanding human health and development.

sons believe they can solve such technical problems. "I am confident," Norman declares, "that better techniques will be developed, which will allow us to do easily the things that now are difficult."

Outside the lab, the Andersons lead quiet lives centered largely on their scientific interests. Leigh lives in a book-filled condominium apartment in Willowbrook, Ill., which he describes as an "average suburb," a short drive from Argonne Laboratory. His parents live about 8 kilometers (5 miles) away in their own house in Hinsdale, Ill., a more affluent suburb. Leigh is a frequent visitor in his parents' home. They share the same circle of friends, most of whom are fellow scientists.

Norman, whose main relaxation is listening to classical music, describes his wife as "extraordinarily tolerant" of his single-minded dedication to work. She says, "It's all part of being a scientist's wife." Mary Lloyd was active in politics when they lived in Tennessee, serving on the Democratic state executive committee. She now spends much of her leisure time pursuing an interest in English history and literature.

Leigh reads books in scientific fields other than his own for relaxation. He switches to science fiction when he tires of this. He watches television sparingly, preferring the Public Broadcasting Service channel and such shows as "Masterpiece Theatre" and "Monty Python." Leigh also will watch "Benny Hill" when he has nothing good to read. "I enjoy English humor," he says.

Norman and Leigh are avid travelers. Scientific meetings provide an opportunity for them to visit interesting places. "I like to go to Paris and Cambridge," Leigh says. "Many of my friends are in science; I visit them, and we play around in laboratories."

The Andersons consider work and recreation as two aspects of the same thing. "We do enough different things in the lab so that work is recreation," Norman remarks. "Work, for most people, is what you get tired of by late afternoon. When we tire of doing one project during the day, we have other interesting projects to do."

Norman feels confident that their long hours and dedication will lead to the accomplishment of their goals. "To be successful," he believes, "you need to have the ability to do what you want to do. But you also need help and encouragement from others, together with a certain amount of luck. I've had encouragement from my father, from teachers such as Karl Wilbur, and from many of my colleagues. And I've been extraordinarily lucky to have been supported in what I wanted to do. I wanted to build things, and I have been able to do this. In the Navy, I wanted to fly and to work in submarines, and I did those things. I've had the opportunity to develop projects I thought were significant. Now, with Leigh's help, I'm optimistic about having the ability, encouragement, and luck to complete a protein index that will be of major importance in fighting disease and increasing understanding of human biology."

Classrooms in the Clearing

By Michael Reed

Nature and science take on a new meaning when students learn about them through direct contact

"Here they come," calls out one of the student teachers from Northern Illinois University (NIU).

"They" are the seventh-grade students from Huntley School in De Kalb, Ill. Sixty-seven of them, with their luggage and four Huntley teachers, fill two school buses. The scene, as they get off the buses, is typical of 12-year-olds in a milling group. Friends separated for the 45-minute trip call out to one another as though years have passed. There is a great deal of laughing, pushing, and general horseplay. The atmosphere is controlled pandemonium.

The Huntley students have gathered here near Oregon, Ill., at the Lorado Taft Field Campus of Northern Illinois University to spend 2½ days experiencing education that uses settings outside the classroom. The 145-acre campus, about 160 kilometers (100 miles) west of Chicago, is one of a number of outdoor-education facilities that are associated with universities throughout the United States.

The Taft Campus serves about 65 schools a year, some from as far away as Chicago. A school may send as many as three groups of students in a year. The program links the training of student teachers from NIU with the introduction of schoolchildren, from grades two through eight, to nature and elementary science. Each group stays from two to five days.

The noise of the Huntley students has died down to a moderate din. "Group A, everyone from group A, over here now," calls NIU student teacher Beth Enbrecht.

"Group D, over here." "Group C here." "Group B." Three other student teachers follow Beth's lead and the Huntley students begin to drift haphazardly into the four groups of 15 to 20 to which they were assigned before they left De Kalb.

Many of the NIU student teachers who work at Taft are studying for careers in outdoor education. The ones who are participating in the Huntley School program, however, are not planning to specialize in this way. But A. Kerby Tink, professor of education at NIU, feels that exposure to the outdoor-education experience at the Taft Campus is of great value to anyone who wants to teach.

The first item on the program is lunch—a delicious beef stew. Harrison Dining Hall, the building that contains the kitchen and dining room, is perched solidly at the edge of a steep embankment that drops precariously down to the scenic Rock River below. A glass wall that runs the entire length of the large dining room overlooks the river and the cliffs and woods that run to its banks. It is October 28, and the remnants of autumn colors streak and splotch the trees. Even in the atmosphere of excitement and anticipation, almost all the students remark on the beauty of it all.

There are seven to 10 at a table, including at least one student teacher. The Huntley teachers, Taft Campus staff, and visitors share a table at the back of the room.

Malcolm Swan, the director of resident programs at Taft, tells about the extensive preplanning that goes into each program. "There is no single process, but generally it begins when the principal or one of the teachers writes or telephones us. One or two of our staff people then visit the school, or the teachers come here. The details of transportation, meals, and sleeping are usually taken care of quickly.

"Next, we discuss broad objectives. A study we conducted in 1979 tells us that parents and students think the most important thing in the program is to learn about the environment. Teachers, however, feel the most important aspects of the program are social, with an emphasis on cooperation, and the increased self-awareness and confidence derived from successfully coping with a drastically different learning situation.

"We also hammer out the program's content. Some teachers want to extend what is being learned in their classrooms to the outdoors. Others want an emphasis on new learning material. Often we try to blend the two."

After the meal ends, there is a brief orientation meeting outside. The weather is unusually warm for late October. Then the Huntley students are off to their first learning sessions. Group A heads for

The author:
Michael Reed is a free-lance medical writer and a former managing editor of *Science Year*.

Huntley student Carrie Mattern is first off the bus at Lorado Taft, *left*. The seventh-graders are soon briefed on the program, *above*.

the Craft Shop, a long, low building that is tucked partway back in the woods.

The Craft Shop is one of 11 buildings that house the Taft Campus facilities. The more important ones include the just-vacated Harrison Dining Hall and Heckman Dormitory, where the boys are housed in nine dorm rooms with space for 78 people. The girls live in Clarkson Dormitory, which has two dormitory rooms, each with 26 beds. All the dorms have an adjoining room or rooms where the NIU student teachers and Huntley teachers spend the night. Clarkson also contains the campus' main offices, a library, and a laboratory. Faculty offices are located in Taft House, and there are large meeting rooms or classrooms in Poley and in Eagle's Nest.

In front of the Craft Shop, a piece of stone sculpture gives the first-time visitor quite a start. It is a life-sized statue of six robed figures bearing a coffin. Called *The Funeral Procession*, it is the work of students of sculptor Lorado Taft, after whom the campus is named. Taft was the guiding light of the Eagle's Nest Colony, where sculptors, painters, writers, and musicians gathered during the summer months from 1892 to 1942. In 1951, Eagle's Nest Colony was deeded to Northern Illinois University and thereby became the Lorado Taft Field Campus.

In the Craft Shop, student teacher Jean Rodriguez is telling the group, "We want you to make something you can really use to remember the Taft Campus by, rather than something small and meaningless that you will throw in a drawer and forget."

Each Huntley student is about to make a harvest wreath, and Jean and the five other student teachers demonstrate the technique. First, they bend a wire hanger into a circle. "I know how to do that," says Chris Canova. "We make basketball hoops that way."

Next, the demonstrators wrap newspaper strips in a spiral around the wire circle and tape or tie them in place. This provides fullness. Then cornhusks and leaves, soaked in glycerine and water to make them pliable, are taped, glued, or tied in place. Glycerine is a humectant, or moisturizing agent. It draws water from the atmosphere and helps keep anything it touches from drying out.

Work goes on quietly at most of the tables in the Craft Shop. When the wreaths are complete, they are laid out on two of the tables for everyone to view. They are remarkably attractive and there is the clear general feeling of a job well done.

It is 4 P.M. — time for all the Huntley students to meet at Eagle's Nest. There, in a large open room, the Huntley teachers give the seventh-graders a choice of things to do before supper. Some choose relaxing games like chess or checkers. One group heads for an open grassy area to play bombardment, also known as dodge ball.

Another group walks for about 10 minutes to adjoining Lowden Memorial State Park to visit *Black Hawk*. This is a huge statue of an Indian that was built by Lorado Taft. Standing 48 feet high and made with 268 tons of cement, *Black Hawk* stares solemnly out over the Rock River. The statue is said to represent the Indians who once lived in the river valley and called it their own, but were forced to leave it.

Huntley student Cindy Hannon looks long and hard at *Black Hawk* and says thoughtfully, "He looks so serious."

"And sad," adds Stephanie Burr.

"I wish I could climb up on it," says Cindy. Without another word, she and Stephanie walk to the statue and climb partway up. There is a strange respect in the gentleness and grace with which they climb.

At supper, the dining room is alive with comparisons of learning experiences. While group A was in the Craft Shop, group B was learning science; group C, survival; and group D, pioneering. Each group will rotate through all of these activities.

The next day, Thursday, is also sunny and pleasantly warm. In Clarkson Dormitory, the alarms begin to go off at 6:45 A.M. The girls in this dorm are scheduled to meet several of the boys in the dining room by 7:30 to set the tables for breakfast at 8.

It is to be a full and busy day. Group A will go through the pioneering and survival programs. And there are plans for Halloween festivities in the evening. Nobody will start the day hungry — breakfast is grape juice, cereal, pancakes, sausages, and milk.

Nature's discards are gathered outdoors, *above,* to be used to decorate the cornhusk wreaths made in the Craft Shop, *left*.

It is a long walk along rough trails through the woods to the large clearing in which the pioneers' log cabin stands. The cabin was built over a period of time by student teachers, visiting students going through the program, and Taft Campus personnel. It is as close to an authentic pioneer cabin as can be built.

"Try to imagine yourself as a pioneer," urges student teacher Karen Jackson, "with no modern tools and in need of a house."

"The best answer to that problem is a log cabin," says student teacher Denis O'Brien, motioning toward the cabin. "Let's see a little of what it took to build one. First, notice that you need logs of a particular diameter to keep the building uniform and stable. Look at the edge of the woods and see how many trees you can spot that would provide the proper size logs."

The students look around with much discussion, pointing, nodding, and headshaking. Tracy Burt is the first to voice their unanimous conclusion, "Not many at all."

"Right," agrees O'Brien and explains that this means that the pioneers often had to bring long, heavy logs from deep in the woods to where they wanted to build the cabin.

One such log is on the ground. O'Brien shows the students how to lift it and place shorter logs beneath it as rollers, demonstrating a basic principle of physics. Then the students move the large log by pushing it atop the small logs.

The large log is heavy, the ground bumpy, and the smaller logs are not nearly as round as a wheel. After the large log is moved a short distance, one of the small logs is uncovered by the progress and must be picked up and moved forward under the front of the large log to support it over new ground to be covered. The work is difficult and slow. Physics principles do not always apply smoothly in practice.

Each of the students also works with a drawknife, which strips the bark off wood to be used for furniture and other special purposes. They learn to use a froe—a cleaverlike tool that is hammered down through short logs to split them into roofing shingles, floorboards, and barrel staves. They experiment with an ax for felling trees and a two-man saw to cut them into logs of the length required.

Next, it is time to make candles. Some of the students tend the fire while the others sit and listen to student teacher Renee Christian point out that candles were the only source of nighttime light for the pioneers. "Their wax was tallow—animal fat," she goes on. "But we will use paraffin—a cleaner, harder wax that the pioneers didn't have."

The students learn that using a double boiler, a vessel within another vessel that contains water, is the safest way to melt the wax. The water in the outer container, a large tin can, reaches the boiling point, and gets no hotter. This temperature is high enough to melt the wax in the inner vessel, a smaller can, but not high enough to set it afire.

Wicks are made by tearing strips from a large sheet of cloth, dipping them in the melted wax, and cooling them repeatedly. With each dip, a thin new layer of wax is deposited on the forming candle. The previous group had dropped a small piece of crayon in the wax pot, so these candles are colored green.

The fire is smoky ("Worse than our Sunday barbecue," quips Huntley student Chris Canova), and the work is tedious. Between this and the labor with the logs, an important point has been learned. Tammy Johnson says it for everybody, "They sure had to work hard in those days, didn't they?"

On the way back from the pioneering program, Tracy Burt stops at the campus library. The library contains 700 doctoral dissertations on outdoor education and related subjects and films to help student teachers in this specialized area. But Tracy is not after any of these. She heads straight for the magazine rack, where Professor Tink has just picked up a professional teaching journal. The rack reflects the nature of Taft Campus. Side by side are journals such as *Instructor and Teacher* and magazines such as *Camping Magazine*, *Scientific American*, and Tracy's choice for a quick reading, *Ranger Rick's Nature Magazine*.

After lunch, group A gathers in the laboratory. The first lesson in survival is how to use a compass. Everybody is asked to find 186° from north. When Huntley student Sally Kaelin suddenly understands how the compass works, she exclaims, "Ooh, let's go get lost!"

Outside in the woods, the Huntley students pair up, two to a compass, to practice using the device. Student teacher Beth Enbrecht tells them to walk 155° from north for about 120 feet, then 40° for about 300 feet. The groups do not end up very close together.

This project is followed by instruction on surviving if lost in the woods. "Where would you build your shelter?" asks student teacher Dan Fiorini.

"In a field," guesses Carrie Mattern.

"No," says Fiorini, "not enough protection from bad weather. Build in a protected area. If you can find it near water, you'll have water to drink, but, also, you'll find the most plant and animal life for food."

Fiorini then points to a large fallen tree that is held partially off the ground by some of its branches. "We'll use that as the initial framework for a shelter. Just find as many branches and leaves as you can and pile them on and over the tree to enclose a cavelike area under its raised portion."

With 16 students working, the shelter quickly takes shape. Stephanie Burr and Tracy Burt are delighted with it and begin to take armloads of dried leaves into it to make a soft, dry "bed."

Next, Fiorini demonstrates how to make a snare to catch animals for food, and there is a lively discussion of what (and who) to use as bait. A young tree is bent almost to the ground to provide the power to close the snare and hold the unfortunate victim. The tree has to

A team of Huntley girls apply the techniques they have learned to build a campfire, *above*. Practice in using a compass, *below,* is also part of the learning process for outdoor survival.

While instructor Denis O'Brien helps Stephanie Burr use a froe to make shingles, *above,* other Huntley students are experimenting with candle-making techniques practiced by the pioneers, *above right.*

be living because a dead tree would snap if bent. Living tissue is flexible and strong, particularly in a tree trunk, which is made up of strong but pliable cylindrical layers that run along its length. These layers provide strength, protection, and channels for the transport of water and nutrients from the roots.

By now it is getting late and everybody is tired. But there is still one more lesson to be learned — how to build a campfire.

First, there is a brief discussion of fire as a chemical process. Fire, the heat and light that come from burning materials, is the result of the rapid combination of oxygen with the materials. Thus, burning, like rusting, is a form of oxidation, the major difference being the speed of the process.

Next, the practical aspects of building a fire are covered. Tinder — such as dried leaves, grass, and tiny twigs — is used to light kindling. The kindling — small pieces of bark, dry twigs, and narrow branches — lights the fuel, which consists of larger pieces of wood. The size of the fuel is then gradually increased until an adequate fire is burning.

As long as the tinder is under the kindling, the kindling under the fuel, and there are enough openings for air to get in, there is no one best way to stack the materials before lighting the fire. The trick is to have the tinder and kindling in the right proportions.

Huntley students trudge through the woods on their way to a science lesson at the Rock River over the hill.

Some of the students go off to find tinder and kindling. Others clear two small areas in which to start two fires. It has become a contest between the girls and the boys. Tammy Johnson has spontaneously become leader of the girls' "team," and is directing construction of the small pile of leaves, grass, and twigs.

The boys' team is less organized, but more energetic. They have collected great quantities of burnable material for a fire that will be much larger than the one the girls will set. And the boys are first to light their tinder, but not by much. Tammy has the girls' fire going less than a minute later.

The boys' fire progresses very slowly. The girls' fire smokes something awful.

"More tinder!" squeals Tammy.

"That will make it worse," warns another student.

Suddenly the boys let out a cheer. As if by magic, their fuel has caught and is burning beautifully. The boys congratulate each other loudly, proclaiming their victory as modestly as peacocks. Later, a student teacher reveals that the boys' fire only started to burn after somebody found a painted board and threw it in. There is some debate as to whether the paint gave the boys an unfair advantage.

The last evening at the Taft Campus for the Huntley students will be busy. In Heckman, some of the students have decided to start by carving pumpkins into jack-o'-lanterns. Others will read or play quiet games. A large number of students have chosen to begin the evening with a square dance.

Close examination – of a water sample from the river, *above,* or the delicate veins in an autumn-turned leaf, *below* – is the first important step in the scientific study of the nature of things.

The social side of the Lorado Taft experience includes the scientific study of square dancing.

The pumpkins are carved more quickly than expected and the reading and quiet games are not very exciting, so everyone gravitates toward the square dance. At first, there is a great deal of shyness, with boys and girls at opposite ends of the room and only student teachers dancing to the record. But gradually, the music gets to the seventh-graders and soon almost everybody is up and dancing. Before the dance is over, an air of warmth and friendship has developed among the whirling dancers — students and student teachers alike.

At 8:15 P.M., everyone sets out for the woods, armed with flashlights. They are headed for the final social event of the program. Under the guidance of Malcolm Swan, a large campfire has been built in a nearby clearing. The Huntley students plunk down around the rim of the fire, placing their newly carved pumpkins, lit from within by candles, at their feet. Then, with a seemingly endless supply of popcorn and lemonade being passed around, a series of songs are sung and stories told.

Friday morning breakfast buzzes with excited conversation about the night before. And then it is time for the final lesson. For group A, the lesson is in science. The group meets in Eagle's Nest where student teacher Nancy Sanders begins by asking, "What is a river?"

"Flowing water," says one Huntley student.

"In a ditch, a channel," adds another.

Sanders reveals that the goal of the lesson is to estimate the age of the Rock River. As background, there is a discussion about the source of river water, how a river cuts into the ground, and other details. As the discussion proceeds, the students get acquainted with some basic physics, chemistry, geology, and agronomy.

They learn that, in general, a young river has little earth material deposited in its bed and along its banks, flows straight and fast, has a V-shaped channel and steep banks, and is likely to have waterfalls, rapids, and canyons. A mature river, on the other hand, has some material deposited in its bed and meanders, or follows a curving course that can create a lake by turning back on itself. This kind of river flows only moderately fast, has a U-shaped channel, less steep banks, and few, if any, falls, rapids, or canyons.

An old river has lots of deposited material, meanders a great deal (creating a large number of lakes), flows slowly, and has a flattened channel and banks. The terms "young," "mature," and "old" represent different time periods for different rivers. It depends on the geology and topology of the area and the speed of the water flow.

On the way to the river, the student teachers pass out magnifying glasses for general nature study. The glasses come in handy as the students trek along the path through the woods. Tammy Johnson is fascinated with the magnified views of fungi and moss that dwell on trees. Chris Canova discovers the minuscule, delicate, veinlike structures on a leaf surface.

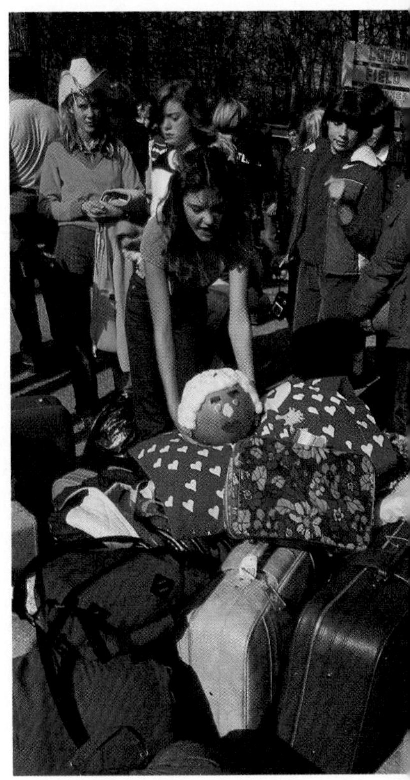

Stories are told and songs are sung around the campfire in the clearing, *above*. The next morning, the Huntley students gather their gear together, *above right,* in preparation for returning home.

The path now follows the river. At one point, the banks are so steep that rain runoff has uncovered some of a tree's roots and a section of strangely chipped and fragmented rock.

"Water gets into the crevices in the rock, freezes, expands, and cracks. And that shatters the rock," explains student teacher Judy Wiesbrock.

Huntley student Tom Anderson examines one of the chipped rocks closely in hopes of finding some fossils, but there are none. Some of the other students collect samples of water from a stream that is feeding the river and from the river itself. Back at the lab, they will test these samples to see what the water contains. As they collect water at the riverbank, they spot hundreds of minnows. "Why are they all here?" Mary Davison wonders out loud.

Student teacher Michele Bjorgo explains that they prefer the shallows near the banks because the sun warms the water more effectively there. Also, larger fish cannot reach and eat them.

When the students return to the lab, some hurry to the microscopes to examine samples of soil, leaves, fungi, nuts, and other things collected while walking to and from the river. A small group gathers to run some simple tests on the stream and river water, and there is a groan of dismay when slight "pollution" (most of it is natural sediment) is discovered in both.

Finally, everyone heads for the dining room for a look at the river from a distance. The students then assemble their clues to the age of the river. The banks are fairly steep, but there are some meanders along with the beginning of a lake where one meander had doubled back upon itself. The water moves fairly quickly, but not as fast as it might, considering the high water level. The students conclude that the Rock River is still young, but it is becoming mature.

It is time for lunch, the last meal at Taft before packing and boarding the buses for home. Everyone tries to assess the value of the experience.

Huntley student Stephanie Burr described it as "a good experience, a different kind of learning."

Cindy Hannon liked the science best. But in general, "I liked it all. I love the outdoors, and now I know more about what goes on there than I did before. My grandfather has some woods, and I love to walk in them. It will be more interesting and meaningful now."

Carrie Mattern "learned a lot of things that I couldn't have learned as well from a book."

Outdoor education has been around as long as the human race. Primitive people learned to wrest food, shelter, clothing, and tools from nature to survive. As civilization developed, people began to understand how to take advantage of their environment and to pass their skills on to succeeding generations. Industrialization reduced the number of people who needed to know how nature worked in order to survive, and eventually this information was available only in textbooks. But, as Johann Heinrich Pestalozzi, an 18th-century Swiss educational reformer, wrote—studying from a textbook "filled children's minds with hazy ideas and meaningless words . . . " but "teaching through observation gave . . . clear ideas, greater knowledge, and more experience in oral expression."

In places like the Lorado Taft Field Campus, Pestalozzi's words ring true to even the casual observer of this learning in action.

There is no central place for locating all the available outdoor-education facilities in the United States. But there are some possible sources of information. One is a nearby university or college. The department of education in your state may also be helpful. Your state's park, recreation, and outdoor and environmental associations are also possibilities. Other places to try are the American Camping Association at Bradford Woods, Martinsville, Ind. 46152, and organizations such as the National Wildlife Federation and the Sierra Club. The 10 regional offices of the National Park Service provide programs in outdoor education. For information, write to: Office of Public Affairs, National Park Service, Department of Interior, Washington, D.C. 20240.

World Book Supplement

Revised articles on subjects in science and technology reprinted from the 1982 edition of *The World Book Encyclopedia.*

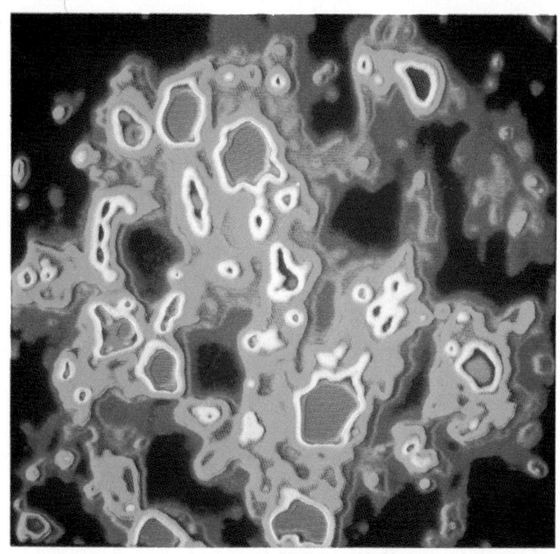

A. V. Crewe, M. Ohtsuki, and M. Utlaut, Enrico Fermi Institute, University of Chicago

Individual Atoms of the metals platinum and palladium magnified about 3 million times appear as yellow dots in this photo made with an electron microscope. The yellow areas with red or purple centers are clusters of atoms. Color was added electronically to improve the image. Atoms themselves have no color.

ATOM is one of the basic units of matter. Everything around us is made up of atoms. An atom is incredibly tiny—more than a million times smaller than the thickness of a human hair. The smallest speck that can be seen under an ordinary microscope contains more than 10 billion atoms.

Atoms form the building blocks of the simplest substances, the *chemical elements.* Familiar elements include hydrogen, oxygen, iron, and lead. Each chemical element consists of one basic kind of atom. *Compounds* are more complicated substances composed of two or more kinds of atoms linked together in units called *molecules.* Water, for example, is a compound in which each molecule consists of two atoms of hydrogen linked to one atom of oxygen.

Atoms vary greatly in weight, but they are all about the same size. For example, an atom of uranium, the heaviest element found in nature, weighs more than 200 times as much as an atom of hydrogen, the lightest known element. However, the diameter of a uranium atom is only about 3 times that of a hydrogen atom.

Robert H. March, the contributor of this article, is Professor of Physics at the University of Wisconsin-Madison and the author of Physics for Poets.

The Parts of an Atom

Tiny as atoms are, they consist of even more minute particles. The three basic types are *protons, neutrons,* and *electrons.* Each atom has a definite number of these *subatomic* particles. The protons and neutrons are crowded into the *nucleus,* an exceedingly tiny region at the center of the atom. If a hydrogen atom were about 4 miles (6.4 kilometers) in diameter, its nucleus would be no bigger than a tennis ball. The rest of an atom outside the nucleus is mostly empty space. The electrons whirl through this space, completing billions of trips around the nucleus each millionth of a second. The fantastic speed of the electrons makes atoms behave as if they were solid, much as the fast-moving blades of a fan prevent a pencil from being pushed through them.

Atoms are often compared to the solar system, with the nucleus corresponding to the sun and the electrons corresponding to the planets that orbit the sun. This comparison is not completely accurate, however. Unlike the planets, the electrons do not follow regular, orderly paths. In addition, the protons and neutrons constantly move about at random inside the nucleus.

The Nucleus makes up nearly all the *mass* of an atom. Mass is the quantity of matter in an atom. Each proton has a mass roughly equal to that of 1,836 electrons, and it would take 1,839 electrons to equal the mass of a

WORLD BOOK illustration by Leonard E. Morgan

The Parts of an Atom

An atom consists of three basic types of particles called *protons, neutrons,* and *electrons.* Protons have a positive electric charge, and electrons have a negative charge. Neutrons are electrically neutral. The protons and neutrons are clustered in the *nucleus,* a tiny region near the center of the atom. The electrons whirl at fantastic speeds through the empty space outside the nucleus.

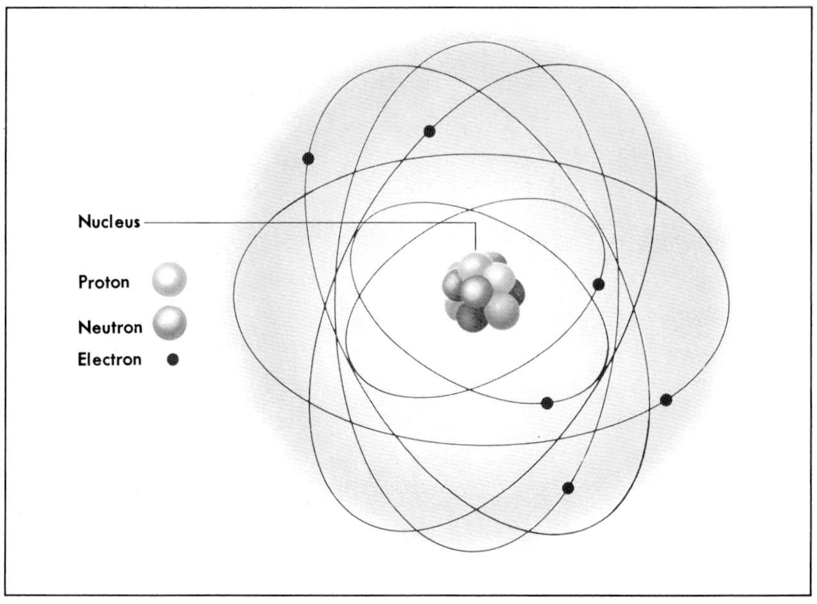

neutron. Each proton carries one unit of positive electric charge. Each electron carries one unit of negative charge. Neutrons have no electric charge. Under most conditions, an atom has the same number of protons and electrons, and so the atom is electrically neutral.

Protons and neutrons are about 100,000 times smaller than atoms, but they are in turn made up of even smaller particles called *quarks*. Each proton and neutron consists of three quarks. In the laboratory, scientists can cause quarks to combine and form other kinds of subatomic particles besides protons and neutrons. All these other particles break down and change into ordinary particles in a small fraction of a second. Thus, none of them is found in ordinary atoms. However, scientists first learned that protons and neutrons consist of quarks through the study of other subatomic particles. For information on these other particles, see PARTICLE PHYSICS and the separate articles on subatomic particles listed in the *Related Articles* at the end of this article.

The Electrons, unlike the protons and neutrons, do not seem to have smaller parts. Electrons have very little mass. The mass of an electron in grams is written with a decimal point followed by 27 zeros and a 9.

Opposite electric charges attract. The positively charged nucleus therefore exerts a force on the negatively charged electrons that keeps them within the atom. However, each electron has energy and so is able to resist the attraction of the nucleus. The more energy an electron has, the farther from the nucleus it will be. Thus, electrons are arranged in *shells* at various distances from the nucleus according to how much energy they have. Electrons with the least energy are in inner shells, and those with more energy are in outer shells.

Each electron shell has a letter name. The shell closest to the nucleus is traditionally called the K shell. The other shells, in order of increasing distance from the nucleus, are the L, M, N, O, P, and Q shells. Each shell can hold only a limited number of electrons. The K shell can hold no more than 2 electrons. The L shell can hold 8 electrons, the M shell 18, and the N shell 32. In theory, the O shell can hold 50 electrons, the P shell 72, and the Q shell 98. However, these outer shells are never completely filled.

The Properties of Atoms

The Atomic Number tells how many protons an atom has. All atoms of the same element have the same number of protons. For example, every hydrogen atom has a single proton, and so the atomic number of hydrogen is 1. The atomic numbers for all the other natural elements range successively up to 92 for uranium, which has 92 protons in each atom. Elements whose atoms have more than 92 protons can be created in the laboratory.

The atomic number determines an element's place in the *periodic table*. This table organizes the elements into groups with similar chemical properties. For a reproduction of the periodic table, see ELEMENT, CHEMICAL.

The Mass Number is the sum of the protons and neutrons in an atom. Although all atoms of an element have the same number of protons, they may have different numbers of neutrons. Atoms that have the same number of protons but different numbers of neutrons are called *isotopes*.

Most of the elements in nature have more than one isotope. Hydrogen, for example, has three. In the most common hydrogen isotope, the nucleus consists only of a proton. In the two other hydrogen isotopes, the nucleus consists of one or two neutrons in addition to the proton. Scientists use the mass number to distinguish the three isotopes as hydrogen 1, hydrogen 2, and hydrogen 3. Scientists also refer to hydrogen 1 as *protium*, to hydrogen 2 as *deuterium*, and to hydrogen 3 as *tritium*.

In most lighter elements, the nucleus of each atom contains about an equal number of protons and neutrons. Most heavier elements, however, have more neutrons than protons. The heaviest elements have about 3 neutrons for every 2 protons. For example, uranium 238 has 146 neutrons and 92 protons.

WORLD BOOK illustration by Leonard E. Morgan

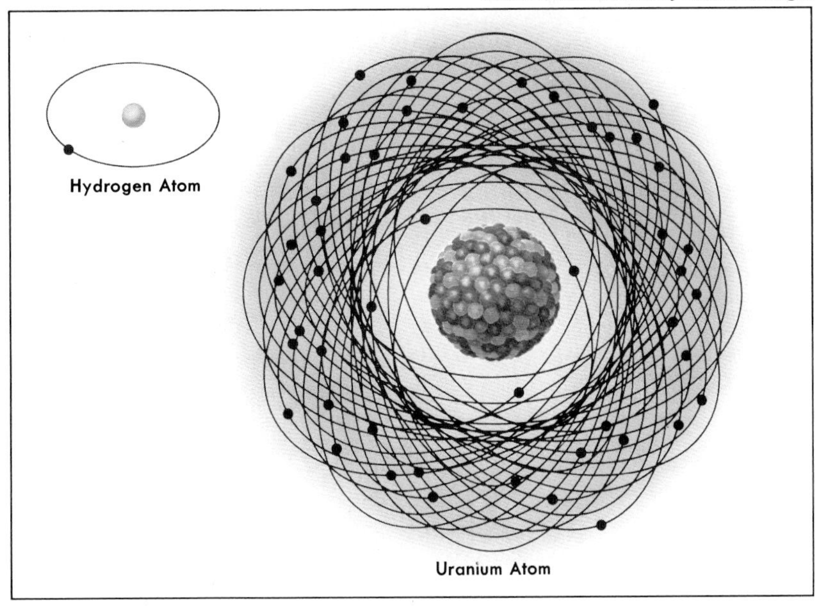

How Atoms Compare in Weight and Size

Atoms vary greatly in weight, but they are all about the same size. The smallest and lightest atom is the hydrogen atom. It consists of 1 proton and 1 electron. The largest and heaviest atom found in nature is the uranium atom. It has 92 protons, 146 neutrons, and 92 electrons. An atom of uranium weighs more than 200 times as much as an atom of hydrogen. However, a uranium atom is only about 3 times as large in diameter as a hydrogen atom.

Electron Shells and Chemical Behavior

An atom's electrons are arranged in *shells*. Starting with the innermost, the shells are labeled K through Q. Each shell can hold only a certain number of electrons. For example, the L shell can hold eight. In chemical reactions, the outermost shell gains, loses, or shares electrons.

WORLD BOOK diagrams by Zorica Dabich

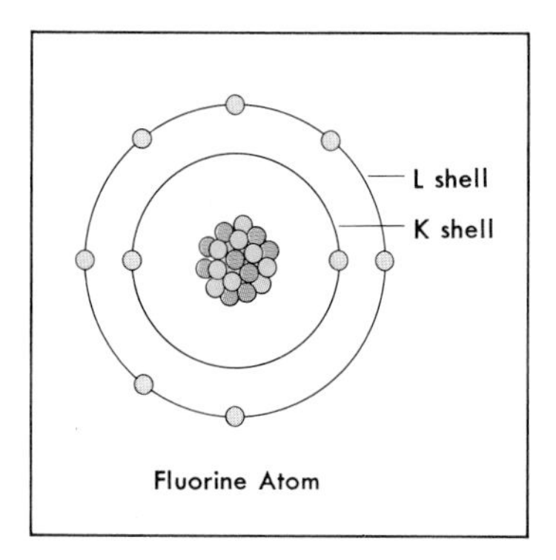

A fluorine atom has seven electrons in its L shell. The atom fills the shell by accepting one electron from another atom.

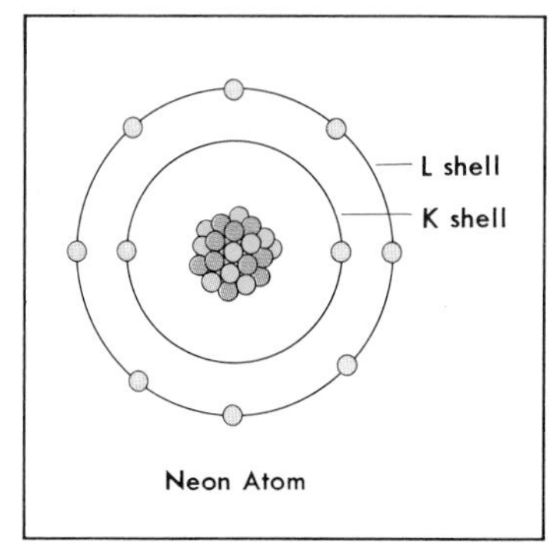

In a neon atom, the L shell is filled. As a result, neon generally does not enter into chemical reactions with other atoms.

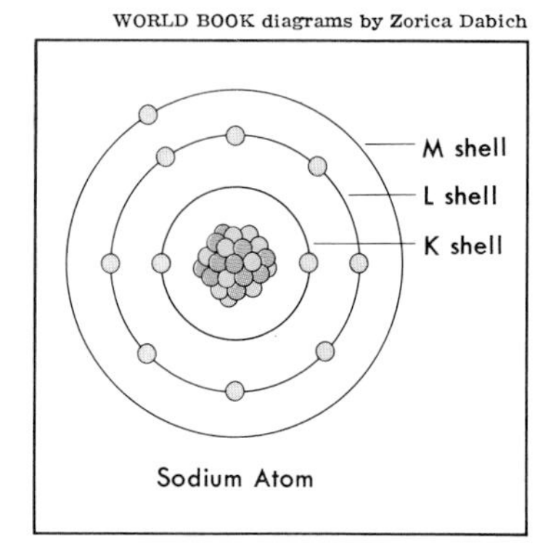

A sodium atom tends to lose the one electron in its M shell. The filled L shell then becomes the outermost shell.

Atomic Weight is the weight of an atom expressed in *atomic mass units* (amu). One amu, also called a *dalton*, equals $\frac{1}{12}$ the weight of an atom of carbon 12. For most atoms, the weight in amu is extremely close to the mass number. Atomic mass units are very small. There are 602 billion trillion amu in a gram.

Scientists determine the atomic weight of an element with more than one isotope by averaging the weights of all the isotopes in the proportions in which they occur in nature. For example, the atomic weight of chlorine is 35.453 amu. This value is an average for the two isotopes chlorine 35 (atomic weight 34.96885) and chlorine 37 (atomic weight 36.96590) in the proportions in which they occur.

Electric Charge. Although an atom is normally electrically neutral, it can lose or gain a few electrons in some chemical reactions or in a collision with an electron or another atom. This gain or loss of electrons produces an electrically charged atom called an *ion*. An atom that loses electrons becomes a *positive ion*, and an atom that gains electrons becomes a *negative ion*. The gain or loss of electrons is called *ionization*.

Chemical Behavior. The chemical behavior of an atom is determined largely by the number of electrons in its outermost shell. When atoms combine and form molecules, electrons in the outermost shell are either transferred from one atom to another or shared between atoms. The number of electrons involved in this process is called the *valence*. The atoms of some elements can have more than one valence, depending on the number and kind of atoms with which they are combined.

If an atom tends to lose electrons to other atoms, its valence is positive. If an atom tends to gain electrons, its valence is negative. For example, sodium tends to lose one electron and thus has a valence of +1. Chlorine tends to accept one electron from another atom and so has a valence of −1. A molecule of ordinary table salt consists of one atom of sodium linked to one atom of chlorine. The sodium atom donates the electron that chlorine is able to accept.

Radioactivity. In some atoms, the nucleus can change naturally. Such an atom is called *radioactive*. The change in the nucleus may be only in the arrangement of the protons and neutrons. Or the actual number of protons and neutrons may change. When a nucleus changes, it gives off radiation. This radiation consists of alpha or beta particles or gamma rays. Atoms of uranium, radium, and all other elements heavier than bismuth are radioactive. Some isotopes of lighter elements are also radioactive. In addition, physicists can create radioactive isotopes of nearly all elements in a laboratory by bombarding atoms with protons, neutrons, or other subatomic particles.

The type of radiation given off by a radioactive nucleus depends on the way the nucleus changes. Gamma rays are given off if only the arrangement of the protons

The Isotopes of Hydrogen

Isotopes are atoms of the same element that have different numbers of neutrons. Hydrogen, for example, has three isotopes. In *protium,* the most common hydrogen isotope by far, the nucleus consists of only a proton. The nucleus of an atom of *deuterium* has one proton and one neutron. Two neutrons and a proton make up the nucleus of the third hydrogen isotope, *tritium.*

WORLD BOOK diagram by Zorica Dabich

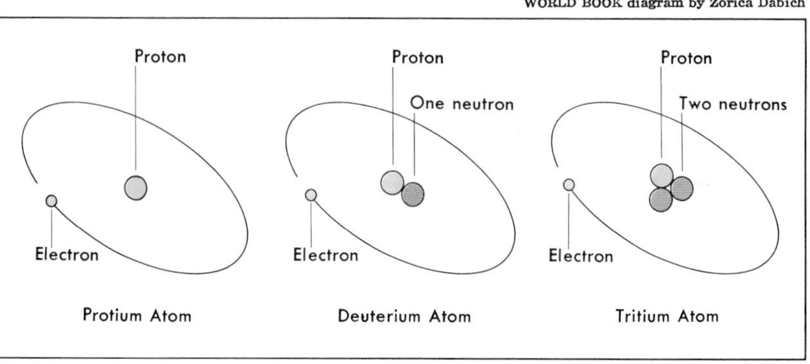

and neutrons in the nucleus changes. But alpha or beta radiation is given off if the number of protons and neutrons in the nucleus changes. The atom then becomes an atom of a different element. This process is called *transmutation* or *radioactive decay*. See RADIOACTIVITY; TRANSMUTATION OF ELEMENTS.

The Forces Within an Atom

The field of physics called *quantum mechanics* deals with the forces inside an atom and the motions of subatomic particles. This field began in 1913, when the Danish physicist Niels Bohr used the *quantum theory* to explain the motion of electrons in atoms. Other physicists further developed quantum mechanics and applied its principles to the nucleus as well as the electrons. See QUANTUM MECHANICS.

Electron Energy Levels. According to quantum mechanics, electrons cannot have just any amount of energy. Instead, electrons are restricted to a limited set of motions, each of which has a specific value of energy. These motions are called *quantum states* or *energy levels*. When an electron is in a given quantum state, it does not absorb or give off energy. For this reason, an atom can gain or lose energy only if one or more electrons change their quantum state.

Just as water always seeks its lowest possible level, electrons seek the state of lowest energy. However, only one electron at a time can occupy each quantum state. If the lower states are filled, other electrons are forced to occupy higher states. If all electrons are in the lowest possible state, the atom is in its *ground state*. This condition is normal for atoms at ordinary temperatures.

When matter is heated to temperatures higher than a few hundred degrees, energy is available to raise one or more electrons to a higher energy level. The atom is then in an *excited state*. However, atoms rarely remain in an excited state for more than a fraction of a second. An excited electron almost immediately drops to a lower state and continues dropping until the atom returns to its ground state. At each succeeding drop, the electron gives off a tiny packet of radiant energy called a *photon*. The energy of the photon equals the difference between the two energy levels of the electron. The photons given off by electrons are detected as visible light and other forms of electromagnetic radiation.

Bohr originally described the quantum states of electrons as orbits like those of the planets around the sun. However, physicists now know that this description is incorrect because an electron is not simply a particle. An electron also has some characteristics of a wave. It is difficult to imagine how something could be both a particle and a wave. This difficulty is one of the problems scientists have in trying to describe the atom to nonscientists. To do so, scientists must use familiar ideas based on our knowledge of the world as we observe it. But conditions inside the tiny atom differ greatly from those in our everyday world. For this reason, physicists can describe the motions of electrons accurately and completely only in mathematical terms.

Forces in the Nucleus. The quantum rules that govern the motions of electrons also apply to the motions of protons and neutrons inside the nucleus. However, the force that keeps the nuclear particles together differs greatly from the electrical attraction that holds the electrons within the atom. Each nuclear particle is attracted to its nearest neighbor by what is called the *nuclear force* or, sometimes, the *strong interaction*. Like electric charges repel each other. However, the powerful nuclear force overcomes the mutual repulsion of the positively charged protons. It thus keeps the nucleus from flying apart. This force dies off quickly, however, unless the nuclear particles are extremely close together. Electrons are immune to the nuclear force.

The nuclear force is highly complicated, and no exact mathematical description of it has been formulated. Nevertheless, a theory known as the *nuclear shell model* provides reasonably accurate estimates of the energy levels in the nucleus.

One neutron and one proton can occupy each quantum state in the nucleus. For this reason, a light nucleus has a nearly equal number of protons and neutrons. But a proton and a neutron in the same state do not have the same amount of energy. Each proton is electrically repelled by all other protons in the nucleus, which in-

Electron Energy Levels in an Atom

An electron in an atom cannot have just any amount of energy. Instead, it is restricted to a limited set of motions, each with a specific value of energy. These motions are called *energy levels* or *quantum states*. An electron absorbs or gives off energy only when it changes from one energy level to another.

WORLD BOOK diagrams by Zorica Dabich

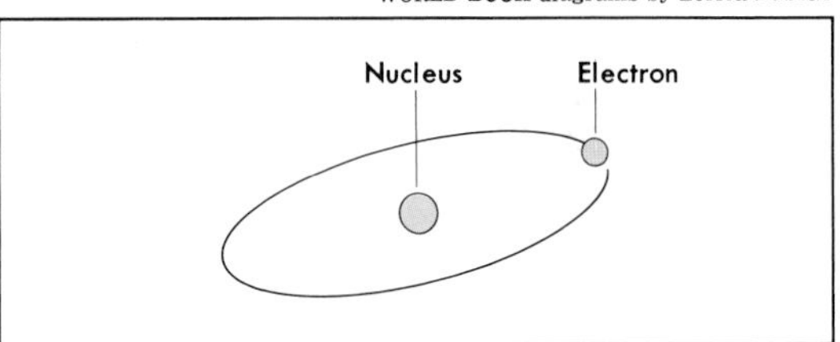

In the atom above, the electron is in its lowest possible energy level. Physicists say that such an atom is in its *ground state*.

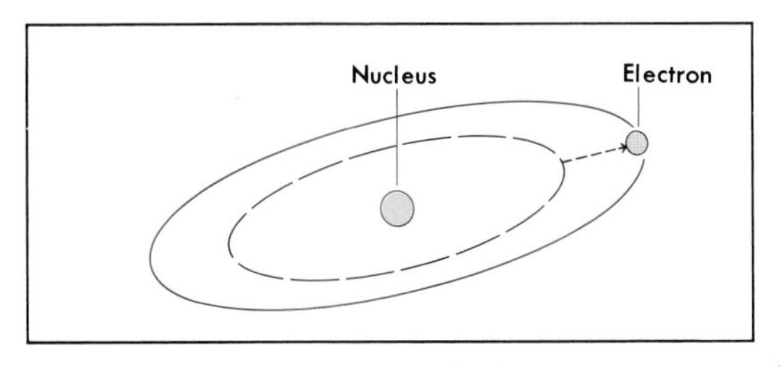

Heating the atom provides energy to raise the electron to a higher energy level. The atom is now in an *excited state*.

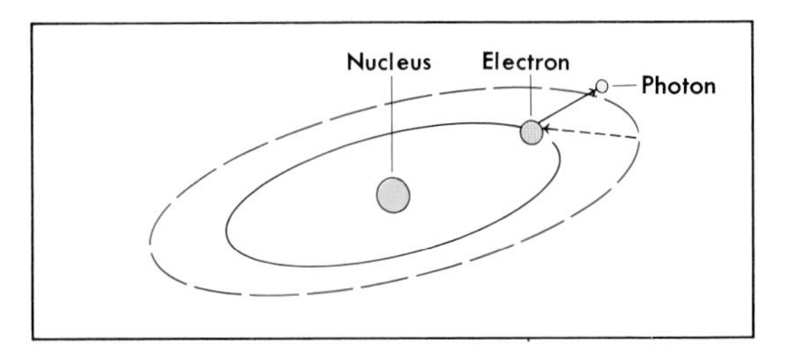

The electron drops back almost immediately. As it does so, it gives off energy in the form of a *photon* (particle of light).

creases its energy. In a nucleus with many protons, the difference in energy levels between protons and neutrons is considerable, and more low-energy states are available for neutrons than for protons. This fact explains why a heavy nucleus has more neutrons than protons.

How Scientists Study Atoms

Scientists use a variety of instruments and techniques to study atoms. The devices and methods used depend on whether the researchers are studying the atoms themselves, the electrons, the nuclear particles, or the quarks.

Researchers use X rays to study the arrangements of atoms in regular, repeated patterns, such as in crystals. When X rays pass through a crystal, the atoms in the crystal *diffract* (spread out) the X rays in a certain way. These diffracted rays produce patterns on photographic film that reveal how far apart the atoms are and how they are arranged. Extremely powerful *scanning electron microscopes* and *field-emission microscopes* enable scientists to observe the positions and movements of individual atoms. However, these instruments cannot reveal any details of the structure of atoms.

Scientists study the motions of electrons chiefly by analyzing the light given off by atoms in heated gases. Instruments called *spectrometers* break up the light into a spectrum with a separate line for each wavelength of light. Each wavelength is related to the difference in energy between two quantum states in the atom. After determining the wavelengths, scientists can draw up a complete list of energy levels. With the aid of quantum mechanics, they can then obtain a description of the electron motions in the atom.

Scientists gain some information about the motions of protons and neutrons by studying the gamma rays given off when a nucleus returns from an excited state to the ground state. However, most of their knowledge of nuclear structure has come from experiments with *particle accelerators*. These devices bombard the nucleus with beams of high-energy electrons or protons. The swift-moving electrons or protons can disrupt the motion of particles in the nucleus and occasionally even knock some of them loose. In some experiments, whole nuclei are accelerated and smashed into stationary nuclei. Nuclear physicists have developed a wide variety of detectors for observing the particles that emerge from these collisions. Most of the detectors produce an electric signal when a particle passes through them.

Particle accelerators are also used to study the behavior of quarks. However, such studies require particles with much greater energies than those that are used to study nuclei. As a result, much more powerful accelerators are required.

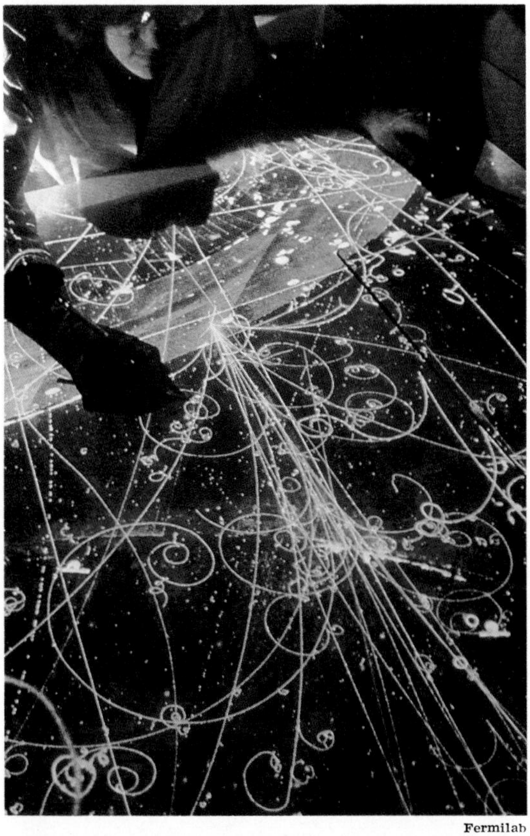

Fermilab

Tracks Made by Atomic Particles from a *particle accelerator*, a device that speeds up the particles, are recorded on film. Physicists study the tracks to learn about the characteristics of the particles that produced them.

Development of the Atomic Theory

The idea that everything is made up of a few simple parts originated during the 400's B.C. in the philosophy of *atomism*. Atomism was founded by the Greek philosopher Leucippus, but his disciple Democritus developed the philosophy more fully. Democritus gave his basic particle the name *atom*, which means *uncuttable*. He imagined atoms as small, hard particles, all composed of the same substance but of different sizes and shapes. During the 300's B.C., a Greek philosopher named Epicurus incorporated Democritus' ideas about atoms into his philosophy. About 50 B.C., the Roman philosopher and poet Lucretius presented the fundamental principles of atomism in his long poem, *On the Nature of Things*. See ATOMISM.

During the Middle Ages, the idea of atoms was largely ignored. This neglect resulted partly from the fact that atomism had been rejected by Aristotle, an ancient Greek philosopher whose theories dominated medieval philosophy and science. The idea that atoms form the basic units of all matter did survive, however. During the 1500's and 1600's, such founders of modern science as Francis Bacon and Isaac Newton of England and Galileo of Italy believed in atoms. However, they could add little more to the atomic theory than Democritus had described.

The Birth of the Modern Atomic Theory. In 1750, Rudjer Boscovich, a scientist born in what is now Yugoslavia, suggested that Democritus might have been wrong in believing that atoms are "uncuttable." Boscovich thought that atoms contain smaller parts, which in turn contain still smaller parts, and so forth down to the fundamental building blocks of matter. He felt that these building blocks must be geometric points with no size at all. Today, most atomic physicists accept a modern form of this idea.

The development of the atomic theory advanced greatly when chemistry became an exact science during the late 1700's. Chemists discovered that they could combine elements to form compounds only in certain fixed proportions according to mass. In 1803, a British chemist named John Dalton developed an atomic theory to explain this discovery. Dalton proposed that each element consists of a particular kind of atom and that the varying properties of the elements result from differences in their atoms. He further suggested that all atoms of a given element are identical in size, shape, and mass. According to Dalton's theory, when atoms combine and form a particular compound, they always combine in a specific numerical ratio. As a result, the composition by mass of a particular compound is always the same.

The First Descriptions of Atomic Structure. In 1897, a British physicist named Joseph John Thomson discovered that atoms are "cuttable." He made this discovery while studying the rays that travel between charged metal plates in a vacuum tube. Thomson determined that the rays consisted of lightweight, negatively charged particles. He had thus discovered electrons. Thomson immediately realized that the electrons must be part of the atom. He proposed a model of the atom in which negatively charged electrons were embedded in a positively charged sphere. Although Thomson's description was far from correct, his work encouraged other scientists to investigate the structure of the atom.

In 1911, the British physicist Ernest Rutherford presented his theory of atomic structure. Rutherford, a former student of Thomson's, declared that nearly all the mass of an atom is concentrated in a tiny nucleus. He also stated that the nucleus is surrounded by electrons traveling at tremendous speeds through the atom's outer regions.

Rutherford based his theory on the results of experiments in which he bombarded thin sheets of gold with alpha particles. Most of the particles passed through the sheets, which showed that the gold atoms must consist chiefly of empty space. However, some alpha particles bounced back as if they had hit something solid. Rutherford concluded that these particles had been reflected by a strong force from the tiny but heavy nucleus of an atom.

Rutherford's theory did not explain the arrangement of electrons in atoms. In 1913, however, a description of the electron structure was proposed by Niels Bohr, a Danish physicist who had worked with Rutherford.

Models of the Atom During the 1900's, physicists have proposed various models of atomic structure. The diagrams below show the three most important early models and a present-day model.

WORLD BOOK diagrams by Zorica Dabich

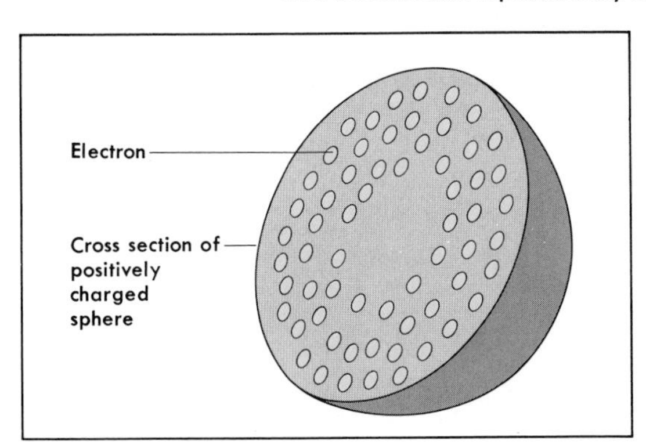

The Thomson Model was proposed by the British physicist Joseph John Thomson in 1904. It showed the electrons embedded in a positively charged sphere like seeds in a watermelon.

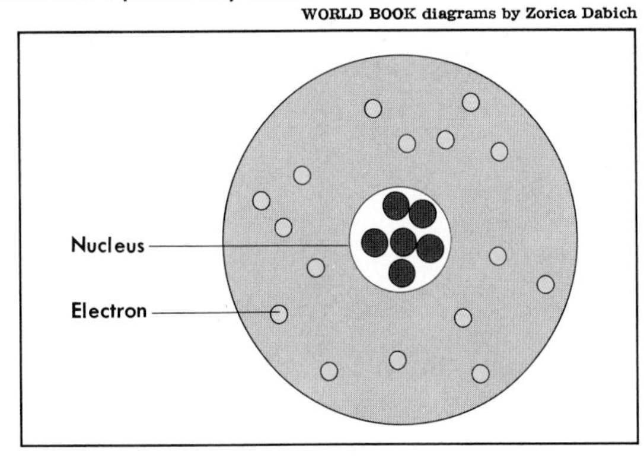

The Rutherford Model showed the mass of the atom concentrated in a positively charged nucleus surrounded by electrons. Ernest Rutherford, a British physicist, proposed this model in 1911.

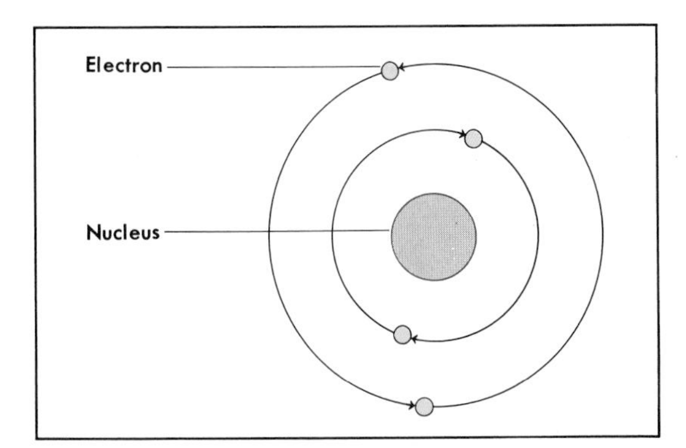

The Bohr Model, proposed in 1913 by the Danish physicist Niels Bohr, gave a description of the electron structure. It showed the electrons traveling in fixed orbits around the nucleus.

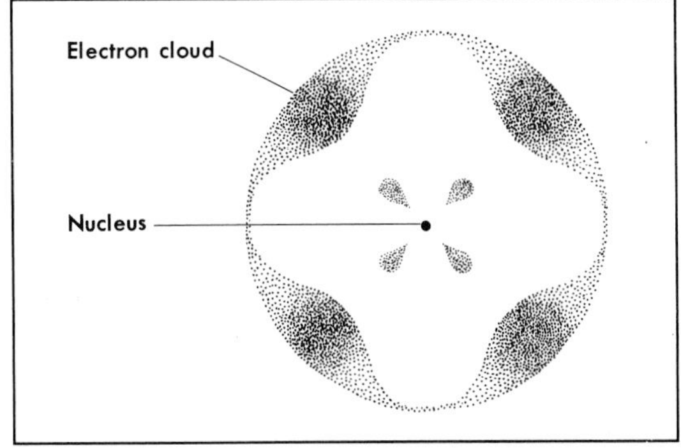

The Electron Cloud Model, a currently accepted model, indicates the regions within the atom where electrons may be found. Electrons are most likely to be where a cloud is darkest.

Bohr suggested that electrons could travel only in a certain set of orbits around the nucleus. Bohr's original, crude picture of the atom was inadequate, but many of the ideas behind it proved correct. In 1924, the French physicist Louis de Broglie proposed that electrons have some properties of waves. By 1928, a correct description of the arrangement of electrons had been obtained with the help of other physicists, especially Erwin Schrödinger and Wolfgang Pauli of Austria and Max Born and Werner Heisenberg of Germany.

Studying the Nucleus. Although physicists understood the motions of electrons by 1928, the nucleus remained largely a mystery. Protons had been discovered in the late 1800's, and Rutherford had determined in 1914 that they must form part of the nucleus. But scientists realized that the nucleus could not consist of only protons. In 1932, a British physicist named James Chadwick discovered that the nucleus also contains uncharged particles, or neutrons. Also during the early 1930's, scientists developed particle accelerators capable of producing energies high enough to study the nucleus.

The pioneers of nuclear physics did not expect that they would soon see a practical use for their knowledge. In 1938, however, researchers discovered that bombarding the nucleus of a uranium atom with a neutron caused the nucleus to split into two parts and release energy. They called the process *nuclear fission.* The discovery came a few months before the start of World War II in 1939, and fission was used in atomic bombs that helped end the war in 1945.

The development of atomic weapons made governments aware of the importance of nuclear physics. As a result, they provided great sums of money for nuclear research after the war. The funds made possible the construction of accelerators of increasing size and energy. As these accelerators revealed more and more details of the nucleus, researchers realized that the proton and neutron could not be simple objects. They also found that the neutron did not completely lack an electric charge. Instead, it contained equal amounts of positive and negative charge. In addition, researchers discovered hundreds of new particles. These particles were sufficiently similar to one another and to protons and neutrons to suggest that all nuclear particles might be merely different arrangements of a few simple parts.

Recent Discoveries. By 1964, researchers had turned up enough clues to indicate what the fundamental parts of protons, neutrons, and other nuclear particles might be like. The American physicists Murray Gell-Mann and George Zweig thus proposed a theory describing these parts. Gell-Mann named the parts *quarks.* By 1971, physicists had demonstrated that these particles were much smaller than protons and neutrons.

The success of the quark theory has led to rapid progress in subatomic physics. An exact description of the force between protons and neutrons has never been formulated because of the complexity of these particles. However, the force that holds quarks together is becoming well understood and may help physicists eventually understand the nuclear force. The question remains whether quarks are the final, elementary building blocks of atoms. Much research is being devoted to answering this question. ROBERT H. MARCH

CIRCULATORY SYSTEM is a network that carries blood throughout the body. All animals except the simplest kinds have some type of circulatory system.

In some *invertebrates* (animals without a backbone), the circulatory system consists of a simple network of tubes and hollow spaces. Other invertebrates have pump-like structures that send blood through a system of blood vessels. In human beings and other *vertebrates* (animals with a backbone), the circulatory system consists primarily of a pumping organ—the heart—and a network of blood vessels.

The human circulatory system supplies the cells of the body with the food and oxygen they need to survive. At the same time, it carries carbon dioxide and other wastes away from the cells. The circulatory system also helps regulate the temperature of the body and carries substances that protect the body from disease. In addition, the system transports chemical substances called *hormones,* which help regulate the activities of various parts of the body. This article discusses mainly the human circulatory system.

Parts of the Circulatory System

The human circulatory system has three main parts: (1) the heart, (2) the blood vessels, and (3) the blood. A fluid called *lymph,* and the vessels that carry it, are sometimes considered a part of the circulatory system.

The Human Circulatory System

In human beings, the circulatory system consists chiefly of a pump—the heart—and a network of blood vessels. These vessels—arteries, veins, and capillaries—carry blood throughout the body.

WORLD BOOK illustration by Colin Bidgood

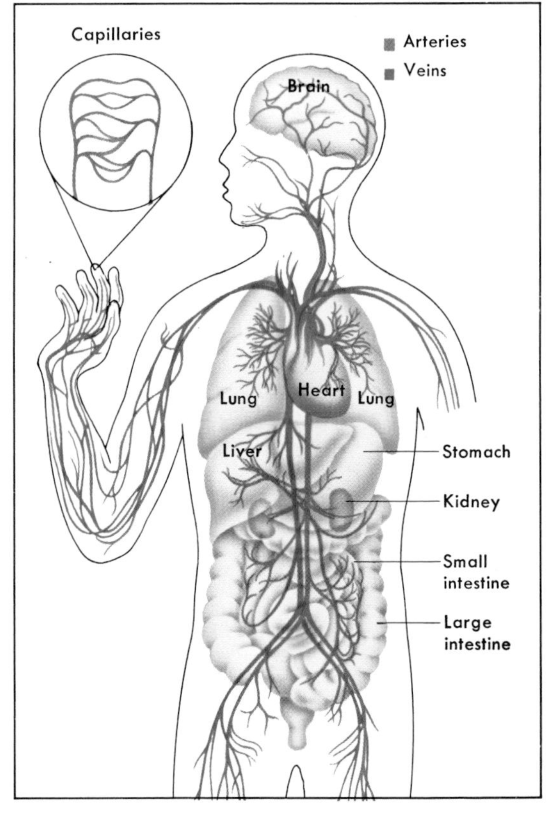

The Heart is a hollow, muscular organ that pumps blood. It consists of two pumps that lie side by side. These pumps relax when taking in blood and contract as they send out blood. The left side of the heart is a stronger pump than the right side. The stronger pump receives blood from the lungs and sends it to cells throughout the body. The weaker pump receives blood from the cells throughout the body and sends it to the lungs.

The Blood Vessels form a complicated system of connecting tubes throughout the body. There are three major types of these vessels. *Arteries* carry blood from the heart. *Veins* return blood to the heart. *Capillaries* are tiny vessels that connect the arteries and the veins.

The Blood consists chiefly of a liquid called *plasma* and three kinds of solid particles known as *formed elements*. Plasma is made up mostly of water, but it also contains proteins, minerals, and other substances. The three types of formed elements are called *red blood cells*, *white blood cells*, and *platelets*. Red blood cells carry oxygen and carbon dioxide throughout the body. White blood cells help protect the body from disease. Platelets release substances that enable blood to clot. Platelets thus aid in preventing the loss of blood from injured vessels.

Functions of the Circulatory System

The circulatory system performs many vital functions. It plays an important role in respiration, in nutrition, in the removal of wastes and poisons, and in several other body processes.

In Respiration. The circulatory system plays a part in respiration by delivering oxygen to the cells and removing carbon dioxide from them. During this process, the blood follows two routes called the *systemic circulation* and the *pulmonary circulation.*

From the left side of the heart, blood full of oxygen is pumped into the systemic circulation. This blood leaves the heart through the *aorta*, the main artery of the body. A number of major arteries branch off the aorta. These arteries, in turn, branch into smaller and smaller vessels, finally emptying into the tiny capillaries. There, oxygen leaves the blood and enters the tissues through the thin capillary walls. In a similar way, carbon dioxide leaves the tissues and enters the blood. The blood, now carrying carbon dioxide, leaves the capillaries and flows through larger and larger veins. Eventually, the blood enters the right side of the heart through two large veins —the *superior vena cava*, which carries blood from the head and arms, and the *inferior vena cava*, which carries blood from the trunk and legs.

From the right side of the heart, the blood is pumped into the pulmonary circulation. *Pulmonary arteries* carry the blood that contains carbon dioxide to capillaries in the lungs. The carbon dioxide passes through the capillary walls into the lungs and is then exhaled. Oxygen that has been inhaled passes from the lungs into the blood in a similar way. The blood returns through the *pulmonary veins* to the left side of the heart and begins its journey again.

In Nutrition. The circulatory system carries digested food substances to the cells of the body. These nutrients enter the bloodstream by passing through the walls of the small intestine into the capillaries. The blood then carries most of the nutrients to the liver.

Some Functions of the Circulatory System

WORLD BOOK illustrations by Colin Bidgood

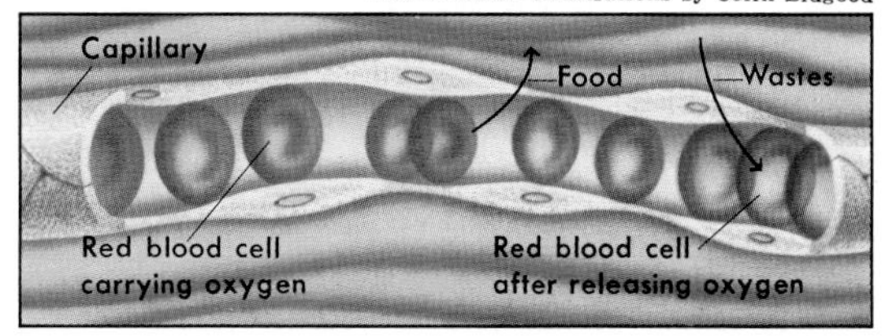

In Maintaining Body Tissues. The circulatory system supplies tissues of the body with essential food and oxygen, and carries away carbon dioxide and other wastes. Substances leave and enter the bloodstream through thin capillary walls.

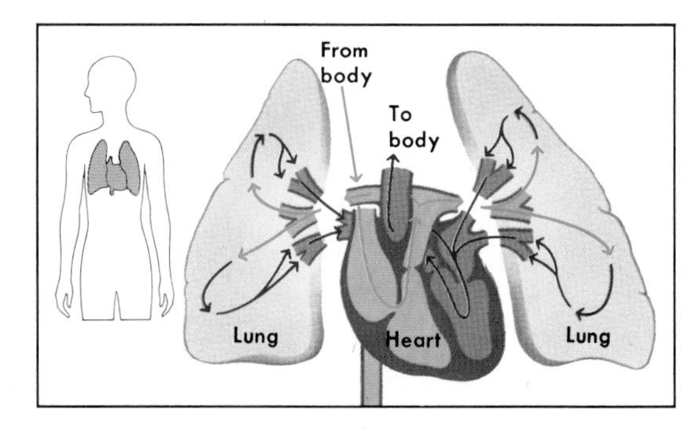

In Respiration. Blood carrying carbon dioxide, *blue,* flows to the heart. The heart pumps this blood to the lungs, where it gives up carbon dioxide and picks up oxygen. The oxygen-rich blood, *red,* returns to the heart and is pumped to all parts of the body.

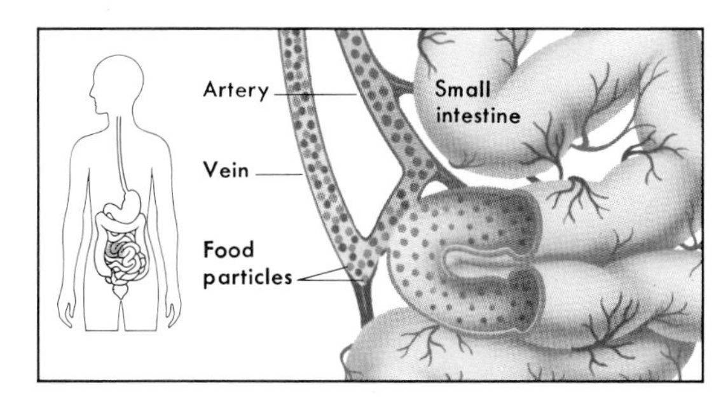

In Nutrition. The circulatory system carries digested food particles to the cells of the body. These particles enter the bloodstream through the walls of the small intestine.

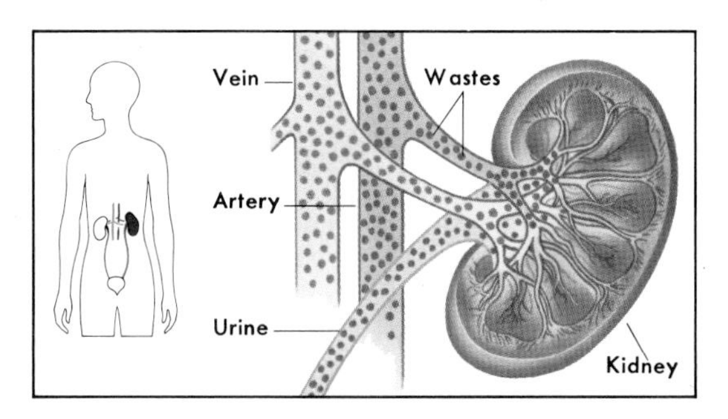

In Removal of Wastes. Waste products from body tissues are carried by the blood to the kidneys. The kidneys filter out these substances and expel them in the urine.

The liver removes certain nutrients from the blood and stores them. It later releases the nutrients into the blood when the body needs them. The liver also changes some nutrients into substances needed by the body. Blood leaving the liver contains nutrients that the cells use in the production of energy, enzymes, and new building materials for the body.

In Removal of Wastes and Poisons. The circulatory system helps dispose of waste products and poisons that would harm the body if they accumulated. These substances include carbon dioxide, salts, and *ammonia*, a by-product of the cells' use of protein.

The liver removes ammonia and other wastes, and various poisons that enter the body through the digestive system. The liver converts the wastes and poisons into water-soluble substances, which are carried by the blood to the kidneys. The kidneys filter out these and other water-soluble wastes and expel them from the body in urine.

Other Functions. The circulatory system helps protect the body from disease. White blood cells engulf and destroy bacteria, viruses, and other harmful invaders. As the blood circulates, it also helps keep the body temperature stable by absorbing heat from the cells' production of energy. If the temperature of the body begins to rise, the flow of blood into vessels in the skin increases. The heat from cells deep in the body is thus carried to the skin, from where it passes out of the body. If the temperature of the body begins to drop, the flow of blood to the skin is restricted. This action enables the body to retain as much heat as possible.

The circulatory system also carries hormones. These chemical substances affect or control the activities of various organs and tissues. Hormones are produced by the endocrine glands, including the thyroid, pituitary, adrenal, and sex glands. These glands release their hormones into the bloodstream.

Disorders of the Circulatory System

The circulatory system can be damaged by disease or injury. One of the most common diseases of the system is *arteriosclerosis*, which results from the accumulation of fatty deposits in the arteries. Such deposits stiffen and thicken the walls of the arteries. As a result, the flow of blood is restricted. In some cases, blood clots develop in vessels affected by arteriosclerosis. Such clots may lead to a heart attack or a *stroke*, a condition in which the brain does not receive enough blood.

Another disease, *hypertension*, commonly called *high blood pressure*, is often associated with arteriosclerosis. Hypertension makes the heart work harder and may lead to such complications as a heart attack, a stroke, or kidney failure.

Treatment for arteriosclerosis and hypertension includes rest, exercise, and changes in the diet. Physicians may prescribe various drugs to lower the blood pressure, strengthen the heart, or prevent infection and blood clots. In extreme cases, a surgeon may remove clots or replace one or more diseased blood vessels.

Other disorders of the circulatory system result from damage or defects in the heart or blood vessels. For example, *rheumatic fever* may harm or destroy the valves that control the flow of blood through the heart. Incomplete development of the heart or its blood vessels before birth may produce defects called *congenital heart disorders*. Some cases of damage or defects can be corrected by surgery.

The Circulatory System in Other Animals

Vertebrates all have a *closed* circulatory system. In this type of system, the blood flows only in the vessels and remains separate from the fluid in the body tissues. Mammals—including human beings—and birds have a heart with two separate pumps. In these animals, the blood in the systemic and pulmonary circulations almost always remains separate. In amphibians and most reptiles, the pumps of the heart are only partly separated, and the systemic and pulmonary blood mixes together somewhat. In fish, the heart has only one pump. The pump collects the blood and sends it to the gills and then to the rest of the body.

Invertebrates have circulatory systems that range from complex to simple. Some invertebrates, such as earthworms and octopuses, have a closed circulatory system. Other invertebrates have an *open* circulatory system, in which the blood is only partially confined to the vessels. It fills the hollow spaces of the body as well. Animals with an open circulatory system include insects, spiders, and most shellfish.

In many invertebrates, the blood is pumped by contracting vessels or by *pumping centers* (contracting portions of vessels), or by both. Among insects, for example, the "heart" consists of an internal contracting vessel that extends almost the length of the back.

The simplest animals with a true circulatory system include certain kinds of worms. Earthworms, leeches, and a variety of sea worms have contracting vessels that pump the blood. A group of simpler worms, called *ribbon worms* or *proboscis worms*, have a circulatory system with no pumping centers and no contracting vessels. The movements of the animal keep the blood flowing through the body.

FRANCIS L. ABEL

MIGRATION, in biology, is the movement of animals to a place that offers better living conditions. Many birds, fishes, insects, and mammals regularly migrate to avoid unfavorable changes in weather or food supply. Human beings also migrate, but they do so for political and social reasons as well as biological ones. For information on human migrations, see IMMIGRATION.

Biologists use the term *migration* to describe several types of movements. Some biologists, particularly those who study insects, refer to one-way journeys as migrations. Such movements take place when animals leave an area in search of better living conditions, and neither they nor their descendants necessarily return to the original area. Other biologists refer to the long-term historical changes in the distribution of animals as migrations. But most biologists define migrations as regular, round-trip movements between two areas. Each area offers more favorable living conditions than the other at some point in the animals' lives. This article discusses such regular, round-trip migrations.

Migrations take place on land, in water, or in the air. Some animals migrate only short distances. For example, many frogs and toads make yearly migrations of only a few miles or kilometers between their breeding and nonbreeding homes. Other migrations cover thousands of miles or kilometers. Arctic terns rank among the animals that migrate farthest. These birds travel as much as 22,000 miles (35,400 kilometers) in a year.

Types of Migrations. Most migratory animals make (1) daily migrations or (2) seasonal migrations. Other migratory animals make only one or a few round-trip journeys during their lifetime.

Daily Migrations take place among many of the small, drifting animals that live in the ocean. These *plankton animals* swim hundreds of feet or meters below the surface during the day. Each night, they migrate to the upper levels of the water.

Seasonal Migrations take place twice a year. They occur in connection with periodic changes in temperature or rainfall. There are three main kinds of seasonal migrations: (1) latitudinal migrations, (2) altitudinal migrations, and (3) local migrations.

Bats, seals, and most species of migratory birds perform *latitudinal migrations*. That is, they migrate in basically a north-south direction. Some mountain-dwelling animals make *altitudinal migrations* up and down the mountain slopes. For example, mountain quail and mule deer spend summer in high elevations and move to lower areas in winter. Many tropical birds and mammals make *local migrations*. They move to moister regions of the tropics during the dry season and return to their original homes when the rainy season begins.

Less Frequent Migrations are made by some animals. For example, salmon are born in freshwater streams but soon migrate to the oceans. After several years, they return to their freshwater birthplaces to breed. Pacific salmon die soon afterward, but some Atlantic salmon swim back to the ocean and return to their birthplaces to breed as many as three times. Female sea turtles also make a number of migrations during their lifetime. Every two or three years, mature female green turtles and loggerhead turtles swim up to 1,400 miles (2,300 kilometers) to the beach where they hatched. There they lay their eggs.

Why Animals Migrate. Migration enables many species to take advantage of favorable weather and abundant food supplies in areas with changing environments. In some parts of the world, for example, food is plentiful in summer but becomes scarce during the cold winter months. Many animals that live in these regions migrate to warmer climates in the fall. They return in the spring when the weather warms up.

Many migrations are related to reproduction. Numerous animals migrate to breeding areas where their young have the best chance for survival. Migratory birds breed in their summer homes, where the food supply is most abundant. Humpback whales, on the other hand, migrate from their polar feeding grounds to give birth in tropical or subtropical waters. The warm waters provide little food for the adults, but the newborns could not survive in the polar seas.

What Triggers Migrations. Many animals begin their migrations after unfavorable environmental conditions set in. But among other species, the factors that trigger migrations are more difficult to explain. Many migratory birds, for example, leave their winter homes in the tropics while conditions there are still favorable. Among such species, migration may be triggered by environmental changes that are associated with the onset of warm weather and increased food in their northern breeding grounds. Experiments show that changes in daylength stimulate the migrations of many species of birds. In spring, the increasing hours of daylight trigger the release of certain *hormones* in the bodies of the birds. Hormones are chemical substances that regulate many body functions. In this case, the hormones stimulate preparations for the northward trip.

In addition to using environmental clues, many seasonal migrators probably have an inborn "calendar" that tells them when to migrate. Some birds, for example, show seasonal migratory behavior even when kept under constant conditions in a laboratory. An inborn timing mechanism probably triggers the migration of salmon and other animals that migrate at different stages of their life.

How Migrating Animals Find Their Way. Research has shown that animals use a number of ways to gather directional information during migrations. Many are guided by the sun, the moon, and the stars. Such travelers must be able to allow for the movements of these heavenly bodies in determining direction. Others follow landscape features, such as rivers or mountain ranges.

Animals rely on more than visual cues when they migrate. For example, salmon find their way back to their birthplace by recognizing the odors of their home streams. Some animals are guided by changes in temperature, moisture, wind direction, or the earth's magnetic field. Sea-dwellers may use information from ocean currents.

Many animals use more than one compass during their migrations. Some species of birds are guided by the sun during the day and the stars at night. Many biologists believe that they use the earth's magnetic field to find their way on cloudy days and nights.

Sometimes, migrating animals are forced from their normal route into an unfamiliar area. In some cases, the "lost" animals seem to be able to determine where they are and how to reach their original destination. This process is called *navigation*. Although there are many examples of what appears to be navigation by animals, scientists know little about how this process works.

Some of the most convincing evidence of animal navigation comes from experiments with shearwaters, sparrows, and homing pigeons. Scientists captured these birds and took them to unfamiliar areas up to thousands of miles or kilometers away. Most of the birds successfully returned to the original capture point.

Other experiments indicate that although young animals are able to migrate, they may not be able to navigate from unfamiliar areas. For example, European starlings normally migrate in a southwest direction from their breeding grounds around the Baltic Sea to wintering areas bordering the English Channel. Scientists captured both adult and young starlings that had reached The Netherlands during a migration. They took the birds to Switzerland and released them. The adult starlings corrected for the move and reached their normal wintering grounds. But the young birds, which were making their first migration, continued to fly southwest. The young birds ended up in Portugal, Spain, and southern France.

Sidney A. Gauthreaux, Jr.

CRYSTAL is a solid that is composed of atoms arranged in an orderly pattern. Most nonliving substances are made up of crystals. For example, metals and rocks consist of crystals, as do snowflakes, salt, and sugar.

Well-developed crystals have a distinctly regular shape as a result of their geometrically ordered arrangement of atoms. Such crystals have smooth, flat surfaces, which intersect to form sharp edges. These surfaces, called *crystal faces*, show definite symmetrical relationships. The faces of crystals of the same substance always meet at the same angle regardless of the shape and size of the crystals.

The scientific study of crystals is called *crystallography*. Crystallographers measure the angles between crystal faces and analyze the symmetrical arrangements of such surfaces. They also examine and identify the atomic structures of crystals with the aid of *transmission electron microscopes* and *X-ray diffraction* techniques (see X RAYS [In Scientific Research]).

Crystallization is the process by which nonliving matter grows into crystals. Crystals may form from vapors, solutions, or *melts* (molten materials). When either temperature or pressure is lowered or evaporation occurs, certain atoms in such substances move close together and join. In most cases, they do so on a *crystallization nucleus*, an impurity or a tiny piece of crystal consisting of a particle or cluster of atoms. The atoms collect on the nucleus and arrange themselves into structural units called *unit cells* to form a crystalline solid. A crystal increases in size by adding atoms to its surfaces in an expanding network of unit cells. See MINERAL (Inside Minerals).

In a few cases, crystals develop smooth, mirrorlike faces. Such crystals are said to be *euhedral*. In nature, euhedral crystals rarely occur because they form only in an unconfined space where they can grow without touching other crystals. Most crystals are *subhedral*—that is, they have poorly formed faces that are rough or pitted. Some crystals, called *anhedral*, have no faces at all. Most rocks are composed of anhedral crystals.

Classifying Crystals. Crystals are classified according to *symmetry*, a balanced arrangement of faces. There are three basic types of crystal symmetry—plane of symmetry, axis of symmetry, and center of symmetry.

A *plane of symmetry* is an imaginary plane that divides a crystal into identical halves. An *axis of symmetry* is an imaginary line through the center of a crystal. When a crystal is rotated 360° about this axis, identical faces will appear from two to six times. If identical faces recur twice, the axis is a *twofold* axis of symmetry. If they reappear three times, the axis is a *threefold* axis. A crystal has a *center of symmetry* if opposite sides are identical. Most crystals have a center of symmetry.

All crystals can be grouped into one of 32 possible combinations of symmetry. These combinations, in turn, can be classified into seven general crystal systems. These systems are (1) isometric, (2) tetragonal, (3) hexagonal, (4) rhombohedral, (5) orthorhombic, (6) monoclinic, and (7) triclinic. Each system may be described in terms of three imaginary axes, called *crystallographic axes*, which intersect in the center of a crystal.

Isometric System. Crystals in this system have three axes of equal length that are perpendicular to one another. The simplest isometric crystal is a cube. Another form is the octahedron, which has eight sides consisting of equilateral triangles. Such minerals as galena, garnet, and pyrite crystallize in this system.

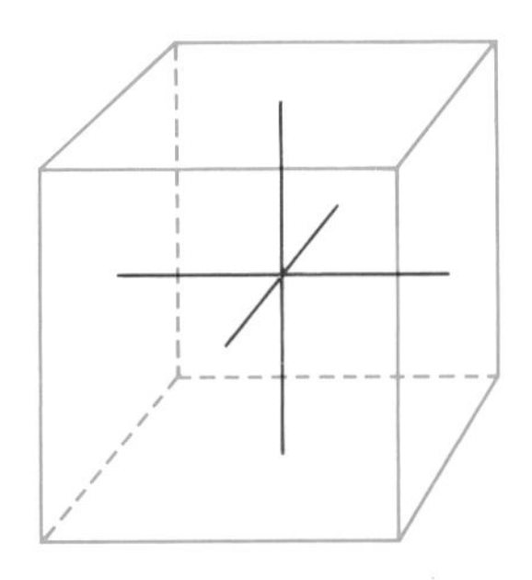

Isometric Crystal

Pyrite

Tetragonal System. Tetragonal crystals have three axes that intersect at right angles. Two of the axes are of equal length. The simplest form of tetragonal crystal is a prism in which the sides are rectangular and the top and bottom are square. Other tetragonal crystals resemble eight-sided pyramids. Their sides are made up of identical *isosceles* triangles, which are triangles with two equal sides. The minerals cassiterite, rutile, and zircon crystallize in the tetragonal system.

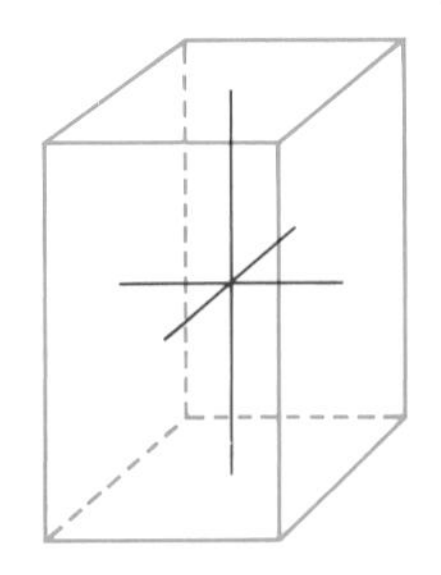

Tetragonal Crystal

Rutile

Hexagonal System. Hexagonal crystals have four axes. Three of the axes are of equal length and lie in a horizontal plane with a 120° angle between one another. The fourth axis is perpendicular to the others and may be of any length. The simplest hexagonal crystal is a

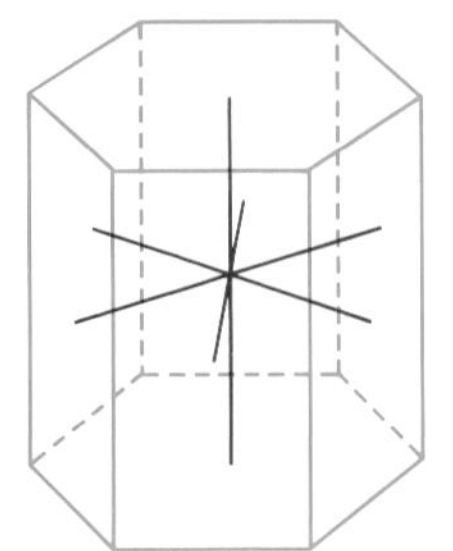

Hexagonal Crystal

Field Museum of Natural History (WORLD BOOK photos)

Apatite

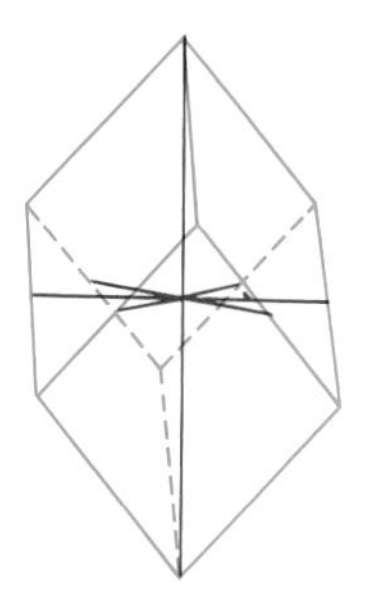

Rhombohedral Crystal

Quartz

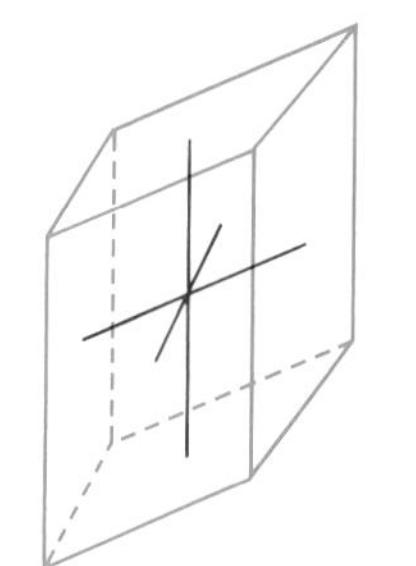

Triclinic Crystal

Field Museum of Natural History (WORLD BOOK photos)

Plagioclase Feldspar

prism that has six rectangular faces parallel to the fourth axis. The minerals apatite, beryl, graphite, and molybdenite form in this system.

Rhombohedral System. Some crystallographers consider the rhombohedral system a subdivision of the hexagonal system because both systems can be defined in terms of the same axes. However, there is one major difference between them. The vertical axis of a rhombohedral crystal is a threefold symmetry axis, but that of a hexagonal crystal is a sixfold axis. The simplest crystal in

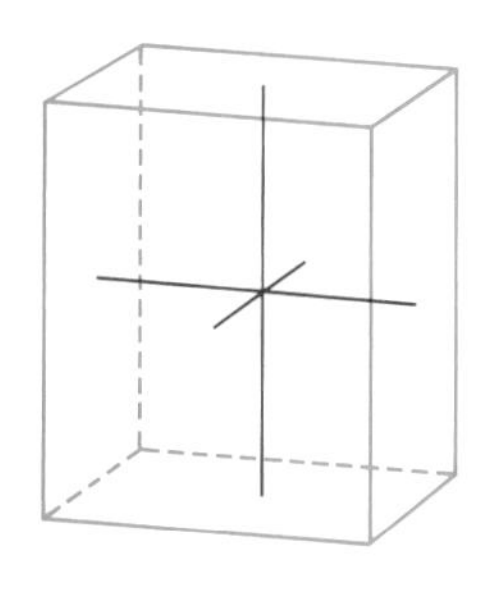

Orthorhombic Crystal

Barite

the rhombohedral system has six rhomboidal faces, each consisting of an equal parallelogram. This system includes crystals of calcite, dolomite, and quartz.

Orthorhombic System. Orthorhombic crystals have three axes of unequal length that intersect at right angles. The simplest crystal of this type is an orthorhombic prism with three sets of unequal rectangular faces that

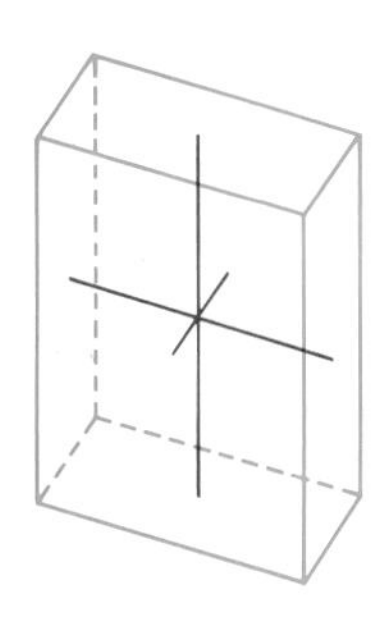

Monoclinic Crystal

Gypsum

meet at right angles. Aragonite, barite, topaz, and certain other minerals crystallize in this system.

Monoclinic System. Monoclinic crystals have three axes of different lengths. Two of the axes are perpendicular to each other, but the third is inclined. A simple monoclinic crystal has two rhomboidal faces and four rectangular ones. The top and bottom surfaces are inclined. Many compounds, including the minerals gypsum, hornblende, orthoclase, and pyroxene belong to this system.

Triclinic System. Triclinic crystals have three axes of unequal length. None of the axes are perpendicular. The faces of these crystals are all different and do not meet at right angles. Plagioclase feldspars and a few other minerals form in this system. WILLIAM B. SIMMONS

See also GEM; MINERAL; SNOW.

RAIN is a form of precipitation that consists of drops of water. Raindrops form when water droplets in clouds combine or when precipitation in the form of ice, such as snow, hail, or sleet, melts.

Rain falls throughout most of the world. In the tropics, almost all the precipitation is rain. However, in the inland of Antarctica and in a few other places, all precipitation occurs as ice.

Raindrops vary greatly in size and in the speed of their fall. The diameter of most raindrops ranges from 0.02 to 0.25 inch (0.51 to 6.35 millimeters). The larger the raindrop is, the faster it falls. At sea level, a large raindrop with a diameter of 0.2 inch (5 millimeters) falls at the rate of 30 feet (9 meters) per second. Drizzle, which consists of drops with a diameter of less than 0.02 inch, falls at the rate of 7 feet (2.1 meters) per second or slower.

The shape of a raindrop depends on its size. Raindrops with a diameter of less than 0.04 inch (1 millimeter) are round. Most larger raindrops become flatter as they fall.

Rain is necessary for life because it provides water for human beings and other animals and for plants. Few forms of life exist in places where little or no rain falls. In rural areas, rain helps prevent the loss of valuable topsoil by stopping dust storms. Rain also cleans the air by washing away dust and chemical pollutants.

Rain can be harmful as well. Too much rain may interrupt communications and cause flooding that destroys property and threatens life. Heavy rainfall also damages crops and speeds up the loss of soil.

Measuring Rainfall

Rainfall is measured in various ways. The most commonly used instrument is the *rain gauge*. It is a cylinder with a narrow tube inside and a funnel on top. Rain falls into the funnel and flows into the tube, where it is measured with a special "ruler."

A network of rain gauges is used to measure the annual precipitation of a region. In winter, the gauges are placed about 10 miles (16 kilometers) apart. In summer, they are set closer together because summer showers occur in narrow bands. The gauges are generally used on level ground. The total precipitation collected periodically throughout the year in all the gauges represents the annual precipitation.

Other instruments measure the *intensity of rainfall*—that is, the rate of rainfall within a certain period, usually an hour. A *weighing-type gauge* may be used. This instrument has a bucket into which the rain falls. The bucket stands on a platform that is attached by springs to a scale. The weight of the rain water gradually pushes the platform down. The movements of the platform are recorded on a special tape that is processed by a computer.

If the intensity of rainfall is too slight to be measured, it is called a *trace of rain.* Rain that falls from a trace to 0.10 inch (2.5 millimeters) per hour is a *light rain.* A *moderate rain* falls at rates from 0.11 to 0.30 inch (2.8 to 7.6 millimeters) per hour. A *heavy rain* falls faster than 0.30 inch per hour.

In some cases, *meteorologists* (scientists who study weather) measure rainfall with radar. This electronic instrument sends out radio waves that are reflected by raindrops. The reflected waves, called *echoes*, appear on a screen as spots of light. The brightness of the echoes depends chiefly on the size and number of raindrops. The echoes indicate the amount and intensity of rainfall. Radar measures scattered showers missed by rain gauges, which are too far apart to measure precipitation in all places.

Rainfall Distribution

World Distribution. The earth receives an average of about 34 inches (86 centimeters) of rain and other forms of precipitation annually. Some regions have a much greater rainfall, and others get much less rain.

Some regions near the equator have received as much as 400 inches (1,000 centimeters) of rain a year. Rain usually falls every day in such areas as western Africa and the Amazon River Basin of South America.

The coastal regions of the tropics also have heavy rains. The heaviest rainfall ever recorded for a 24-hour period occurred at Cilaos, on the tropical island of Reunion in the Indian Ocean. Cilaos received 74 inches (188 centimeters) of rain on March 15-16, 1952.

Other regions of the tropics receive little rain. They include the vast deserts of Australia, northern Africa, and the Arabian Peninsula. The tropical desert of Chile had the longest recorded dry period. No measurable precipitation fell at Arica, Chile, in a 14-year period, from 1903 to 1917.

Some Rainfall Records

The Earth's Average Annual Precipitation (including rain, snow, and hail) is about 34 inches (86 centimeters).

Greatest Rainfall in the World occurs at Mount Waialeale in Hawaii. An average of about 460 inches (1,168 centimeters) of rain falls there yearly.

Least Rainfall in the World is recorded at Arica, Chile, a desert town that receives an average of 0.03 inch (0.76 millimeter) a year.

Least Rainfall in the United States occurs in Death Valley, California. An average of 1.8 inches (4.6 centimeters) falls there annually.

In the *temperate zones,* the regions between the tropics and the polar circles, cyclones bring heavy rains to the western coasts of some continents. However, deserts lie in the interior of continents in this zone. Other regions of low precipitation occur around the polar circles.

Distribution in North America. The distribution of rainfall in the United States varies greatly. Less than 2 inches (5 centimeters) of rain falls yearly in Death Valley, in California. On the other hand, the northwest coast receives up to 150 inches (381 centimeters) a year. In general, the eastern half of the U.S. mainland has more precipitation than the western half. Rain seldom falls in the Great Basin, a desert area that covers parts of Oregon, California, Idaho, Utah, Wyoming, and Nevada.

The rainfall in Canada is distributed similarly to that in the United States. For example, some areas of

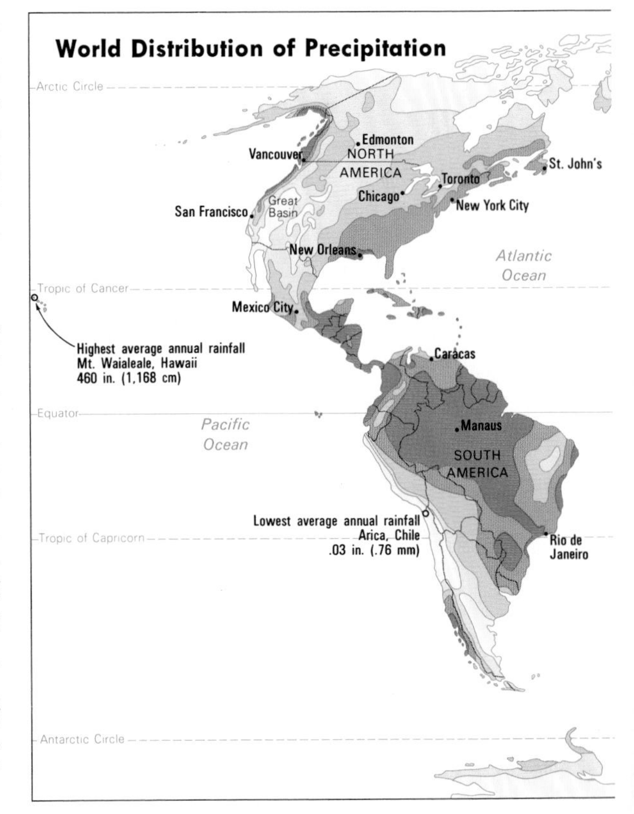

Canada's west coast get more than 100 inches (250 centimeters) of precipitation a year. The eastern half of the country generally receives more rain than the western half. However, the lowest precipitation in Canada occurs in the areas near the Arctic Circle. These northern areas receive less than 10 inches (25 centimeters) annually.

What Causes Rain?

Formation of Rain. Rain develops from water vapor in the atmosphere. This vapor forms when the heat of the sun causes evaporation from the oceans and other bodies of water on the earth. The warm, moist air cools as it rises, and the amount of vapor it can hold decreases. The temperature at which air holds as much vapor as it can is called the *dew point*. When the temperature drops below the dew point, some of the vapor condenses into water droplets, forming clouds.

Water droplets form on tiny particles of matter known as *condensation nuclei*. Such nuclei consist of dust, salt from ocean spray, and chemicals given off chiefly by industrial plants and motor vehicles. As the water droplets form, heat is released, making the clouds warmer. The warmth helps the clouds rise, and they become cooler. The formation of raindrops in such clouds is explained by the *coalescence theory* and the *ice-crystal theory*.

The Coalescence Theory applies to much of the rain that forms over the oceans and in the tropics. According to this theory, different sizes of droplets form in clouds. The larger droplets fall faster through a cloud than the smaller droplets do. As a larger droplet falls, it collides and combines with smaller droplets. This process is called *coalescence*. If a large droplet falls about 1 mile (1.6 kilometers) through a cloud, it may combine with a million smaller droplets. In this way, the droplets become too heavy for the air to support them. Some fall to the earth as raindrops. Others having a diameter of more than 0.25 inch tend to split into smaller drops. These drops will move upward if the cloud is rising rapidly. As they begin to grow, they again fall and repeat the coalescence process.

The Ice-Crystal Theory accounts for much of the rainfall in the temperate zone. The process of rain formation based on this theory probably occurs more frequently than coalescence. The ice-crystal process occurs in clouds in which air temperature is lower than 32° F. (0° C), the freezing point of water. In most cases, such clouds consist of droplets of *supercooled water*. Supercooled water is water that remains in a liquid state at temperatures below 32° F. In clouds of this type, ice crystals form on microscopic particles called *ice nuclei*. Most ice nuclei consist of extremely fine particles of soil or volcanic dust.

Ice crystals form when droplets of supercooled water freeze on ice nuclei. When the temperature drops to −40° F. (−40° C) or below, the droplets freeze without ice nuclei. Under certain conditions, ice crystals may also form directly from water vapor. In such a case, water vapor is deposited on ice nuclei and freezes without first condensing into droplets.

Ice crystals that form near droplets of supercooled

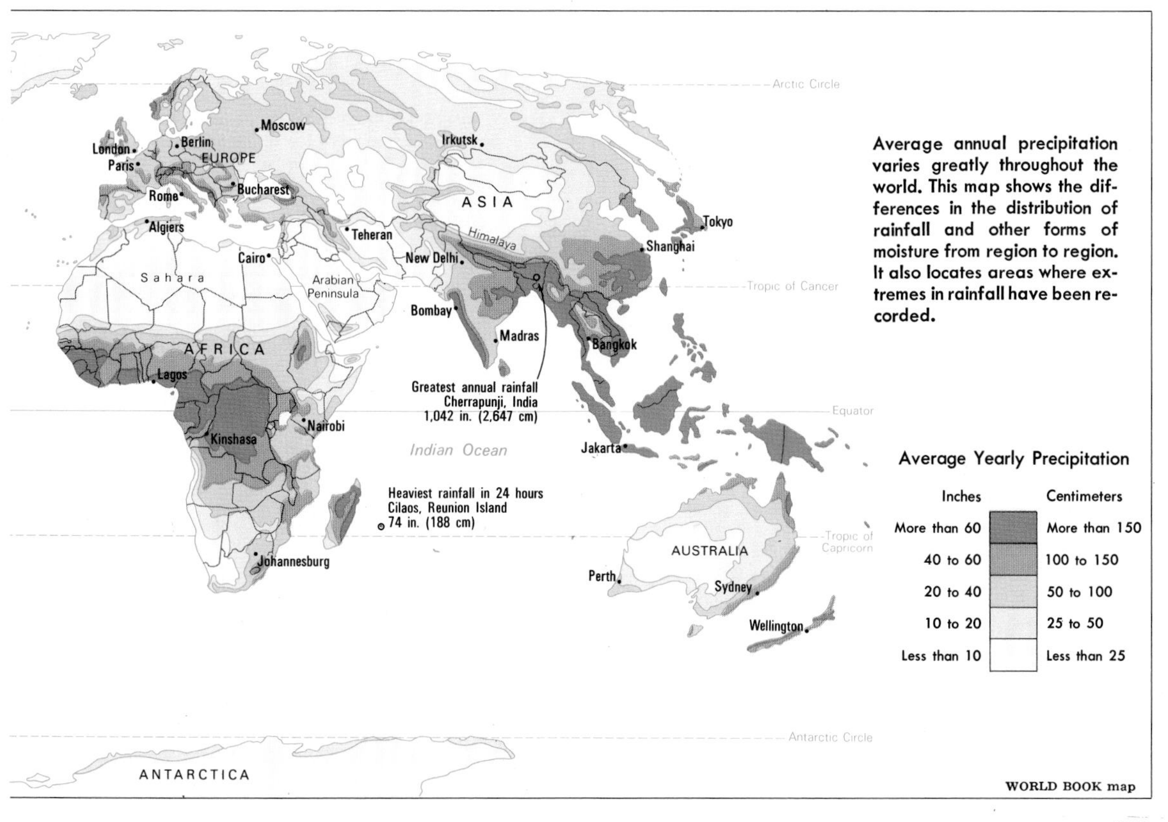

Average annual precipitation varies greatly throughout the world. This map shows the differences in the distribution of rainfall and other forms of moisture from region to region. It also locates areas where extremes in rainfall have been recorded.

How Rain Forms Weather experts have developed two theories of rain formation—the coalescence theory and the ice-crystal theory. The diagrams below illustrate the processes described by each of these theories.

WORLD BOOK diagrams by Leonard E. Morgan

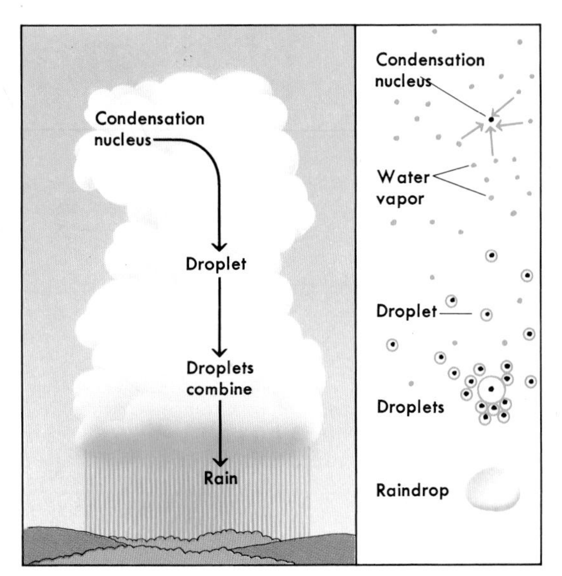

The Coalescence Theory explains how different sizes of water droplets form in clouds. A droplet forms when water vapor condenses on a particle called a *condensation nucleus.* As a droplet falls through a cloud, it combines with smaller ones. When it becomes too heavy for the air to support, it falls as a raindrop.

The Ice-Crystal Theory applies to clouds of supercooled water droplets. Such a droplet, formed by condensing water vapor, freezes on a particle called an *ice nucleus.* The resulting ice crystal combines with others to form a snowflake. The snowflake becomes rain when it falls through air warmer than 32° F. (0° C).

water increase in size when water vapor from cloud droplets is deposited on the crystals. As the crystals fall through a cloud, they may collide and combine with other crystals or with supercooled droplets. Crystals that become too heavy for the air to support fall out of the cloud. Such ice crystals become raindrops if they fall through enough air that is warmer than 32° F.

Experiments in *rainmaking,* also called *cloud seeding,* are based chiefly on the ice-crystal theory. In these experiments, various substances are put into clouds to serve as ice nuclei. This procedure sometimes helps produce rain and snow by promoting the formation of ice crystals. See Rainmaking.

Variations in Rainfall. Rainfall is affected by such factors as latitude, large bodies of water, land features, air currents, and cities. These factors largely determine the variations in rainfall that occur in different areas of the world.

In general, rain falls more frequently in latitudes near the equator than in those close to the poles. At the equator, the intense heat of the sun causes large amounts of moisture to evaporate in the warm air. Because the polar regions receive little sunlight, the air there is too cold to hold much moisture.

Areas near large bodies of water receive more rain than locations in the dry interior of a continent. The larger amount of rainfall results from evaporation of moisture from nearby sources of water, including oceans, lakes, and irrigation systems. The lack of rain in the deserts of west central Asia is due primarily to their great distance from the sea.

Places on the windward slopes of mountains generally have more rain than areas at a lower elevation. The slopes help produce rain by lifting warm, moist air to a higher altitude. There, the air cools, forming clouds and then rain. Most of the slopes away from the wind are dry because the wind carries little moisture across the top. In Asia, the southern slopes of the Himalaya receive 200 to 600 inches (510 to 1,500 centimeters) of rain annually. The northern slopes average less than 10 inches a year.

Seasonal rainfall, especially in regions near the tropics, is caused by winds that blow in an opposite direction in winter than in summer. Such winds are called *monsoons.* The monsoon that blows across southern Asia in the summer brings extremely heavy rains. The greatest amount of rain ever recorded in one year fell on the town of Cherrapunji, India, near Shillong. Cherrapunji received almost 1,042 inches (2,647 centimeters) of rain from August 1860 to July 1861.

Meteorologists believe cities promote rainfall, but they are not certain why. One possible explanation is that clouds may form more quickly in the heat generated by automobiles, heating systems, and sun-warmed concrete. Also, pollutants in the air over a city may act as condensation nuclei for raindrops.

Pollutants also cause *acid rain,* which forms when moisture reacts with nitrogen oxides and sulfur dioxide. These chemicals are released by motor vehicles, factories, and certain power plants. Such rain pollutes lakes and streams, endangering wildlife. It also damages crops, forests, and soil.

Norihiko Fukuta

Related Articles. See the Climate section of the articles on the continents, countries, states, and provinces. See also:

Climate	Evaporation	Rainmaking
Cloud	Humidity	Storm
Cloudburst	Rain Gauge	Water
Desert	Rainbow	Weather

Index

This index covers the contents of the 1981, 1982, and 1983 editions of *Science Year,* The World Book Science Annual.

Each index entry is followed by the edition year in *italics* and the page numbers:

Botany, *83*–234, *82*–230, *81*–253

This means that information about Botany begins on the page indicated for each of the editions.

An index entry that is the title of an article appearing in *Science Year* is printed in boldface italic letters: ***Archaeology.*** An entry that is not an article title, but a subject discussed in an article of some other title, is printed: **Plate tectonics.**

The various "See" and "See also" cross references in the index are to other entries within the index:

Neuroscience, *83*–292, *82*–286, *81*–306.
See also **Brain.**

Clue words or phrases are used when the entry needs further definition or when two or more references to the same subject appear in *Science Year.* These make it easy to locate the material on the page:

Maya: archaeology, *83*–219, *82*–217, *81*–236;
Special Report, 83–12

The indication *"il."* means that the reference is to an illustration only, as:

Magnetic plant, *il., 83*–234

Index

A

B

C

Index

D

E

F

G

H

N

O

P

Index

T

U

V

W

X

Y

Z

Acknowledgments

The publishers of *Science Year* gratefully acknowledge the courtesy of the following artists, photographers, publishers, institutions, agencies, and corporations for the illustrations in this volume. Credits should be read from top to bottom, left to right, on their respective pages. All entries marked with an asterisk (*) denote illustrations created exclusively for *Science Year*. All maps, charts, and diagrams were prepared by the *Science Year* staff unless otherwise noted.

Cover
Stephen Dalton, Natural History Photographic Agency

Advisory Board
7 University of Pennsylvania; Harvard University; Cornell University; University of California; Argonne National Laboratory; Harvard University; California Institute of Technology.

Special Reports
10 © Dan McCoy; Stephen Dalton, Natural History Photographic Agency; © Presidents and Fellows of Harvard College 1972. All rights reserved. Peabody Museum, Harvard University (Hitlel Burger)
11 International Flavors and Fragrances; William M. Harlow, Photo Researchers; Steve Hale*
12 © Presidents and Fellows of Harvard College 1972. All rights reserved. Peabody Museum, Harvard University (Hitlel Burger)
15 R. E. W. Adams, University of Texas at San Antonio
16 © Lee Boltin; R. E. W. Adams, University of Texas at San Antonio
17 R. E. W. Adams, University of Texas at San Antonio; B. L. Turner, Clark University
18-20 Charles McBarron*
22 R. E. W. Adams, University of Texas at San Antonio
24 Charles McBarron*
26 Didier Boremanse
28 Stephen Dalton, Natural History Photographic Agency
30 Lois MacBird, California Institute of Technology
31 Kupferstichkabinett-Staaltl. Museem PreuB. Kulturbesitz, West Berlin
32 Patricia Wynne*
33 Lois MacBird, California Institute of Technology
34 Michael Wotton; Warren Garst, Tom Stack & Assoc.; Gary Milburn, Tom Stack & Assoc.
35 Masakazu Konishi, California Institute of Technology
36 Lois MacBird, California Institute of Technology
37 Eric Knudsen; Lois MacBird, California Institute of Technology
39-40 Lois MacBird, California Institute of Technology
42 © J. L. Mason, ARDEA London
45 From *Carnivorous Plants* by Randall Schwartz © 1974 by Randall Schwartz. Reproduced by permission of Holt, Rinehart & Winston Publishers
46 © Leonard Lee Rue III, Bruce Coleman Ltd.; © Hans and Judy Beste, ARDEA London
47 Jane Gate, Alphabet & Image; Donald E. Schnell, M.D.
48 Jane Gate, Alphabet & Image; Robert Hynes*; Robert Hynes*
49 © Hans Pfletschinger, Peter Arnold; Robert Hynes*; Robert Hynes*
50 © Kim Taylor, Bruce Coleman Ltd.
51 © William M. Harlow, Photo Researchers; © P. Morris, ARDEA London; © P. Morris, ARDEA London
52 S. E. Williams, Lebanon Valley College
54 Robert Hynes*; Jane Gate, Alphabet & Image; © Yolande Heslop-Harrison
56 S. E. Williams, Lebanon Valley College
58 Anne Norcia*
61 Anne Norcia*; Lowell Observatory
62 Anne Norcia*
63 Hale Observatories
64 Kitt Peak National Observatory; R. L. Waterfield, Woolston Observatory near Ascot; Royal Astronomical Observatory; Hale Observatories
65 Hale Observatories; Kitt Peak National Observatory; Helwan Observatory
67 Naval Research Laboratory
69 C. Nicollier
70 Copyright © David Scharf 1977
71 © Matt Herron, Black Star
73 Leonard E. Morgan*; © David Strick, Black Star; Steve Whiteley, Medfly Project, CDFA/USDA
74 © David Strick, Black Star
75 Leonard E. Morgan*; © Mickey Pfleger
76 Tropical Fruit and Vegetable Research Laboratory, Western Region, U.S. Department of Agriculture; Steve Whiteley, Medfly Project, CDFA/USDA; © David Strick, Black Star
77 Tom McHugh, Photo Researchers
79 Steve Whiteley, Medfly Project, CDFA/USDA; © Ted Streshinsky
80 Leonard E. Morgan*
83 Steve Whiteley, Medfly Project, CDFA/USDA
87 M. Abbey, Photo Researchers; Brent Jones
89 Carmen Raventos and Ronald L. Nagel, M.D., Albert Einstein College of Medicine
90 Lou Bory*
92 Lemuel Diggs Collection, National Heart, Lung, and Blood Institute, Sickle Cell Disease Branch, National Institutes of Health
93-94 Lou Bory*
97 Isabel Tellez and Ronald L. Nagel, M. D., Albert Einstein College of Medicine
98 Albert L. Babb, University of Washington; M. Abbey, Photo Researchers
100 Steve Hale*
103 Alice Dole; Private Collection; Private Collection; Private Collection; Private Collection; Robert Frerck*
104-105 Brian Zakem
106 Bettmann Archive; Brian Zakem
107 Brian Zakem; Private Collection
109 Doug Stewart; Alice Dole
110 Brian Zakem; Steve Hale*
111 Brian Zakem
112 Brian Zakem; Robert Frerck*
114 Joe Rogers*; Milt and Joan Mann; Frederik D. Bodin, Picture Group; Milt and Joan Mann; Vance Henry, Taurus
119-121 Joe Rogers*
122 Scripps Institution of Oceanography, University of California, San Diego
123 Joe Rogers*
124-125 State University of New York at Buffalo
128 © Most Media
129 Pioneer Video Inc.
131 BBC Hulton Picture Library
132 Nebraska Videodisc Group
133 Pioneer Video Inc.; Pioneer Video Inc.; Zenith Radio Corporation
134 James Teason*
137 Jack Ayers Associates (Milt and Joan Mann*)
138 Sears, Roebuck and Co. (Milt and Joan Mann*)
139 © J. Pugh, FPG; British Tourist Authority
140 American Heart Association
142 Plasma Physics Laboratory, Princeton University
146-147 Leonard E. Morgan*

148 Leonard E. Morgan*; Sandia National Laboratories
149 © Dan McCoy, Rainbow
150 Lawrence Livermore National Laboratory
151 Leonard E. Morgan*
152 Plasma Physics Laboratory, Princeton University
153-154 Leonard E. Morgan*
156-166 Steve Hale*
168 Rob Wood*
171 National Geographic Palomar Observatory Sky Survey
173 Kitt Peak National Observatory
174 Rob Wood*
175 Rob Wood*; H. C. Arp, Mount Wilson and Las Campanas Observatories
177-179 Rob Wood*
182 George Suyeoka*; © Harry Cutting, Animals Animals; Dan Miller* (Steve Hale*)
186 George Suyeoka*; Scala/EPA (Steve Hale*)
187 Gary Beauchamp, Judy Wellington and Charles Wysocki, Monell Chemical Senses Institute
189 James Kostelc, Monell Chemical Senses Institute; Illinois Institute of Technology (Dan Miller*)
190 Wolf Heck, University of Manitoba; © Jane Burton, Bruce Coleman Inc.
191 © William Franklin McMahon, *People Weekly*
192 George Suyeoka*; Dan Miller*; *World Book* photo; Alice Dole (Steve Hale*)
193 International Flavors and Fragrances
194 Steve Hale*
196-197 Norb Bielat*
200 Ralph Morse
201 High Energy Physics Group, Purdue University; High Energy Physics Group, Purdue University; High Energy Physics Group, Purdue University; © Dan McCoy, Rainbow
202-206 Norb Bielat*

Science File

210 J. Porter, University of Georgia; Henrique Lins de Barros, Darci Motta Esquivel and Jacques Danon, Centro Brasileiro de Pesquisas Fisicas, Rio de Janeiro, and Richard B. Frankel, Francis Bitter National Magnet Laboratory, Massachusetts Institute of Technology; U.S. Department of Agriculture
211 European Southern Observatory; Smithsonian News Service; National Center for Atmospheric Research/National Science Foundation
212-214 U. S. Department of Agriculture
215 David Pilbeam, Harvard University
216 Leslie G. Freeman, University of Chicago
217 Yang Limen, New China Pictures
218 NYT Pictures
219 Smithsonian News Service
221 Tom Dillehay, University of Kentucky
222 NASA
223 Sovfoto
224 National Center for Atmospheric Research/National Science Foundation
225 Drawing by Stevenson; © 1982 The New Yorker Magazine, Inc.
226 European Southern Observatory
230 The Perkin-Elmer Corporation
234 Henrique Lins de Barros, Darci Motta Esquivel and Jacques Danon, Centro Brasileiro de Pesquisas Fisicas, Rio de Janeiro, and Richard B. Frankel, Francis Bitter National Magnet Laboratory, Massachusetts Institute of Technology
235 U. S. Department of Agriculture
236 General Motors Corporation
237 General Electric Research and Development Center
239 C&D Batteries, Allied Corporation
241 © University Museum, University of Pennsylvania; The René Dubos Center for Human Environments; Kaiser-Permanente Medical Care Program
242 University of California; Edo Lonig, Black Star; Columbia University
245 Applied Physics Laboratory, Johns Hopkins University
248 United Press Int.
250 National Museums of Kenya (Peter Kain)
251 A. H. Coleman, Harvard University
252 R. L. Fillion, National Museums of Canada
254 National Center for Atmospheric Research/National Science Foundation
255 NASA
257 J. Porter, University of Georgia
259-260 Oak Ridge National Laboratory
262 Sinclair; Panasonic; Sinclair
263 © Sidney Harris
264 Sony; Biofuel Inc.
266 Enertec Systems
269 Energy Technology Visuals Collection
271 U. S. Department of Agriculture
272 Picture Group; Wide World
273 Alfred Nordheim, Mary Lou Pardue, Achim Möller and Alexander Rich, Massachusetts Institute of Technology and Eileen M. Lafer and B. David Stollar, Tufts University School of Medicine
274 Herbert A. Lubs, Enrique Lujan and Charles Norman, University of Miama
278 Ronald E. Goldstein, D.D.S., Emory University School of Dentistry
279 University of Chicago Medical Center
280 Richard A. Miller, M.D., David Maloney, Roger Warnke, M.D., and Ronald Levy, M.D., Stanford University Medical Center
281 National Cooperative Gall Stone Study
282 Terry Amor, *Medical World News*
283 Miles Laboratories
284 Technicare Corporation
285 L. H. Wilkinson, M.D., Albuquerque Surgical Group, P.A.
287 Philip Katz, Harold L. Schwartz, Henry Brenman, D.D.S., and Louis Lowry, M.D., Thomas Jefferson University
289 © M. Twohy from *Audubon*
291 International Business Machines
294 U. S. Department of Agriculture
297 Harshaw Chemical Company
298 Gregory Tarle, University of California
299 Lawrence Berkeley Laboratory, University of California
300 Argonne National Laboratory
301 © Sidney Harris
303 International Business Machines
305 Lawrence Livermore Laboratory, University of California
307 Drawing by Frascino; © 1982 The New Yorker Magazine, Inc.
312 Lawrence Berkeley Laboratory, University of California
314-315 NASA
316 S. Brown, Wheeler Pictures
317 © New York Zoological Society
318 Tohoku Safari Park and A. Yoshikawa Co., Ltd.
319 © M. Twohy from *Audubon*
320 University of Kansas

Science You Can Use

323-328 John Faulkner*
329 Activision
330-335 John Faulkner*

People in Science

336-338 Robert Frerck*
341 Robert Frerck*; Mr. and Mrs. N. Anderson
343 Robert Frerck*
344 Robert Frerck*; Robert Frerck*; Argonne National Laboratory; Robert Frerck*
345-367 Robert Frerck*

These beautiful bookstands–

specially designed to hold your entire program, including your editions of *Science Year*.

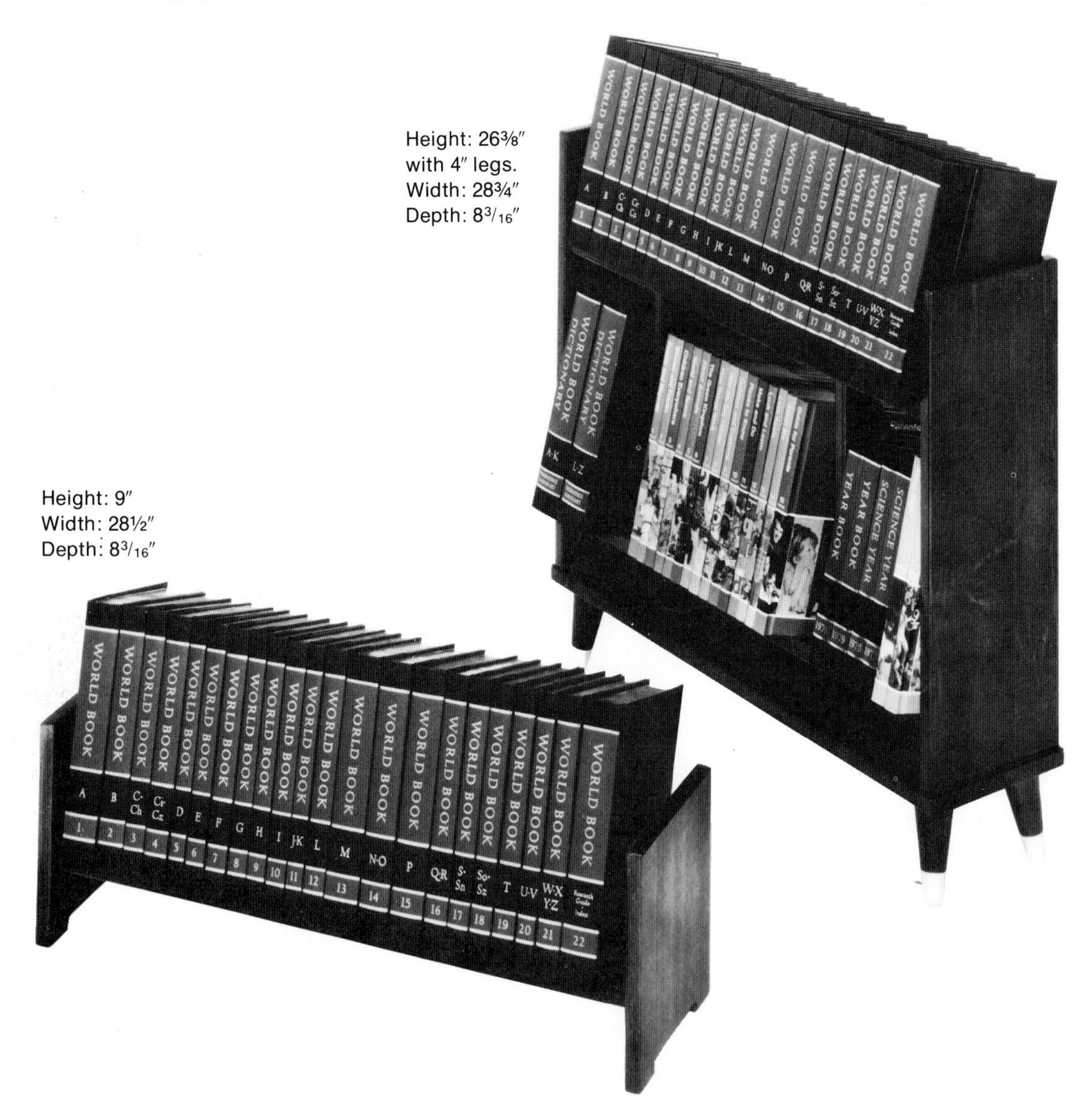

Most parents like having a convenient place to house their *Science Year* editions and their *World Book Encyclopedia.* A beautiful floor-model bookstand —constructed of solid hardwood —is available in either walnut or fruitwood finish.

You might prefer the attractive hardwood table racks, also available in either walnut or fruitwood finish. Let us know by writing us at the following address:

Science Year
Post Office Box 3737
Chicago, IL 60654